POWER TOOL WOODWORKING FOR EVERYONE

POWER TOOL WOODWORKING FOR EVERYONE

by R. J. DeCristoforo

MAGNA PUBLICATIONS · MENLO PARK, CALIFORNIA

POWER TOOL WOODWORKING FOR EVERYONE

Printed in the United States of America

a word from the author to the user*

Many people still feel that power tools are complicated machines, to be operated only by skilled technicians. Actually they are a means for almost anyone to achieve high-quality workmanship with a minimum of practice.

Power tools are woodworking experts. They do not require the long period of apprenticeship needed to accomplish fine work with hand tools. The essentials of woodworking are reduced to a few fundamentals of proper machine setup. Accuracy, speed, and power are built into the machine; the operator merely sets it and guides it.

Anyone who has ever tried to cut a board with a handsaw will probably agree that a certain amount of skill is required for even this most elementary woodworking operation. With a table saw, however, the operator merely sets the fence or miter gauge, turns on the motor, and moves the board forward. The saw cuts the board quickly and easily, producing an edge that is straight and square.

A power tool does not care who flicks the switch. It will perform in exactly the same way whether the operator is skilled or unskilled, male or female, mechanic or clerk. It does a good job—a **consistently** good job. All the little variations, all the small discrepancies that must occur in handwork, are eliminated.

The purpose of this book is to supplement the self-confidence that comes with ownership of power tools. All the information needed for any basic power-tool function is included in this volume. Any woodworking project can be completed through use of the techniques and procedures described. Even highly advanced techniques are shown to be no more than step-by-step procedures that can be followed by anyone.

R. J. De Cristoforo

* Most books are for **readers**; this one is designed for **users**.

CONTENTS

CONTENTS

1 THE TABLE SAW

**Basic use • adjustments • blade types and mounting
crosscutting • ripping • tapers • the squaring board • mitering
using sliding tables • beveling • compound angles • dadoing and grooving
joinery • rabbeting • splines • tenons and slots • notching
tongue-and-groove and lock-corner joints • wedges
drawers • coving • saucer cuts • spirals • wood bending • moldings
inlays • rabbeting circles • pattern sawing • panel raising
chamfering • the molding head • cutoff wheels • trouble shooting**

Table-saw height adjustment is simplified by use of the scale that is part of the rip fence.

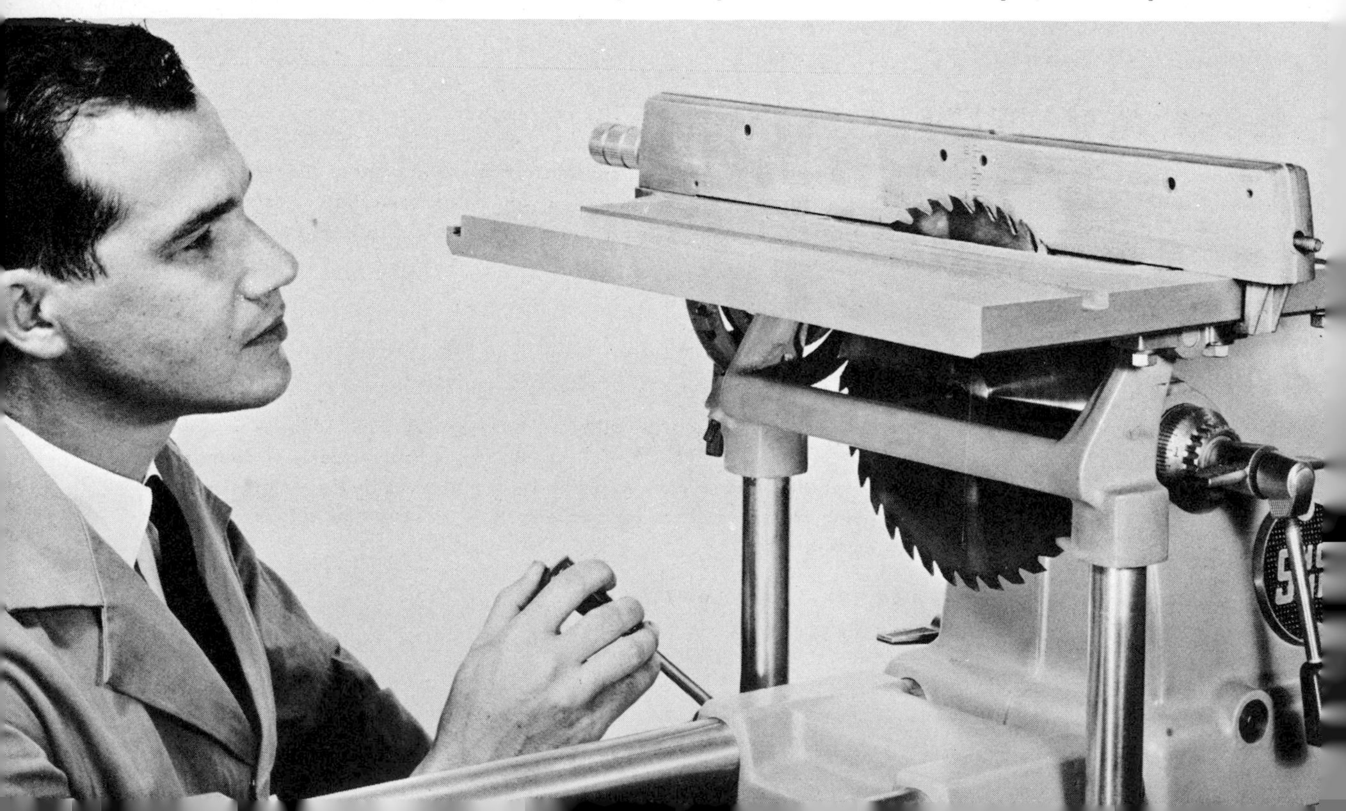

The table saw makes it easy to do the basic shop jobs of crosscutting and ripping.

CROSSCUTTING wood to give it a square edge and ripping stock to make it of uniform width are basic woodworking operations. The simplest joint you can make—a butt joint requires smooth, square mating surfaces if it is to hold with maximum strength. By hand, even such an elementary procedure as making a butt joint is difficult.

The value of the table saw is obvious the first time you use it. All you do is set the saw and guide the stock. The saw does the work, crosscutting square edges and exact lengths and ripping smooth and precise widths.

Using the table saw without becoming familiar with its mechanical features is as dangerous and unwise as starting an automobile trip without knowing how to drive. Know your machine—for safety and for professional results. Supplement the brief explanation of the table saw that follows with the information supplied by the manufacturer.

The table rests on two heavy-walled steel tubes that pass through holes in the carriage. The steel tubes are racked to mesh with two gears activated by the table-raising lever. Because the spindle on which the saw blade arbor is locked is in a fixed position, the table itself is adjusted up or down to change blade projection. Full range of elevation and depression of the saw table is available through use of the table-raising lever. A convenient butterfly-type handle, clearly marked for use, locks the table at any height setting. It is important always to make sure the table-height lock is tightened after each change in table setting.

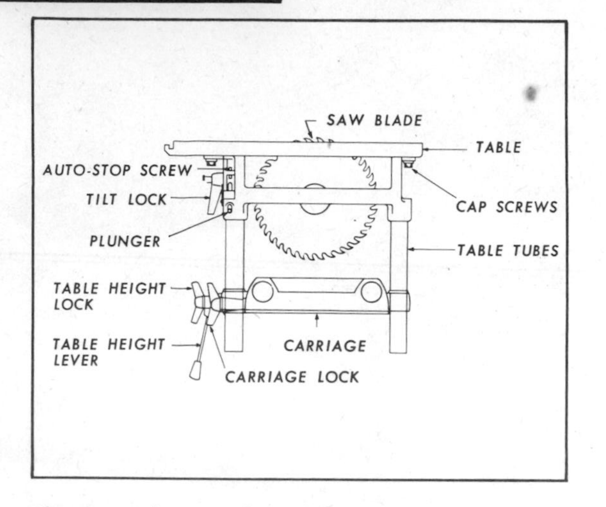

Shown and named in the diagram above are the principal parts of the table saw.

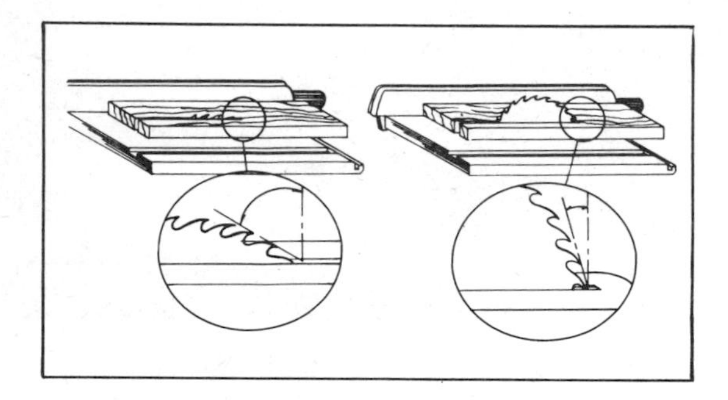

A saw blade projecting as little as shown at left gives a long cutting angle. Angle shown at right works better but is dangerous. Best shop practice in most situations calls for a blade projection of 1/4″ to 1/2″—or exposure to deepest gullet.

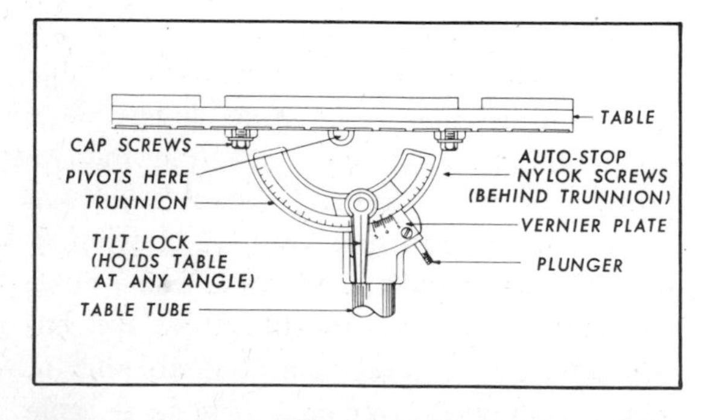

Named here are the principal parts of the trunnion and tilt mechanism of the table saw.

To place the saw table so it can be lowered over the blade, follow this procedure:

1. Raise table high enough to clear the saw blade.

2. With the arbor-mounted saw blade locked on the spindle, slide the carriage toward the headstock until the slotted screw on the headstock side of the carriage butts against the headstock casting.

3. Lower table over blade and check to see if blade is centered in insert slot.

4. If it isn't, loosen the hex nut that secures the slotted screw, and adjust the screw until the saw blade is centered. Then lock the nut. (Many craftsmen adjust this screw to place the blade nearer the left side of the slot. This gives more leeway for the quill adjustment of the multi-purpose tool.)

Use the scale stamped on both sides of the rip fence when setting blade height.

For average work, you should avoid excessive blade projection over the thickness of stock being cut. While a low projection creates a longer cutting angle for the blade (center sketch at left) and requires more power, the added safety justifies it. When the blade projects a considerable amount above the work, the cutting angle is shortened and the blade cuts more easily. The safest method is to limit projection to about 1/2″.

An efficient saw guard (photograph at top of opposite page) is available for the multi-purpose tool as an accessory. It covers the blade, both over and under the table, and moves easily to permit passage of the stock. It is equipped with a splitter to keep the kerf open, thus preventing even green wood from binding the blade. Anti-kickback fingers prevent the blade from throwing work back at the operator.

The entire assembly moves with the quill and does not interfere with the quill feed for fine saw blade adjustments. The lower guard has a chute to which a cloth bag may be attached for collecting sawdust. **CAUTION: If a cloth bag is used, be sure to empty it fre-**

quently—especially each time you use an abrasive wheel to do metal cutting. Before attaching the guard, be sure to read carefully the mounting information supplied by the manufacturer.

The guard prevents your hands from accidentally moving into the saw blade and **should be used whenever possible.** The photographs in this book do not show the guard in place; this is because the operations can be seen more clearly without it.

In addition to using the guard, observe the other safety rules listed at the back of the book. Be just a little bit afraid of the machine. Don't become careless. By all means be confident in the mechanical performance of the saw but never in its ability to think for you. The saw will not stop when confronted by a finger instead of a piece of wood.

The circular saw of the multi-purpose tool has a tilting table. Another common type is the tilting-arbor, on which the blade, not the table, tilts for bevel cutting. In the past there has been much debate about the merits of each but power tool manufacturers are generally in agreement today that for about 95 per cent of home-workshop jobs the tilting-arbor saw holds no advantage over the tilting-table. While the tilting-arbor may be a bit more convenient for some types of cross-bevel cuts, the tilting table, with its cradle-for-work support formed by the rip fence and the tilting table, is more convenient for bevel ripping. Neither operation constitutes a major proportion of most work.

A calibrated trunnion (bottom sketch opposite) is used to tilt and lock the table at any desired angle within its limits.

Because the pivot center of the table is below the table top, the saw slot moves in an arc as the table is tilted. This necessitates advancing the saw blade so it may be centered in the saw slot with the table at the angle of tilt needed. This is done by advancing the blade and tilting the table at the same time. An alternate method is to tilt and raise the table, then advance the saw blade and lower the table over it. Once the table has been tilted and locked in position, it may be raised or lowered in the usual manner to adjust for depth of cut.

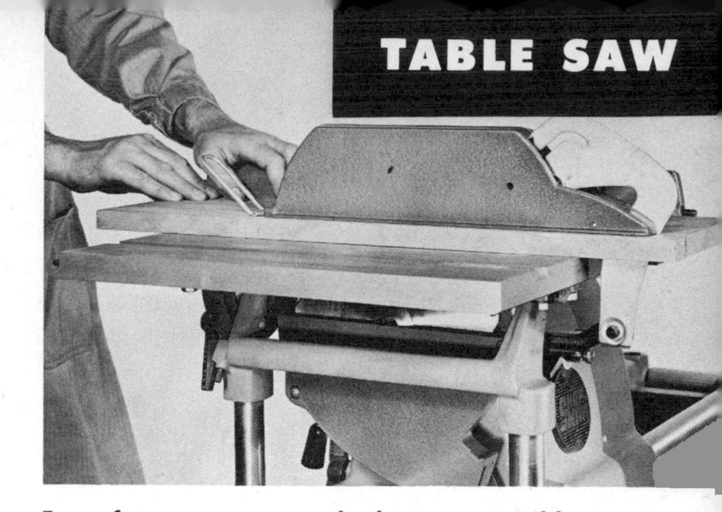

For safety: use saw guard whenever possible.

Here's a typical procedure for setting the table at one of the commonly used angular positions: To tilt to 45°, pull plunger out and tilt table to maximum setting; then push plunger in and return table until 45° auto-stop set screw bears against pin. When returning to "0" setting, pull plunger out and tilt table until plunger is clear of 45° auto-stop; push plunger in and tilt until the table rests against "0" auto-stop.

For a rip cut the fence may be locked approximately in place, then the final adjustment made by advancing the blade (photograph below). Take the measurement from the side of the blade facing the rip fence, and from a tooth set in the direction of the fence.

Use quill feed to make final, hairline adjustment between blade and rip fence.

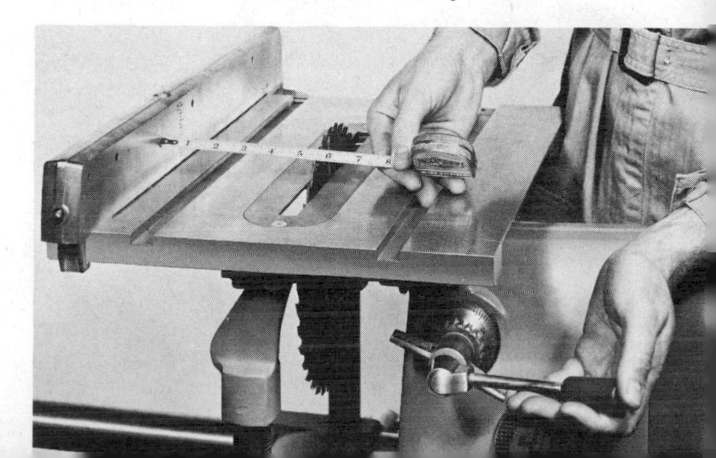

Adjusting the Table Saw

The table saw is constructed to perform its various operations correctly and accurately. But, as with any machine, continued use may cause misalignments that produce substandard results until corrected.

If your table saw is to operate as it should, the parts sketched at the right must meet this description:

1. The table slots in which the miter-gauge bar slides, the rip fence, and the saw blade must be parallel.
2. Rip fence, blade, and miter-gauge head must be perpendicular to table surface.
3. When miter gauge is set at 90°, it must be at right angles to blade and fence.

Each of these factors is easily checked by going through the following procedures. For setting the saw table square to the saw blade:

1. Lock the table at "0" setting.
2. Lock saw table at lowest position.
3. Lock headstock, and then carriage, so table is about 1/8" from saw blade.
4. Use a square, as shown in photograph below, to check the angle between the blade and the table top. It should be exactly 90°. Be sure the square rests against the face of the blade, between two teeth.

If necessary, adjust as follows:

1. Loosen table-tilt lock and pull out trunnion plunger.
2. Set table at exactly 90° (check with square) and secure table-tilt lock.

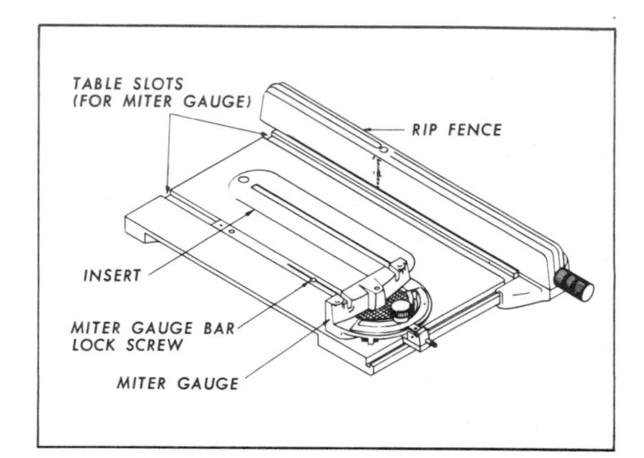

For accurate sawing, these parts must be parallel or perpendicular, as listed at the left.

Saw table must be square with blade. (Don't use a hollow-ground blade for this check.)

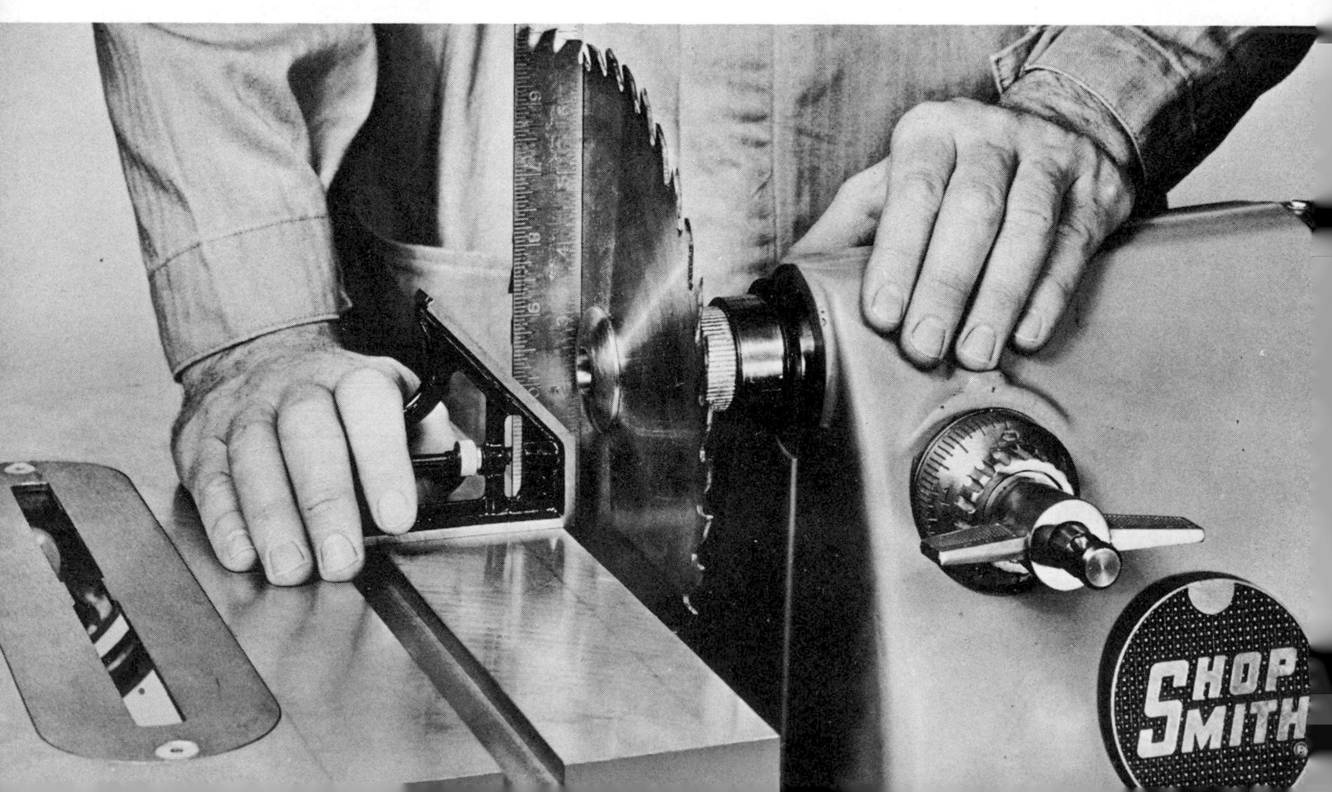

Make sure that the table slots and the saw blade are exactly parallel.

3. Push in plunger and turn Nylok set screw until it just bears against plunger.

4. Adjust trunnion vernier plate until middle calibration is lined up exactly with "0" mark on trunion.

5. Set table over saw blade. Make a trial cut, and check the work with a square.

To set 45° auto-stop, follow this procedure:

1. Tilt table until middle calibration on vernier plate lines up exactly with 45° mark on trunnion. Lock table.

2. Push in plunger and adjust Nylok set screw until it just bears against plunger.

3. Make a trial cut with table set at 45°, and check the work with a square.

The next step is to square the table slots to the blade (photograph above), an easy operation if a miter-gauge stop rod is available. Use it this way:

1. Lower the table over the blade until it is about ⅛″ from the top of the headstock. Lock headstock, carriage, and table.

2. Place the miter-gauge in the right-hand table slot and set it at the 90° position.

3. Set the miter-gauge stop rod (or clamp the Allen wrench to the face of the miter gauge) so that the end protrudes to the left of the miter gauge, in line with a tooth on the saw blade.

4. Adjust the blade by advancing the quill until one tooth, nearest the front of the table saw, just touches the end of the stop rod. Lock the quill, and mark the tooth.

5. Rotate the saw blade by hand toward the rear of the table (opposite to normal rotation). Move the miter gauge and stop rod, and check on the same tooth.

If necessary, adjust as follows:

1. Loosen the four hex-head cap screws that secure table to trunnion and rear bracket. Do not loosen more than one full turn.

Make sure that miter gauge, set at 90°, is exactly at a right angle to the table slots.

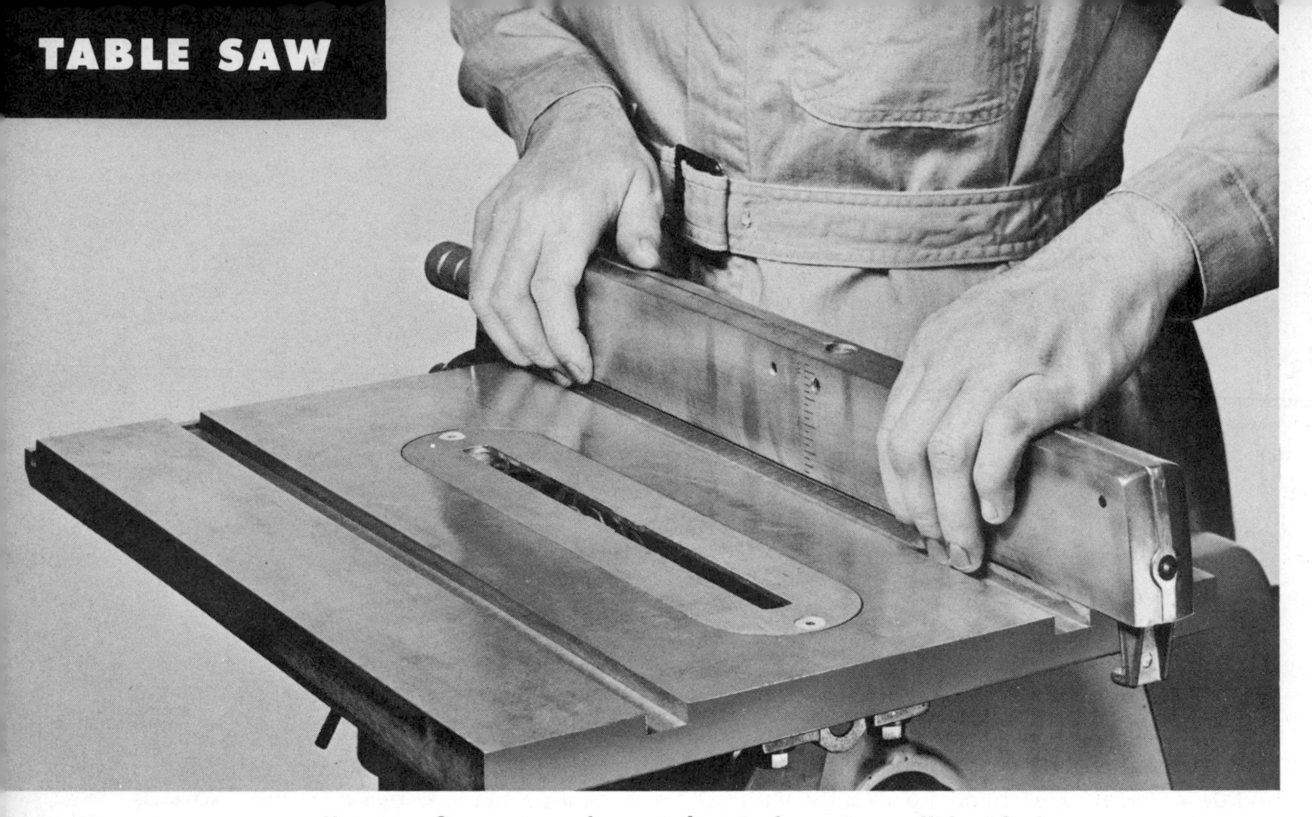

Use your fingers to make sure that rip fence is parallel with slots.

2. Tap the table lightly with the heel of your hand to rotate it into alignment.

3. Lock the four cap screws, turning each one a small amount, and repeating until all are secured.

4. Make a trial cut, and check the work with a square.

Next, check the miter gauge to see if it is at right angles to the table slots:

1. Set the miter gauge in either slot, and use a square as shown on preceding page.

2. Be sure one arm of square is held firmly against the face of the miter gauge. Be sure the other is flush against the side of the other table slot.

3. If angle between miter gauge and slot is not exactly 90°, adjustment is required.

If necessary, adjust as follows:

1. Loosen lock knob and pull out miter-gauge plunger.

2. Adjust miter gauge exactly square to slot, and lock in place.

3. Push in plunger and adjust Nylok set screw until it bears against plunger.

4. Adjust miter-gauge vernier plate until middle calibration is lined up exactly with 90° mark on miter gauge.

5. Make a trial cut and check it with a square.

To set 45° auto-stops, follow this procedure:

1. Loosen lock knob, and turn miter-gauge head until center mark on vernier plate is lined up with 45° mark on miter gauge.

2. Push in plunger and adjust Nylok set screw until it bears against plunger.

3. Make a similar adjustment on the opposite 45° auto-stop.

4. Make trial cuts at each setting and check with a square.

Finally, adjust the rip fence so it is parallel to the table slots:

1. Place the fence on the table and lock it in line with one table slot, as shown in the photograph above.

2. Use your fingers as shown to check the side of the fence to see if it is perfectly in line with the side of the slot.

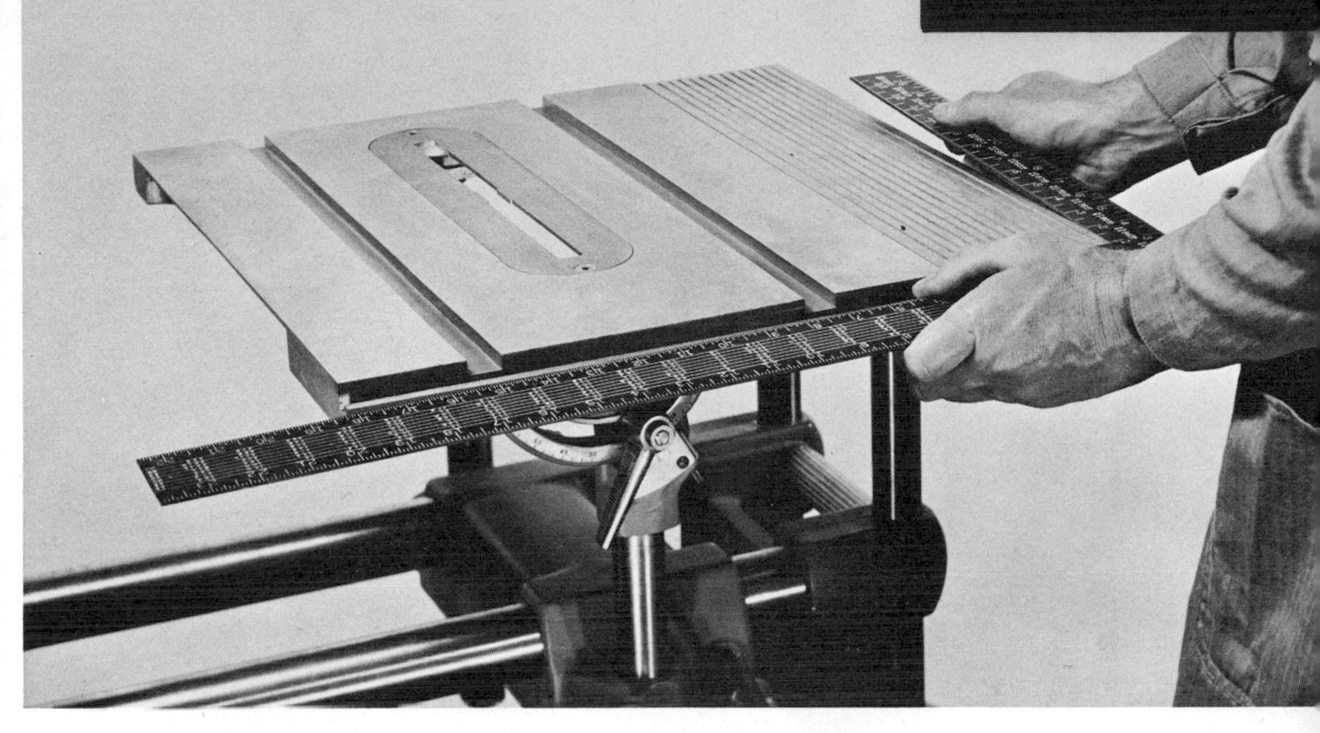

Extension table must be parallel with saw table. Front surfaces must be in line.

If necessary, adjust as follows:

1. Loosen the two cap screws on the underside of the fence base casting.

2. Adjust the fence until it is exactly parallel to the table slot.

3. Tighten the two screws.

Check the extension table to be sure it is parallel to the saw table, and in line across the front surfaces (photograph above):

1. Mount extension table and lock at same height as saw table.

2. Move saw table and butt it against edge of extension table.

3. Check for alignment of front surfaces with a straightedge.

If adjustment is necessary, follow this procedure:

1. Loosen the four cap screws which secure the extension table to its mounting bracket.

2. Adjust extension table so it butts flush against saw table throughout its length.

3. Tap extension table forward or backward until front edge is in line with front edge of saw table.

4. Tighten the four cap screws again, turning each one a small amount at a time, until all four are secure.

When these points have been checked, and necessary adjustments made, your table saw will give you square, true cuts. Remember these warning signals and when they appear check the saw before going any further:

1. The work shows a tendency to move away from the rip fence.

2. The saw produces an unusually wide kerf.

3. The work binds between saw blade and fence, perhaps burning inside face of kerf.

4. A crosscut does not check square, or shows a slight bevel.

5. The work binds when crosscutting.

6. The work shows a tendency to move to the right or left when crosscutting.

7. A miter cut does not check with the setting on the miter-gauge scale.

An assortment like this of the most-used saw blades will step up your cutting efficiency.

Circular Saw Blades: The Types and Their Uses

Most generally useful of the many types of blades available are the seven shown above. They are described below, from **right** to **left.**

1. This special all-purpose combination blade is standard equipment on the multi-purpose tool. It does a fast, clean job on both crosscutting and ripping.

2. The crosscut blade is designed for use when a great deal of crosscutting is done. It is not intended for ripping.

3. The ripsaw, like the crosscut blade, does just one job well. It is designed for maximum efficiency when doing production ripping. Don't use it for crosscutting.

4. The hollow-ground combination blade will function as both a ripsaw and a crosscut saw. Its special design produces a cut as smooth as a planed edge, and it is often called a planer blade. The diagram at the top of the next page shows the hollow-ground feature of the blade. Because of this innovation and the fact that the teeth are not set, the cut it makes is smooth. The diagram also shows the path of such a blade through a cut. It can be seen that if there is not sufficient blade projection above the work, the blade will tend to bind in the kerf, and may burn. Use the blade for fine work only and for mitering cuts; do not use it for general sizing cuts. Whenever you do use it, be sure that the blade projects at least ¾″ over the work.

5. The cutoff wheel is an abrasive disc that mounts on a 5/8″ arbor. It will slice through steel and other metals in solid, extruded, or tube shapes. It should never be used under great pressure, nor should excessive pressure be exerted against the side of the wheel. It may be used, however, to sharpen tools such as lathe chisels. When using the cutoff wheel, it is wise to employ flanges that are at least 1/3 the diameter of the wheel itself. The flexible, or reinforced, cutoff wheel of the kind shown here is much safer than the rigid variety.

6. The Magna Dado is an ingenious single-blade dado assembly. It has a heavy blade and a geared hub assembly to permit adjustments from a normal kerf (5/32″) up to a 7/8″ slot. The minimum cut is at "A" position, the maximum at "Z". An Allen wrench is used for the settings.

7. The "safety-cut" blade, a relative newcomer in the field, usually has only eight teeth, yet performs with maximum efficiency at minimum power consumption. It too is a combination blade, crosscutting and ripping equally well, and it produces a smooth cut. One of its outstanding features is that it reduces kickback to a minimum.

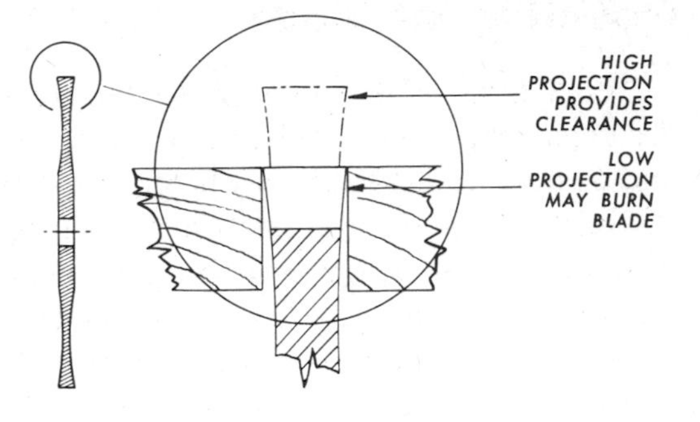

The shape of the hollow-ground blade demands a greater projection above the work. Otherwise there may be a tendency to bind, or the work or the blade may burn.

The drawing below shows simplified views of the teeth on the various blades, making a chart useful for identifying the different types. An additional blade in quite common use is a flat-ground combination blade similar in appearance to the hollow-ground one in the center of the photograph. It may be used for both crosscutting and ripping but it will not produce the smooth cut of the hollow-ground blade.

Use this chart of tooth styles to identify the various types of saw blades in common use.

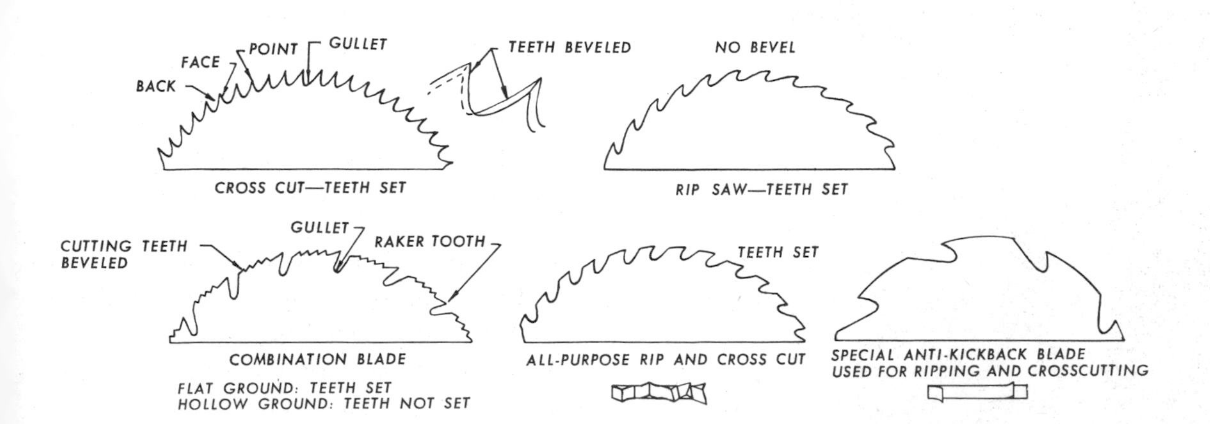

Mounting the Blade

The spindle of the multi-purpose tool is designed to permit rapid change of arbors and all other tools which may be mounted on it. To mount an arbor (sketch at right) place it on the spindle as far as it will go. Always be sure that the hole in the arbor is free from wood chips and other shop dirt. Tighten the set screw against the tapered flat with the Allen wrench provided. The tapered flat is a great safety feature since even a loose screw will wedge against it to prevent the arbor from flying off the spindle.

The 9-inch saw blade mounts on a special 1¼″ saw-blade arbor. Remove the arbor nut by turning it clockwise. (Thread is left-hand so nut will tend to tighten as saw turns.) Hold the arbor with the flats pointing toward your left. Slip on the saw blade with the teeth pointing in your direction. Replace the nut and finger-tighten by turning counter-clockwise. Place the arbor on the spindle with the

Lumber grips saw teeth for easy loosening of arbor nut without taking arbor off spindle.

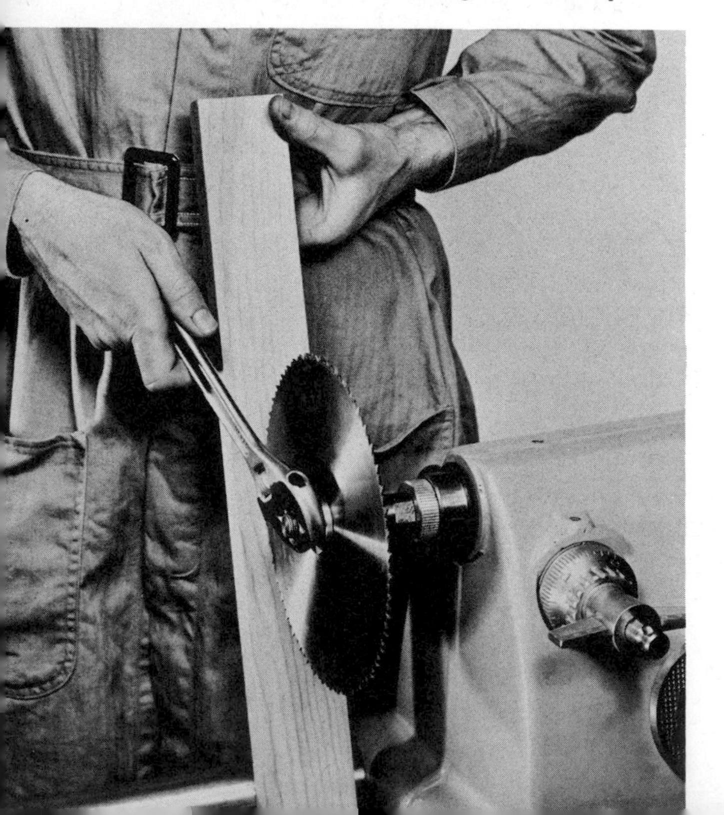

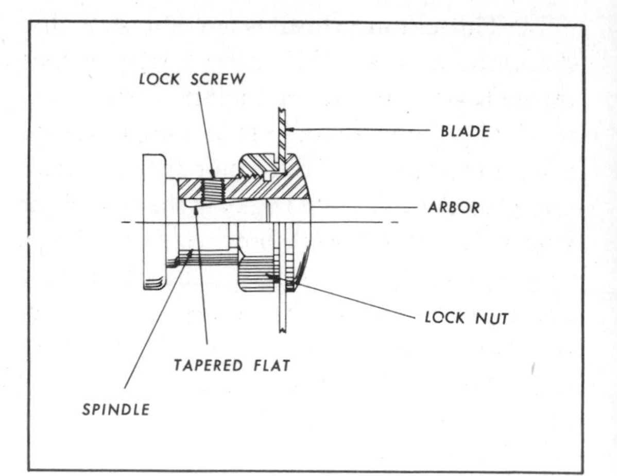

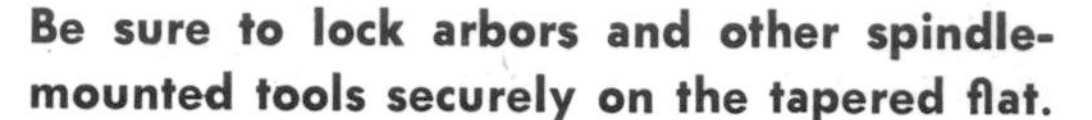

Be sure to lock arbors and other spindle-mounted tools securely on the tapered flat.

set screw positioned over the tapered flat, and lock in place with the Allen wrench. Hold the arbor flats with one wrench and the arbor nut with the special wrench provided, and tighten.

To loosen the arbor nut on a conventional arbor, use a scrap piece of wood as shown in photograph at lower left. (This method works also on the special 1¼″ arbor.) Brace the wood against the blade and the inside edge of the front tube, and use a wrench on the arbor nut. To tighten the nut, place the scrap piece of wood against the back of the blade and the inside edge of the rear tube.

When using this method, always be sure to stand so the wood protects you from the blade, and **always be sure that the power is off.** Checking the switch is not enough. When making **any** major adjustment on any power tool, **always remove the plug** from the power source. This may sound old-maidish, but many accidents have happened after the operator turned off the switch—because it was turned on again by someone brushing against it or by a tool dropping on it.

Once the blade is on the arbor, lower the table over it and place it so the blade is centered in the saw slot. This setting is constant after the initial adjustment of the screw on the headstock side of the carriage.

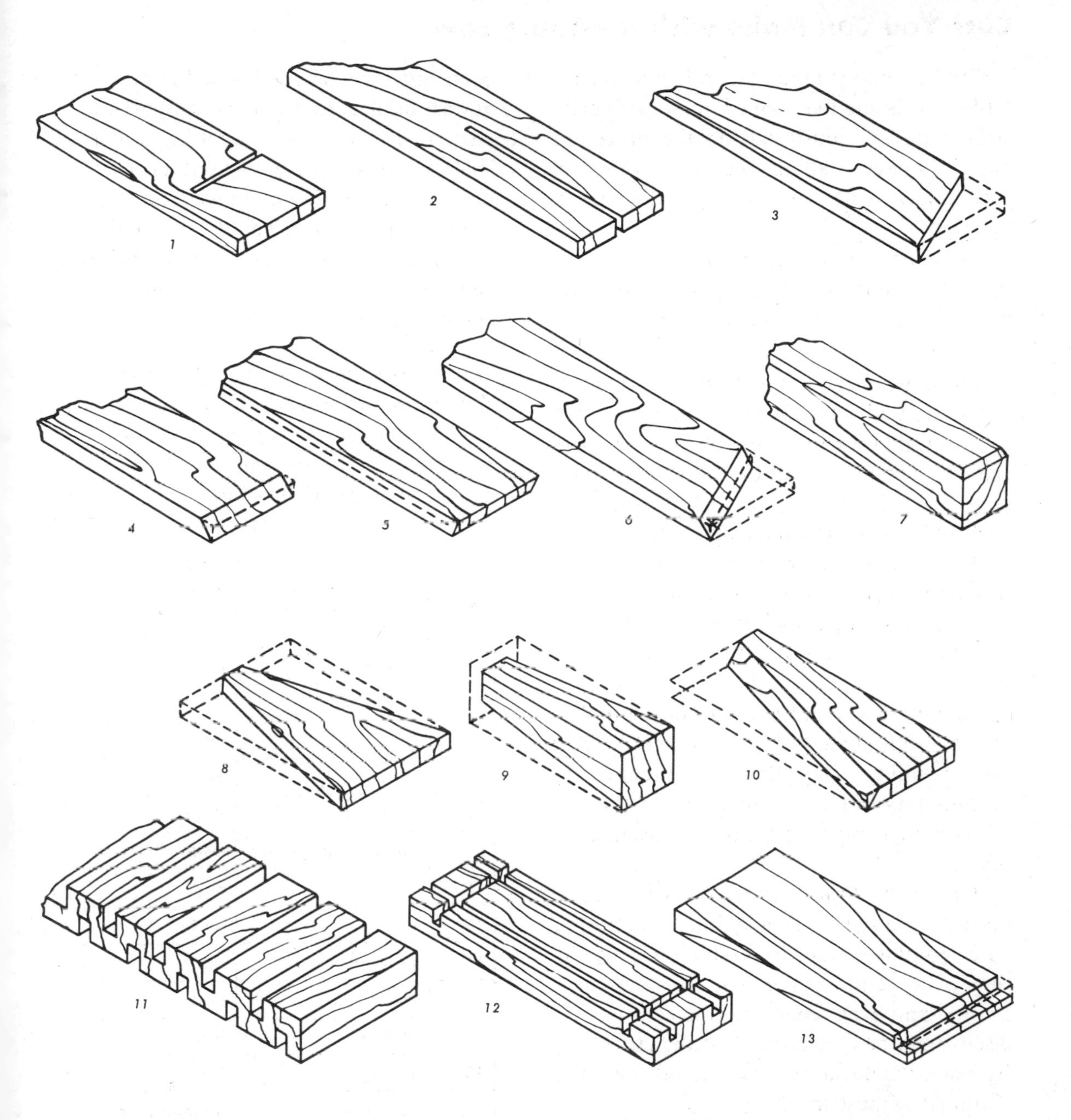

These are saw cuts possible with a regular blade. Their names, and the pages on which more information about them can be found, are:

1. **crosscut, page 14**
2. **rip cut, 24**
3. **miter, 30**
4. **cross-bevel, 36**
5. **rip-bevel, 36**
6. **compound miter, 39**
7. **chamfer, 68**
8. **two-sided taper, 29**
9. **four-sided taper, 29**
10. **compound rip-bevel, 39**
11. **kerfing, 64**
12. **kerfing, 63**
13. **rabbet (two-pass), 44**

Cuts You Can Make with the Table Saw

Cuts of many kinds are possible on the table saw. Some that can be made with basic equipment are illustrated on the preceding page. Others, calling for accessories or special techniques, are shown on the page at the right.

These two groups of diagrams give you a quick look at the many cuts possible and provide a handy reference guide for this chapter of the book.

Those who know how to use a table saw but are not advanced in procedures may wish to start right off with a project, making use of these two charts. If, for example, the project calls for a finger-lap joint on a box corner, refer to Number 15 on the opposite page and find that the procedure is explained and illustrated on Page 48. If the joint calls for a stud tenon or a through slot, refer to Number 8 or Number 10 and find that they are illustrated on Page 51.

Beginners who are not familiar with power tools should study the text carefully from the beginning. Then they may practice the various types of cuts, finally going through all of them, using the page references listed in the charts.

The charts **do not** illustrate sawing curves on the table saw. This may be accomplished with templates and forms which permit cutting of a gentle curve, but the method is limited and even when extreme care is exercised it can be dangerous. Cutting curves is a jig saw or band saw operation and should be confined to those machines.

Work that can be done with a molding head is illustrated in the charts. This is a table-saw accessory, popular with both beginners and experts. It consists of a steel or aluminum head which mounts on an arbor or directly on the spindle. Shaped or straight knives (usually in sets of three) are locked in the head. It is especially useful for surface cuts, but may be used also for many operations similar to those accomplished on a shaper. In addition to cutting full profile shapes, the knives can be used for partial cut, or cuts with different knives may be combined. Thus with a small but carefully selected assortment of molding knives it is possible to shape a virtually unlimited range of standard and original designs.

The saw cuts shown at the right are those calling for accessories or special techniques. The list below identifies the saw cut, indicates the accessory used to make it, and gives the page of this book on which more information about it appears.

NO.	NAME OF CUT	ACCESSORY	PAGE
1	dado	dado	40
2	groove	dado	41
3	hollowing	dado	41
4	rabbet	dado	44
5	rabbet	dado	44
6	notching	dado	47
7	tongue-and-groove	dado	53
8	stud tenon	dado	51
9	slot	dado	53
10	through slot	dado	51
11	true tenon	dado	50
12	coving	blade	57
13	coving	blade	56
14	surface cuts	molding head	73
15	finger lap	dado	48
16	dovetail		120
17	special groove	dado	42
18	molded edge	molding head	71
19	coved edge	molding head	71
20	molding or edge	molding head	73

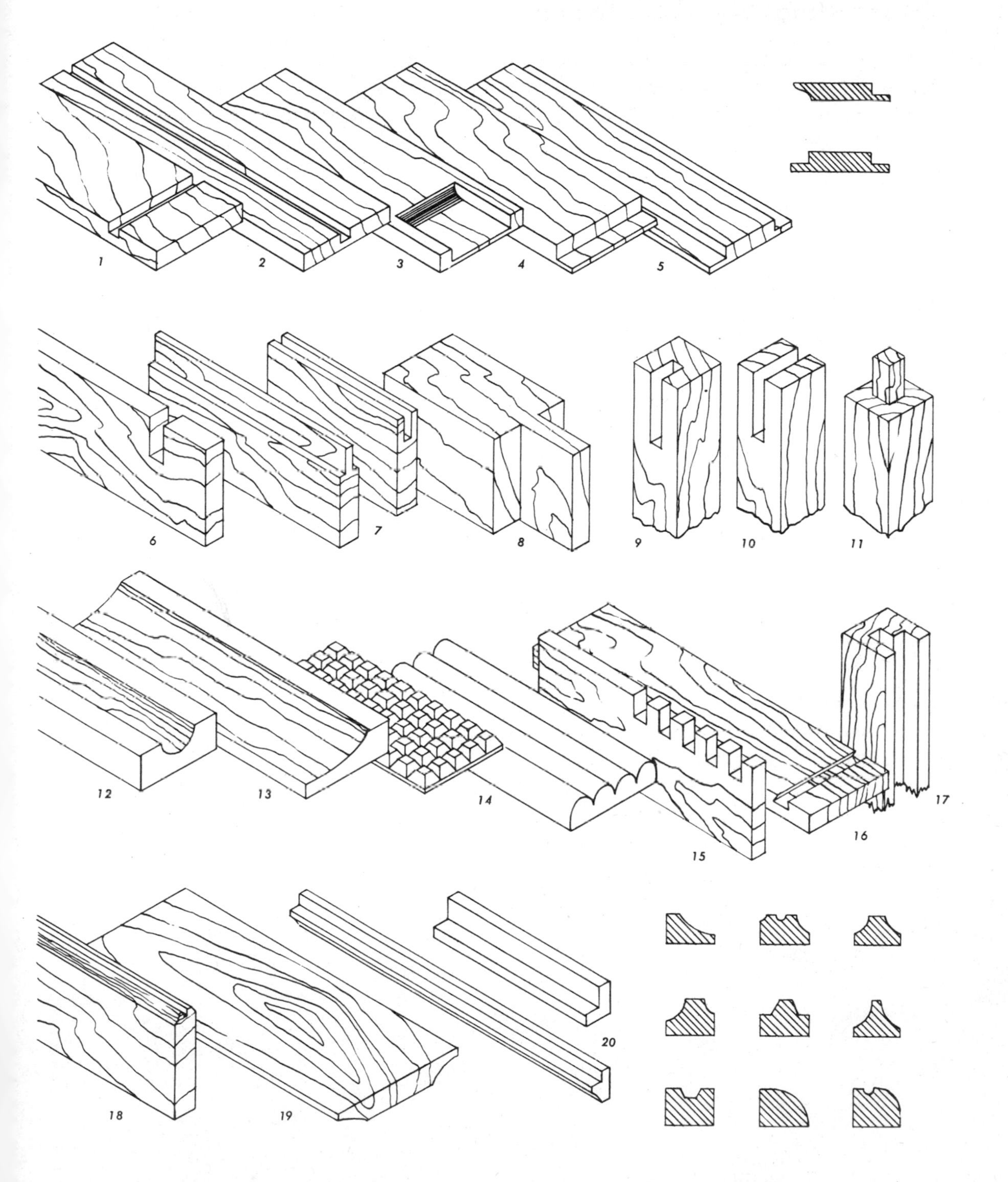
1
2
3
4
5
6
7
8
9
10
11
12
13
14
15
16
17
18
19
20

Crosscutting: The Basic Techniques

Simple crosscutting (photograph below) is done by placing the work against the miter gauge and advancing both work and gauge past the blade.

The position of the operator—and particularly of his hands on the work—is important. Although the miter gauge may be used in either of the table slots, most workers find it more convenient to use the slot to the left of the blade. Assume a posture almost directly behind the miter gauge, with the fingers of the left hand lightly holding the work against the miter-gauge head and the right hand, as shown, feeding the work. This position places the operator out of the line of cut. Never force the work against the blade.

Do not consider the cut complete until the work has passed the blade. It is important to understand that while the pass is complete when the work has been advanced past the blade the **operation** is complete only when the work and the miter gauge have been returned to the starting point.

Since most crosscutting operations may be accomplished with one hand, many cabinetmakers habitually use one hand both to hold and to feed the work. This is not a bad practice, when the work is light.

Recently the manufacturers of the multipurpose tool introduced a new miter-gauge hold-down. This accessory, which is easily mounted on the standard miter gauge, auto-

When crosscutting, hold stock firmly against miter gauge and place hands as shown here.

matically bears down on the work when the handle is gripped. The action of the hold-down rod, which is adjustable to accommodate varying stock thicknesses, holds the work firmly down on the table and snug against the miter-gauge head. This increases safety, accuracy, and convenience on almost all sawing operations. On miter cuts it counteracts creep, the tendency of the saw blade to pull the work as the pass is made. It is shown in use in the photograph below.

Never use the free hand to push against the free end of the work. This binds the blade and can result in a dangerous kickback. Use the free hand as a guide only, or for additional support.

Many beginners make the mistake of using the free hand to pick up a cutoff while the blade is still running. Many thoroughly unwelcome things can happen. The hand holding the miter gauge could slip into the blade; the free hand might nudge the cutoff into the blade, causing it to be thrown back against the operator; the action of the blade on the cutoff might knock the free hand into the blade. **Never pick a free piece off the table while the blade is running, unless it is a long one.** It takes only a few seconds for the blade to stop after the switch has been turned off, and it's worth the wait.

Avoid wearing loose sleeves. Either button them tightly at the wrists or roll them up well above the elbows. Do not allow a tie to hang free. If you wear a shop coat, paper clips are useful for holding the sleeves tight at the wrists.

The miter-gauge safety grip adds to convenience, safety, and accuracy when crosscutting.

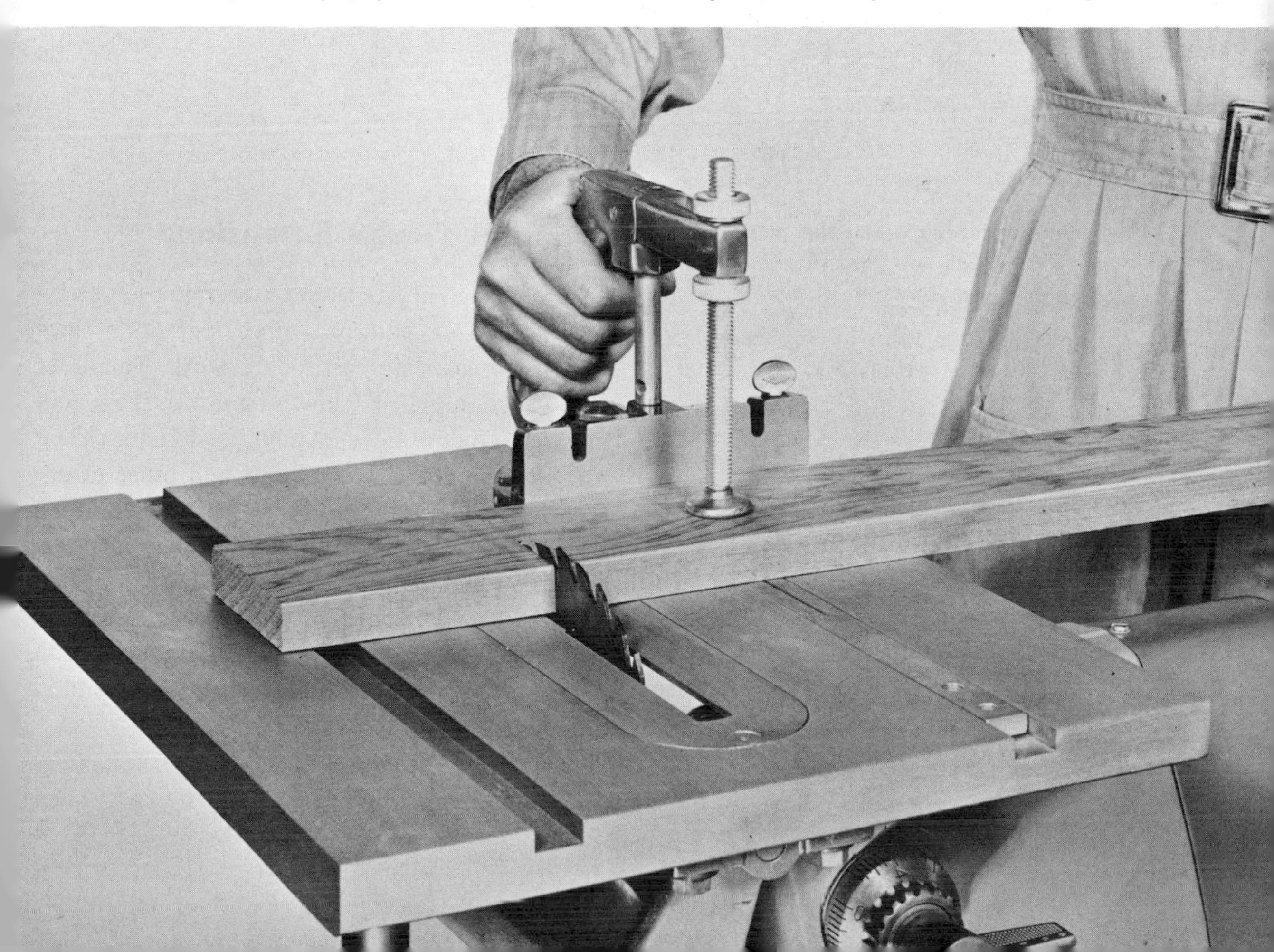

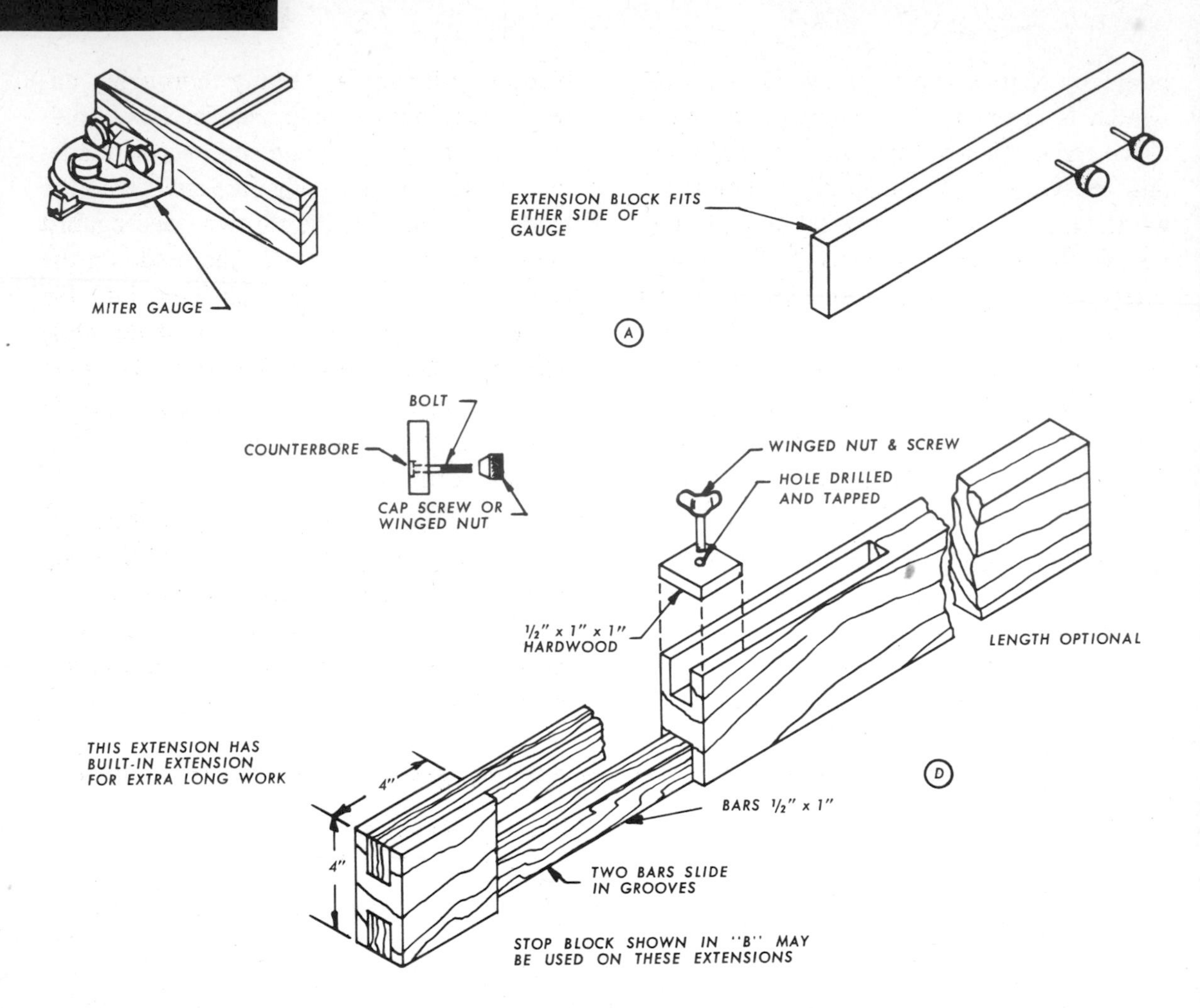

You can easily make the miter-gauge extensions and stop blocks shown in drawings above.

Miter gauge has slots for mounting extensions.

Miter-Gauge Extensions

It is good practice to use a miter-gauge extension for all crosscutting operations, since it increases support for the work. The miter gauge supplied with the multi-purpose tool has a pair of slots cut in its head (photograph at left) for mounting this and other extensions. The extensions may be reversed in the gauge or used on either side of the blade. It is a good idea to have several on hand, each for a specific purpose. A pair of ¼″ machine or carriage bolts about 1½″ long, fitted with washers and wing nuts, may be used to hold homemade extensions in place.

The photograph at right shows an extension being used to provide support when

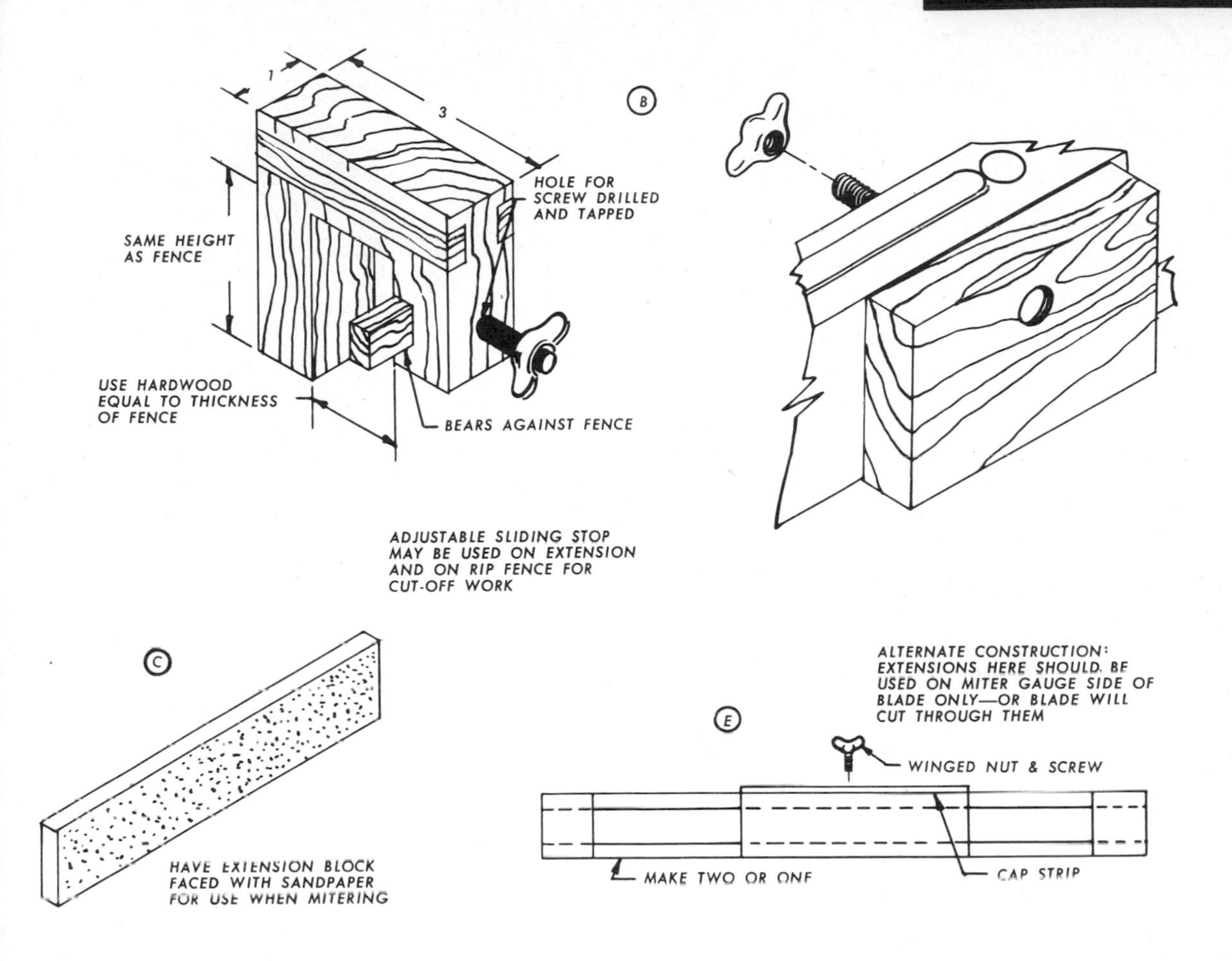

crosscutting a very short piece. It also shows how an extension can be used as a guide to determine the line of cut. Measure the work to the length required, pencil-marking the edge which rests against the gauge. Line up this mark with the slot in the extension, and the saw kerf will be where you want it. It is also a good idea to use a square, when marking to length, and to mark right across the board. Then you can judge the squareness of the cut.

An extension faced with sandpaper (sketched above) provides a high-friction surface especially useful when making mitering cuts. The sandpaper may be applied to the extension with rubber cement for easy removal.

Use hold-down block on small work. Line up mark on work with slot in extension.

Use a miter-gauge stop rod like this to cut one piece or many pieces to an exact length.

Determine length of work by measuring from rod to point of one tooth set in its direction.

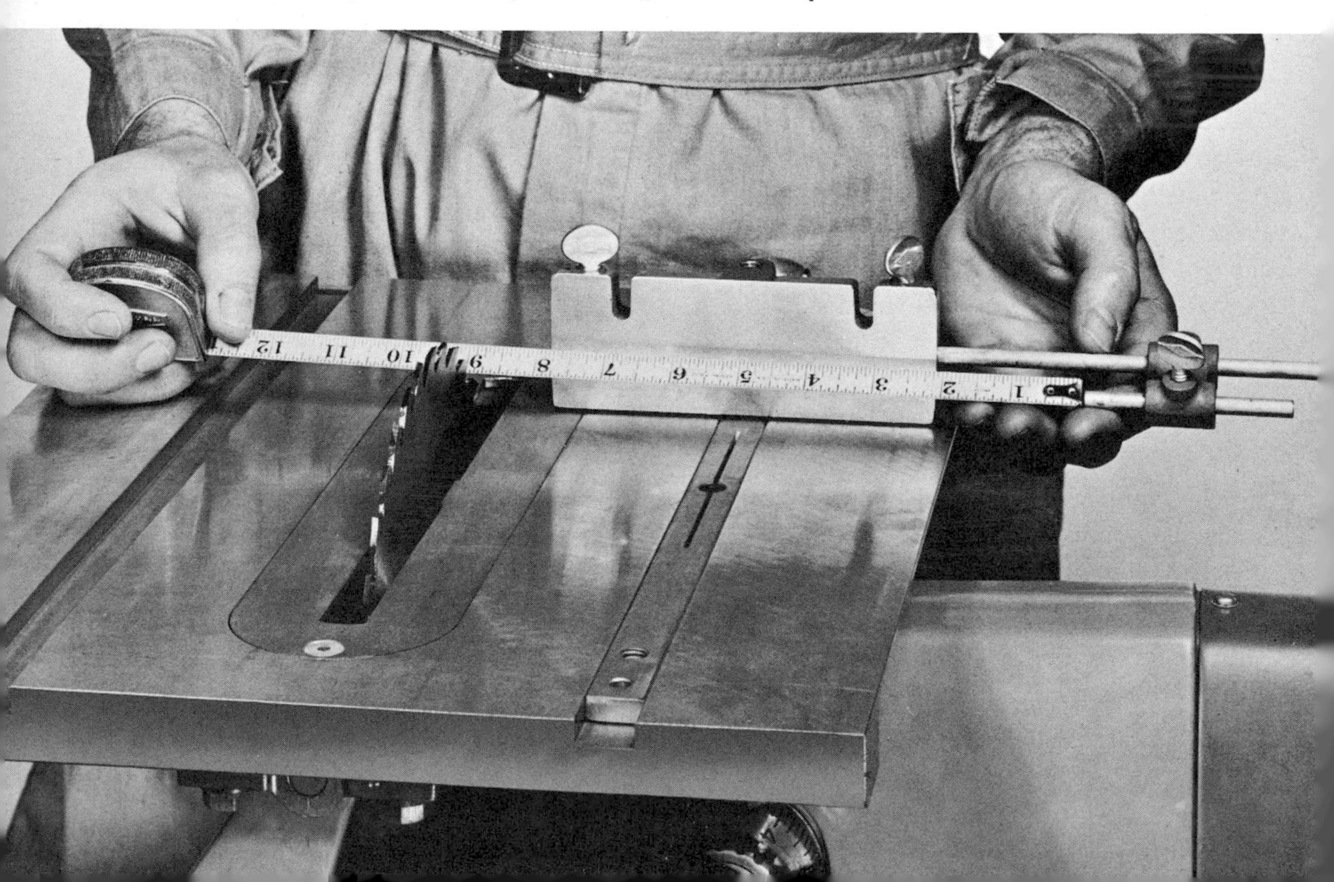

Use of stop block bolted to rip fence is another way to gauge length of duplicate pieces.

Crosscutting to Length

Except for squaring off the end of a board, crosscutting operations are usually done to cut pieces to exact lengths. When only one piece is required, the simplest method is to use the extension with a saw kerf through it, lining up the pencil mark with the kerf. When you need more than one piece, use the miter-gauge stop rod as shown in the upper picture on the opposite page. This rod may be used at either side of the gauge, which makes it usable with the miter gauge in either table slot. When short pieces are cut, the short rod is held in the miter gauge. When longer pieces are required, the long rod is held in the gauge and the short rod is adjusted for length of cut.

Gauge the cut as shown in the lower photograph. Move the rod with the left hand while the right hand holds the scale. Measure from a tooth set in the direction of the rod. Fasten the rod in position with the thumb-screw. Once the setting is made, any number of pieces may be cut to the same length by butting the end of the work against the rod and making the pass.

When a long piece of stock must be cut up into equal-size pieces, it is sometimes more convenient to use another method. (Beginners often attempt to use the rip fence as a stop to determine the length of the work—a dangerous practice.) The correct method is to use a stop block on the rip fence to gauge length of cut (photograph above). The block should be fastened in place on the fence at a point which will permit the front edge of the work to clear the blade. The work is butted against the stop block and the pass made.

Stop blocks of this type are easily made (drawing at top right on page 17) and will prove handy on many jobs. If you have Allen head set screws available, use them in place of wing nuts so the stops may be secured with the Allen wrench provided with the machine.

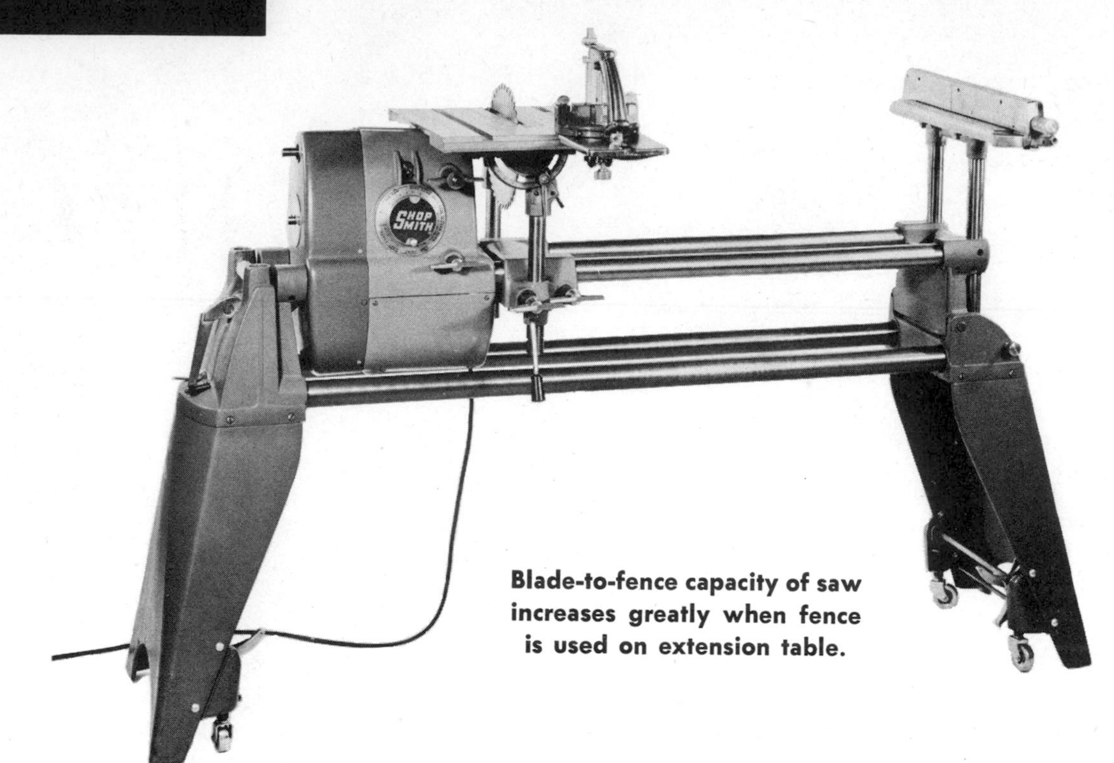

Blade-to-fence capacity of saw increases greatly when fence is used on extension table.

Use an extension floor stand for the extra support needed when crosscutting very long stock.

Crosscutting Long Work

A basic rule in machine woodworking is to provide maximum support for the workpiece. When you are crosscutting stock that extends without support beyond the saw table, the overhang tends to lift the work from the table, binding the blade and producing a kickback.

By taking advantage of the multi-purpose tool's extensions (top of page opposite) you can set the machine to provide support for various lengths of work. For example, the size of the table is 14″ x 18⅜″, but when you move the headstock and saw table to the left end of the ways and mount the table extension at the other end, you have an effective table-size of 18⅜″ x 36½″.

With the headstock to the right and the table extension at the left end, the effective table size is increased to 18⅜″ x 56″. This provides a capacity of 48″ between fence and saw blade—enough to cut to the center of an 8′ plywood panel. Since headstock and table carriage can be moved freely back and forth, there is great latitude in arrangement to provide support where needed.

For crosscutting excessively long stock, an adjustable floor stand is a necessity. Construction details are given below. Dimensions and design of the stand permit adjustments so it may be used at any table height. The extra roller top is used in crosscutting; the full-length roller is used in ripping.

Use these details to construct an extension floor stand. Use it with long roller for ripping, short rollers (shown at bottom and on opposite page) for crosscutting.

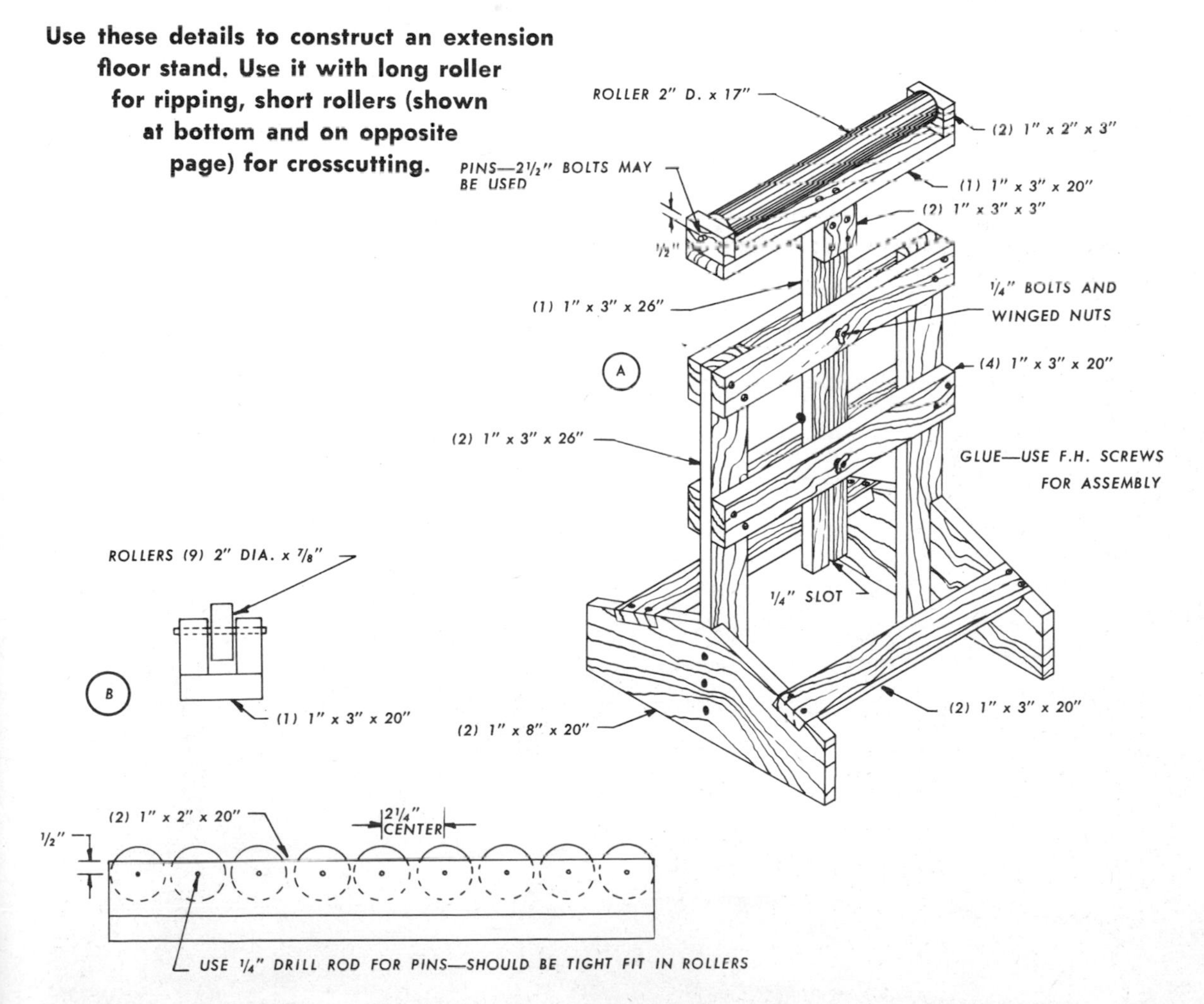

When using the stand, set it to equal the height of the table. Crosscutting even a very long and heavy piece of work is simple when the weight of the work rides on the rollers. When the table extension is placed between the table and the stand, it provides a center support for the work.

If you do not care to do the lathe job required to make rollers, you can substitute standard 1¾″ handrail stock, available from most lumber dealers.

Crosscutting wide boards requires maximum support in front of the blade. Actual table length in front of the blade, with the blade set to cut ¾″ stock, is about 7″—good support for average-size work. The trick of turning the miter gauge around and using it backwards in the slot (opposite page) increases the available table length somewhat, because it eliminates the space needed for the miter-gauge head. With this method a board 12″ wide can be cut with ease. The use of a front table extension increases the table size in front of the blade another 7″.

For crosscutting extra-wide work, such as glued stock or plywood panels, place the saw table and the extensions in positions that will provide the most support for the work. When there is considerable overhang, use the floor stand in one position to start the cut, then stop the saw and move the floor stand forward to provide support at the end of the cut. Crosscutting a plywood panel 4′ wide eliminates use of the miter gauge, so it is best to treat all such panel cuts as ripping operations.

Extra-long miter-gauge extensions can be used to provide additional support for long stock. These may be just straight pieces of wood or, as shown in the drawings on pages 16 and 17, they can be made to provide adjustment in length at one end (D) or both ends (E).

Duplicate cutting of long work can be handled with a stop block on the extension fence, as shown below. Notice how the end of the extension is supported by the extension table. The left hand is used for support and guidance; it should not be used to push the work. Forward motion should always be provided by the hand working the miter gauge. Pushing at other points will cause the blade to bind.

For duplicate cutting of long work: stop block on long gauge extension.

How to simplify cutting wide stock: just use the miter gauge backwards like this.

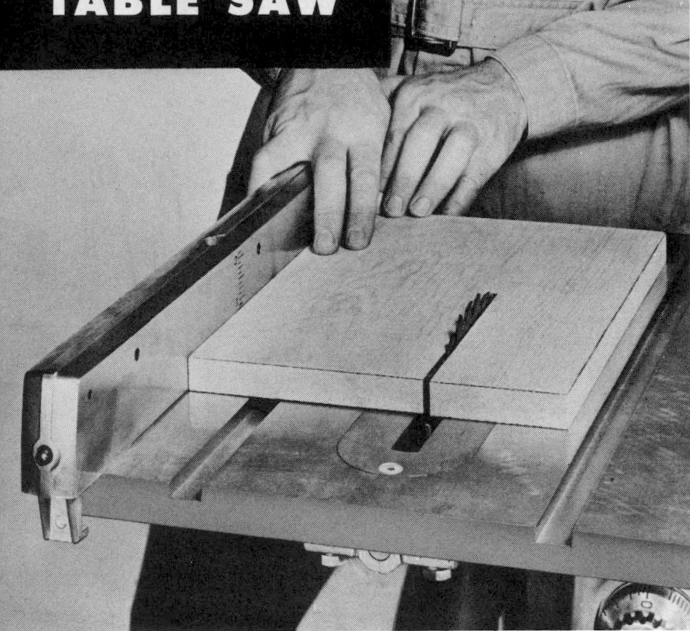

Keep finger hooked over fence on rip cuts.

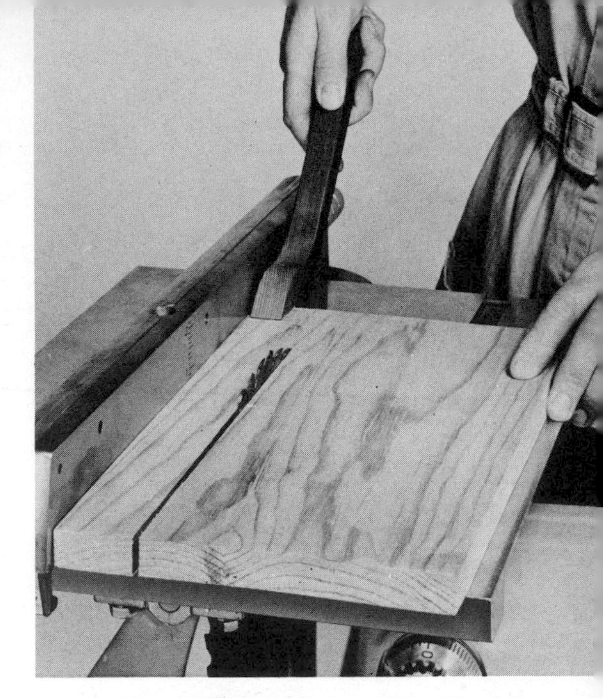

Use pusher when blade is within 3″ of fence.

Ripping

In ripping, the rip fence is used throughout the length of the work as a guide and as a control to maintain the width of the cut.

A simple ripping operation is shown at left above. The job is started with both hands, the left holding the work against the rip fence and the right feeding the work into the blade. The cut is completed by removing the left hand and using the right, **with fingers hooked over the fence** to feed the work until the cut is complete. There is no return on a ripping cut.

A handy little trick is to push the work past the blade until the overhang at the rear of the table causes the back edge of the work to tilt up into the palm of your hand. Then lift it from the table.

Start narrow ripping operations in the same manner but when your hand comes to within 4″ of the blade, use a pusher stick.

A simple way to make the pusher stick shown at left in drawing below is to use a wooden clothes hanger. Separate it at the center line and you have two pusher sticks that need only a notch at one end to be complete.

Push sticks like these are easy to make. For safety, use them whenever necessary.

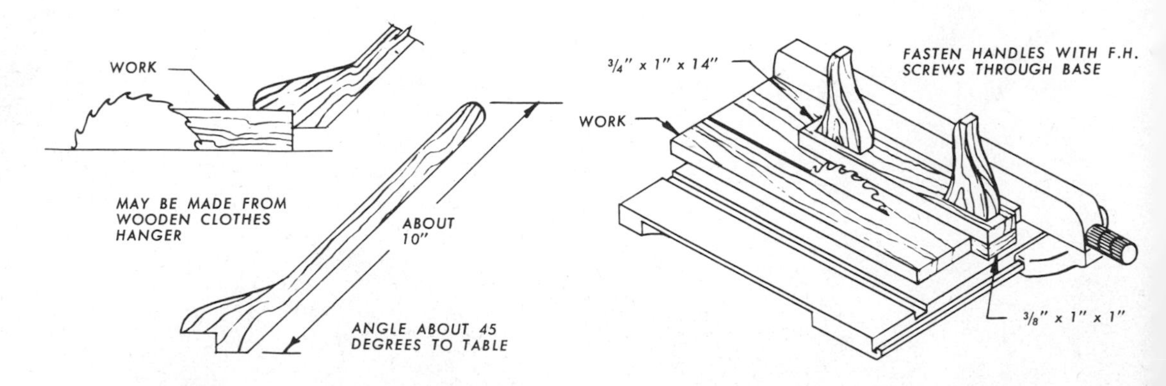

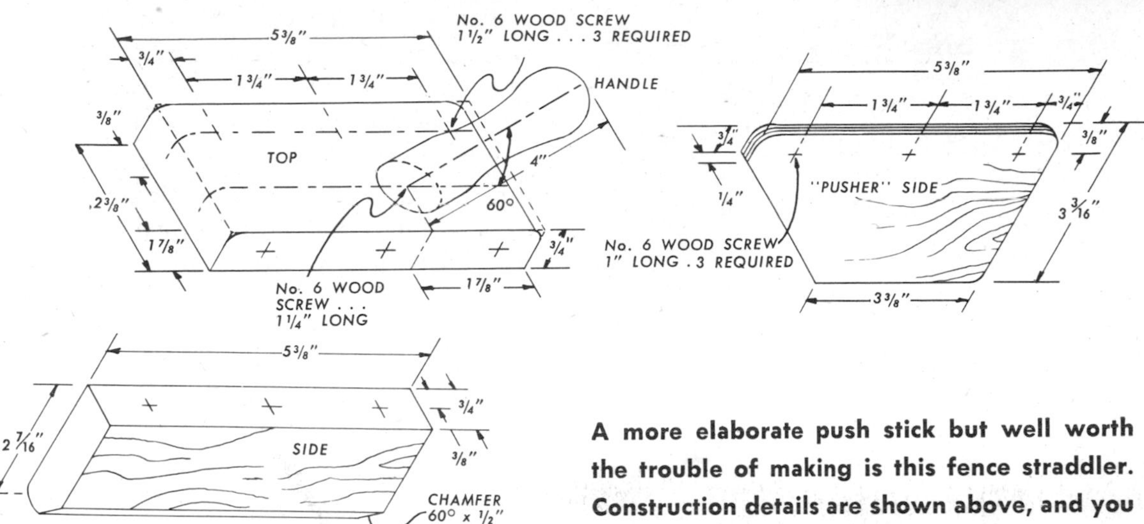

A more elaborate push stick but well worth the trouble of making is this fence straddler. Construction details are shown above, and you can see it in action in the photograph below.

The combination pusher-hold-down shown in right-hand drawing below is useful in grooving and in some edge-rabbeting, jointing and shaping operations.

The type shown above and at right provides additional safety by straddling the rip fence, keeping the hands far from the blade.

Ripping a somewhat longer piece of stock calls for starting the cut with your stance more to the left of the blade so the left hand can hold the work firmly against the rip fence. Use your right hand to support the back edge of the work and feed it forward until the table supports it. Then change your position to normal and complete the pass as usual. These steps are illustrated below.

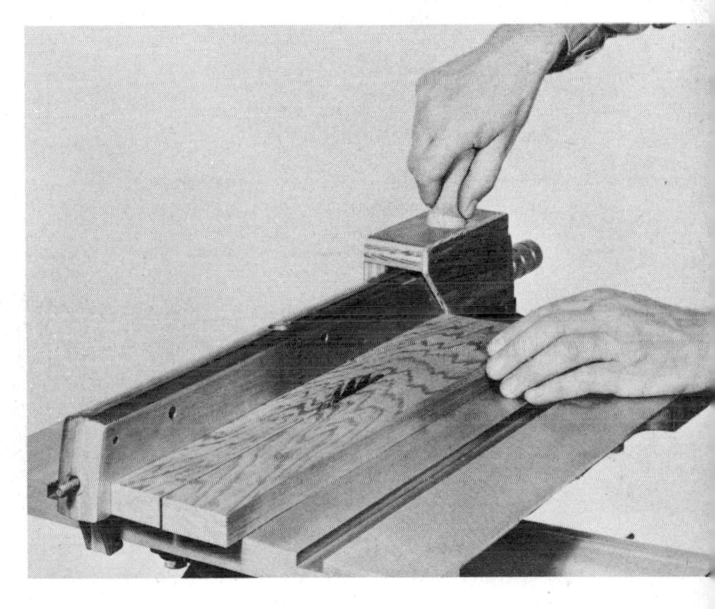

For a rip cut on a longer board, begin with hands placed this way. Near end of cut . . .

. . . remove left hand and complete pass with right, keeping fingers hooked over rip fence.

Ripping Long Work

The roller-top extension stand makes it simple to rip very long work. After setting the rip fence, place the stand as close to the machine as you can without allowing the weight of the overhang to lift the front edge of the work from the table. When starting the cut, stand at the left of the blade and use both hands to feed the work forward (upper photograph). When the board extends about 2 feet beyond the rear of the table, take a position at the back of the machine, as shown in lower photograph. Finish the cut by pulling the work through.

For production work, a two-man operation—one to place and feed the work at the front and the other to pull it through and dispose of it—makes for a fast and a safe procedure.

When ripping wide panels, use the extension table to support the work along the free edge.

Boards up to 20′ are easily ripped when an extension floor stand is used. Begin the cut as shown above. When the work reaches the position below, move around behind the machine as shown and finish by pulling the stock through.

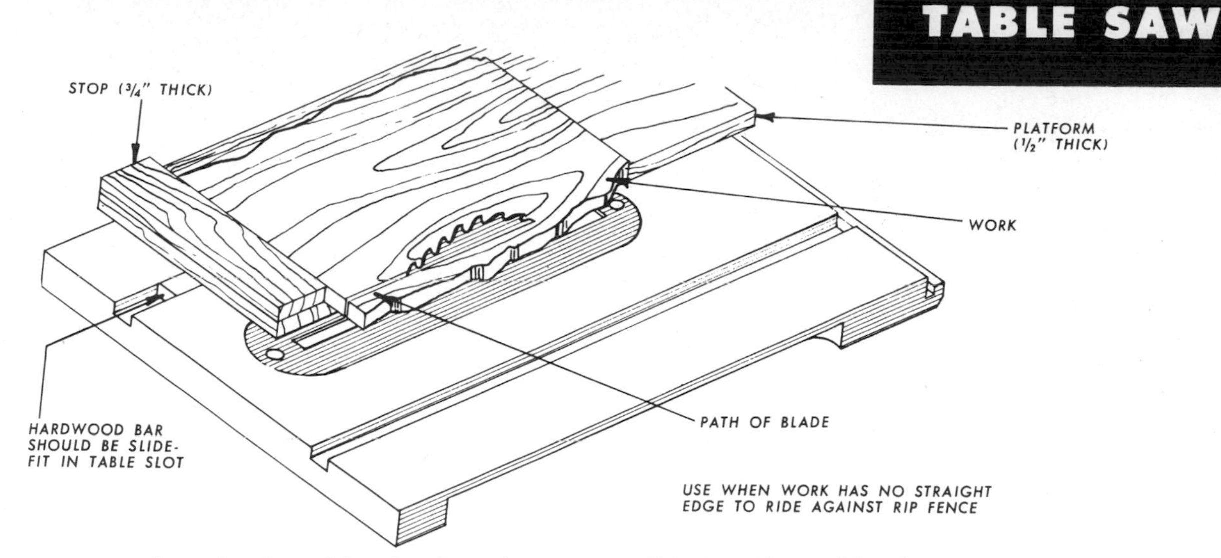

Squaring board has hardwood runner to slide in either table slot.

The Squaring Board

There are times when a piece of stock does not have a straight edge which can be used against the fence. The stock may be a piece that has been jig-sawed or band-sawed on both edges, or a rough piece of lumber that has been knocking around the shop. In order to obtain one straight edge, a jig known as a squaring board is used. This consists of a sliding table with a guide to fit the saw-table slot fastened to its underside. A cleat is fastened to the forward edge of the sliding table, at right angles to the saw blade. The work to be sawed is butted against the cleat, and the whole assembly is pushed past the blade.

Of course there is a size limit to work which can be handled in this fashion. Very large work, such as plywood panels or glued stock with rough edges, may be squared another way. A straight, narrow piece of stock is clamped or tack-nailed to the underside of the panel, to be used as a guide **along the edge of the saw table.** Placement of the guide strip will determine how much of the rough edge is cut off. To handle large panels, place headstock of multi-purpose tool at left end of ways, table extension at tailstock end.

The squaring board permits making a straight rip cut on stock having uneven edges.

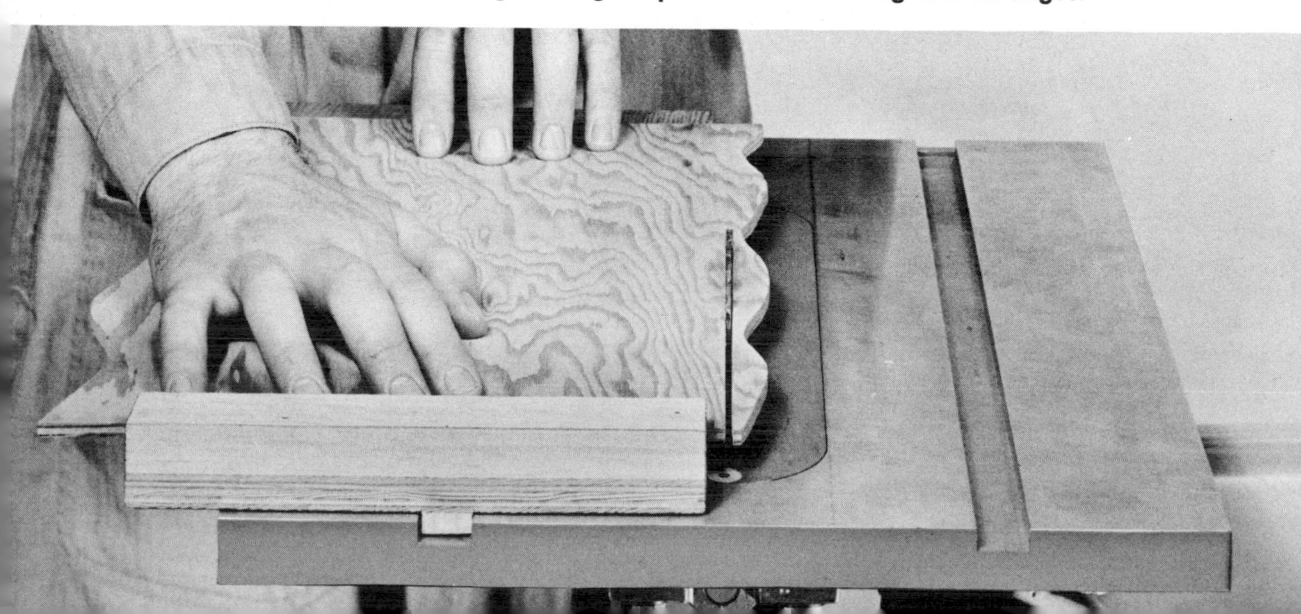

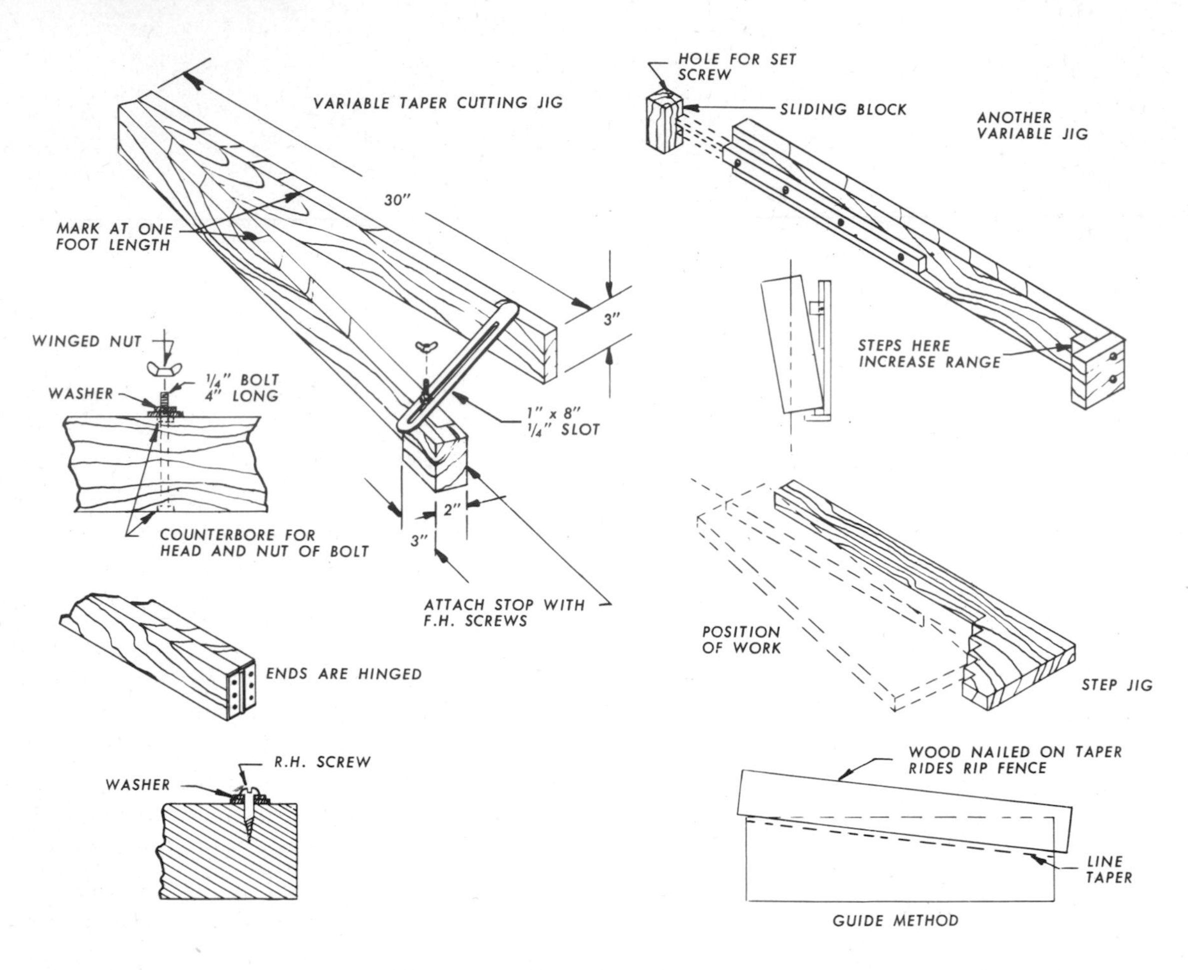

Jigs for cutting tapers: variable jig at left and another version at upper right; step jig for easy repetition of several tapers. Guide method for long work is at lower right.

To find taper per foot at any setting, measure across jig at points 12" from hinged end.

By marking the crossbar as shown here, you can calibrate the jig for presetting.

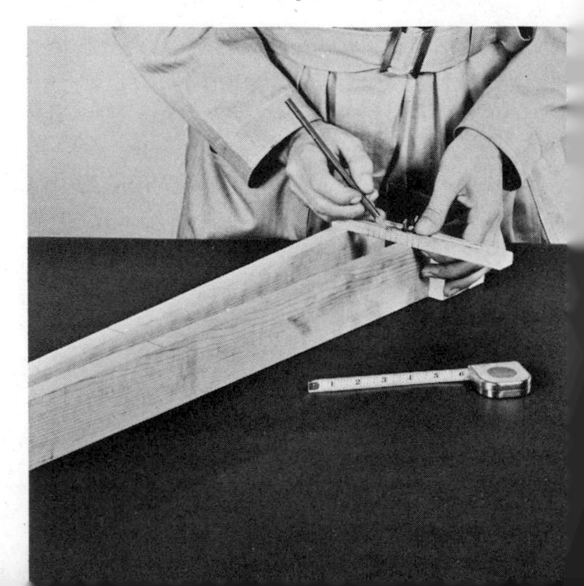

Taper Ripping

Taper cuts—needed for many projects—call for a jig with one straight side for riding the rip fence and a slanted side to gauge the taper. Such a jig is diagrammed on the opposite page. When hinging the ends, keep the two pieces clamped together. The crosspiece or brace that secures the setting can be made of metal or hardwood.

When the jig is complete, mark a line across both pieces 12″ in from the hinged end. Set the jig by measuring between these two marks (photograph at lower left) to determine the taper per foot.

If you are making a stool with legs that are 1′ long and 3″ wide at the top and 2″ wide at the bottom, you would require a 1″ taper per foot. By opening the jig 1″ at the 1′ mark, you'll have the setting.

To provide a scale for future adjustments, you can open the jig to various dimensions across the 1′ marks and pencil in the settings on the cross brace (see right-hand photograph on opposite page).

Use the jig as shown in the photograph at the right. Notice that the table saw has been brought to the right end of the ways and lined up with the extension table to increase the table area at the right of the blade.

Square legs with a taper on each face are made by setting the fence to equal the combined width of the jig and the work. Make one pass, then make the second pass on an adjacent face. Adjust the jig to twice the original setting and make the third and fourth passes on the next adjacent faces. When the work is square, the rip-fence setting need not be changed.

The step jig sketched on the opposite page is good for production work because it eliminates setting the variable jig for different tapers. The steps gauge the taper and are dimensioned for the various tapers needed. One corner of the work is placed in the correct step, while the other end rides against the arm of the jig.

For taper on one side of stock, use the taper jig as shown above. To taper second side, turn tapered side against fence and make a second pass with jig setting doubled.

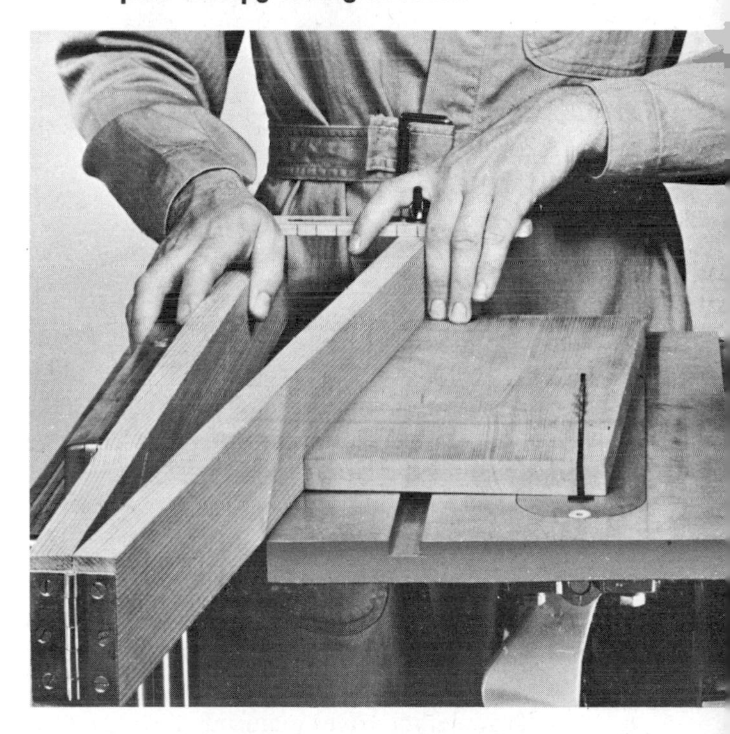

For long work that cannot be handled in a jig, use the guide method (lower right in drawing). Draw the line of taper on the work and nail a board with straight sides to it, one edge parallel to the taper line and about 1/4″ away from it. The opposite edge of the guide rides along the rip fence, which is set to cut on the taper line.

Safety Grip counteracts creep, increasing accuracy as well as safety on miter.

Mitering

A miter cut is an operation that requires a miter-gauge setting. Some examples of miter cuts used to form four-, six-, and eight-sided figures are given on the upper half of the opposite page, along with the miter-gauge settings used for each. The lower half of the page shows bevel-cutting.

The cut pieces, joined to make the forms, are called segments. When the work is not a shaped piece (such as molding), segments are cut as shown in the detail marked 4-3-2-1. This method saves material.

The miter cut can be accomplished with the gauge in either a closed or an open position. A closed position is shown in the upper left sketch. In the open position the miter gauge would be set in the opposite direction. The closed position is more convenient for small work, the open position for large.

While the miter cut sounds simple, it is actually one of the more difficult passes to make. No matter what precautions you may take, or how accurate the machine, the forward motion of the blade pulls the work, causing it to creep—maybe just enough to spoil a perfect miter. So a miter cut needs extra attention.

The miter-gauge safety hold-down shown above is most efficient in this operation since, by holding the work firmly on the table and against the miter gauge, it counteracts the tendency of the saw blade to pull the work.

A miter-gauge extension may be used to provide additional support for the work.

Use these settings of miter gauge or table for cutting 4-, 6-, or 8-sided figures. Drawings on the upper half of the page show miter-gauge settings, lower ones table settings.

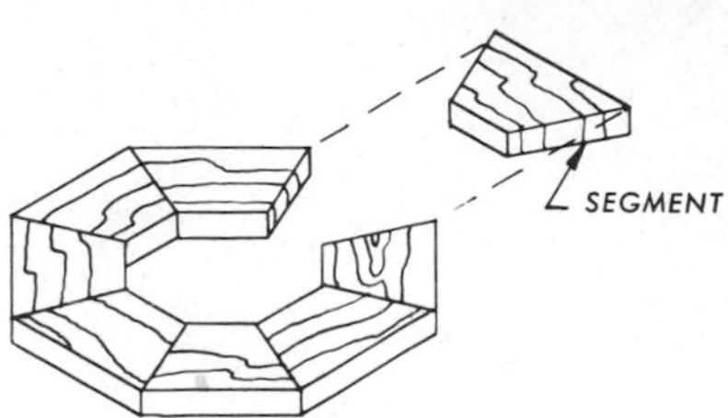

FOR OCTAGON (8 SIDES), SET MITER GAUGE AT $67\frac{1}{2}^{\circ}$

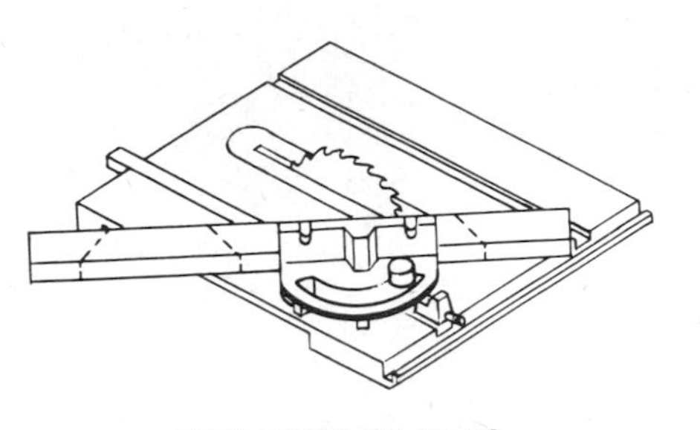

MITER GAUGE SET AT 45° FOR CUTTING SEGMENTS OF SQUARE (4 SIDES) AS SHOWN BELOW

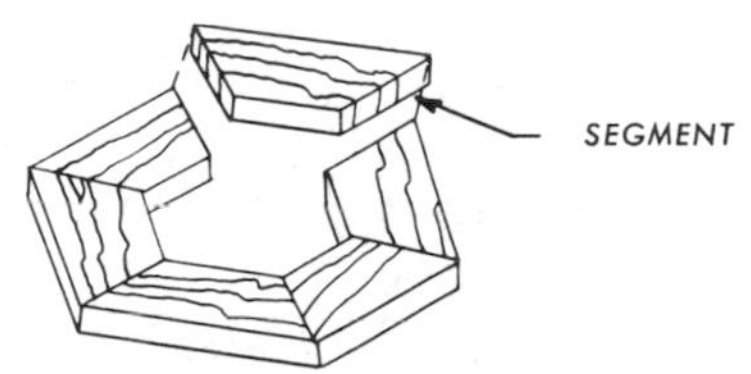

FOR HEXAGON (6 SIDES) SET MITER GAUGE AT 60°

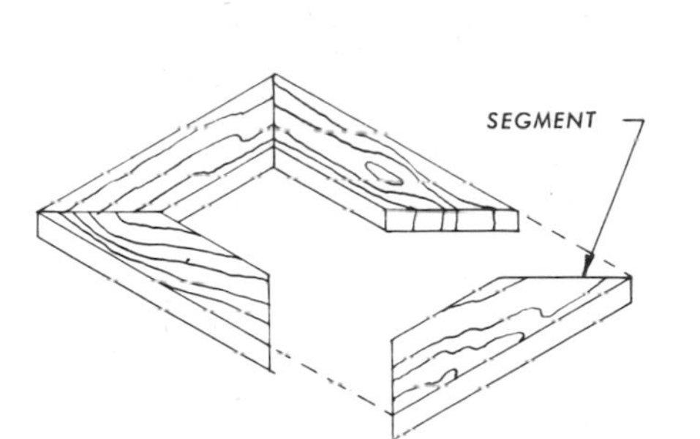

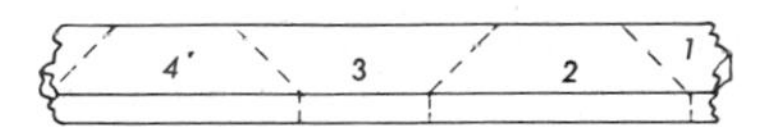

CUT STOCK AS ABOVE FOR BEST ECONOMY AND LEAST EFFORT

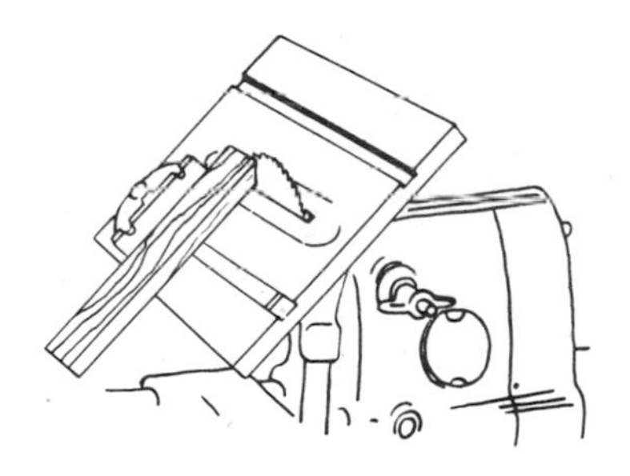

FOR BEVEL CUTTING, SET TABLE AT ANGLE REQUIRED AND MITER GAUGE AT 90°

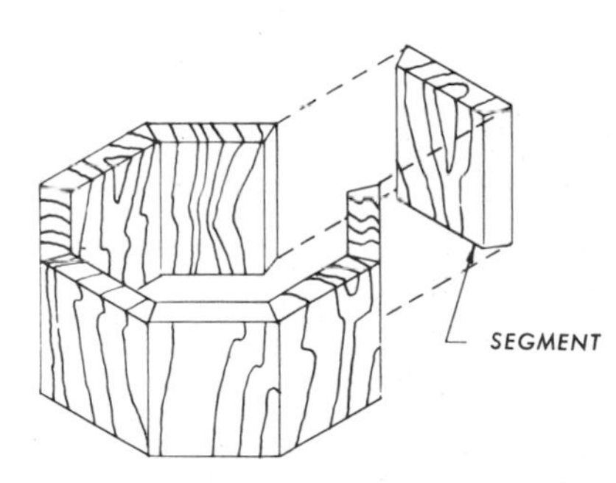

FOR OCTAGON, SET FOR BEVEL OF $22\frac{1}{2}^{\circ}$

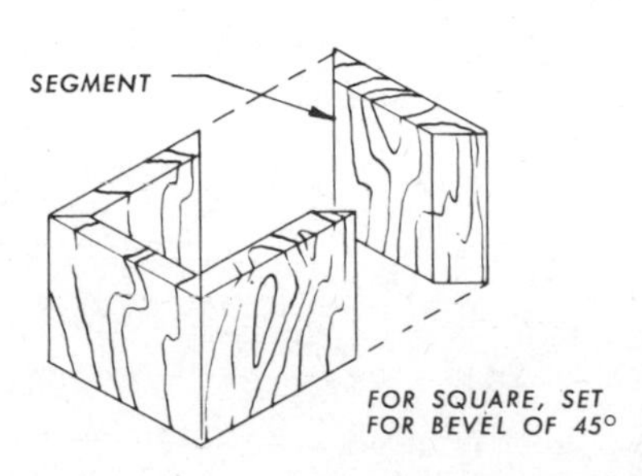

FOR SQUARE, SET FOR BEVEL OF 45°

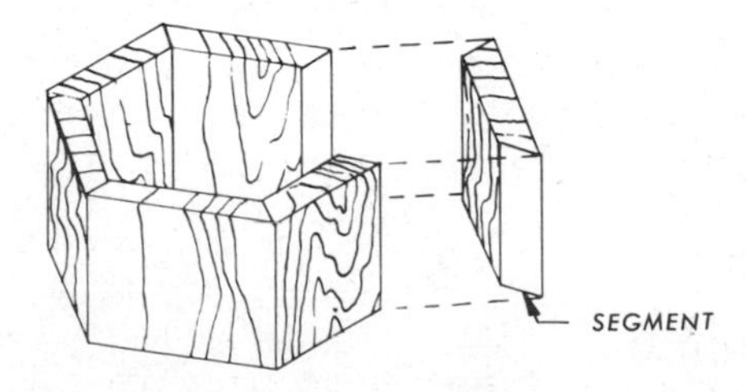

FOR HEXAGON, SET FOR BEVEL OF 30°

Face miter-gauge extension with sandpaper; it will give you a better grip for cutting miters.

Use the miter-gauge stop rod on miter cuts too when making a number of identical pieces.

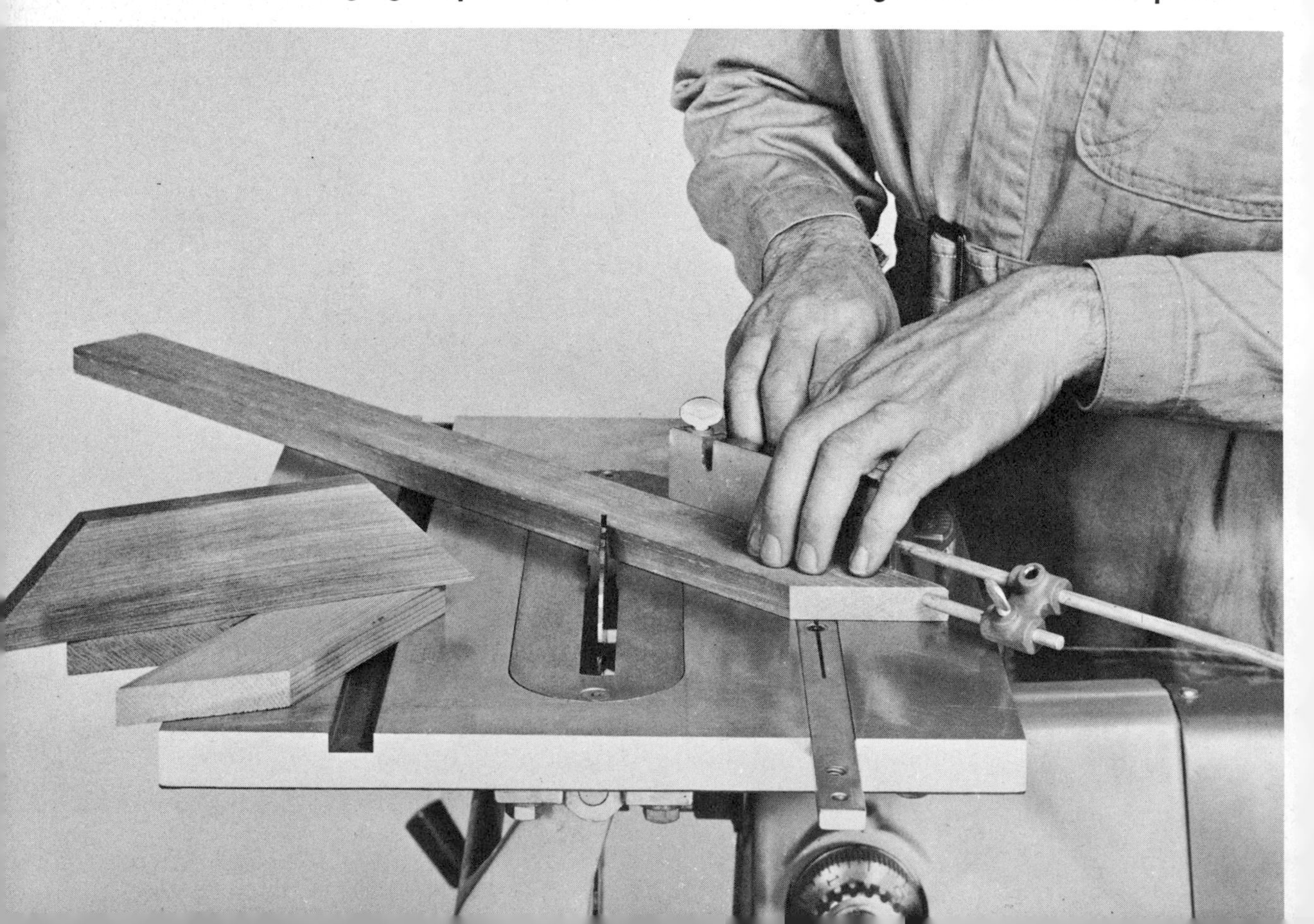

Facing the extension with sandpaper provides a gripping surface which helps to counteract creep. Always hold the work tightly against the miter-gauge head (upper photograph on opposite page) and feed it very slowly.

Here are some things that will cause inaccurate miter joints:

1. Improper alignment of the machine;
2. Saw blade dull or teeth incorrectly set;
3. Work warped or otherwise imperfect to begin with;
4. Work allowed to creep;
5. Pass made too fast.

Mitered segments must be perfectly matched in size and shape if they are to join together in a perfect union. The miter-gauge stop rod can be used as shown in lower picture on opposite page to gauge the length of the segments. First make a full-size, or accurate scale, drawing of the form, then pick off the true length of one segment. Square a piece of stock to this length. Set the miter gauge to the angle needed, and miter both ends of the segment. Then use it to set the stop rod on the miter gauge. Other segments are cut from one length of stock by mitering it at one end, then holding the mitered end against the stop rod. Be sure that you turn the work over for each new pass.

Here are examples of mitered segments, partly assembled. Note the use of splines.

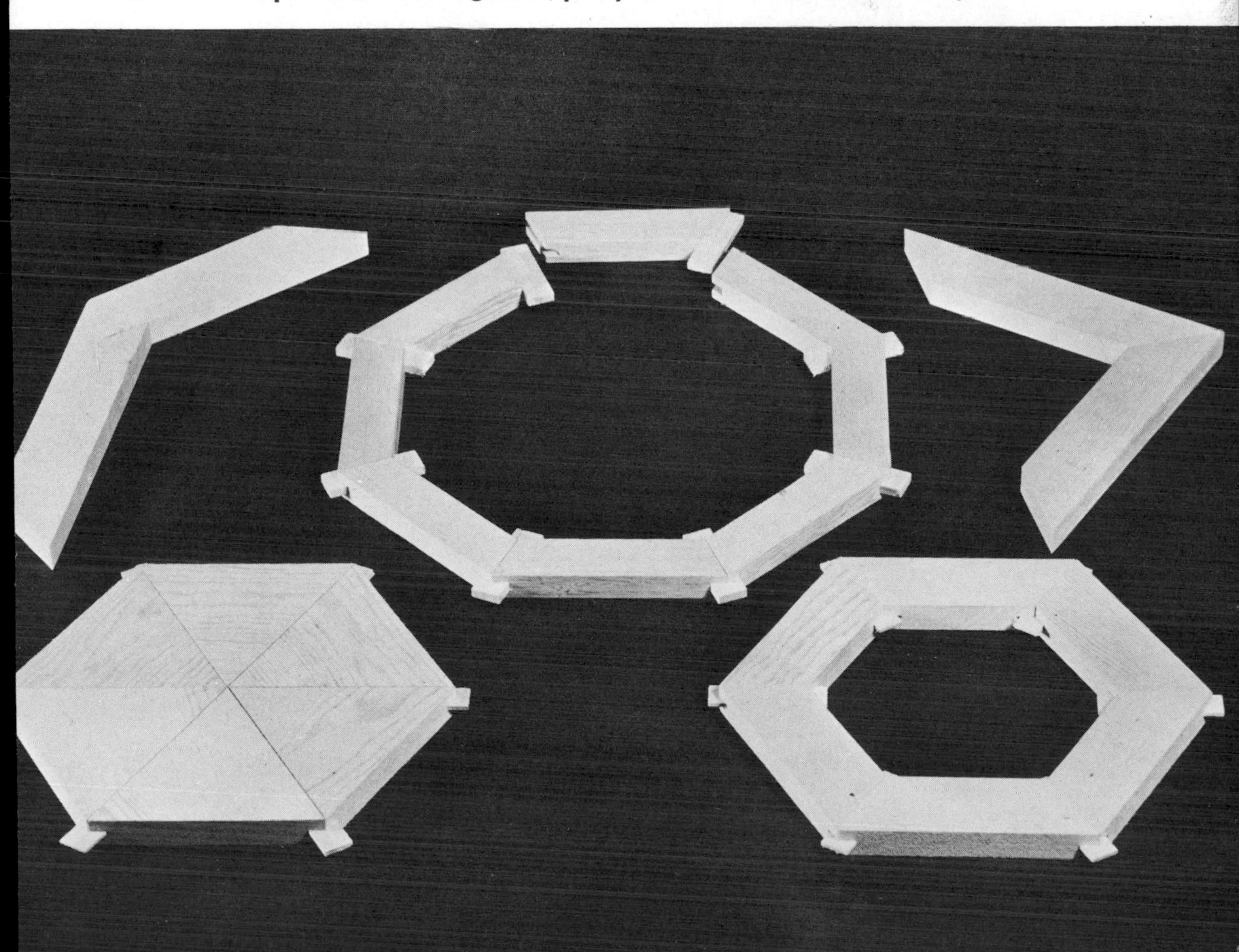

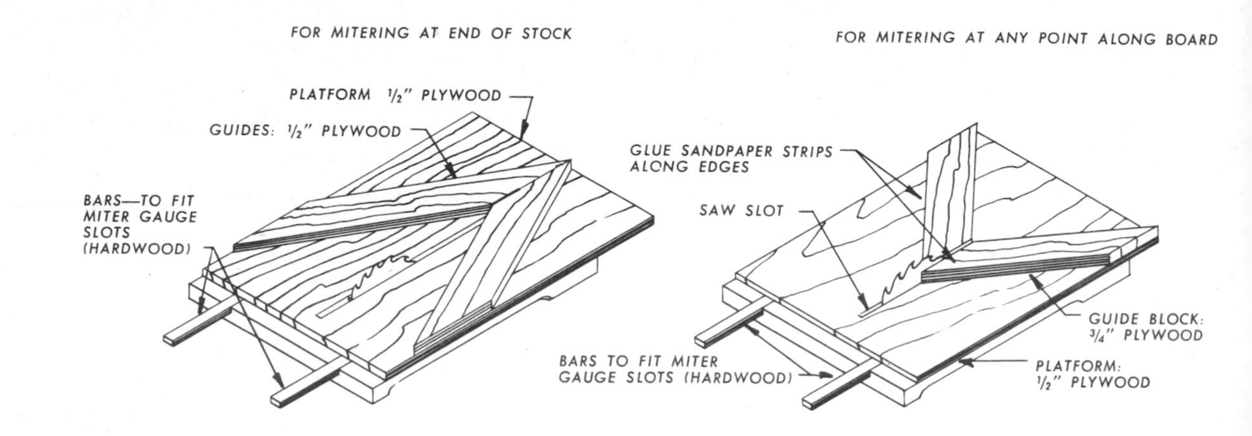

The sliding table in the left-hand drawing is shown in use in the photograph below. The drawing at the right shows how to make the sliding table pictured on the opposite page.

This type of sliding table permits an accurate miter cut at any point along board.

Sliding Tables for Mitering

In addition to the difficulty of cutting perfect miters, there's the problem of matching up the right-hand and left-hand cuts. Changing the setting of the miter gauge so that it may be used alternately in the table slots results in some discrepancies. Using two miter gauges will help to some extent, but a better solution is a simple sliding-table jig.

The left-hand drawing opposite shows how to make a sliding-table jig for mitering stock that has been precut to exact length. Construct it carefully, since the accuracy of the work it will produce depends on the careful alignment of the table and the saw blade.

First cut the plywood platform to size (about 20″ x 24″). Cut the bars to be used as guides riding in the table slots. These may be metal or kiln-dried hardwood—birch or maple. Put the bars in the slots, with the table raised to clear the saw blade. Place the platform on the table; mark off the positions of the bars. Fasten the bars in place; then clamp the sliding table to the saw table. Use the table-height lever to lower the table, so the blade (preferably hollow-ground) will cut its own slot in the platform. Remove the clamps and lengthen the slot. Construct two lines from a common point on the slot to a 45° angle to the slot. The important thing is that the guides form a perfect 90° angle and that the saw slot bisect this angle. A fence may be added, but it is not actually needed.

Jigs of this type should be protected from dampness; sand them carefully and apply three or four coats of shellac, starting with a wash coat (half alcohol and half shellac) and ending with full-strength applications.

This type of sliding table has other uses; in cutting the diameters of circular work; or to cut a true diagonal across opposite corners of a square; and again, to cut slots diametrically across the ends of cylinders or turning squares, before mounting for lathe work.

A second type of sliding table, one which permits cuts at any point on the stock, is shown in use above. Its action is the same and its construction is similar (see right-hand drawing on opposite page) but the platform should be about 5″ longer. This kind of table naturally is limited to one angle, in this case 45°.

For cross bevels on long stock, place table and headstock at extreme right end of tubes. The miter-gauge hold-down is as good as an extra hand on jobs like this (below).

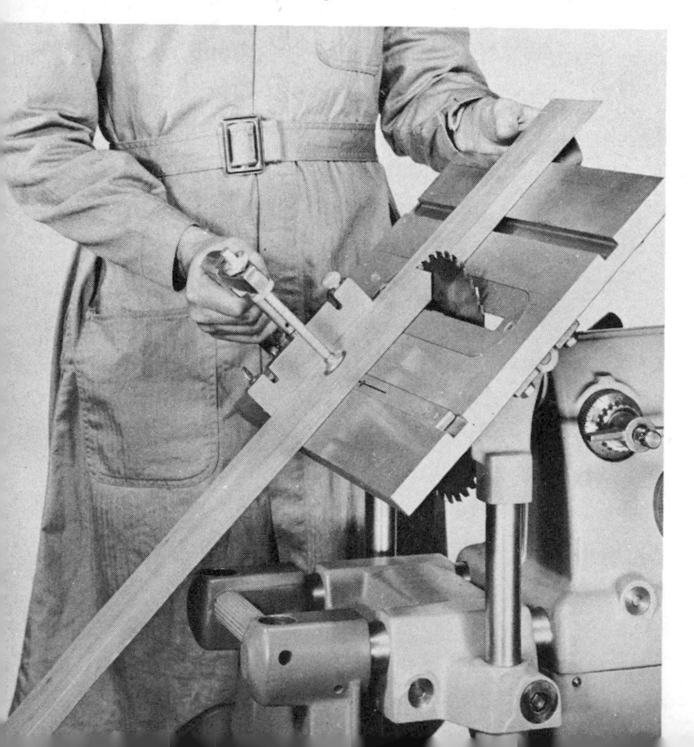

Beveling

Beveling is an operation calling for a table tilt. The distinction between a cross bevel and a miter is a fine one: when crosscut bevels are joined, the result is called a miter joint, so a cross-bevel cut might be termed a miter cut. But, for the sake of clarity, all cuts made with a miter-gauge setting will be called miters, those with table tilted will be called bevels.

Examples of bevel-cut segments are shown on the lower half of Page 31, with table-tilt settings for four-, six-, and eight-sided figures.

A bevel cut across the stock is made with the miter gauge set at 90°. On the multi-purpose tool, the table should be at the extreme right end of the ways. This permits handling long stock, within the limitations set by the distance from floor to ceiling. The bevel cut is not as difficult as the miter but the work should receive maximum support and the pass should be made very slowly. You should stand well to the right of the blade, your right hand holding the work, your left feeding it.

A rip bevel is made with the table tilted, the work riding on the rip fence. It is a comparatively simple operation.

Tilt the saw table for a rip bevel. Play safe by using a push stick on narrow stock.

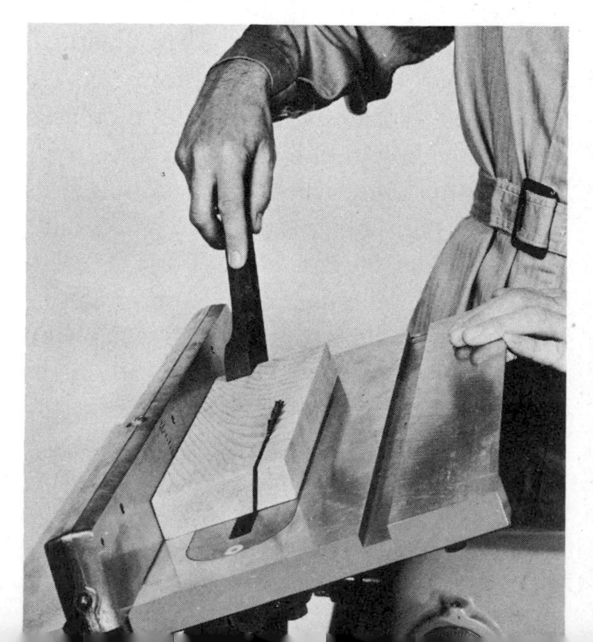

Cutting Compound Angles

While a miter requires a miter-gauge setting and a bevel calls for a table tilt, a compound angle requires both at once.

Any frame or open structure with sloping sides requires a compound-angle cut. A peaked figure with any number of sides, such as you might require for a fencepost top or the roof of a bird house or doll house roof, calls for a compound-angle cut.

Of all table-saw operations, compound-angle cuts are probably the toughest to make perfectly. Work slowly, check each setting carefully, and be sure of each cut **before** you make the pass. This type of cut sometimes requires alternating the miter gauge in the table slots, which means changing the miter-gauge setting each time. Check each setting carefully before making the pass, or use two miter gauges. Make the pass very slowly and provide maximum support for the work. Stand well to the side of the blade. Keep your hands away from the blade, especially when working the left miter-gauge slot.

The angle of cut will be limited at the left side of the blade because some settings will put the miter-gauge head in the line of cut. **For this reason, always make a test pass with the switch off.** When possible, work the miter gauge backward to provide extra support for the work in front of the blade.

Here is a typical procedure, based on a four-sided frame using the popular 60° work angle, which may be followed when making frames with compound-angle joints. First decide the over-all size of the frame and from this determine the lengths of the four pieces required. Cut and square these pieces to **exact** length.

By referring to the chart on the next page you will discover that the 60° work angle requires a table tilt of 21° and a miter-gauge setting of 49°. Set table and miter gauge **exactly** at these settings. If the machine is not set correctly, you will not get a good joint. Now carefully cut each end of each piece as shown below, making each pass slowly. Use the Miter Gauge Safety Grip if you have one. Gauge each cut to remove exactly the same amount of material. If necessary, clamp a stop block to the table to position the work automatically for the pass. The four parts should fit together snugly, forming a perfect right angle at each corner.

This method does involve wasting some

Making a compound-angle cut requires both tilting the table and setting the miter gauge.

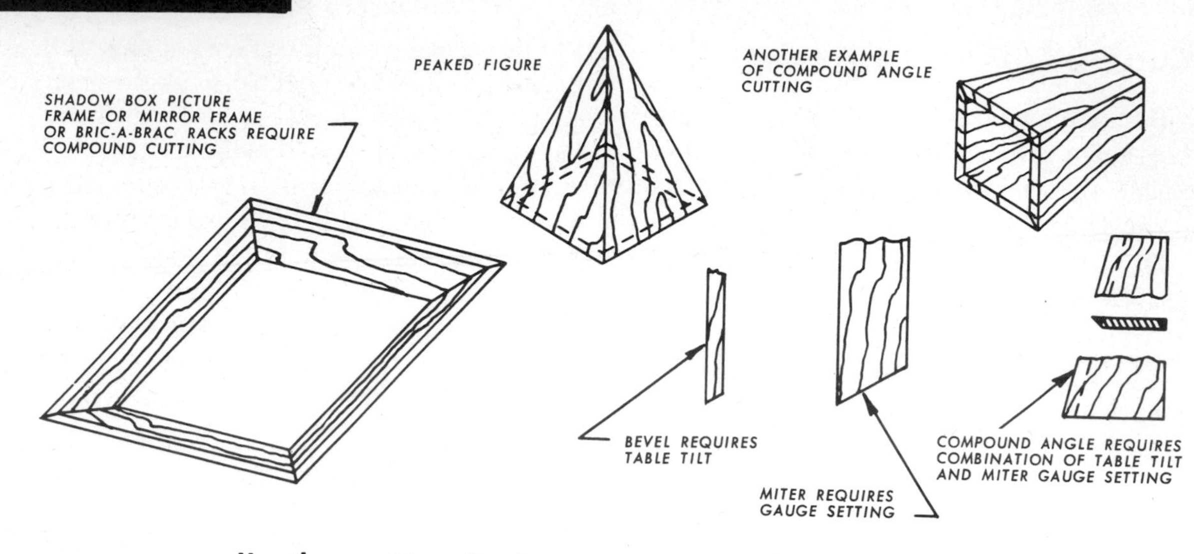
SHADOW BOX PICTURE FRAME OR MIRROR FRAME OR BRIC-A-BRAC RACKS REQUIRE COMPOUND CUTTING
PEAKED FIGURE
ANOTHER EXAMPLE OF COMPOUND ANGLE CUTTING
BEVEL REQUIRES TABLE TILT
MITER REQUIRES GAUGE SETTING
COMPOUND ANGLE REQUIRES COMBINATION OF TABLE TILT AND MITER GAUGE SETTING

Use these settings for the most common compound-angle cuts.

WORK ANGLE	FOUR-SIDED FIGURE		SIX-SIDED FIGURE	
	table setting	miter-gauge setting	table setting	miter-gauge setting
15°	43¼	75½	29	81¾
30°	37¾	63½	26	74
45°	30	54¾	21	67¾
60°	21	49	14½	63½

wood, but attempting to cut each part of the frame consecutively from one long board is extremely difficult. Cutting off the four pieces to exact length, as suggested, pays off in accuracy and convenience.

A compound miter is more easily assembled—and greatly strengthened—if a spline is used. The groove for the spline is easily cut, without changing the table setting, by following this procedure. It is illustrated at the upper right on the opposite page. Move the rip fence close to the blade and lock it where the blade will cut a groove in the exact center of the stock. (The micro-quill feed is useful for this fine setting.) Adjust table height so blade projection will cut a groove half the width of the spline to be used. Then, holding the stock on edge, make the pass shown. It is important that similar surfaces of the work be held against the rip fence when making the pass. After the grooves are cut, put the splines in place (left center photograph). This use of splines greatly facilitates assembling the parts and holding them together for gluing and clamping.

Compound-angle rip cuts are made as shown in the photograph at right center.

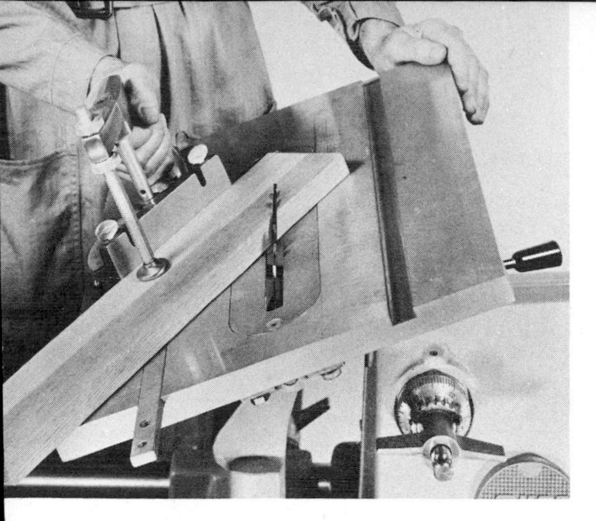

The Miter Gauge Safety Grip holds work firmly, is especially valuable on compound angles.

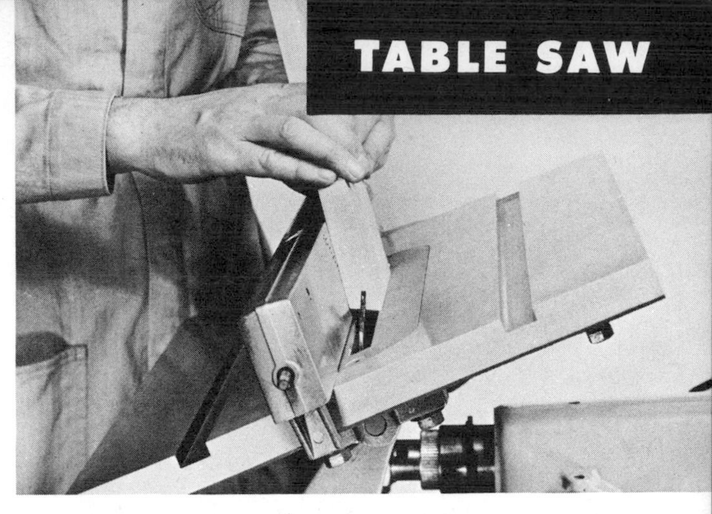

Use this method to cut spline grooves in compound angles without disturbing setting.

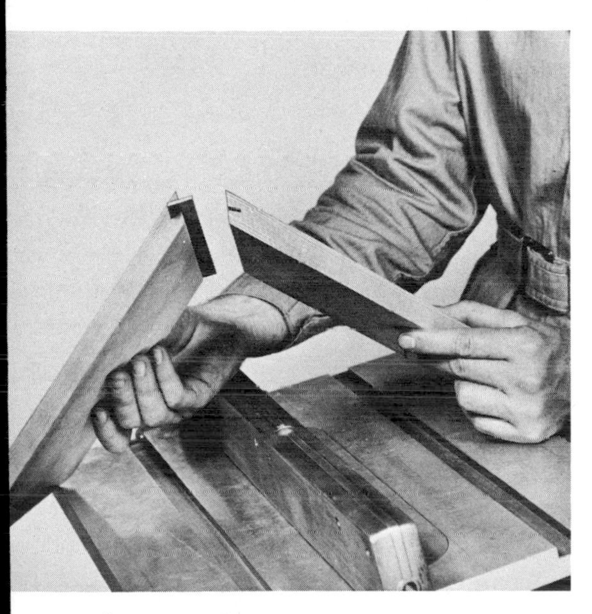

Spline strengthens joint, eases assembly.

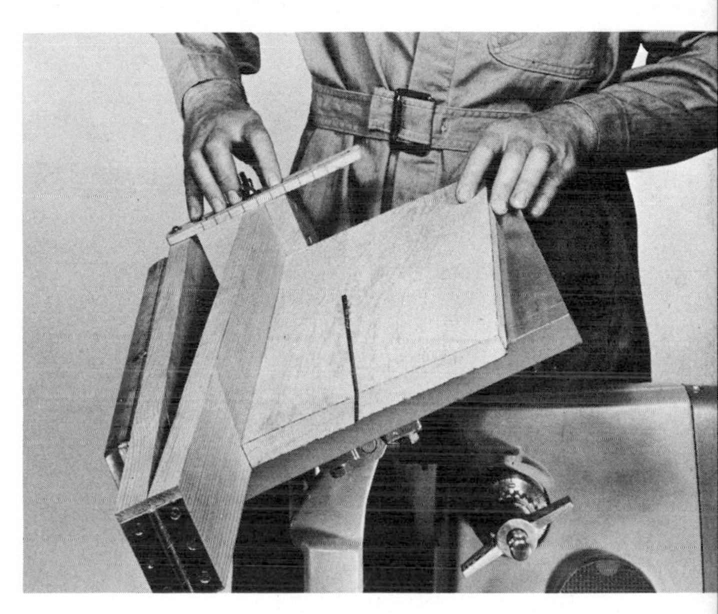

Taper jig may be used on compound-angle cuts.

Note the use of splines in these examples of assembled compound-miter joints.

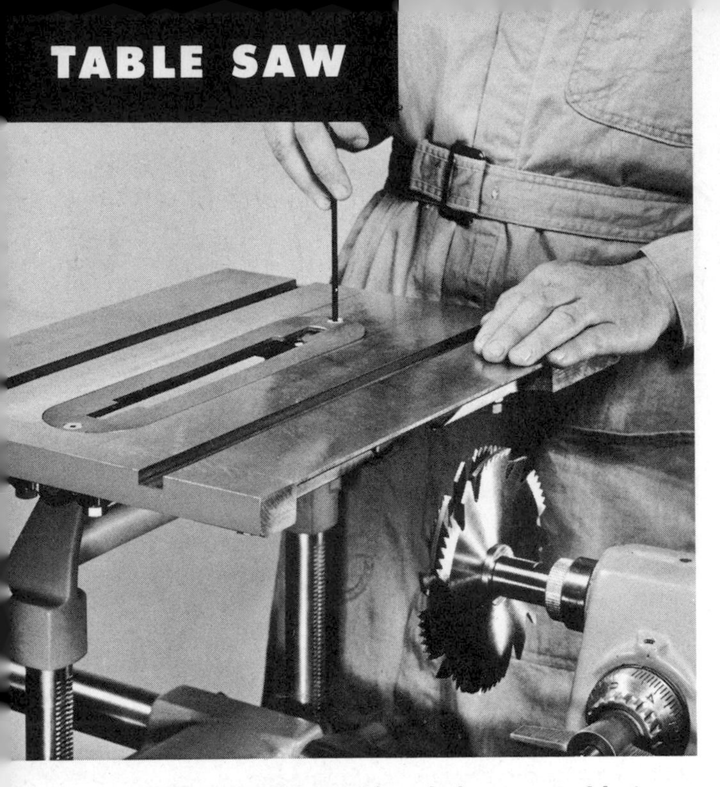

When working with a dado, use a table insert with a slot wide enough for widest cut.

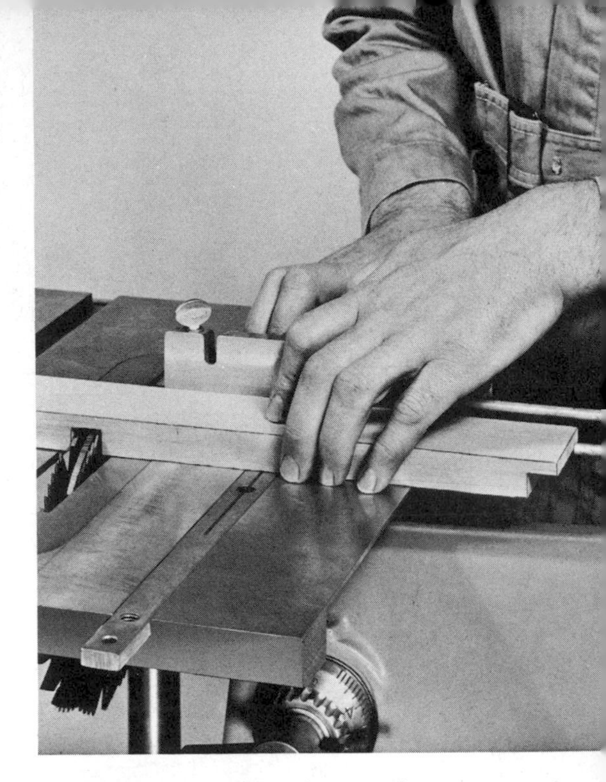

A dado is a cut like this, made across grain. Stop rod is useful in gauging cut.

Dadoing and Grooving

In joinery and some other special applications, it is often necessary to make a cut considerably wider than the saw kerf. For this type of work, a dado-blade assembly is used.

The dado assembly consists of two saw blades and a number of chippers which are fitted on the arbor between the blades. The blades each cut a kerf ⅛″ wide, and the chippers remove the wood between the kerfs. The chippers are made in various sizes; width of cut is controlled by their number and size.

The dado requires a special table insert (photograph above) with a slot wide enough to accommodate the dado assembly at its widest setting.

Blades are always set lower than the thickness of the stock when cutting a dado, which is a cut made across the grain of the wood. Dadoing calls for no special technique except that the work should be fed slowly. When a deep cut is needed, it is best to make more than one pass, adjusting the table height for each pass.

The miter-gauge stop rod (photograph at upper right) can be used to control the distance of the dado from the end of the stock. When several dadoes are needed on a long board (shelf grooves for a bookcase, for example) use on the miter gauge a long extension slotted to provide a check point for the cut.

The grooving cut—like a dado, but made **with** the grain of the wood—is made with the work riding against the rip fence, as shown at top left on opposite page. On an operation of this type, the combination pusher-hold-down may be used. Another trick that helps hold down the work is to use the mortising hold-down on the rip fence, positioning it on the fence just high enough for the work to slide under it. A pusher stick can be used to complete the pass.

A hollowing cut—for fashioning a scoop, for example—is made with the work against the rip fence. A rip-fence block is used, as shown at upper right on opposite page, to gauge the length of cut. The width is con-

The dado cut made with the grain is called a groove. Pusher hold-down is helpful.

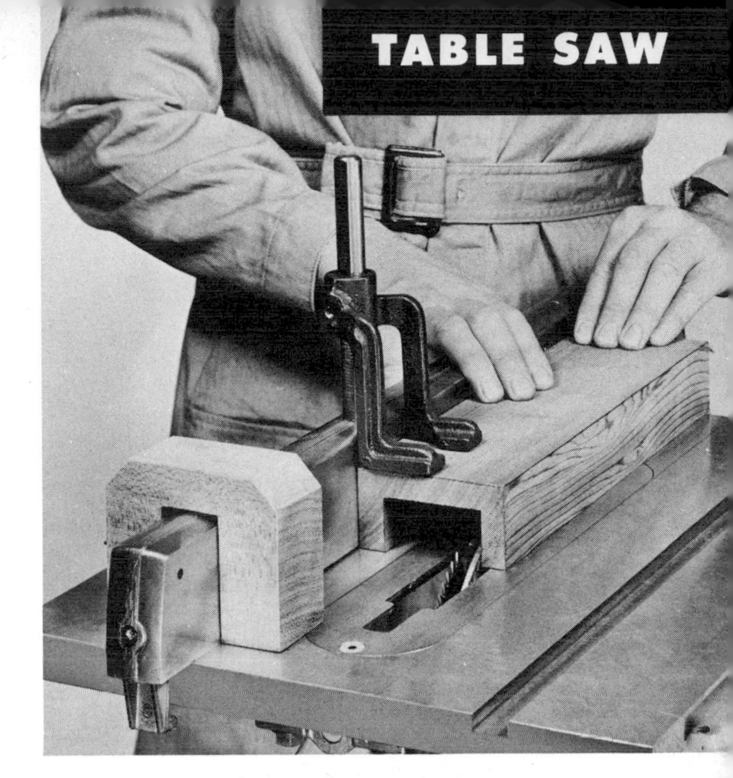

Block limits length of cut, mortising hold-down keeps work on table in hollowing job.

trolled by adjusting the fence after each pass.

To cut a cavity in a block, use two stop blocks—one to start the cut and one to end it. Lower the work over the dado—slowly. For a deep cavity, make several passes, raising the dado a bit each time. A very shallow cavity may be cut in one pass.

When a dado is needed that is wider than the widest cuts possible with the assembly, the cut may be gauged by a notched stick clamped to the table (lower photograph). Such a dado is often needed when joining two-by-fours or heavier stock. The notched stick is precut to specific dimensions and each successive pass is gauged by using the next step in the block.

A simple step block, clamped to the saw table like this, will gauge extra wide dados. It will speed up spacing for each pass and also automatically turn out a dado of exact length.

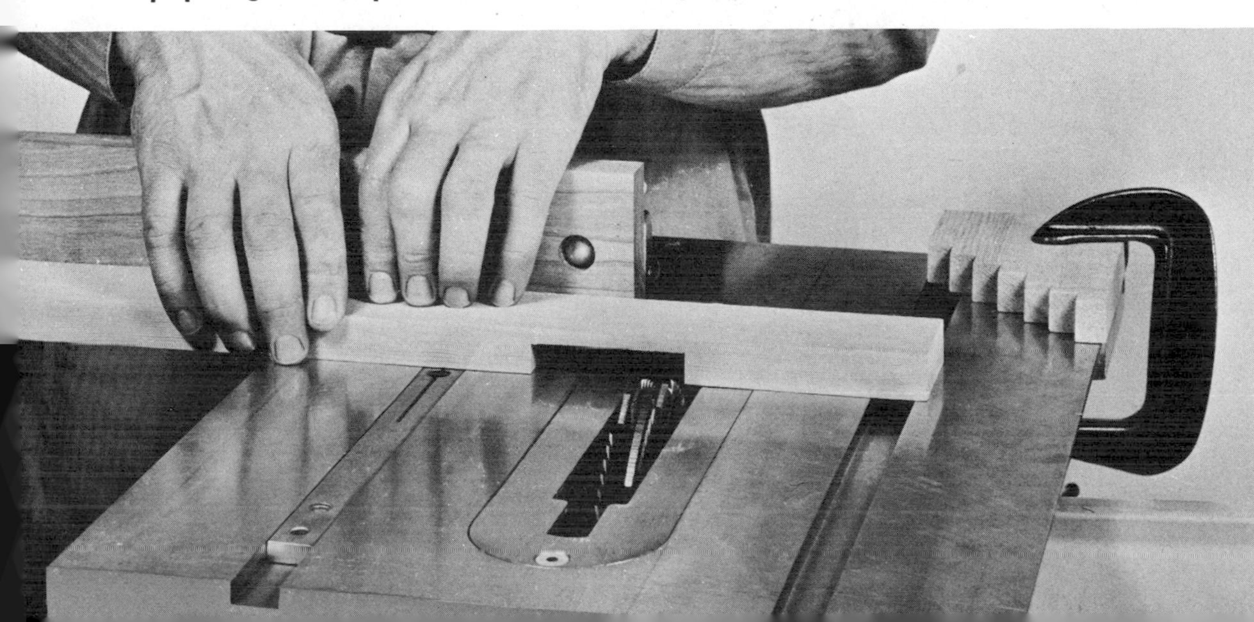

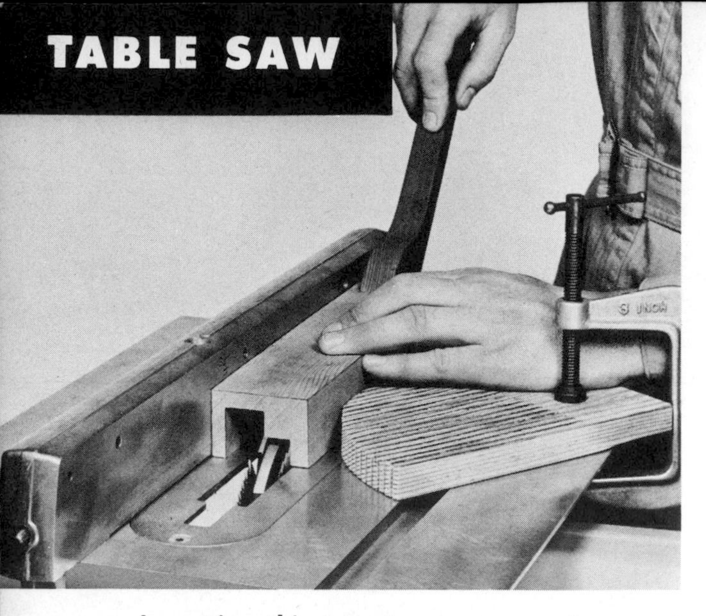

In cutting this two-step groove, note use of spring stick (next page) and push stick.

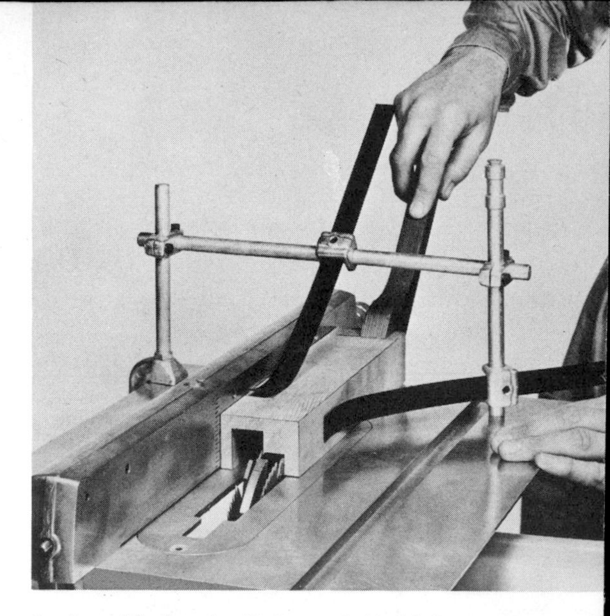

Spring blades in Universal Hold Down press stock firmly against saw table and fence.

Special grooves, such as the two-step, are done as shown above. The first groove is cut with the blades set at one height; the second, with the rip fence adjusted and the blades lowered. It is essential when doing operations of this type that the work be set to bear on the table at each side of the dado assembly. Although a feathering stick may be used, a Universal Hold Down (right, above) does a better job of holding the work firm throughout the pass. Notice that, when it is set up as illustrated, the springs may be used to hold the work **down** on the table, as well as snug against the fence.

The single-blade dado saw, such as the Magna Dado (described on pages 8 and 9), is becoming increasingly popular. It is a good idea to make the notched stick shown below, with a cut for each of the settings marked on the hub of the dado, to use in checking the width of a required dado or groove.

Use notched stick to check thickness of stock so Magna Dado may be accurately preset.

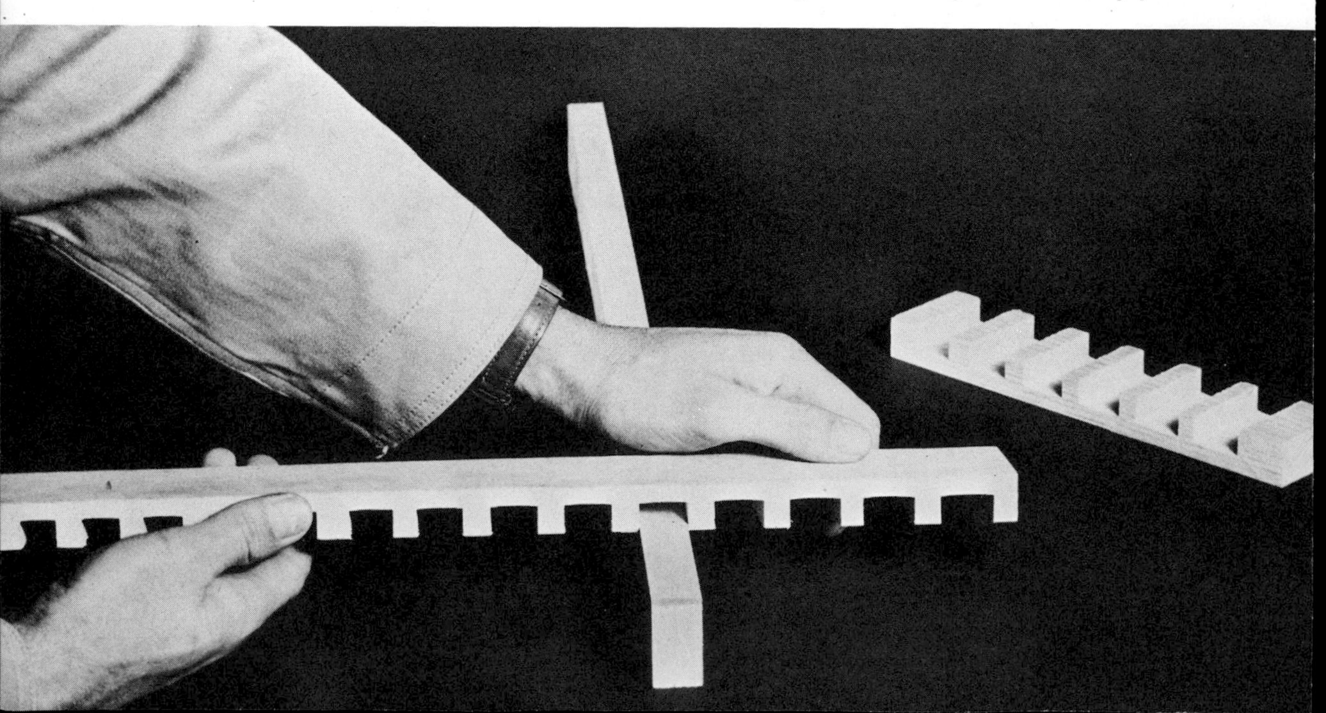

Joinery on the Table Saw

All the joints shown below may be cut on the table saw. If you are to progress to cabinetwork, you should become familiar with these. They are used in all types of framework and in drawer-making.

One or more sets of spring sticks, made as sketched at the right, will prove useful as hold-downs, when cutting joints and in other operations. One is shown in use at upper left on the opposite page.

Spring sticks may be made in various sizes to fit different jobs; ¾″ pine, with saw kerfs spaced about 3/16″ apart, will do a good job in many situations.

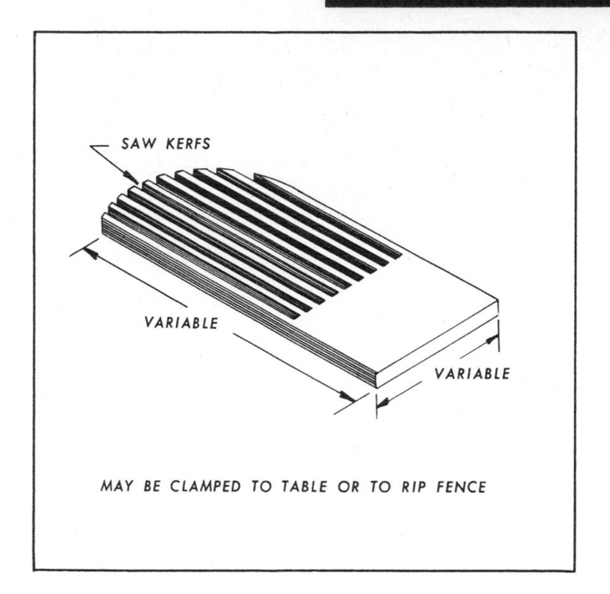

Wooden spring hold-downs are easy to make.

Some of the common woodworking joints that can be cut on the table saw, using a regular saw blade or a dado, are: 1—butt; 2—rabbet; 3—dado and groove; 4—splice lap (end); 5—middle lap; 6—end lap; 7—lapped miter; 8—dado and rabbet (box corners); 9—notch; 10—true tenon; 11—stud tenon; 12—slot (for stud tenon); 13—miter; 14—mitered bevel.

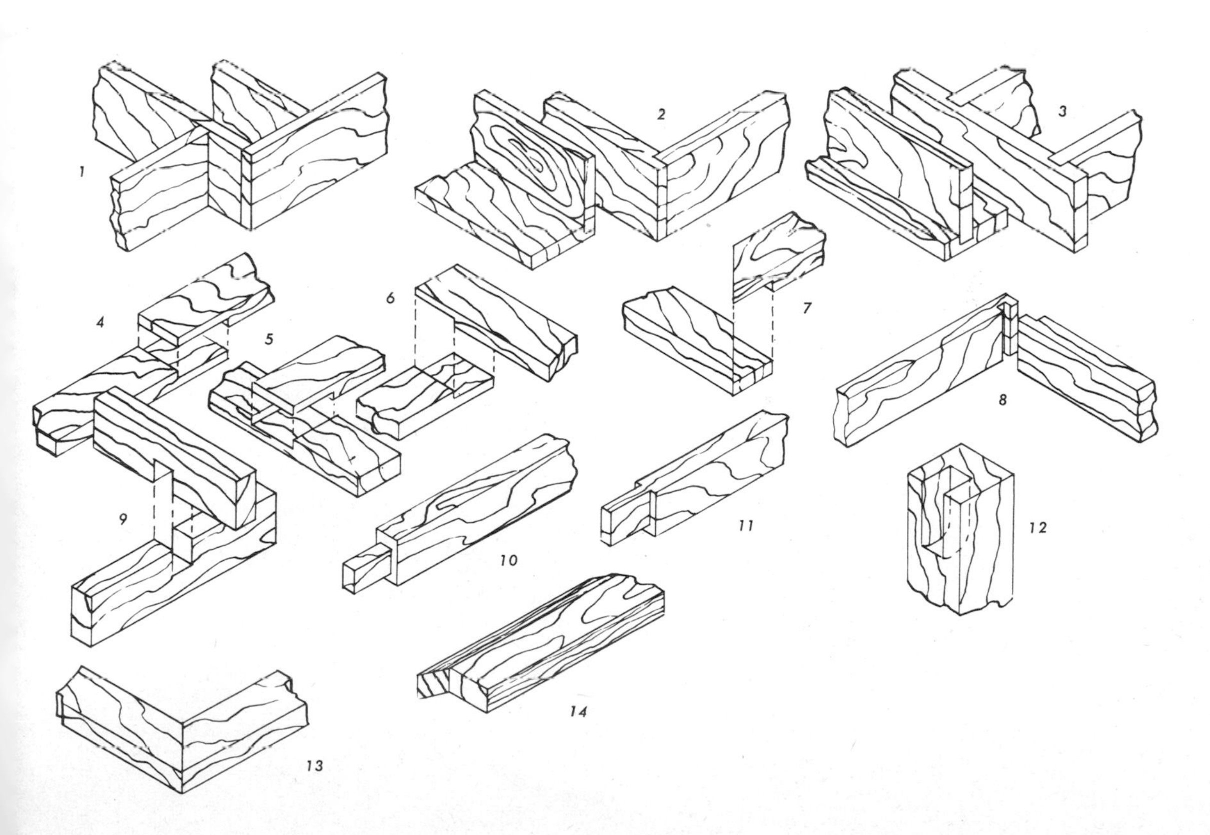

Miter-gauge extension often helps when cutting an end rabbet with a dado.

Rabbeting

A rabbet is an L-shaped cut, made on the end of stock (as shown above) or along the edge (photograph below). The width of the cut may be gauged with the miter-gauge stop rods or by using a stop block on the rip fence.

When rabbet cuts are needed along the length of stock (this may be called for when the back of a bookcase or other project is recessed into the frame), the rabbet is cut with the work riding the rip fence.

The size of the rabbet is determined by the piece that will be joined to it. For example, if you were recessing a ¼″ panel into the back of a bookcase frame made of ¾″ stock, the rabbet would have to be ¼″ deep (to accommodate the panel) by about ½″ wide (to provide nailing area).

Always hold the work flat on the table during the pass. Make the pass slowly. If the cut is deep make it in two or more passes.

Note the safe hand position recommended for rabbeting an edge with a dado.

Cutting Spline Grooves

Splines are slim pieces of wood used to reinforce joints. Using them is often called feathering when applied to picture frames.

A simple jig (drawing and photograph at right) helps in cutting grooves for splines. Make it so it will slide smoothly on the rip fence.

Spline grooves in segments may be made, as shown at lower right, with a spring stick clamped to the table to help hold the work against the fence. If you find that the edge of the work is not wide enough to span the insert slot, make an insert of wood. Use the regular insert as a pattern. Drill and countersink the holes for the hold-down screws. When you lower the table with the new insert in place, the blade will cut its own slot.

Beveled edges require the setup sketched below. Cut two guides at the same angle as the beveled edge, by cutting a straight piece of stock down the center. When splining short bevels, fasten the guides together with a tie block at each end, as shown, and clamp each block to the table. When the stock is too long for this arrangement, omit the tie blocks and use four clamps, one at each end of each guide, to hold them down.

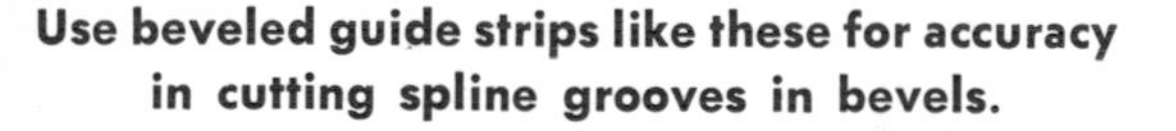

Use beveled guide strips like these for accuracy in cutting spline grooves in bevels.

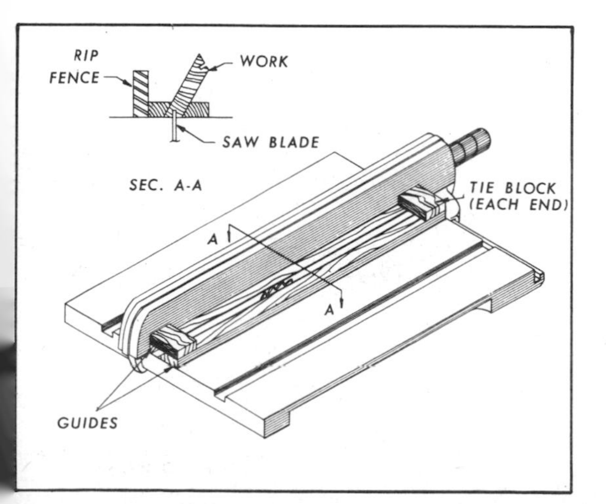

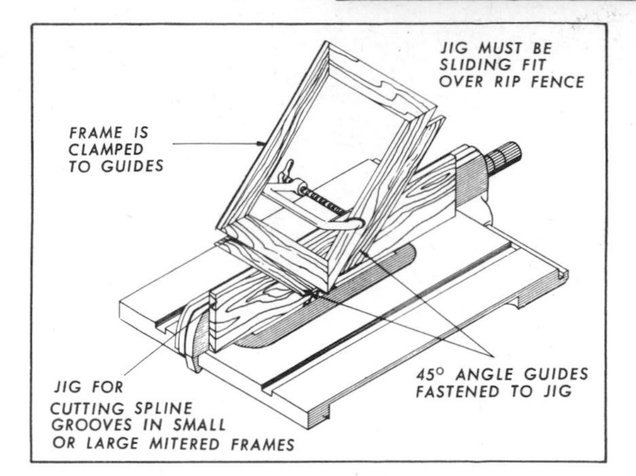

Follow details above to make jig shown below for cutting spline grooves in mitered frames.

Hold similar surfaces against fence when cutting spline grooves in mitered segments.

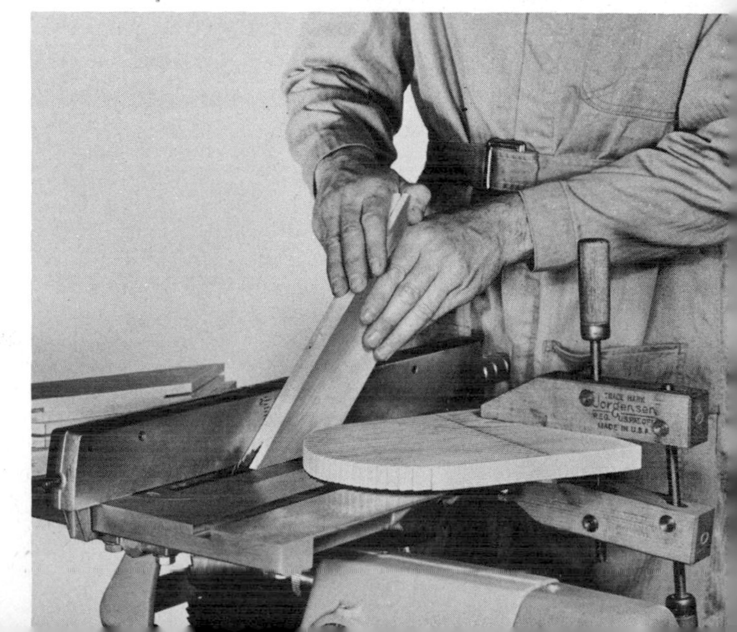

Resaw boards this way to make splines. Both Universal Hold Down and auxiliary fence help.

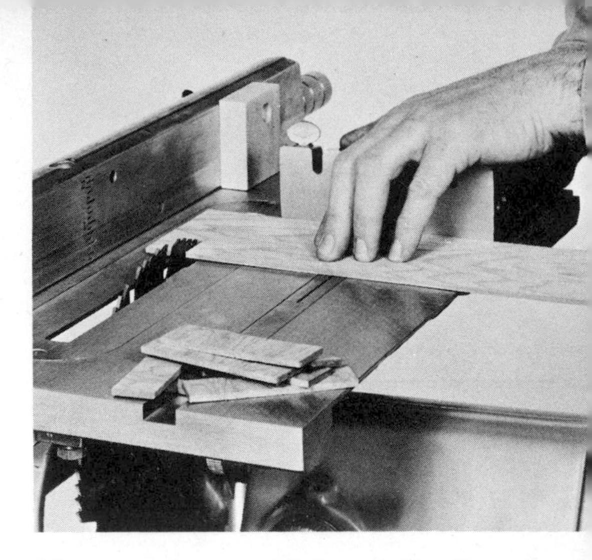

After resawing, as at left, cut off splines. Stop block on fence is used to gauge width.

Making Splines

Strength of a spline depends on its grain's running at an opposed angle to the joint. Therefore grain must run across the narrow width of a spline, not along its length.

Making splines is not difficult, and if the same blade is always used to cut the grooves, splines may be made in advance for use whenever needed.

Start by sizing a piece of stock to ¾″ by 4″ by about 24″ long (this will produce splines 4″ long).

Resaw the stock three times to produce three pieces about ⅛″ thick. Thickness is determined by rip-fence setting.

When resawing on the table saw, make one pass with the stock on edge, then turn the stock over and make a second pass with the stock resting on the opposite edge (photograph at left above).

Cut the splines to width by using a stop block on the rip fence, as shown above. To keep the thin stock from splitting, use a hollow-ground blade. Width of splines may vary, of course, depending on depth of spline groove but about 1″ wide is usually adequate.

When the length of splines is such that they cannot be produced by resawing on the table saw, they may be cut from the end of a piece of stock as wide as the length of the splines needed. This is shown below.

Sanding the splines to exact length is best accomplished with a drum sander, set up for thickness sanding. (How to do this is shown in the chapter on abrasive machines.)

Follow steps sketched at right to make long splines. Cut them off as shown at left.

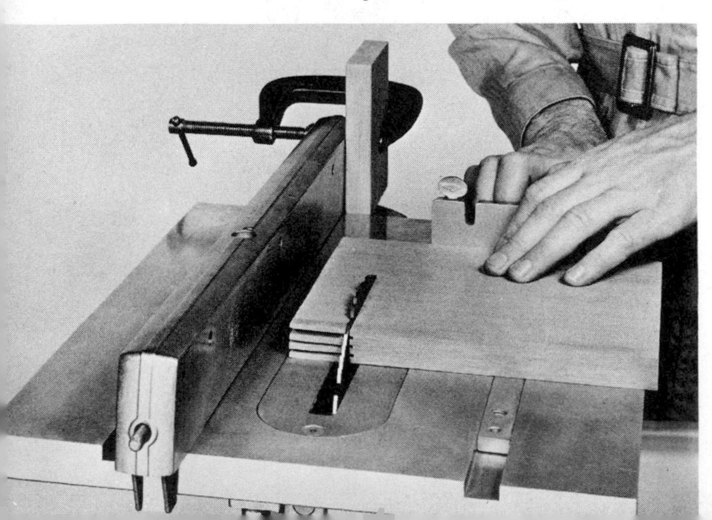

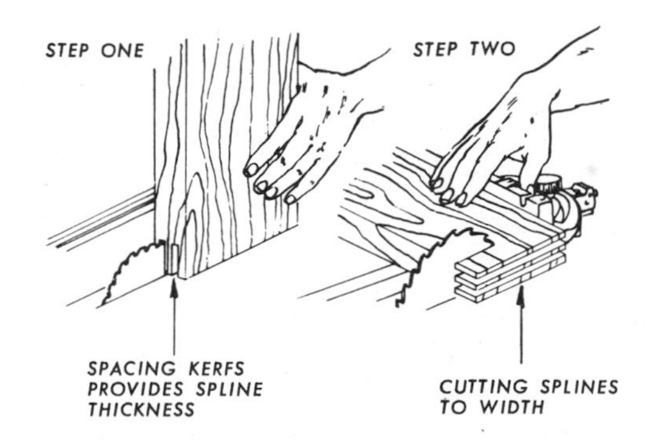

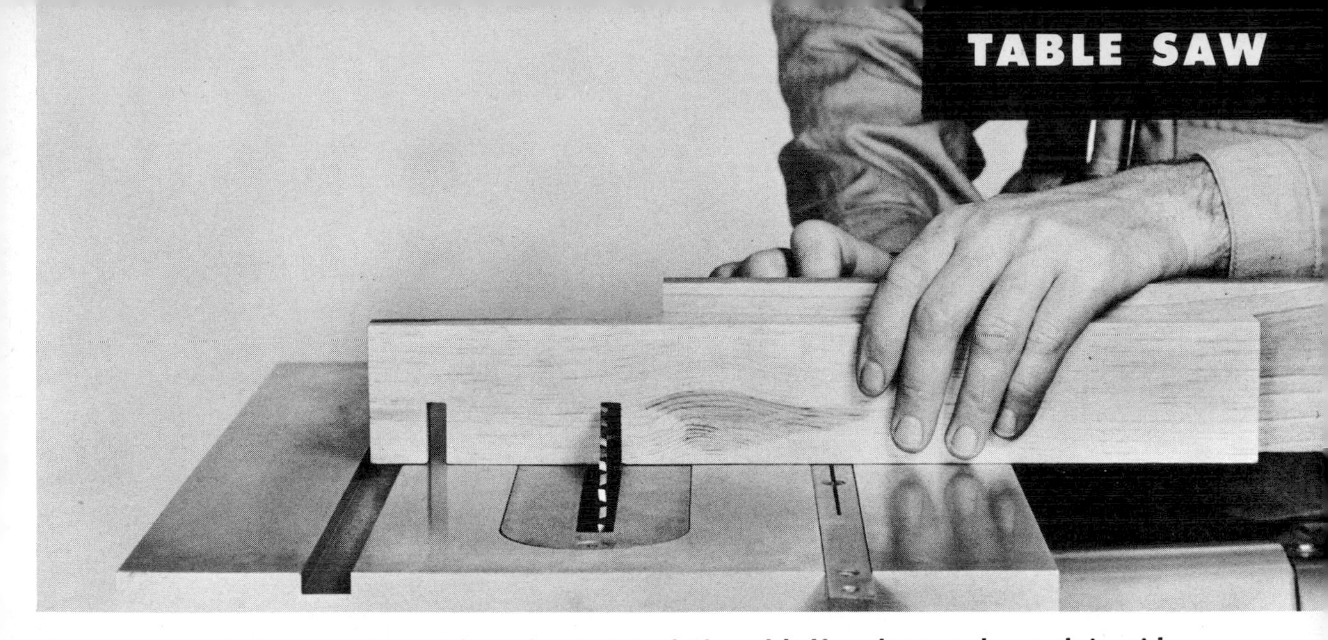

Half-lap joint calls for a notch as wide as the stock is thick and half as deep as the stock is wide. Magna Dado is being used to cut these notches.

Notching

The notching cut is a dado cut across the thickness of the stock and to half its width, as pictured above. The mating pieces produced must, as with all joints, fit together accurately. This is a simple joint since the saw controls the width of the notch, which is the same for both pieces. However, the height of the blade must be carefully set so that when the pieces are joined the surfaces will be even and true.

Below are some details of corner joints you're likely to use in making boxes and drawers. The multiple finger lap, shown in the lower right corner, provides a lot of surface for gluing—which is one reason for its great strength. It is especially useful on box corners and drawers and is frequently used where it will show—because the interlocking fingers form such an interesting pattern.

A simple jig made from a miter-gauge extension facilitates cutting both halves of the joint at the same time. Once made, this jig

Of these corner joints, only the finger lap (lower right) calls for the notching cut.

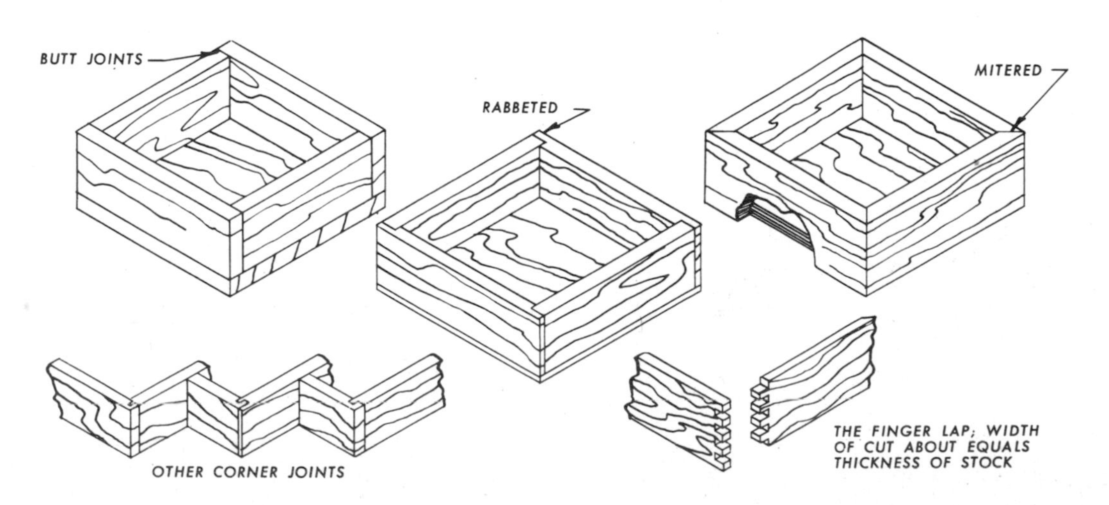

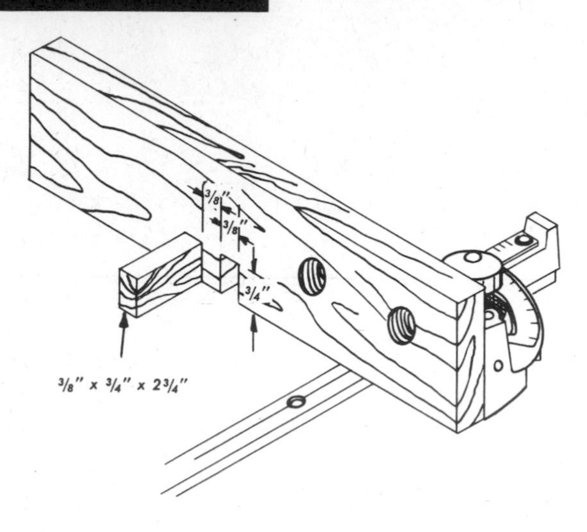

A miter-gauge-extension jig for producing finger-lap joints is made as shown above.

In using the finger-lap jig, line up the guide block, dado, and notch like this.

With finger-lap jig, first cut a notch in one piece (upper sketch), from then on notch both simultaneously (bottom sketch).

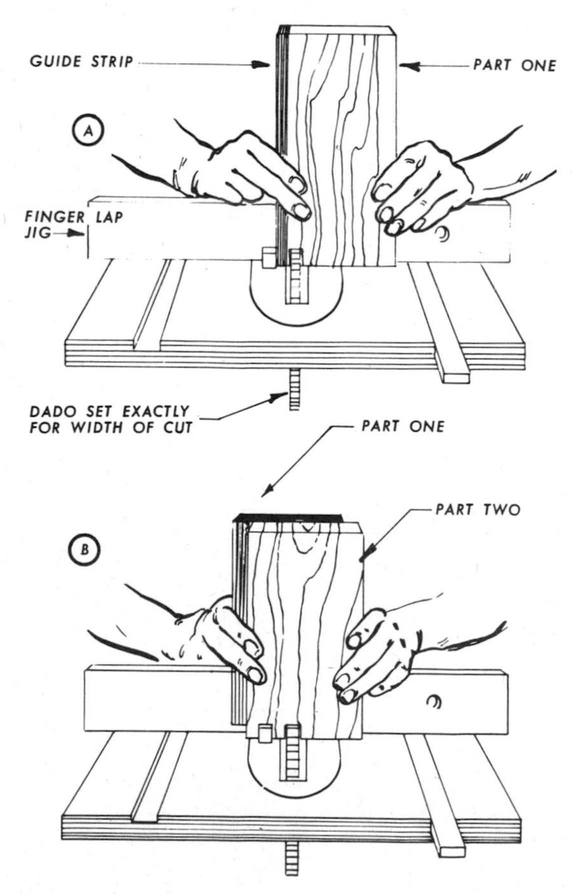

may be used over and over again without limitation on width of work. This makes it possible to use the joint on boxes or drawers, whether shallow or deep.

Generally the width of the fingers should be about equal to the thickness of the stock; but on a shallow project made of 3/4″ stock or thicker, the heavy fingers appear incongruous. A good width, most useful since it applies to materials 3/8″ to 1″ thick, is 3/8 inch.

When making the jig, sketched at upper left, be sure measurements are exact. This is important if pieces are to fit snugly together. Set the dado for a cut exactly 3/8″ wide; height of dado above table should be exactly 3/4″ (for 3/4″ stock). Before cutting the notch in the miter-gauge extension, be sure it fits snugly in the miter-gauge slots and that the lock nuts are securely tightened, then make the pass. Make a second notch exactly 3/8″ away from the first one. The guide block, which measures exactly 3/8″ wide by 3/4″ high by about 2 3/4″ long, is then glued in place in this second notch.

The photograph at right shows how the guide block and notch should line up with the dado assembly.

The first cut, made in one piece only, is gauged with a guide strip exactly 3⁄8″ thick (top drawing A at left). This first L-shaped cut is then butted against the guide block (lower drawing B), and the mating part put in place.

Remaining cuts are made simultaneously in both pieces (photograph at left) and automatically spaced by fitting preceding cuts over the guide block.

A jig of this type will serve only if the same thickness of stock is to be cut continuously. It may be made variable by slotting the holes for the bolts which hold it to the miter gauge and substituting a guide pin for the guide block, as sketched at upper right on this page. This will require more care, since the jig must be correctly set for each job and the cuts gauged by holding their inside faces firmly against the guide pin.

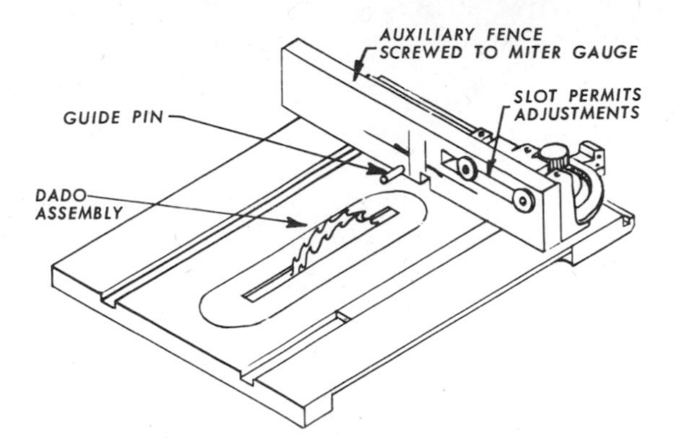

Follow these details to make a finger-lap jig adaptable to stock of varied thicknesses.

Guide block in finger-lap jig controls position of work as subsequent cuts are made.

Cut a rabbet on four adjacent sides—and you have a tenon. Stop rods keep cut accurate.

Tenons and Slots

The tenon is an integrate projection on the end of a piece of stock which fits into a mating cavity in another piece. This cavity, called a mortise, is a drill-press job.

One method of cutting the tenon is shown above; the miter-gauge stop rod is used to gauge the cut so all four shoulders will be true.

A second method is shown in the drawing and photograph at left of the opposite page; a tenoning jig rides the rip fence, which provides adjustment for the thickness of stock being cut. The work is clamped to the jig, and the jig is fed forward. The jig may be used with a dado to cut cheek and shoulder of the tenon at the same time.

A conventional blade may be used with the jig to make the cheek cuts first (drawing at far right). The shoulder cuts are made separately with the miter gauge. Blade projection should be just high enough to meet the first cuts. This is similar to cutting four rabbets, one on each face of the work.

The through slot is cut with the tenoning jig also, using a dado saw set to cut the thickness of the tenon, as pictured at upper right on opposite page.

Another type of slot, which is the mating part for the stud tenon (see 11 and 12 in the drawing on page 43), is cut in the same way as a groove. The stop block is used to gauge the length of cut. Since the dado saw leaves a radius in the corner where the cut is stopped, you can make the cut long enough so this radius does not interfere with the tenon; or you can cut a square-cornered slot with a mortising chisel and bit.

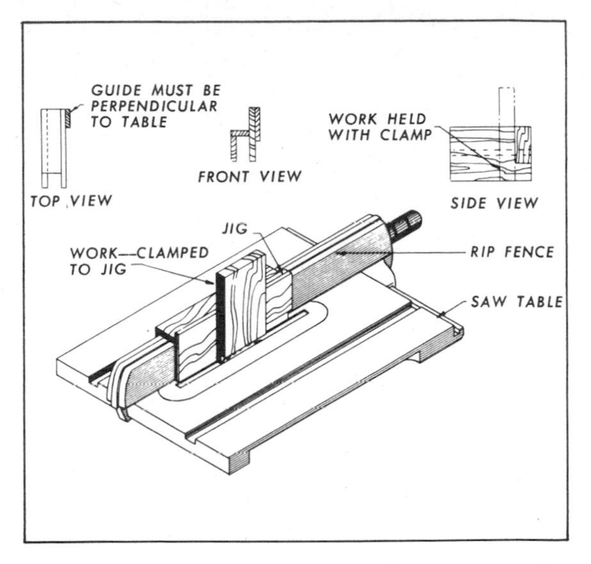

When you make a tenoning jig like this one, be sure it slides smoothly on the rip fence. Guide block must be perpendicular to table.

A tenoning jig is helpful in holding stock firmly and in the correct position. When used with a dado instead of with an ordinary blade (as in this photograph) it will cut cheek and shoulder of the tenon at the same time.

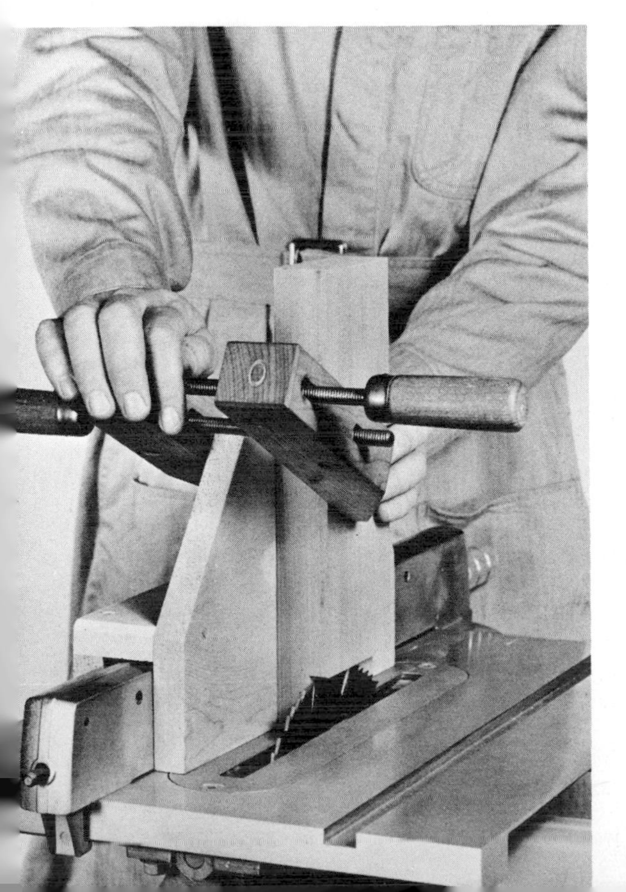

The tenoning jig is handy for cutting slots too. (What appears to be a saw blade in this picture is actually a Magna Dado.)

Make cheek cuts, then shoulder cuts, when cutting a tenon with a regular saw blade.

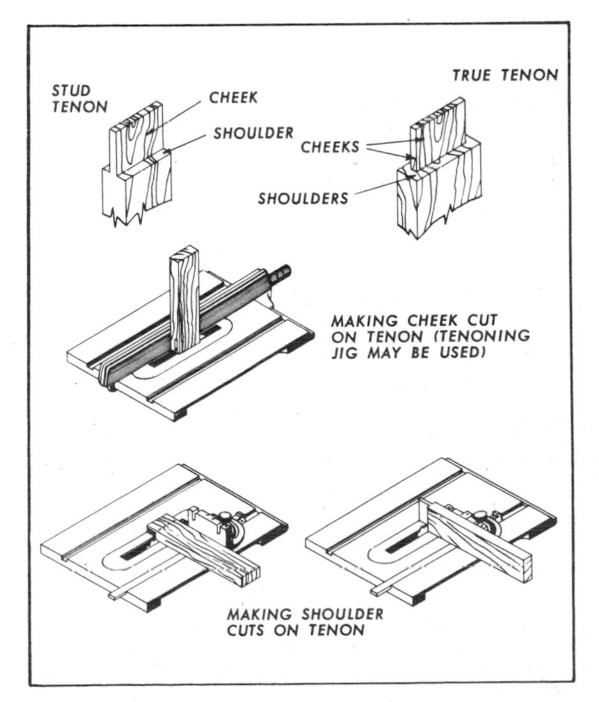

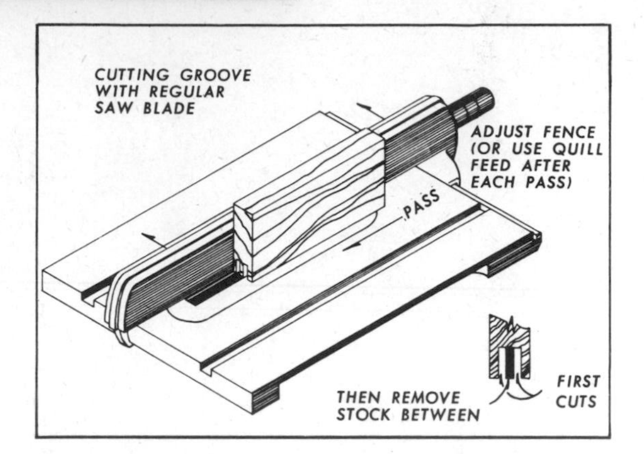

When cutting the groove with a regular saw blade, follow the procedure sketched above.

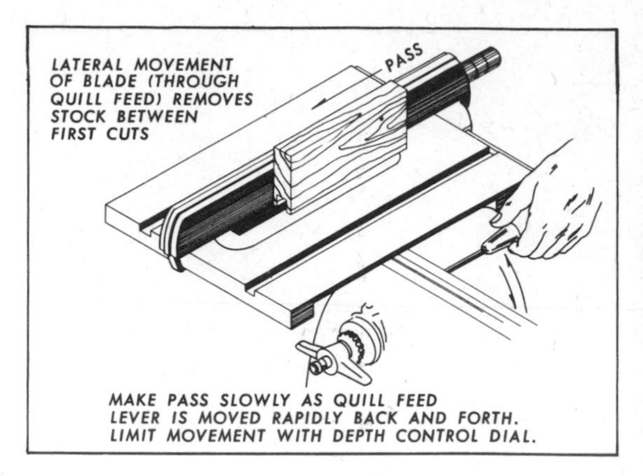

On the multi-purpose tool, use the quill feed for quicker removal of stock between kerfs.

Cut tongue for tongue-and-groove joint this way if you are using a regular saw blade.

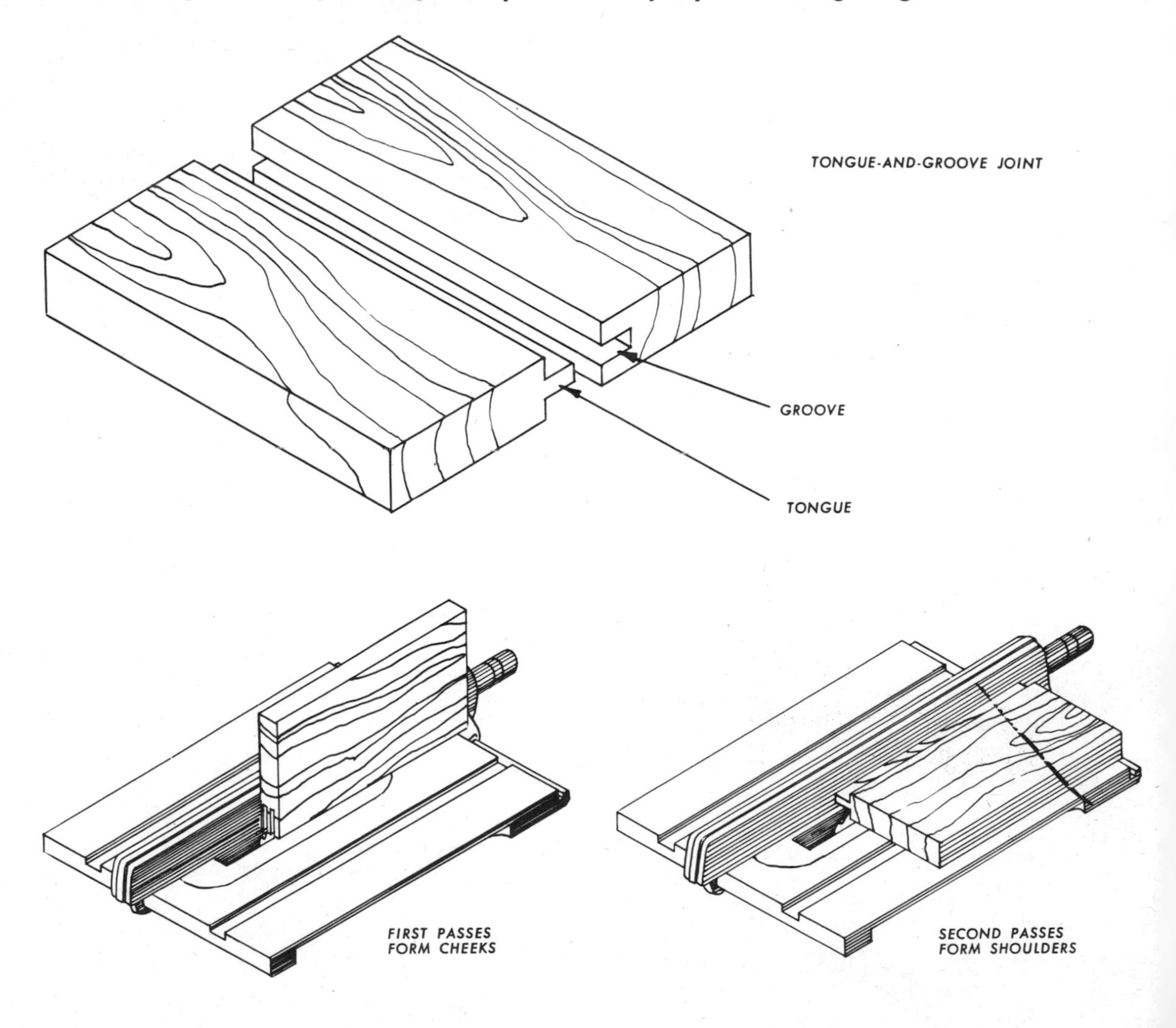

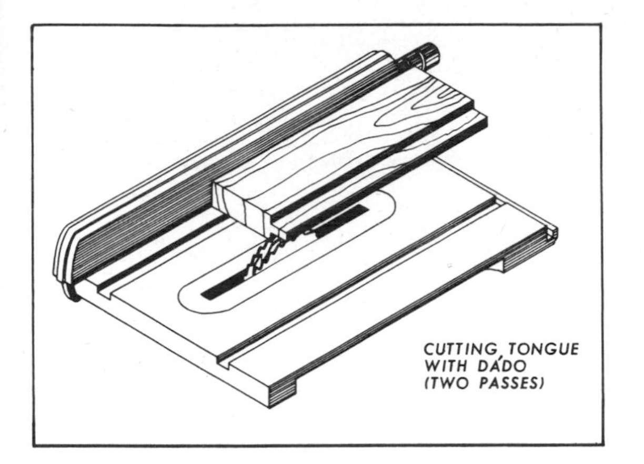

If you use a dado, you can cut a tongue for a tongue-and-groove joint in just two passes.

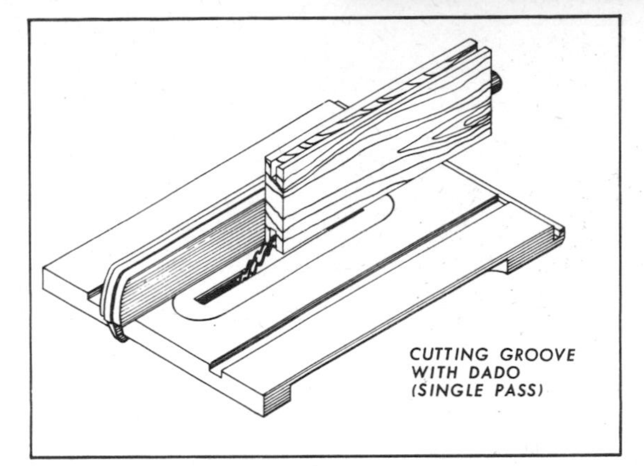

A single pass like this is all that's needed for cutting a groove when a dado is used.

Making a Tongue-and-Groove Joint

The tongue-and-groove joint may be cut on the table saw by a combination of passes with a conventional saw blade, or by using a dado.

When using a single blade, form the tongue by making passes to cut the cheeks and two additional passes to form the shoulders, just as if you were cutting a long tenon. This is shown in the drawing at the bottom of the opposite page. Cut the groove by making a series of passes to remove waste material. On the multi-purpose tool, it is possible to use the quill feed to remove waste material from between the two kerfs that determine the size of the groove. The depth-control dial on the quill feed may be set to limit quill movement.

The procedure with a dado (sketch above) does not radically differ, except that fewer passes are required since the dado may be set to cut cheek and shoulder in one pass. The groove also may be accomplished in one pass, as shown at upper right.

It is good practice to make the tongue slightly shorter than the groove, thus providing room for excess glue between tongue and bottom of groove.

Lock-Corner Joint

This joint must be made accurately. Follow the steps shown below, cutting a dado in the first part ⅝″ from the edge; then a ⅛″ x ⅛″ rabbet on the same edge and a ⅛″ x ½″ rabbet at the other corner. In the second part, make a groove ¾″ deep and ⅜″ wide; then make one pass with a regular blade.

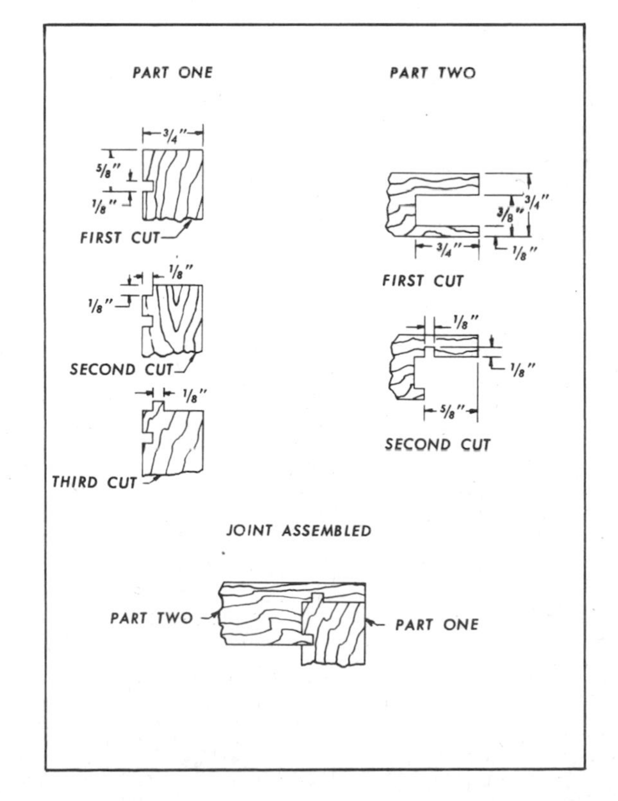

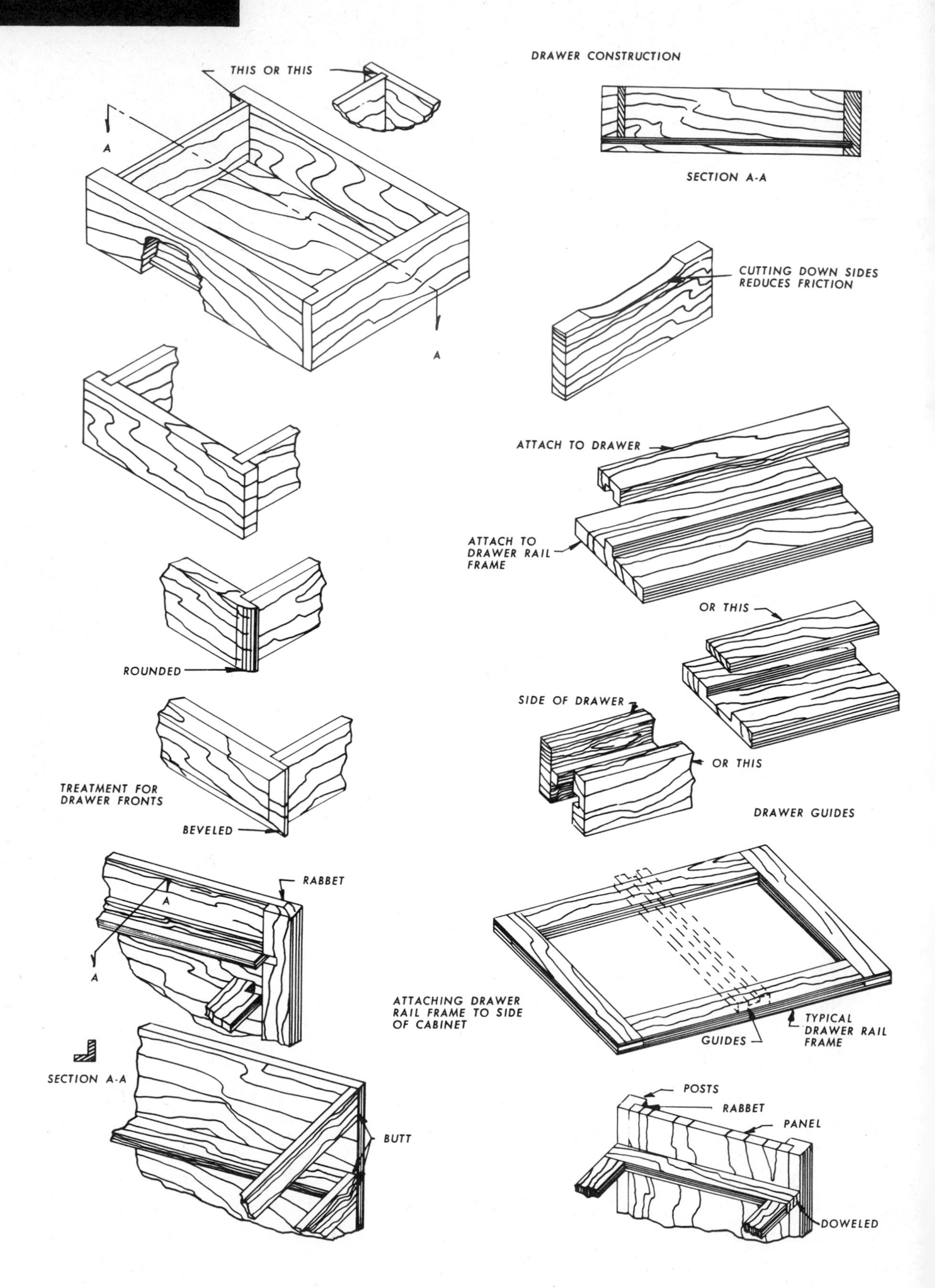
DRAWER CONSTRUCTION
THIS OR THIS
A
A
SECTION A-A
CUTTING DOWN SIDES
REDUCES FRICTION
ATTACH TO DRAWER
ATTACH TO
DRAWER RAIL
FRAME
OR THIS
ROUNDED
SIDE OF DRAWER
OR THIS
TREATMENT FOR
DRAWER FRONTS
BEVELED
DRAWER GUIDES
RABBET
A
A
ATTACHING DRAWER
RAIL FRAME TO SIDE
OF CABINET
TYPICAL
DRAWER RAIL
FRAME
GUIDES
SECTION A-A
POSTS
RABBET
PANEL
BUTT
DOWELED

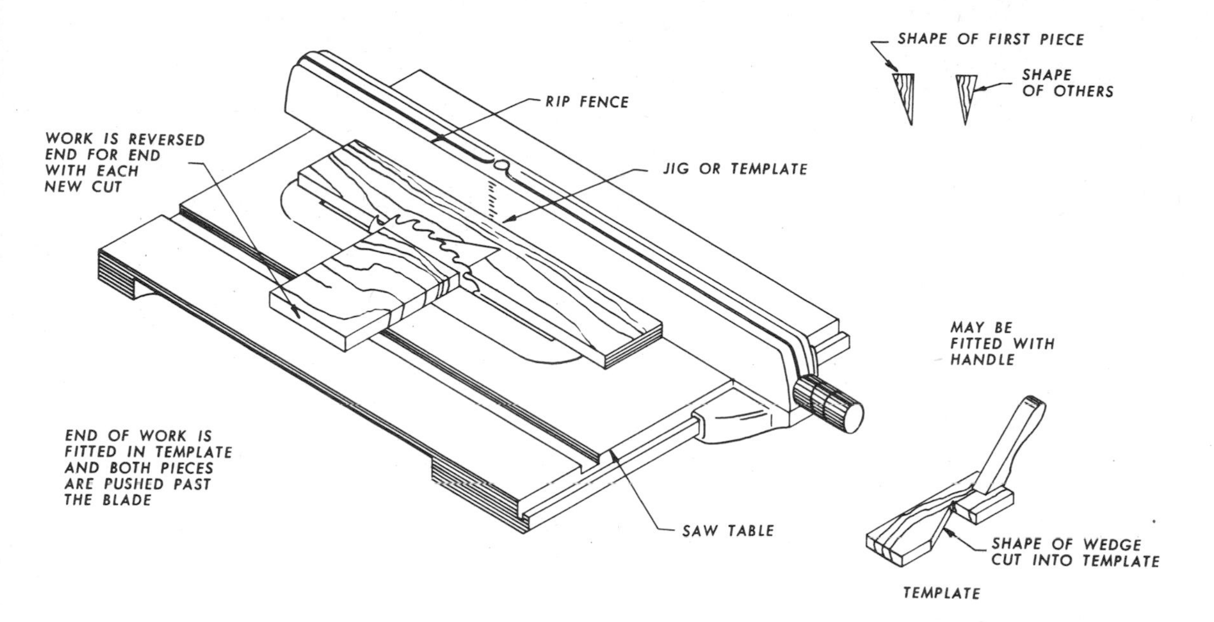

These jigs make it easier to cut wedges.

Making Wedges for Use in Joints

Some joints call for a wedge to be used to spread a projection in a cavity made for it. The end of the projection is split and the wedge is driven into the cut.

Wedges may be cut freehand but it is better to make a small jig (above), using it as shown at the right, since the wedges are usually needed in quantity. The shape cut into the guide block decides the shape and size of the wedge.

Grain in wedges should run along the length of the piece, not across the width.

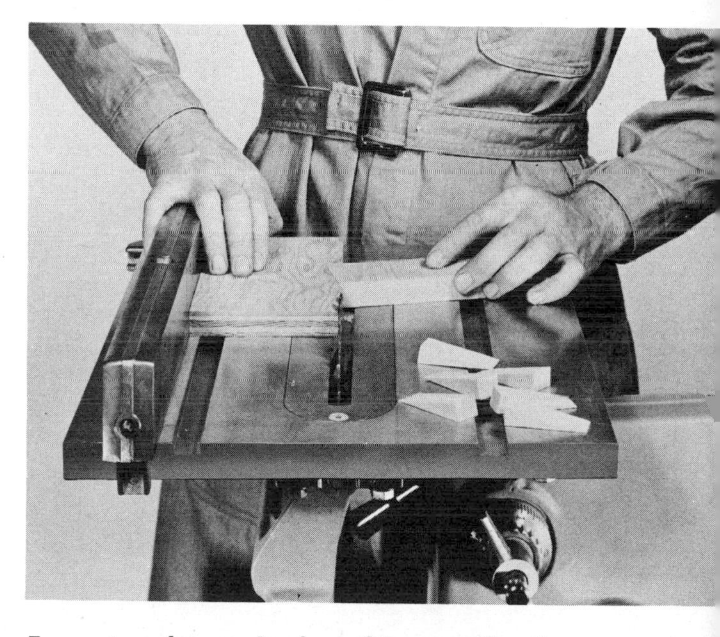

Even a template as simple as this one will make it easier and safer to cut wedges.

Making Drawers and Drawer Rails

Worked out as a guide to drawer-making for use when building pieces of your own design, the chart at left shows the most useful basic designs. All are simple table-saw operations—except the dowel joint, which is described in the chapter on the drill press.

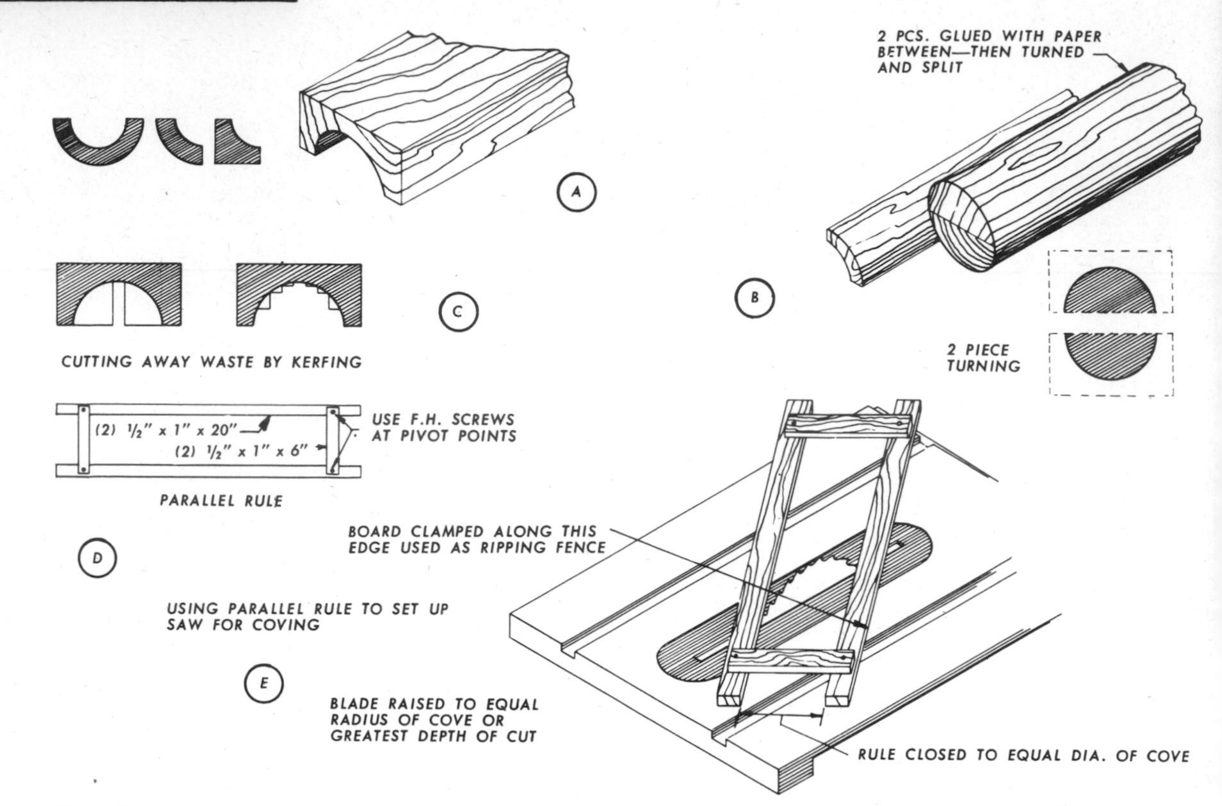

Coving

Coving cuts are very useful. The cove is frequently found on modern furniture; and even the job of making a wooden rain gutter for your roof requires cutting one. How can a blade made for straight sawing cut a round slot? Oblique sawing is the answer.

A variation of the technique is shown in sketch B above. The work is first turned on the lathe, then split, and then coved. The coved pieces are then cut in half, lengthwise. This form is often seen at the ends of shelves and table tops.

Use a combination blade with set teeth for this work. A dado assembly (especially the Magna Dado) set to cut a small dado permits a deeper cut and a faster job.

Although the cove cut is not a true semicircle, a little sanding will true up the arc.

You can speed up coving by first removing most of the waste material by kerfing, as shown at C above.

Here are coving procedures and the parallel rule that's handy in setting up for them.

The coving method may also be used on edges.

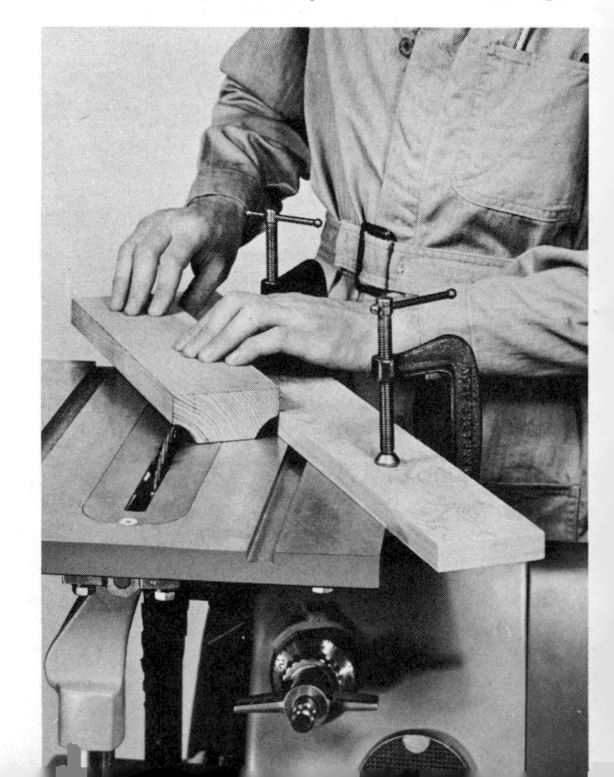

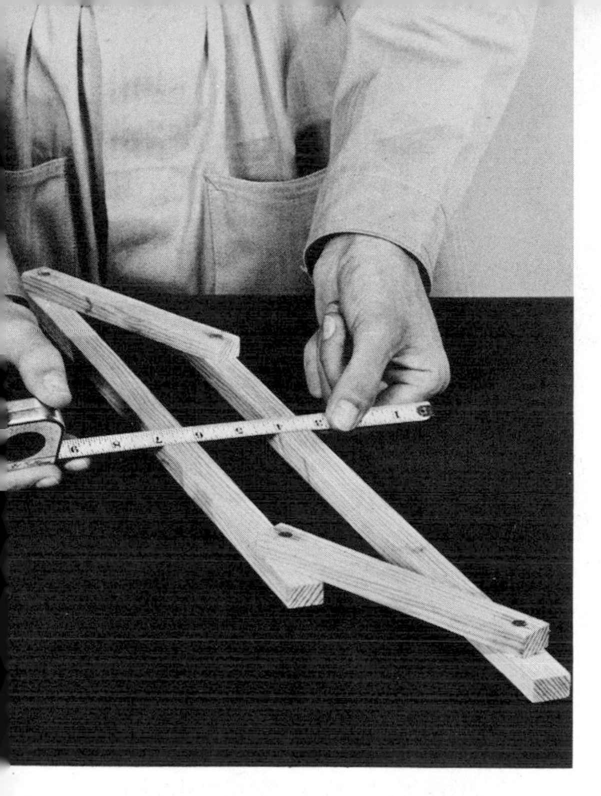

1. Begin by making this parallel rule, also shown in the drawing on the opposite page. Set the rule so its inside measurement (above) equals the diameter of the cut wanted.

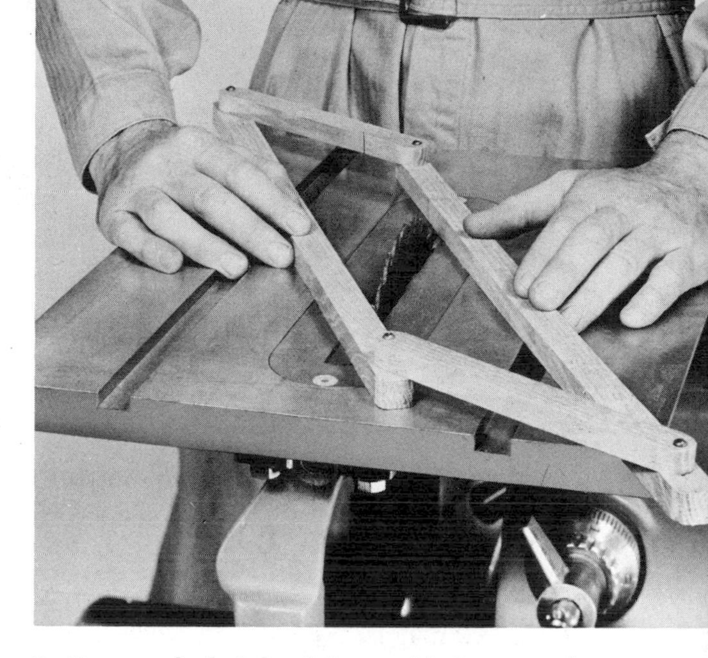

2. Next set the height of the saw blade to equal the radius of the cove desired. Place parallel rule on table so its inside edges just touch front and rear teeth of blade.

3. Clamp a guide to the table at an angle fixed by parallel rule. Place it so cut will be down center of work. Raise the table till the blade projects only about 1/16″.

4. Pass the work over the blade very slowly. Make successive passes with the table lowered 1/16″ for each. A combination blade with set teeth is best for this work.

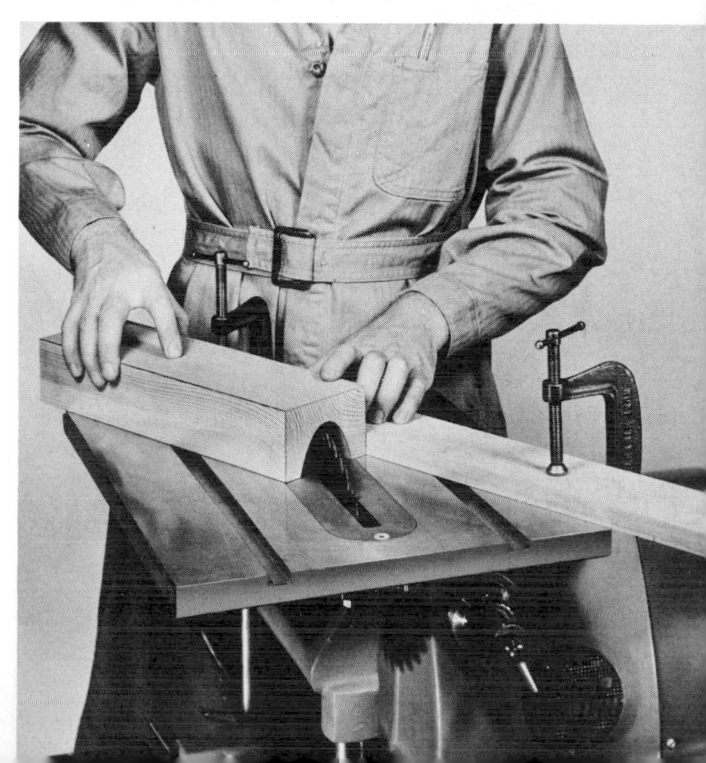

Use the V-jig shown here to cut this saucer-like depression.

Making a Saucer Cut

The technique that permits coving on the table saw may be used to form bowl-shaped depressions.

Stock to be hollowed is first cut to circular shape. This may be done on a jig saw or band saw, or excess corner stock may be removed with miter cuts, the disc sander being used to bring the piece to final round.

A V-jig clamped to the table acts as a guide for the cut. Set the jig so the intersection of perpendicular diameters of the circle to be formed is exactly on the saw-blade center. Place stock in the V-jig and slowly rotate it. Blade projection should be 1/16″ to start with and should be increased no more than 1/16″ after each turn of the stock.

The higher the blade, the deeper will be the bowl and the greater its diameter. The diameter of the depression may be increased, after the initial cuts, by moving the V-block closer to the blade and making additional passes.

When square stock requires such a depression, you can improvise an overhead pivot by using parts of the Universal Hold Down.

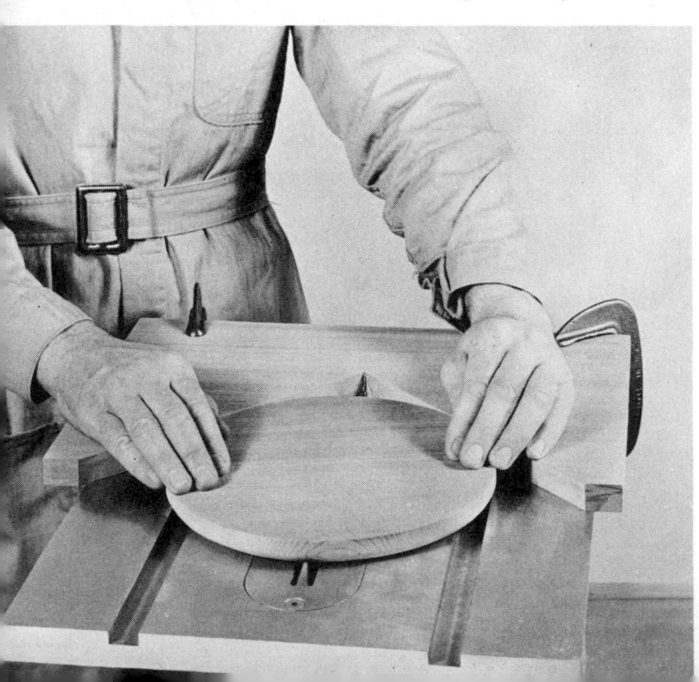

Rotate work while holding it firmly in the V.

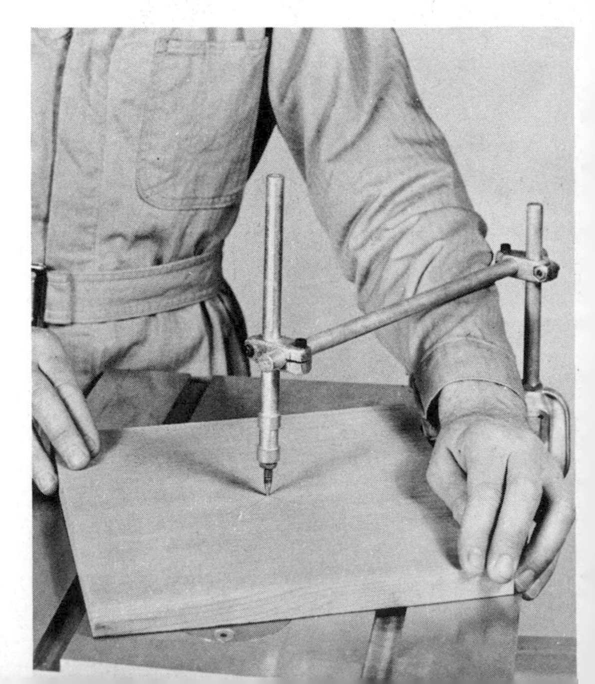

Stock not round calls for an overhead pivot.

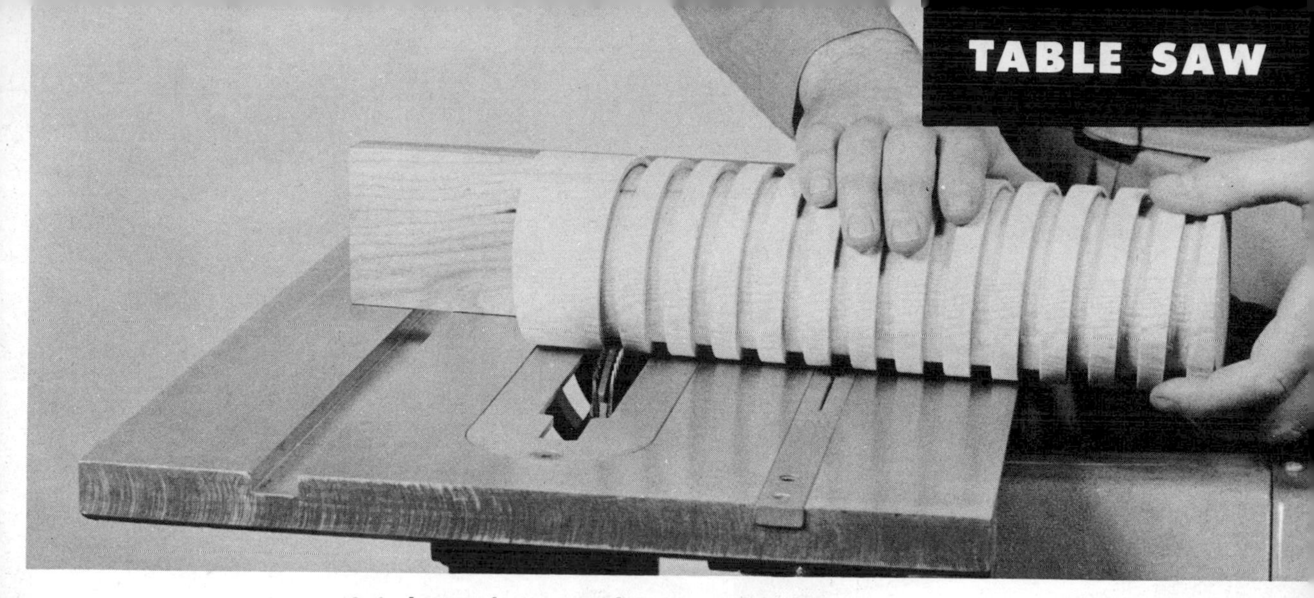

Spirals may be cut on the saw with a dado.

Cutting Spirals

Forming spirals is usually considered a lathe operation. Stock is mounted between centers, but the lathe only holds the work while the spiral is cut by hand. The table-saw technique here will reduce considerably the amount of material that must be removed by hand (usually with hand files) and will automatically shape an even, uniform spiral.

With the dado set to cut a groove of the desired size, secure the miter gauge, with extension attached, to the table. Use a C-clamp or the miter-gauge-bar lock-screw. The angle at which the miter-gauge head is set determines "lead" of the spiral, so the grooves may be formed close together or far apart.

Depth of cut is determined by the position of the miter gauge and the height of the dado above the table. It is best to keep projection to a minimum. When starting the cut, hold the stock firmly against the miter-gauge extension; lower it slowly over the turning dado. When the stock is firmly down on the table, slowly turn it toward the dado. Hold the stock **firmly**, and **remember to turn it slowly.**

There is no limit to the length or diameter of work which may be handled this way. Even a dowel may be spiraled, by using a saw blade instead of the dado.

Use a regular blade to cut spiral in dowel.

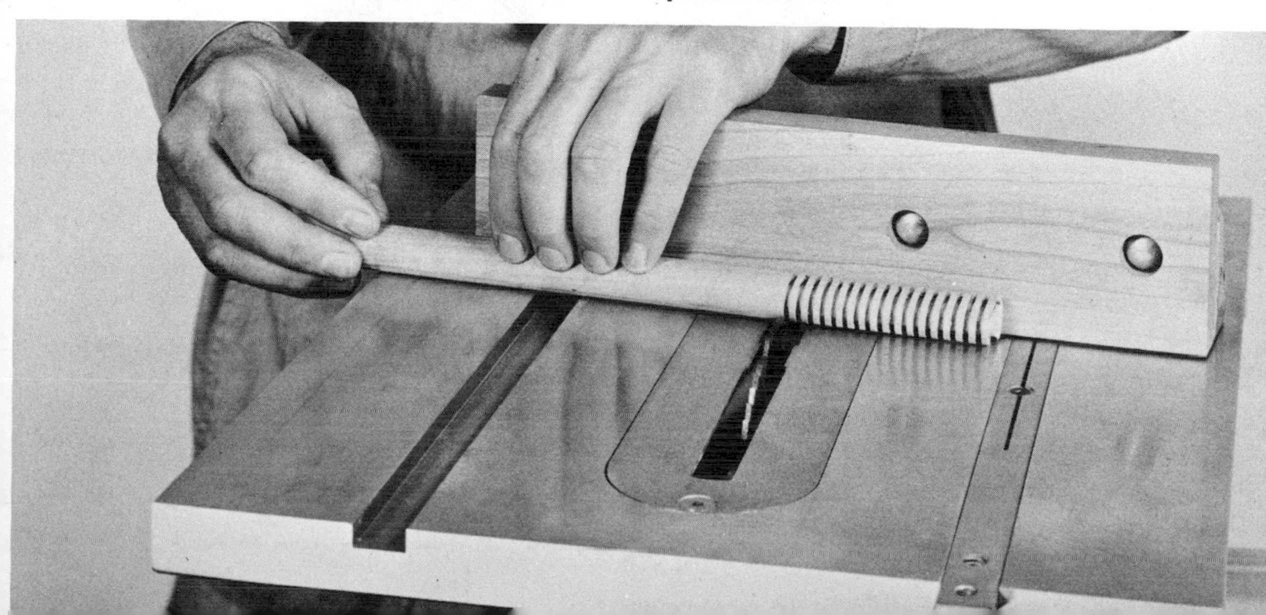

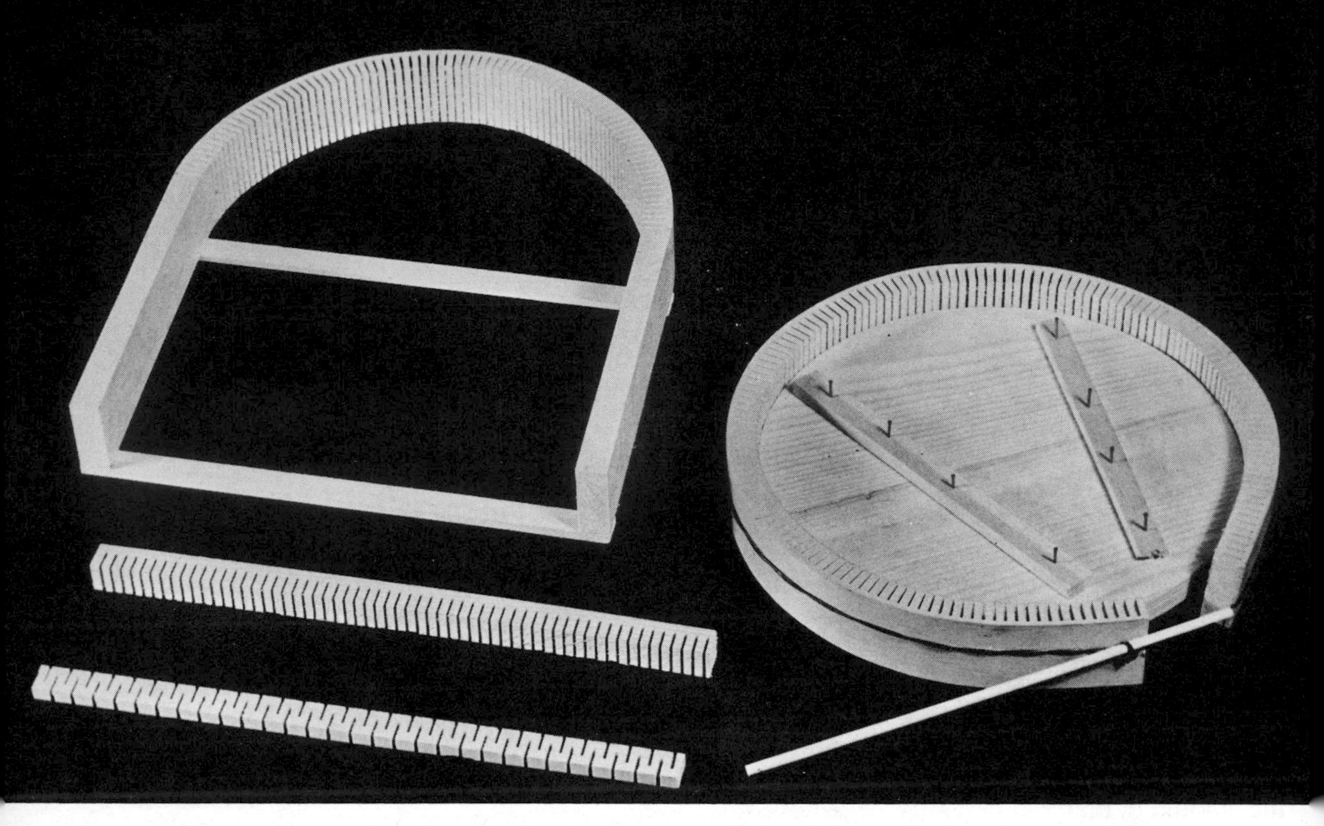

You can bend a strip by kerfing part of it (at left) or all of it (shown at right).

Follow these details for methods of bending wood by kerfing instead of steaming it.

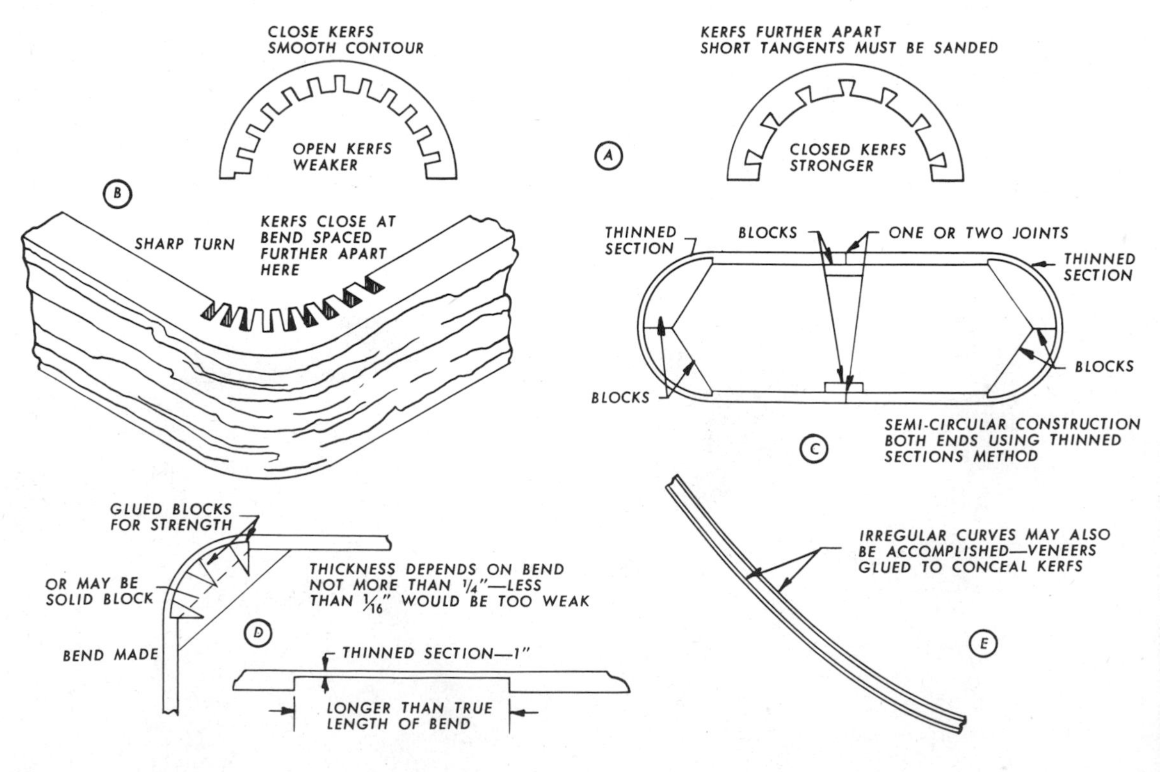

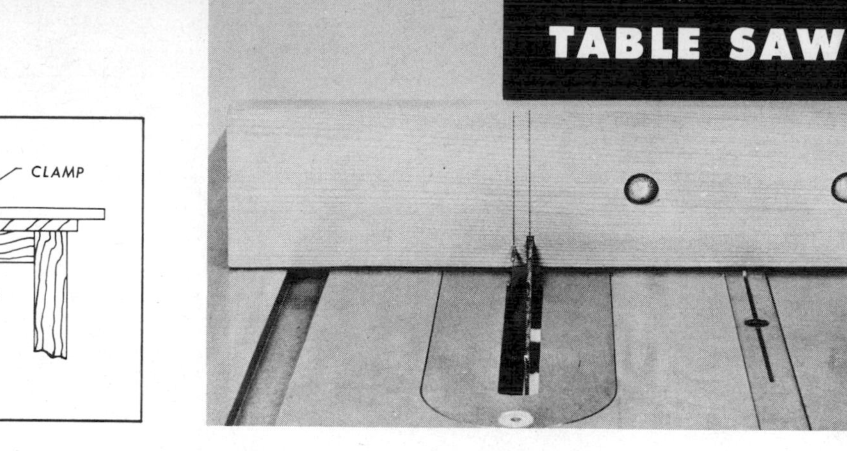

Determine correct kerf spacing this way.

Pin-to-blade distance fixes kerf spacing.

Bending Wood Without Steaming

Home craftsmen and workers in cabinet shops often find it necessary to bend a piece of wood to a particular shape. It may be needed for a garden arbor with an arched top or for a wide edge on a drum table or stool (photograph on opposite page). When problems like these arise, you must bend the wood by steaming it (which calls for special equipment) or by kerfing (which may be accomplished right on the table saw). Kerfs are shown in the drawing on the page to the left. As shown at B, when a board must make a bend around a radius the kerfs are confined to that area of the board making the turn.

If the board is weakened in the kerfed area, glue blocks may be used to strengthen it at the bend. If the spacing is properly determined and the closed kerfs reinforced with glue, the work may be stronger than the wood was.

Kerf spacing is established by a simple test (drawing at left above). Make a sample kerf in the stock to be bent. (In ¾″ stock the kerf would be about ⅝″ deep.) Place the stock, kerf up, on a flat surface. Clamp it on the right side of the kerf, as shown. Then lift the stock at the other end until the kerf closes, and measure the amount of lift, as in the sketch. This distance is the spacing required.

Most jobs of this type call for a considerable number of kerfs correctly spaced, and for a special miter-gauge-extension jig as at left below. Run a saw slot through the extension and use a nail as a guide, spacing it away from the slot the same distance as the kerf spacing.

The photograph above shows the setup of the blade, the slot, and the pin guide. The first kerf is made with the end of the work butted against the pin. The remaining cuts are gauged by placing each new kerf over the guide pin (below). When the kerfs must

Miter-gauge-extension jig helps space kerfs.

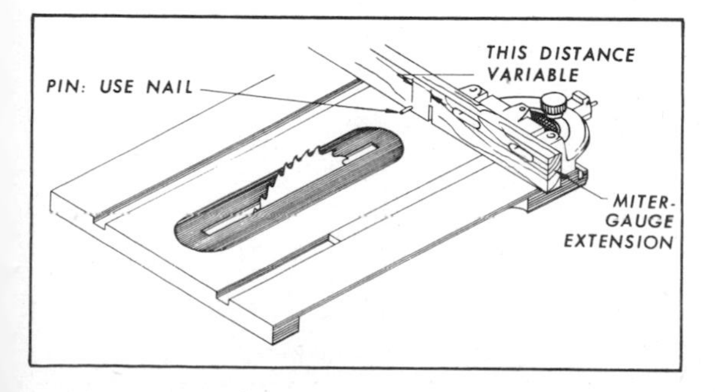

Gauge each subsequent cut by placing the preceding one over the guide pin.

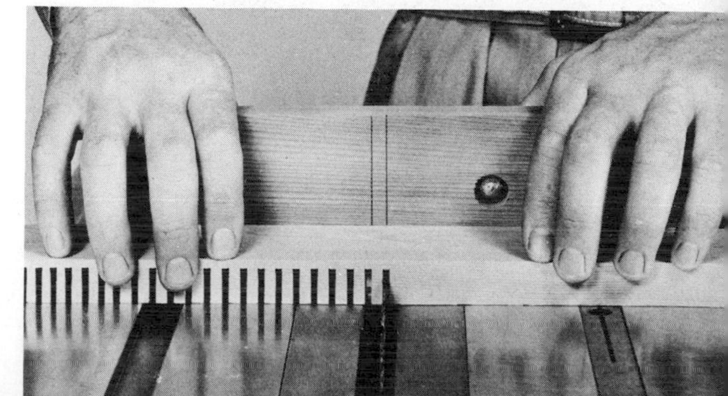

Make a wide cut like this—it's quickest with a dado—to thin out stock for bending.

be cut in an area away from the end of the stock, make the first cut without the jig.

After the kerfing is complete, bend the work slowly until it matches the curve needed. Wetting the wood with warm water will help the bending process, while a tie strip tack-nailed in place will hold the shape until the part is attached to the assembly.

Even irregular curves may be formed in this manner by kerfing both sides of the work. When the kerfing is exposed, veneers may be glued over it to hide the cuts. Outdoor work demands that the kerfs be coated with waterproof glue before the bend is made. Wood putty may be used to fill the crevices afterward. When the work has been sanded, shellacked, and painted, only a close examination will reveal the method used to produce the bend.

Another way to make a bend is the thinning-out method. Instead of kerfs, a very wide dado is cut, as is shown in the photograph above. The thinned-out section must be reinforced with glue blocks. When bending wood that has been thinned-out, soak it first in hot water and make the bend slowly. An example of how surprisingly small a radius may be turned by using this method is shown in the photograph at the lower left.

The width of the thinned-out sections can be controlled by using the step-stick clamped to the table. This is sketched below.

Thinning permits bends as sharp as these.

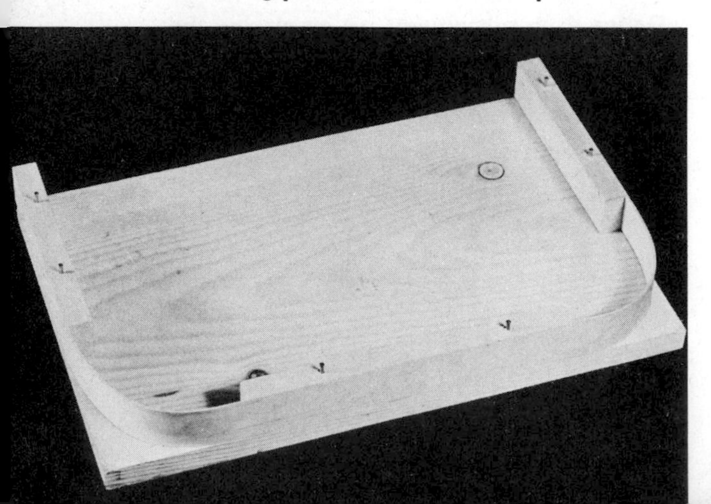

Guide block is gauge for thinning out stock.

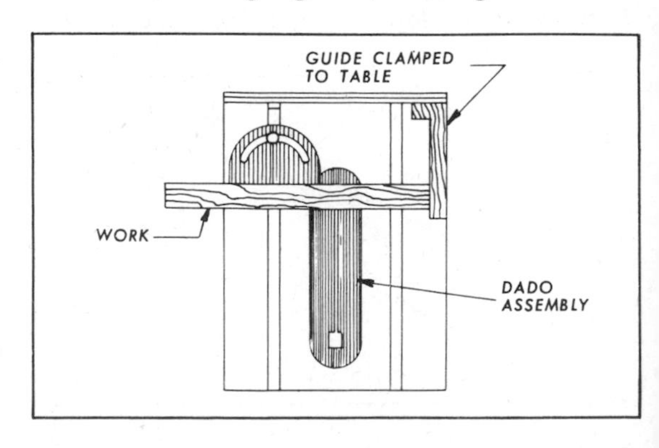

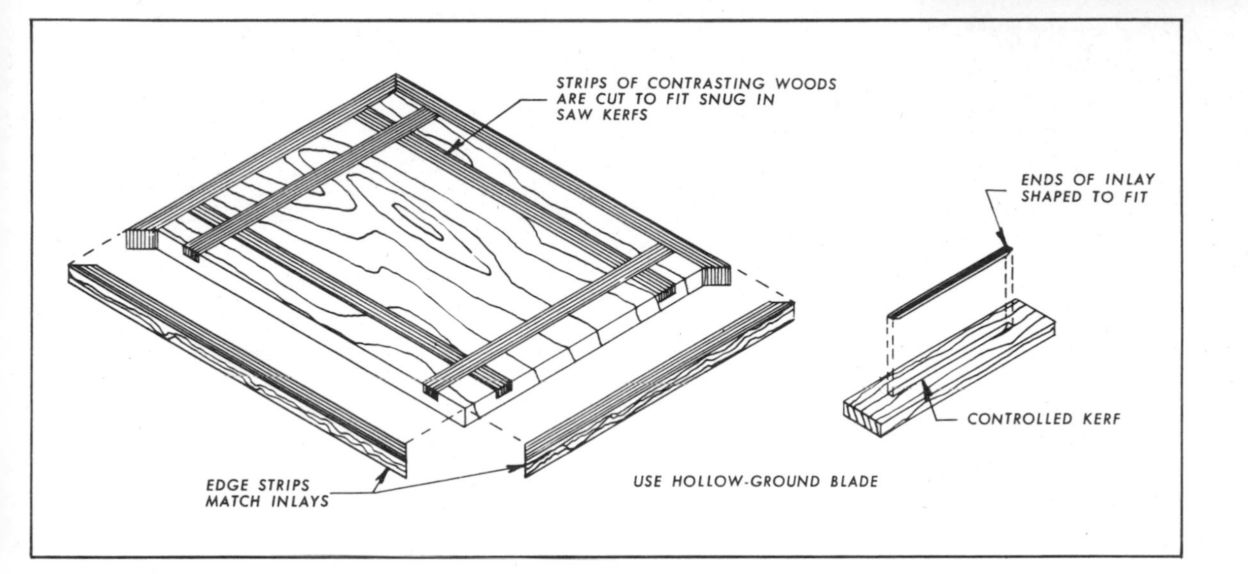

Simple Inlays

The drawing above and photograph below show how to make a simple inlay. Cut a shallow kerf into the surface or edge of the stock, then fill it with a contrasting wood cut to fit. The edges may be veneered with thin strips that match the inlay.

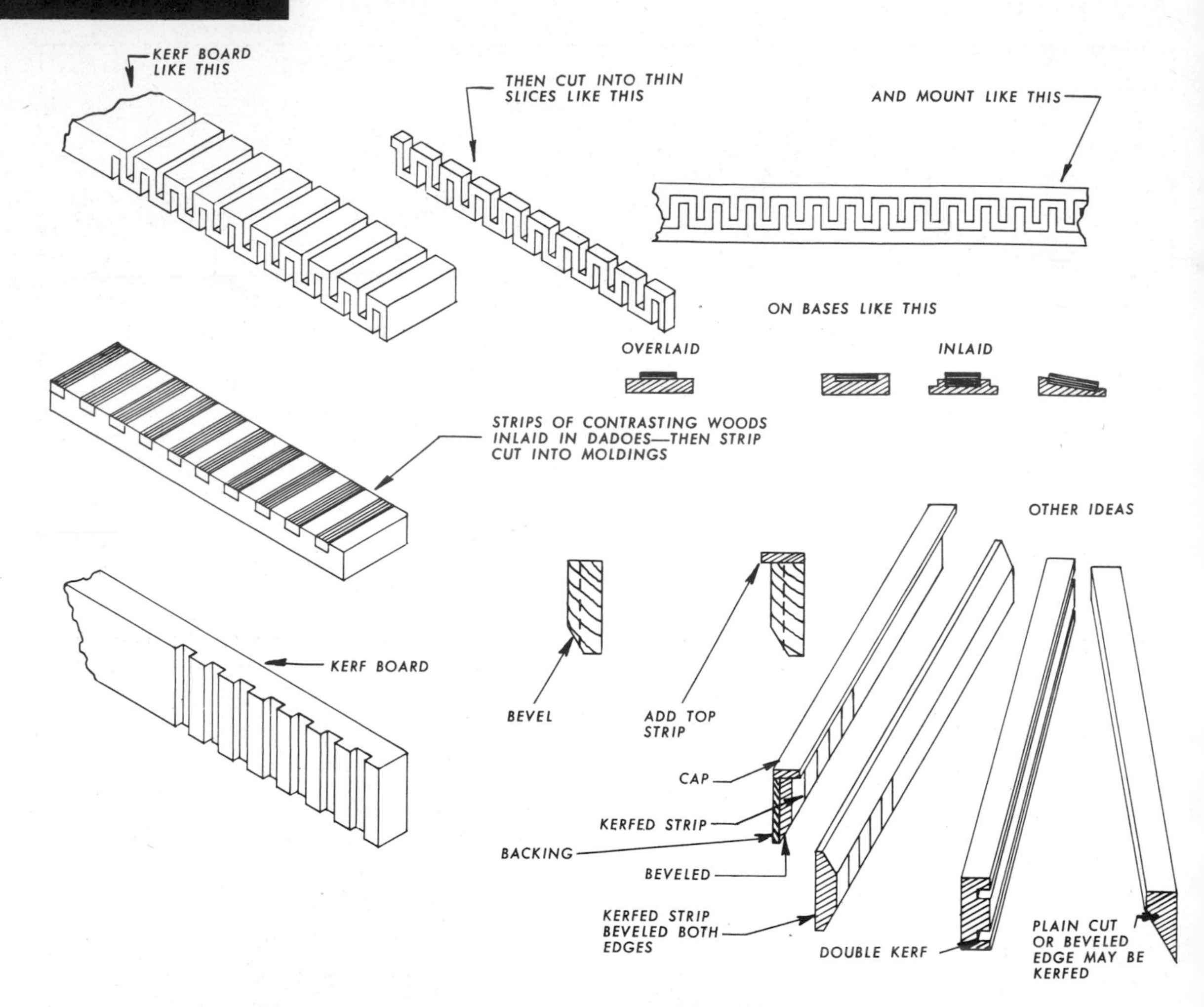

Kerfing can produce fancy moldings, as above. Picture below shows how alternating the kerfs on opposite surfaces makes a material that can be strip-cut into neat dentil molding.

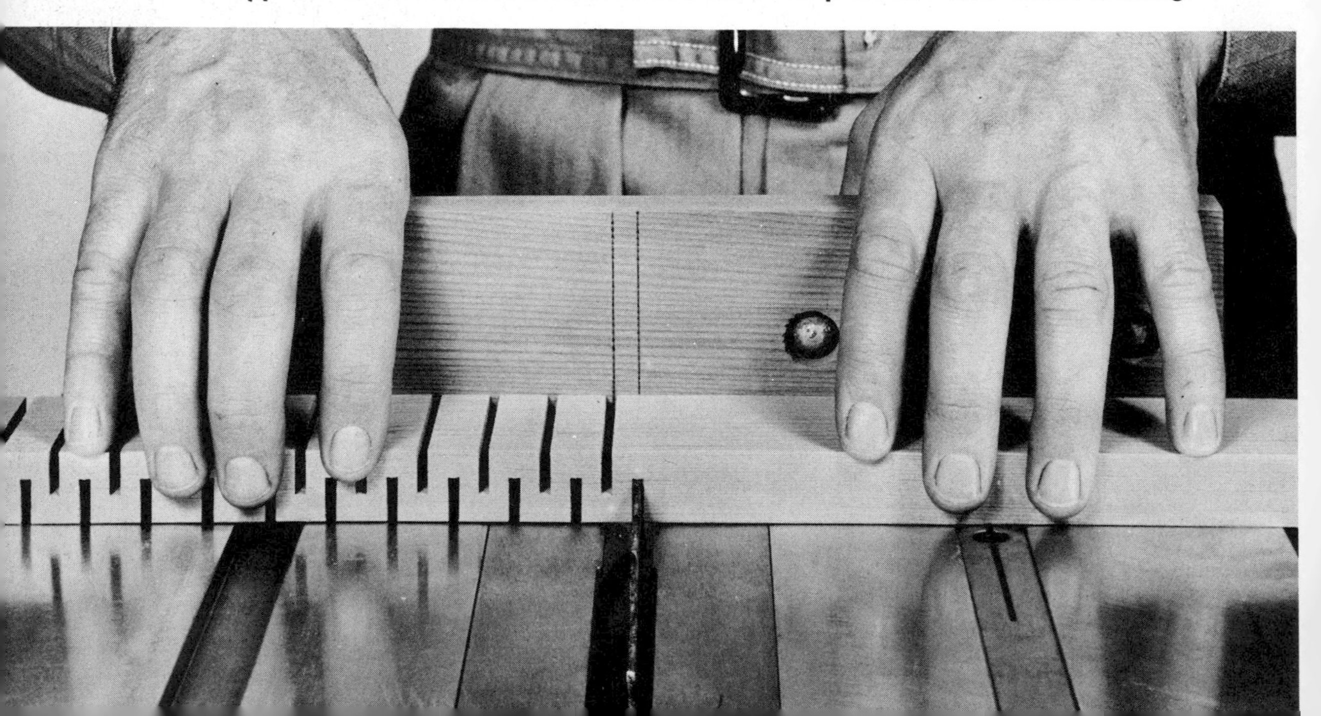

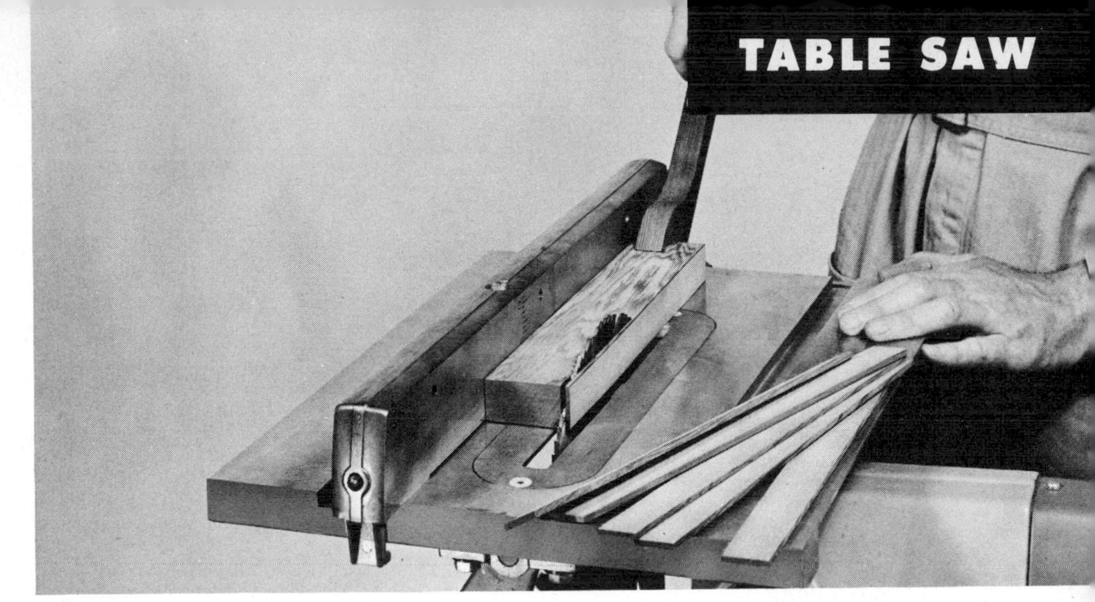

Use a hollow-ground blade and a push stick when cutting thin strips.

Special Moldings and Strip Cutting

You're often likely to want a special molding of the sort shown in the drawing on the left-hand page to individualize your work. When needed in quantity, moldings made this way save you money.

One type is easily made by using the miter-gauge-extension jig used for kerfing. Instead of the kerfs being made on one face of the work, the work is turned over for each new cut, as shown at left. The notching jig used for the finger-lap joint can also be used. Notches are cut instead of kerfs. Stock that has been surface-cut with a molding head can also be strip-cut into slim moldings.

One way of strip-cutting the decorated pieces is by advancing the blade for successive cuts, as in the photograph above. For this you need a dado-blade insert and a hollow-ground blade. The only disadvantage is that the strips may be drawn down through the insert slot at the end of the cut. To overcome this, clamp a piece of wood to the rip fence so that it projects horizontally over the work at the rear of the table and acts as a hold-down for the pieces being cut. This method permits precise cutting through use of the quill-feed lever, the cuts being gauged with the depth-control dial. Be sure the quill is locked securely after each adjustment.

Strips may also be cut by use of a special wooden insert. This is just like the regular saw-table insert except that it is made with a slot just wide enough for the blade.

A third method is sketched below.

Any of these methods can be used to cut strips as fine as 1/64″ thick.

For this production setup for cutting thin strips, begin by making an auxiliary table to fit the saw table. Then lower the blade beneath the table. Set the rip fence away from the blade by a distance equal to the thickness of the auxiliary fence plus the thickness of the slat to be cut. Clamp auxiliary table to saw table, then raise the blade so it cuts its own slot. Clamp auxiliary fence to rip fence. Use a push stick when cutting the strips.

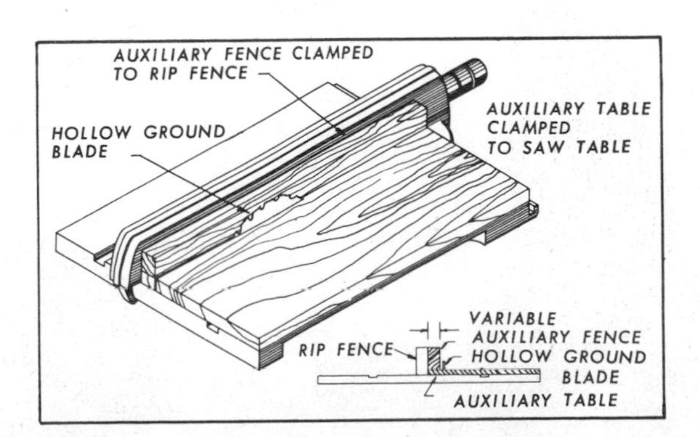

How to Rabbet Circular Work

Cutting a rabbet in a piece of round stock is usually a shaper operation. But there are some edge shapes, used on table tops, which call for a deep rabbet that cannot be cut with normal procedures. Even when the work is rabbeted as shown below, the shaper may be used for final touches—to round off the edge or to mold it to some particular design.

Construction details of the jig are shown in the drawing.

A single blade may be used, and the cut deepened by advancing the blade to take another cut, or a dado saw may be used to take the full bite in one pass.

When starting the cut, place the work in the semicircular guide very slowly (or clamp it in place and lower the table). Once it is seated in the guide, revolve it slowly until the pass is complete.

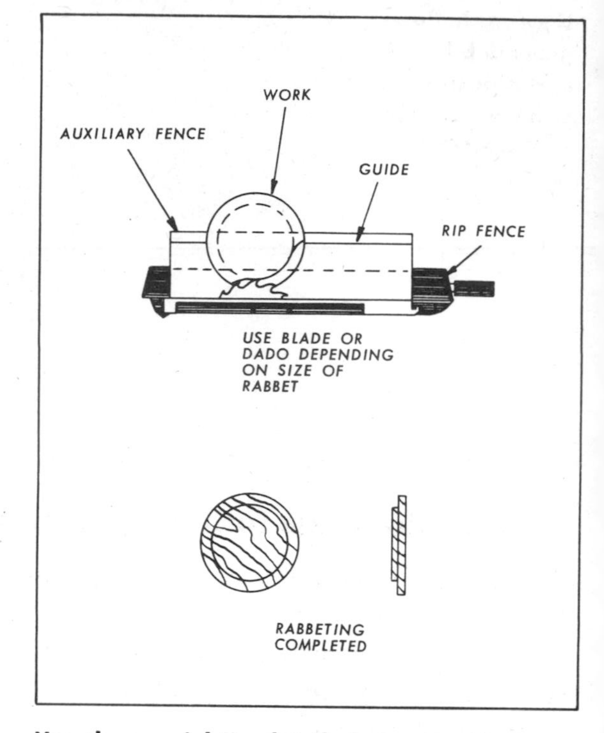

Use the special jig detailed above and shown in use below to rabbet circular pieces. To make the rabbet, simply turn stock in guide.

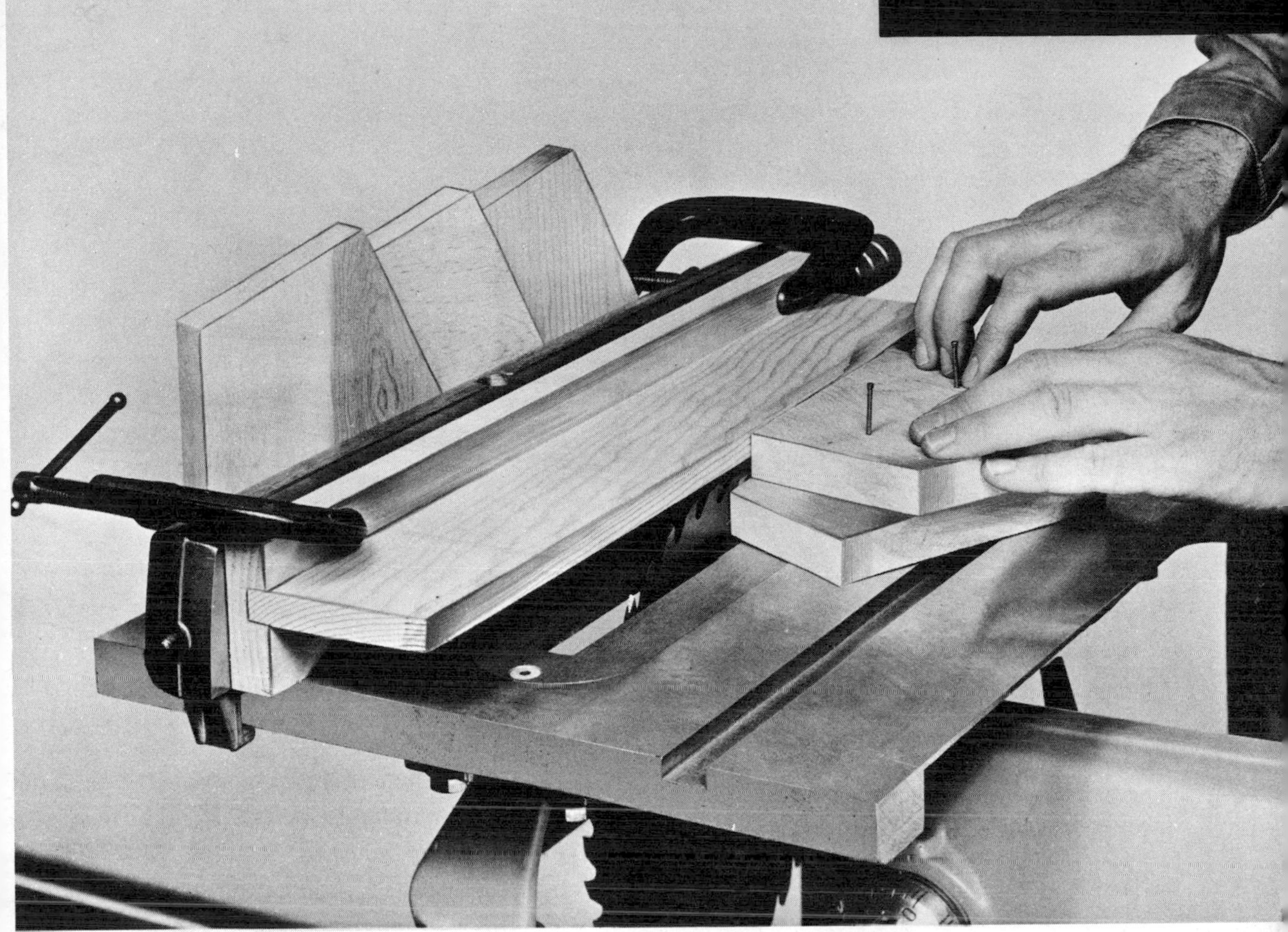

The pattern, shown riding along the guide strip, is fastened to the work. This quantity method is useful for production shops and for spare-time-income work in a home shop.

Pattern Sawing for Production Work

To cut an odd-shaped piece in quantity, start by making a pattern. Cut a piece of stock to exact shape and size.

Then cut other pieces to approximate shape and size.

Drive two nails through the pattern just far enough to project slightly.

Then press the pattern down on the work. Run it through the saw with the pattern riding the guide block as in the photograph above. Each piece will be exactly the size and shape of the pattern.

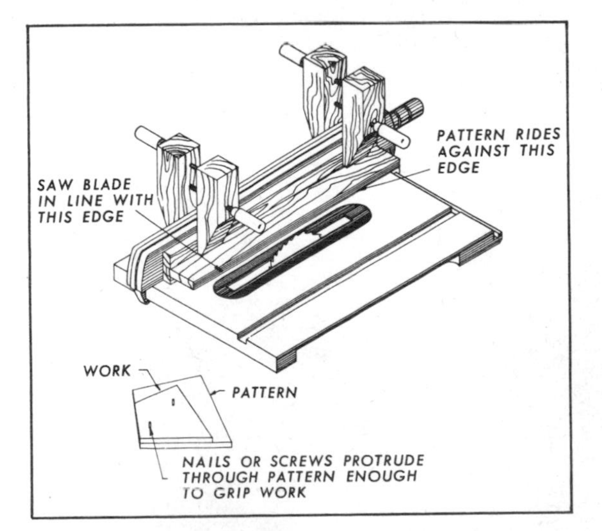
PATTERN RIDES AGAINST THIS EDGE
SAW BLADE IN LINE WITH THIS EDGE
WORK
PATTERN
NAILS OR SCREWS PROTRUDE THROUGH PATTERN ENOUGH TO GRIP WORK

Here are the details of the jig for cutting a quantity of irregular pieces just alike.

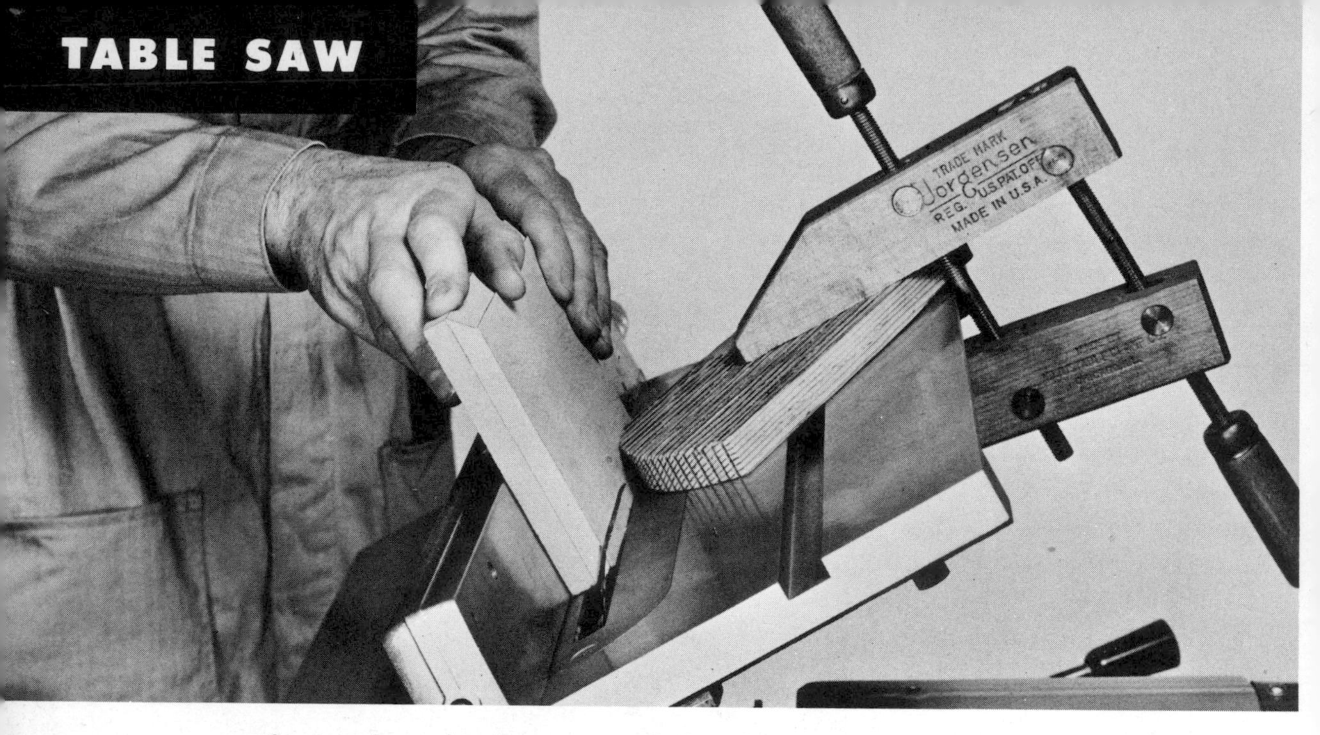

This bevel cut that leaves a small shoulder on the work creates a panel effect.

For a chamfer, make a bevel cut that doesn't remove the entire edge of the stock.

Raising a Panel

Raised panels are seen most often on closet doors, radio cabinets, etc. Making them is a bevel job, done with saw table tilted and rip fence adjusted so that the cut is just deep enough to make the bevel—leaving a slight shoulder on the work.

Sometimes a shallow kerf is cut on the surface of the panel, bordering the edges, and the bevel is cut so that it will meet the kerf. Either way the method of beveling is the same, and is shown above.

Chamfering

You can chamfer on the table saw by tilting the table to the angle of the chamfer and setting the rip fence to gauge the cut.

Operations of this type are made with comparative ease on the multi-purpose tool, especially on production runs, by using the saw at the right end of the ways. You can then stand at the end of the tool with your work on a table at your left and place the finished pieces on a table at your right.

How to Use a Cutoff Wheel

Cutoff wheels have come into their own in the home workshop because of the innovation of making them of abrasive-coated, laminated linen sheets.

They are safe, and easy to use on the table saw, if these rules are carefully followed:

1. Never run the wheel slower or faster than the manufacturer's recommended minimum and maximum operational speeds.
2. Use side flanges which are at least one third the diameter of the wheel.
3. Wear safety goggles.
4. Use the saw guard.
5. Never stand in line with the wheel.
6. Never exert side pressure against the wheel.

The cutoff wheel will cut easily through steel, aluminum, and other materials in bar stock, extruded shapes, and tubing forms. Feed should always be slow, and the work should be held tightly.

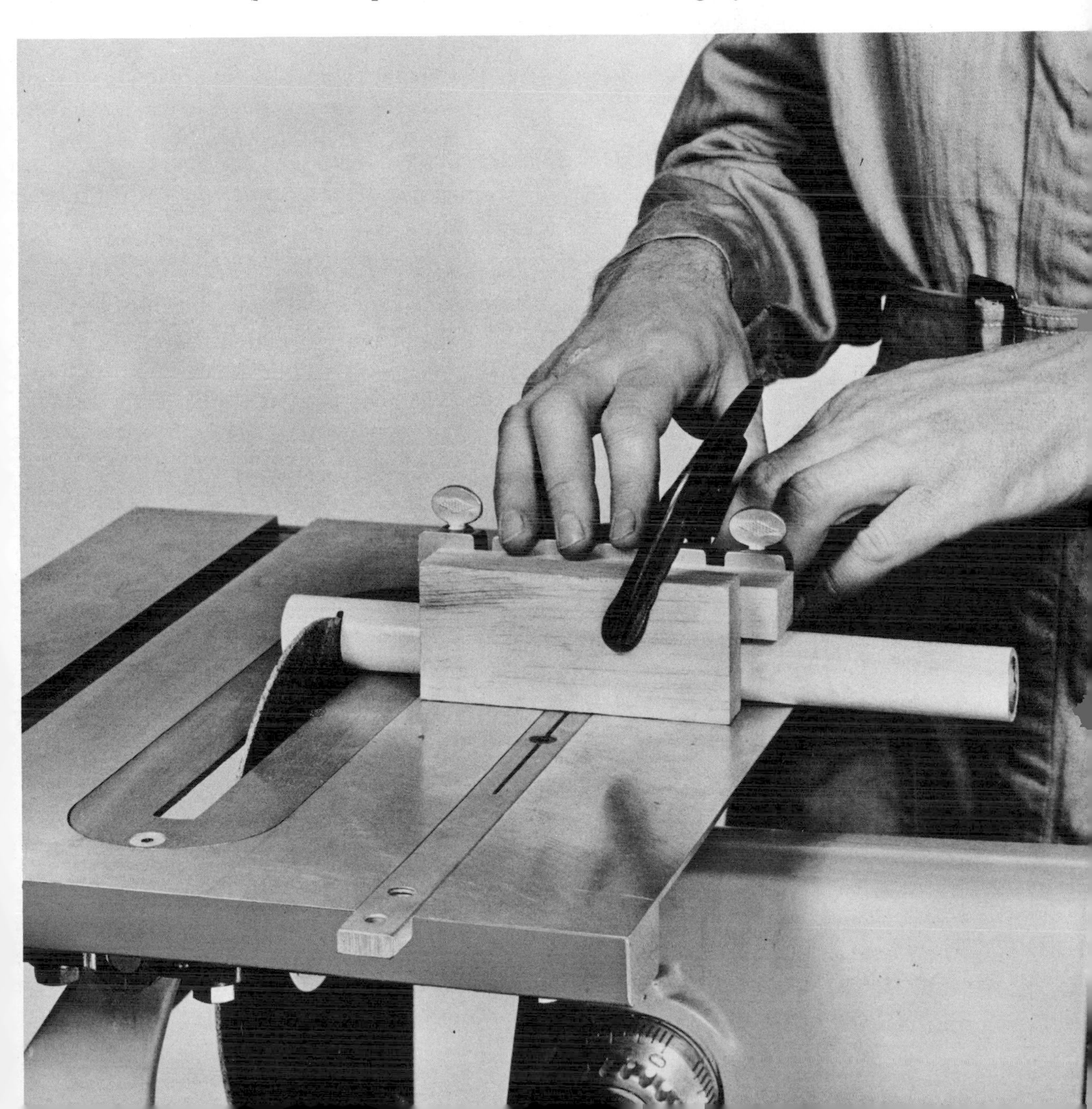

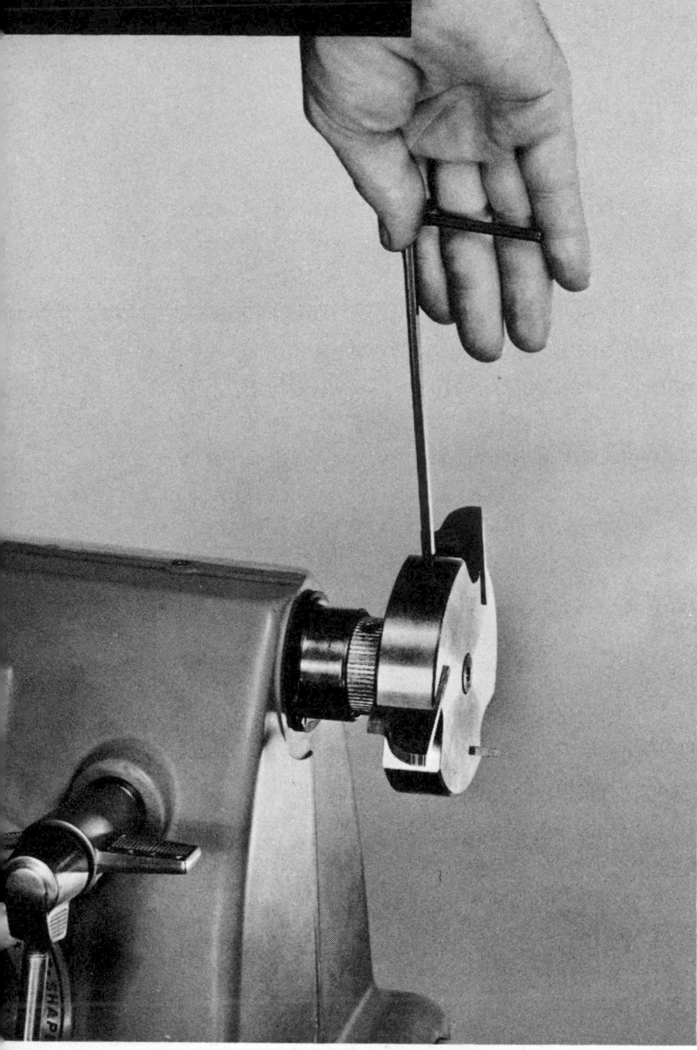

Molding head can be locked right to spindle.

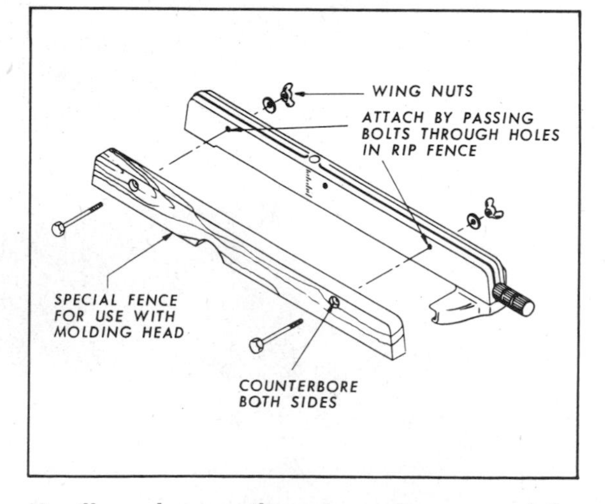

You'll need an auxiliary fence for many of the operations done with the molding head.

How to Use the Molding Head

The molding head is a practical, easy-to-use table saw accessory that enables you to add a professional touch to almost any project. With it you can shape table edges, form cabinet door lips, make your own sash, make strong glue joints, and do many other standard operations. It also enables you to shape virtually unlimited standard or original molding designs.

The molding head, of steel or aluminum, can be secured directly to the spindle or it can be mounted on a ⅝″ arbor. When mounting it on the spindle, seat the set screw securely against the tapered flat. When mounting it on an arbor, place the head between thin washers with their undercut sides against the head, and secure it with the arbor nut.

Most molding-head knives are about 1″ wide and call for use of a dado insert. If the dado-insert slot is too narrow for the knife, make a special insert of plywood or Masonite, shaped to duplicate the regular insert. Drill and countersink two holes for the table-insert hold-down screws; make the opening for the knife by slowly lowering the table as the molding head is turning. Always turn the molding head by hand before turning on the power, to be sure the knives clear the insert. By adding a wood facing, as sketched at lower left, you can use the rip fence for molding-head operations. To make the semicircular cutout, bolt the facing to the rip fence. With a blank blade mounted and turning, lower the table slowly until the cutout is about 1″ deep. If the holes for the bolts are counterbored on both sides of the wood facing, it may be used on either side of the rip fence, putting it to either left or right of the molding head.

Do not cut too deep or too fast when using the molder. If very deep cuts are required, make them in stages, lowering the table after each pass until full depth of cut

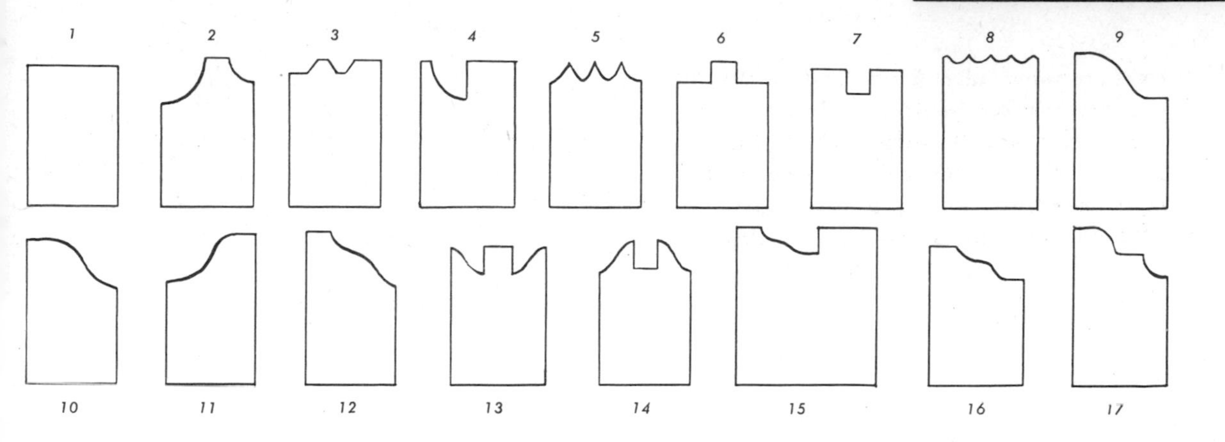

With a good assortment of knives you can turn out thousands of standard moldings and shapes of your own design. The knives shown above are:

1. **blank cutter blade**
2. **¼", ½" quarter round**
3. **glue joint, ½" stock and up**
4. **cabinet-door lip**
5. **"V"-flute molding**
6. **groove cutter**
7. **tongue cutter**
8. **four-bead molding**
9. **ogee molding**
10. **ogee molding**
11. **ogee molding**
12. **reverse ogee**
13. **panel-insert cutter**
14. **panel-insert (cope) cutter**
15. **1⅜" sash cutter**
16. **1⅜" sash cope cutter**
17. **bead-and-cove molding**

is reached. If the molding head should slow up or if the work chatters, you are cutting too deep or too fast. Move the work back, let the molding head attain full speed, then resume cutting.

Cuts made with the grain (below, left) are always easier and smoother than cross-grain cuts (below, right). Cuts made with the grain, whether they are at the edge or somewhere along the width of the work, are made like rip cuts—with the work riding the wooden facing on the rip fence. Cross-grain cuts are made by advancing the work with the miter gauge.

In shaping adjacent edges or all four edges of a workpiece, always make the cross-grain cuts first. The final with-the-grain cuts will remove the slight imperfections that are inevitable when working cross-grain.

In addition to cutting full profile shapes,

With-the-grain cuts like this one are made with the work riding against the rip fence.

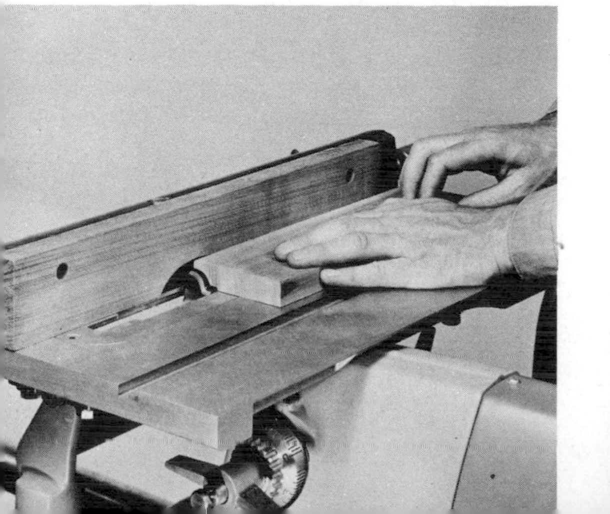

Just as with an ordinary blade, use the miter gauge when making cross-grain cuts.

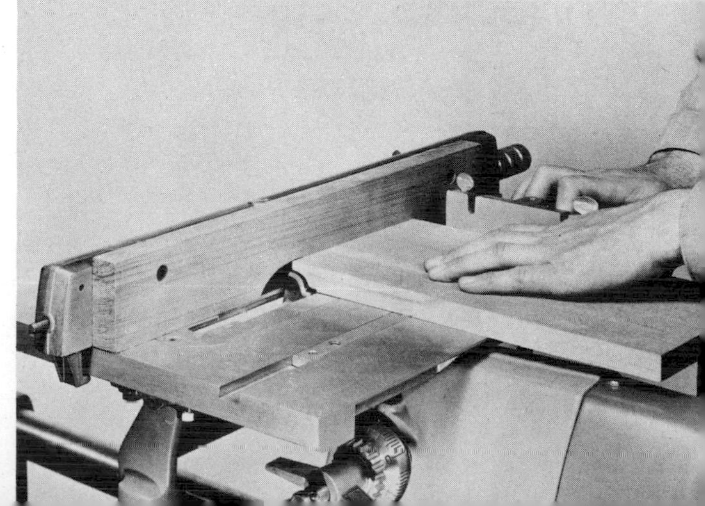

Here are some cutter knives and examples of forms that can be produced with them. The knives are: 1—blank cutter blade; 2—¼″, ½″ quarter round; 3—bead and cove molding; 4—ogee molding; 5—"V"-flute molding; 6—ogee molding; 7—groove cutter.

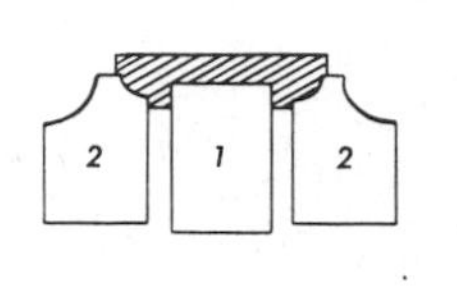

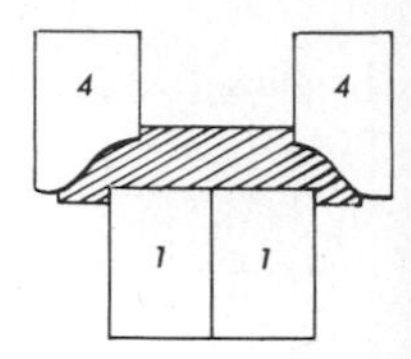

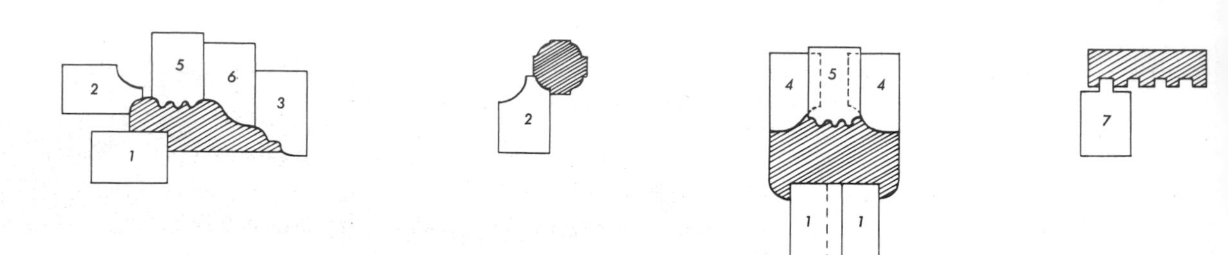

the knives can be used for partial cuts or they can be used in combination to produce almost any original molding design.

Knives like the cabinet-door lip, sash cutters, glue joint, four-bead molding, are designed to do a specific job; they are usually set to produce the full profile cut. Other knives, like the ¼″ and ½″ quarter-round, may be described as combination cutters; and they usually are set to shape a portion of the profile. This portion cut may constitute the entire operation. Or it may be just one part of an edge to be completed by several passes with different blades.

The drawing above indicates some methods of producing molded shapes through combination cuts. It is a good idea to keep a record of the knives you acquire. This record

Detailed and shown in use here are V-blocks for molding the edges of circular pieces.

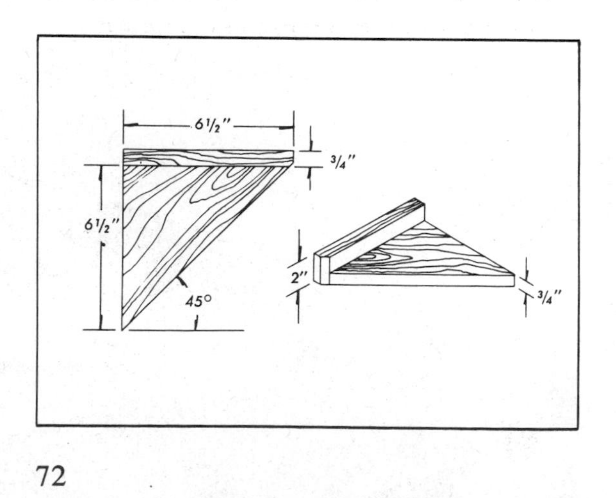

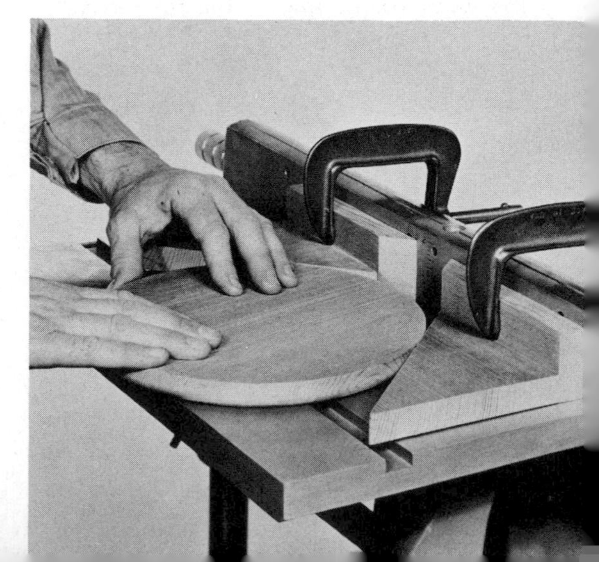

may be in the form of paper profiles or simply outlines on tracing paper. These can then be overlaid on a drawing of the shape needed. The profile, or the section of profile, which fits in with the design can be marked off for reference when you make the cuts.

You do not have to limit molding-head operations to straight cuts; circular pieces, small or large, are easily handled through the use of the simple V-block arrangement shown in the photograph and drawing below. The blocks are situated to suit the size of the work, then clamped to the rip fence. The rip fence is positioned for width of cut. Move the work in slowly until it seats firmly in the V; then rotate it slowly against the direction of rotation of the molding head. Start with a shallow cut and attain full depth of cut by easy stages.

When molding is needed in quantity, strips should be precut to size on the table saw, then fed through the simple jig shown in use at the top of this page. The jig is a length of stock rabbeted to take the strips. This is clamped to the rip fence and the precut material is fed through, as shown.

One operation that nearly always calls for the molding head is making decorative cuts on the surface of stock, as shown at the right and below.

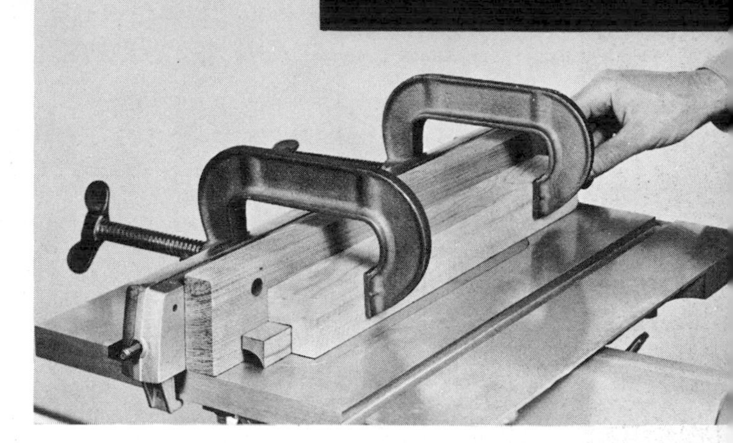

Use this method when cutting a number of slim pieces with the molding head.

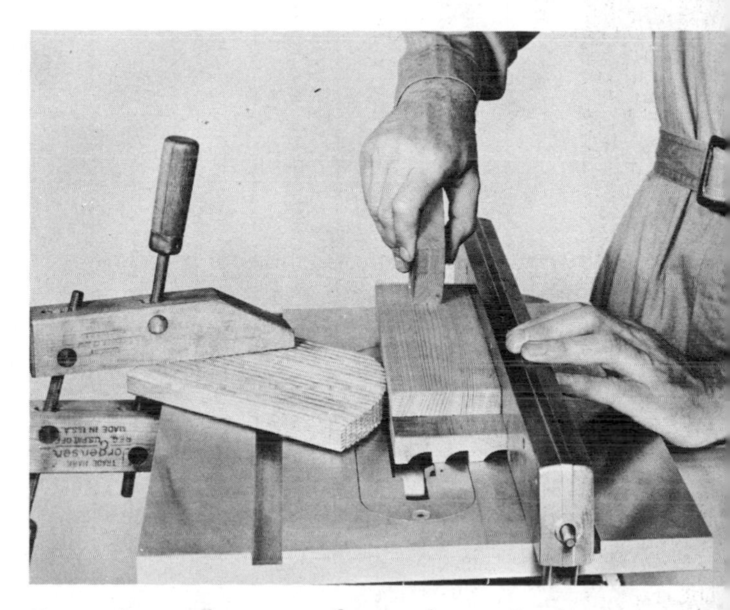

Decorating surfaces—as shown above—is almost exclusively a job for the molding head. Below are some examples of work.

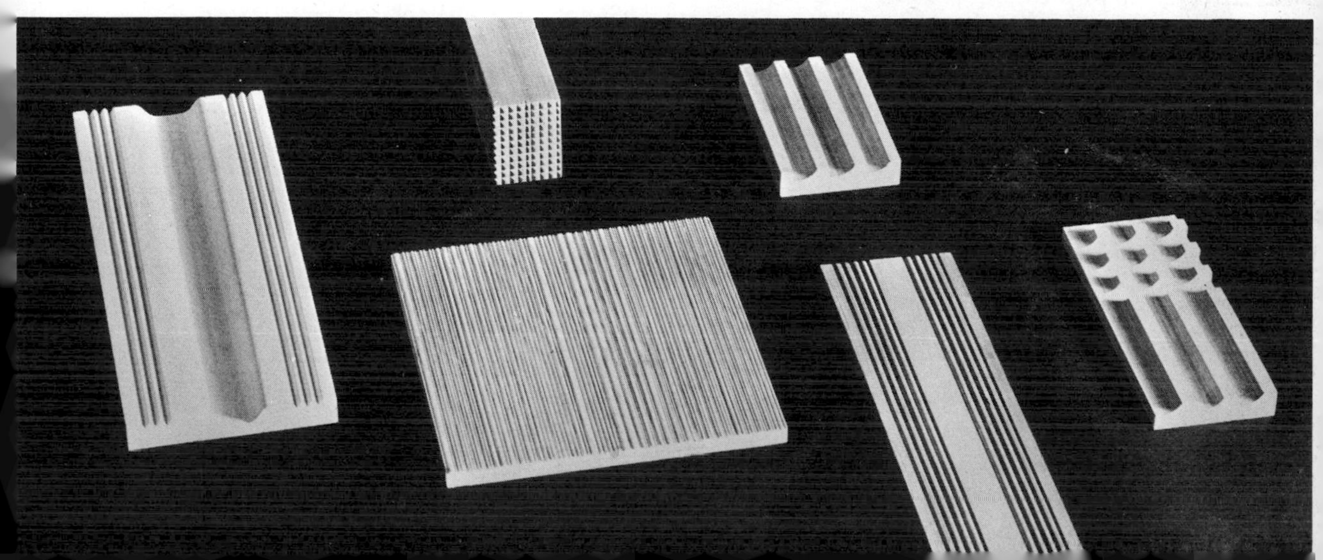

TROUBLE-SHOOTING CHART FOR THE TABLE SAW

RIPPING

THE TROUBLE	POSSIBLE CAUSES	THE CURE	SEE PAGE
WORK MOVES AWAY FROM FENCE AT BACK OF BLADE OR WORK JAMS BETWEEN FENCE AND BLADE	misalignment	be sure table slots are parallel to blade and that rip fence is parallel to table slots	4-6
	incorrect feed	be sure work is snug against fence throughout pass	25
	uneven work edge	joint edge which rides rip fence	82, 83
WORK ABOUT 1/8″ NARROWER THAN REQUIRED	measuring from wrong side of blade	be sure to measure from side of blade nearest fence and from tooth set toward fence	3
CUT EDGE HAS SLIGHT BEVEL	table not square to blade	adjust auto-stop at "0" setting on table trunnion	4
	work warped	surface stock after ripping slightly oversize—then rip to size	88
45° RIP-BEVEL CUT INACCURATE	incorrect setting	adjust auto-stop at 45° setting on table trunnion	5
SIDES OF CUT GOUGED	blade chatter	feed more slowly—be sure blade is sharp—use correct rpm	—
BLADE STALLS WHEN CUTTING SIDES OF CUT BURN	dull blade	sharpen	324
	tough wood	lower rpm for greater power	—
	accumulation of pitch and gum on blade	clean in turpentine or similar solvent	—
	incorrect projection on hollow ground blade	3/4″ projection above stock is minimum	9
BLADE BINDS IN KERF	kerf closes after cut—green wood	use splitter	2

CROSSCUTTING	CUT NOT SQUARE	miter-gauge head not square to table slots	adjust auto-stop at 90° setting on miter gauge	6
	WORK JAMS	miter gauge square to slots but slots not parallel with saw blade	be sure table slots are parallel with saw blade	5
	CUT NOT CONGRUOUS WITH MITER GAUGE SETTING	misalignment	check and adjust miter gauge auto-stops at 45° and 90° settings	6
		work allowed to creep	hold work securely when making pass—use Miter Gauge Safety Grip	30
	CUT HAS SLIGHT BEVEL	misalignment	adjust auto-stops at "0" setting on table trunnion	4
	MITER GAUGE HEAD ROCKS	uneven base setting	adjust nylon glides in base of miter gauge	—
	MITER GAUGE HARD TO PUSH	miter gauge bar too snug in table slots	be sure miter gauge bar lock screw is not tightened—clean bar and table slots—apply wax and rub to polish	—
	BLADE BINDS IN KERF	excessive overhang tilts work	provide adequate support to keep work level on table	20
DADOING—MOLDING	GROOVE BOTTOM UNEVEN	dado chippers uneven—usually lower than outside blades (common fault even with new set)	joint and sharpen	—
		inconsistent radial placement on arbor	mark blades and chippers and consistently line up marks when placing on arbor—do this in conjunction with sharpening and jointing	—
	GROOVE BOTTOM HAS SLIGHT RADIUS	lateral movement of single blade dado does this	characteristic of single-blade dado—provides room for glue	—
	EXCESSIVE VIBRATION	excessive speed	use lower rpm	—
	DADO OR MOLDING HEAD STALLS	cutting too deep	attain full depth of cut with successive passes	70
	WOOD, DADO, OR MOLDING KNIVES BURN	feeding too fast cutting too deep	feed slowly and attain full depth of cut with successive passes	70
		gum and pitch accumulation on dado or molding knives	clean with turpentine or similar solvent	—
		dull blades and chippers or knives	sharpen	—
	SPLINTERING OR EXCESSIVE FEATHERING AT END OF CUT	breaking out of cut too fast	avoid by finishing cut very, very slowly	—

2 THE JOINTER

Adjusting for accuracy • for depth
adjusting guard and fence • edge jointing
jointing wide boards and making an auxiliary fence
jointing uneven edges • end grain
surfacing • rabbeting • beveling • tapering • chamfering
making octagonal shapes • trouble shooting

Ideally the jointer and the table saw should operate simultaneously.

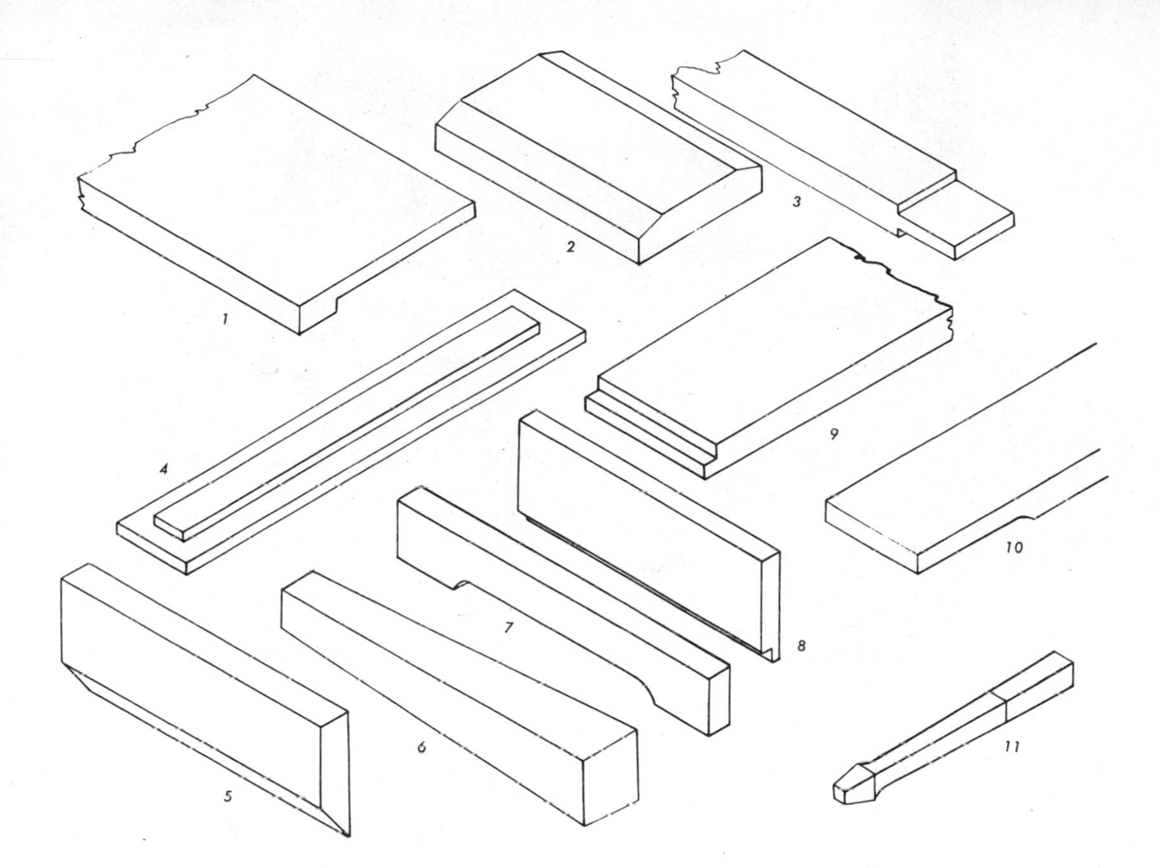

These are typical jointer cuts. You'll find information about making each of them on these pages: 1—wide rabbet, page 90; 2—chamfer, 94, 95; 3—stud tenon, 91; 4—raising (four rabbet cuts), 90; 5—bevel, 92; 6—tapers, 92, 93; 7—recessing, 94, 95; 8—edge rabbet, 90; 9—end rabbet, 90, 91· 10—surfacing, 87-89; 11—leg shapes, 92, 93.

THE JOINTER is designed to accomplish quickly and accurately many operations that would require tedious hours of labor if done by hand. It's basically a rotary cutter that will plane edges smooth and square, ready for gluing or assembling. It will do a fine job on light surfacing cuts also but should not be confused with the thickness planer, as jointers often are. The thickness planer is a heavy industrial machine designed to dress stock to exact thickness and perfectly parallel surfaces.

The basic usefulness of the jointer is illustrated by a quick preview of standard operational procedure on a saw-jointer combination—such as is available with the multipurpose tool. When cutting stock to width, you first establish a smooth, square work-edge by making a jointing cut on one edge of the stock. This edge is placed against the fence during the rip cut on the saw. The rip cut is made oversize to allow for stock removal when making the second jointing cut. Thus you have sized your stock to exact dimensions and also obtained smooth, square edges requiring no further attention. In addition the jointer is used to accomplish all the cuts shown in the drawings above.

Height of the jointer knives should be set to the horizontal plane of the outfeed table.

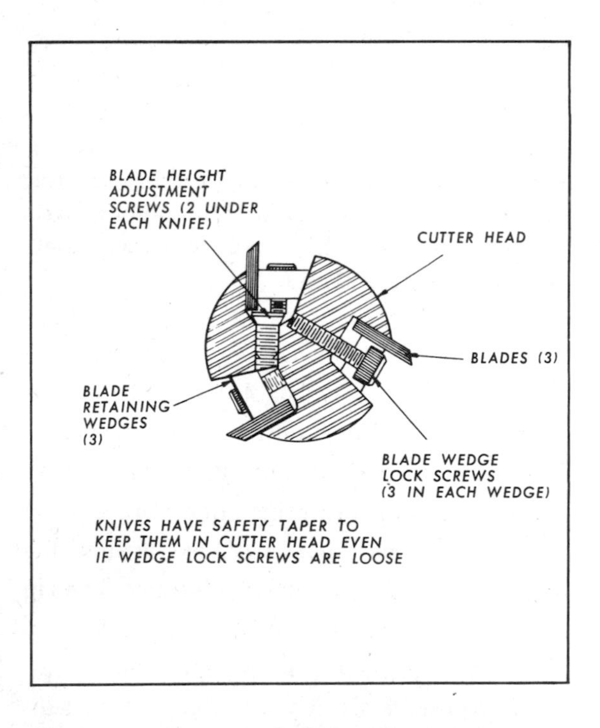

The knives sit on two height-adjustment screws and are locked in place with wedges. The knives have a safety taper to keep them in the cutter head even if wedge lock screws work loose.

Machine Adjustment

The most critical jointer adjustment is the one that determines knife height in relation to the horizontal plane of the outfeed table. However, a jointer with a fixed outfeed table, cast integrally with the base, and knives that can be screw-adjusted for height makes even that adjustment a simple matter.

The horizontal plane of the outfeed table must be tangent to the cutting circle of the knives. To check this, place a straightedge on the outfeed table so that it juts out over the cutter head. Turn the cutter head by hand (use hand on flexible coupling) until one knife is poised at the topmost point of the cutting circle. The knife should barely scrape the straightedge. If the knife lifts the straightedge from the table, it is an indication that the knife is set too high. If the knife doesn't touch at all, it is set too low. Make this check at both ends of each knife, as shown in the photograph appearing at the top of this page. If adjustment is required, loosen the three

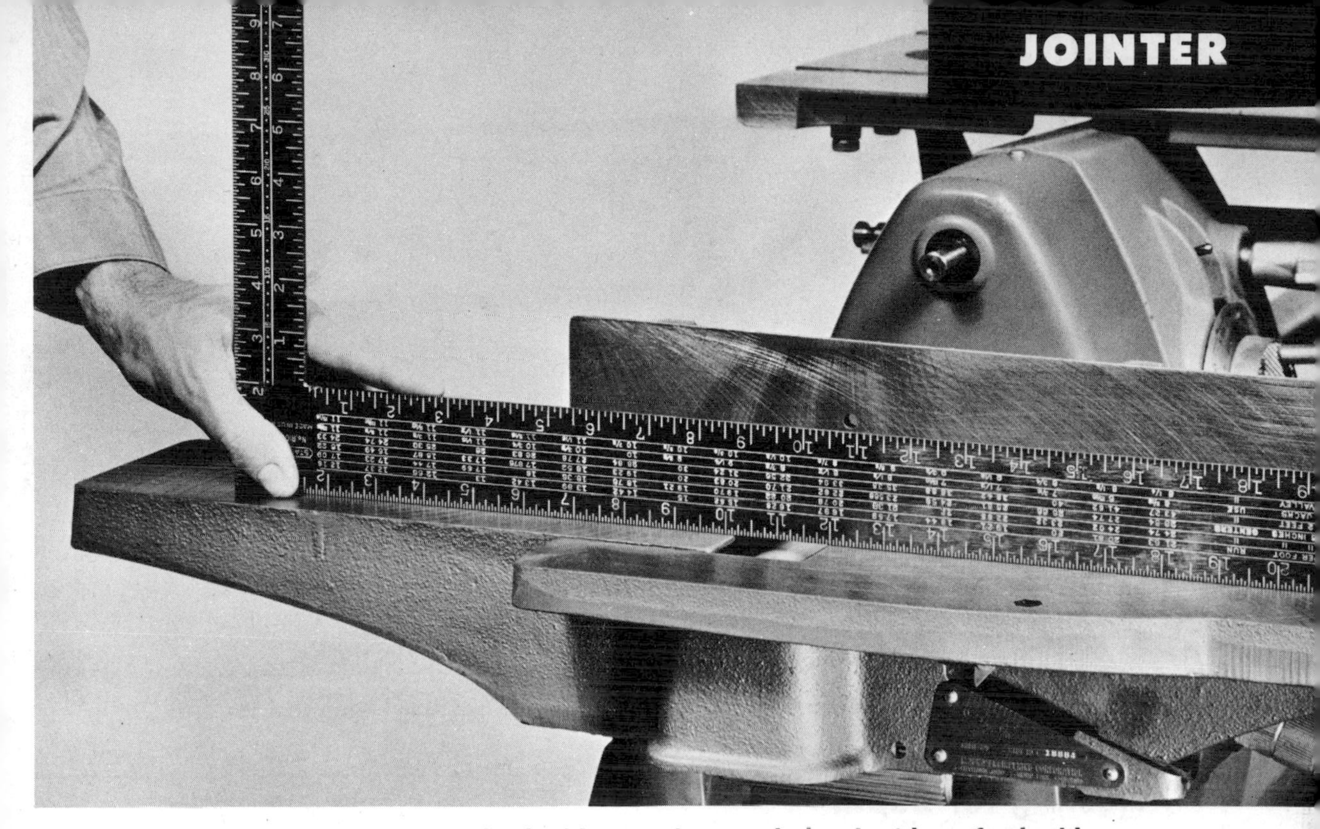

With depth indicator at "0" infeed table must be exactly level with outfeed table.

Allen screws which lock the blade-retaining wedges. Adjust the two Allen screws on which the knives rest (see drawing on opposite page) either up or down, depending on whether the knife is too high or too low.

After the knife is adjusted for height, check it for position in the cutter head. The forward edge of the knife (edge nearest the rabbeting ledge) should extend about 1/16" beyond the front edge of the outfeed table. If it doesn't, the work will not clear the outfeed table during a rabbet cut. Lock each wedge in place with the three Allen screws.

When knife height is correct, use a straightedge (photograph above) to see if the infeed table is level with the outfeed table. A further check can be made by taking a length of wood with a straight edge and making a pass with the power turned off. It should move over the gap between the tables and slide smoothly onto the outfeed table without hitting its front edge or being the least bit above it.

Operational danger signals which indicate misalignment are shown in the diagram below. If, after passing over the cutter head, the edge of the work hits the front edge of the outfeed table and must be forced across, the knives are set too low; if the work drops slightly near the end of the pass producing a gouged or tapered end, the knives are too high.

Here's what will happen if jointer knives are set too low or too high in cutter head.

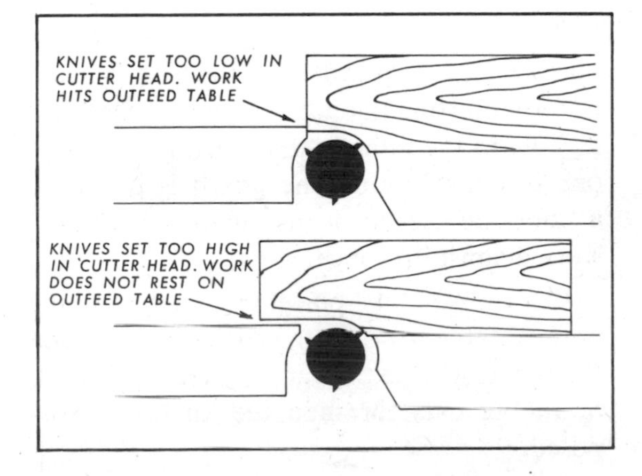
KNIVES SET TOO LOW IN CUTTER HEAD. WORK HITS OUTFEED TABLE
KNIVES SET TOO HIGH IN CUTTER HEAD. WORK DOES NOT REST ON OUTFEED TABLE

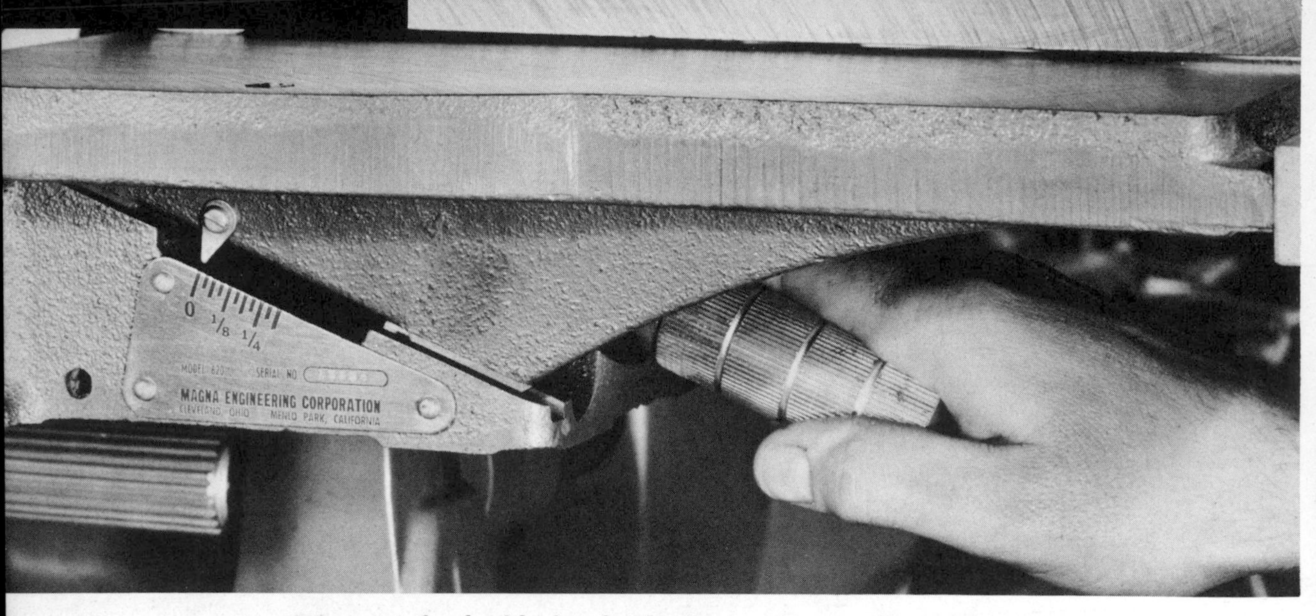

Lower infeed table for depth of cut, taking readings from this scale.

Adjusting for Depth

Turning the hand knob clockwise (photograph above) lowers the infeed table for depth-of-cut adjustments.

To check the accuracy of the pointer on the depth scale, set it at 1/8″ and make a trial cut. Measure the cut; if it is not correct, raise or lower the table until a cut measures exactly 1/8″. Then set the pointer exactly on the 1/8″ mark on the scale. Depth-of-cut settings for the full range of the scale will then read correctly.

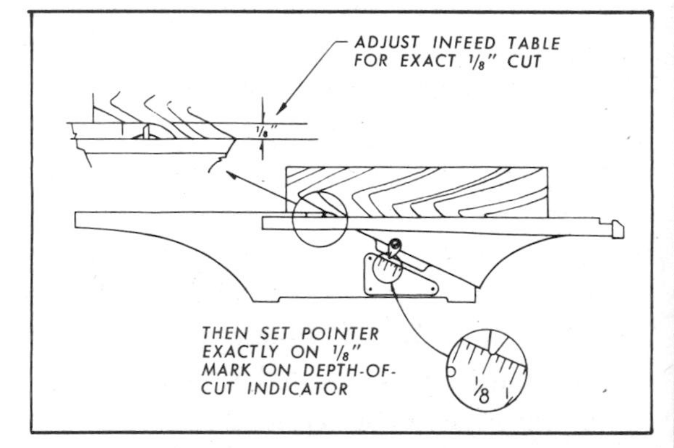

This is how to adjust depth-of-cut scale.

Adjusting the Guard

The cap on the guard contains a spring that keeps the guard over the cutter head. Before inserting the hex pin of the guard into its hole in the infeed table, turn it clockwise one full revolution. The guard is primarily a safety device but it also helps to hold the work against the fence.

On rabbet cuts place the guard on the outfeed table to cover the cutter head behind the fence. Use extra care at start and finish of rabbet cuts for then the knives are exposed.

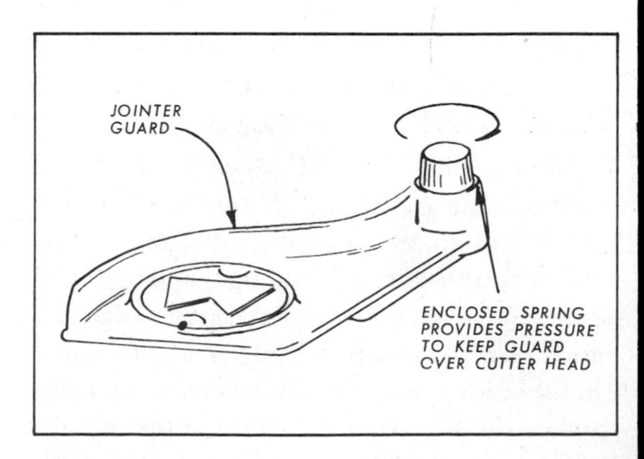

Never work without the guard if you can possibly help it. When guard is omitted from a picture, it is only so cut may be clearly seen.

Adjusting the Fence

In normal operating position the fence should be perpendicular to the horizontal plane of the tables. Check this with a square (photograph at right). If adjustment is necessary, follow this procedure:

1. Use the two-socket wrench to loosen the nut that secures fence tilt.

2. Set the fence on the quadrant "0" mark and lock it. Check the setting with a square.

3. If the fence requires adjustment, loosen the two slotted screws which secure the fence bar to the infeed table, and (see top sketch at right) adjust the bar until the fence checks out exactly square to the table. Then securely lock the two slotted screws.

This adjustment is important since it controls the squareness of all jointing cuts. Like any adjustment it should be checked periodically.

The auto-stop for the 90° position may be adjusted now. Keep the fence locked at "0" setting on the quadrant; bring the stop forward (middle sketch) and thread the Nylok screw down until its end bears against the stop.

To adjust the auto-stops for the 45° settings on the quadrant, lock the fence in position and follow the same procedure used for adjusting the "0" setting auto-stop. Do this with the fence tilted 45° forward—and again with the fence tilted backward 45°. Thus you have accurate, automatic stops at the three most-used fence positions.

In addition to angular settings for bevel cuts, the fence may be moved across the tables (bottom sketch). For example, the width of a rabbet cut is gauged by the distance from the end of the knives to the fence. If you want a rabbet cut 1″ wide, move the fence across the table and lock it 1″ away from the end of the knives. Setting of the fence in any position across the tables is locked with the two-socket wrench.

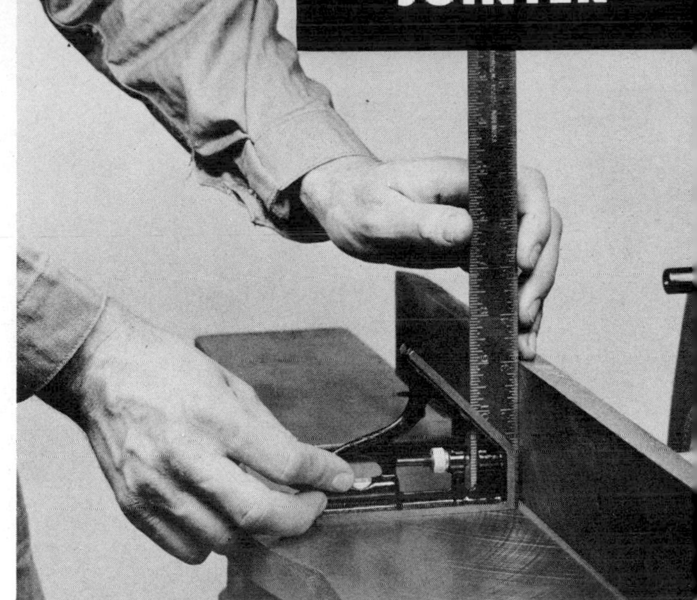

For accurate jointing, the fence must be square to the tables when set at "0".

Top sketch shows how to square fence to tables by adjusting fence bar. Middle sketch shows how Nylok set screws provide automatic stops at most commonly used fence positions. How the fence moves across the tables—an essential for rabbet cuts—is at bottom.

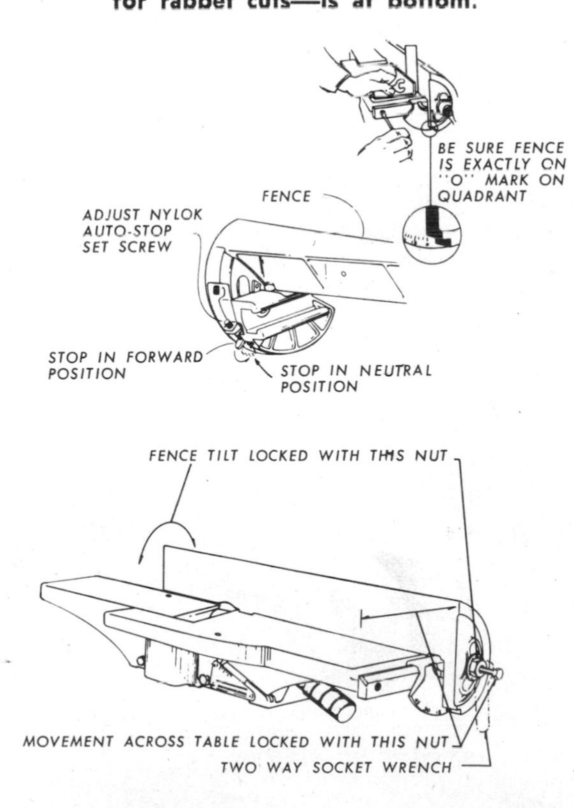

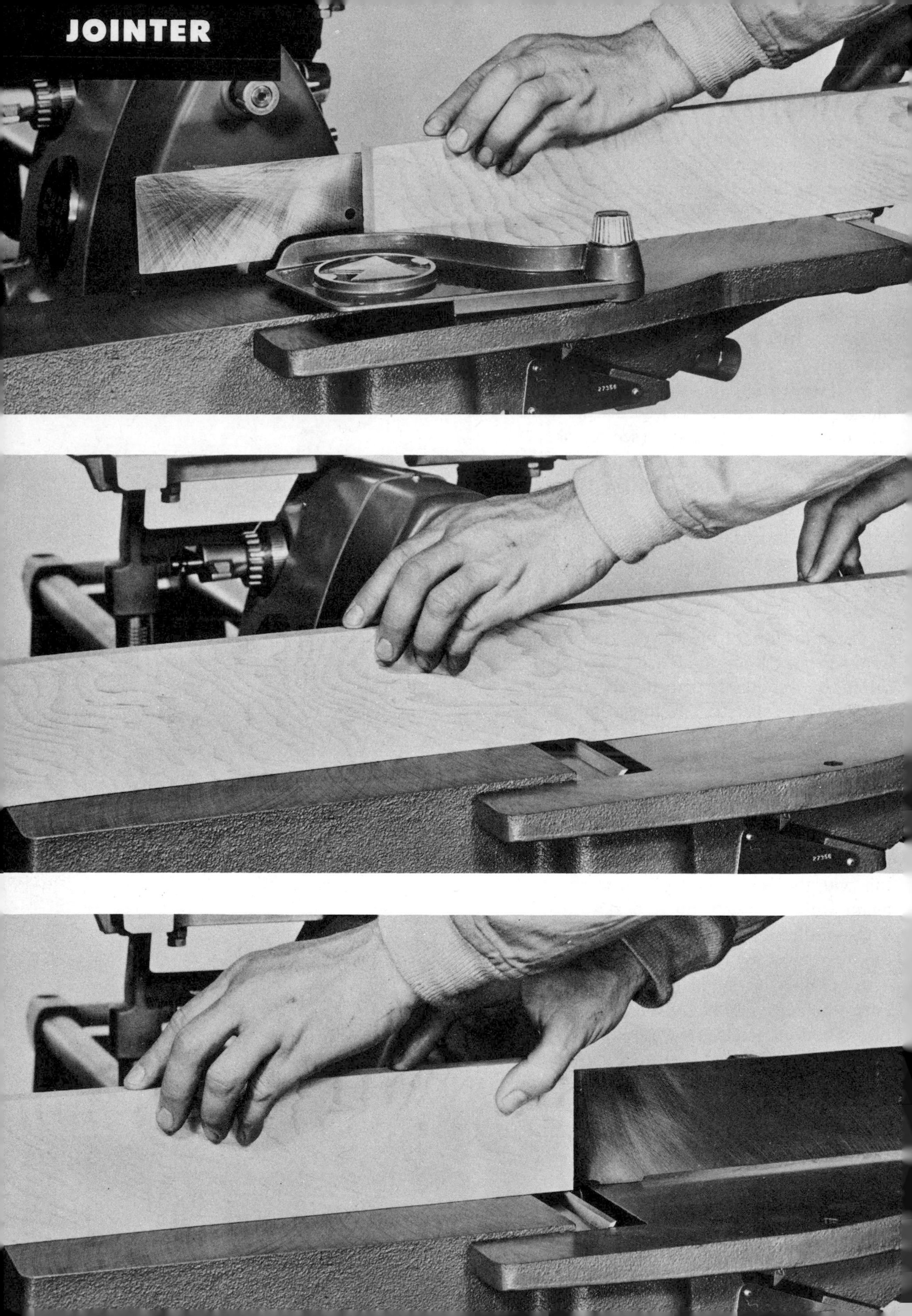
27356
27356

Edge Jointing

The jointing cut is always accomplished by moving the work so the knives will be cutting **with the grain** of the wood (sketch at right). Working **against the grain** seldom produces a satisfactory surface; it also increases the danger of kickback and splintering.

If the cutting action is not smooth or if you feel the work pushing back against your hands, the chances are that you are working against the grain. Stop the pass immediately and reverse the position of the wood.

If you have to make a cut against the grain, take a very light cut—and make the pass very, very slowly.

Depth-of-cut settings on jointing cuts never should exceed ⅛". A setting of from 1/32" to 1/16" usually does the best job and wastes less wood.

Although the jointing cut is a smooth movement from start to finish, it may be thought of in the three steps shown on the opposite page. The better side of the stock is placed against the fence with the work edge down on the infeed table. Hands should be placed to hold the work down on the table and snugly against the fence. The left hand rests on the front edge of the work, thumb on top, fingers against the side. This permits both side- and down-pressure to hold the stock firmly against the fence and flat on the table. The right hand is placed near the end of the stock—**against** the end if the piece is short enough—and feeds the stock forward.

As the work advances over the cutter head,

The photographs show three stages in a jointing cut. At start of cut, shown at the top, distribute pressure equally down on the table and against fence. Middle picture shows hand positions with cut half done. At bottom is the end of the cut, when it is important to avoid too much down pressure. (The safety guard has been omitted only for picture clarity.)

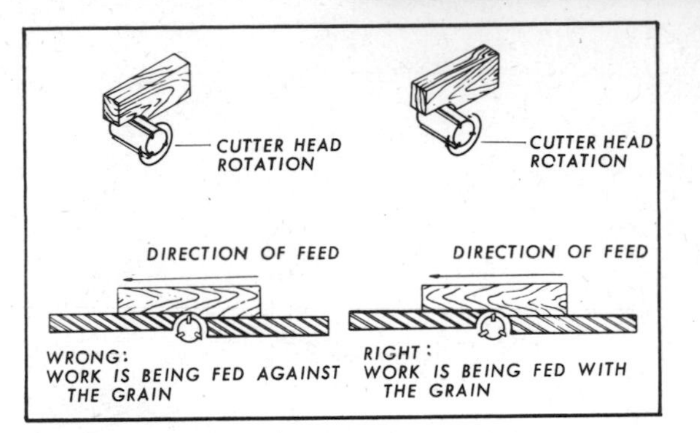

Make jointing cuts with—not against—grain.

the guard moves aside to permit its passage. The left hand does most of the work of keeping the stock snug against the fence and down on the table, while the right hand moves it forward.

Some operators object to passing either hand over the cutter head, but if the work is wide enough and the guard is used there is little danger when the hands are placed as shown. Always try to keep hands hooked over the top of the work.

At the end of the cut, the hands are still in about the same position on the work. Avoid heavy downward pressure at the end of the cut, since this might tilt the work into the cutter, resulting in a gouged end.

If the machine is in proper adjustment and the pass is made correctly, the jointed board will have edges that are square with its face. Edges of a group of jointed boards will fit against each other without gaps, checking out in all respects shown in the drawing below.

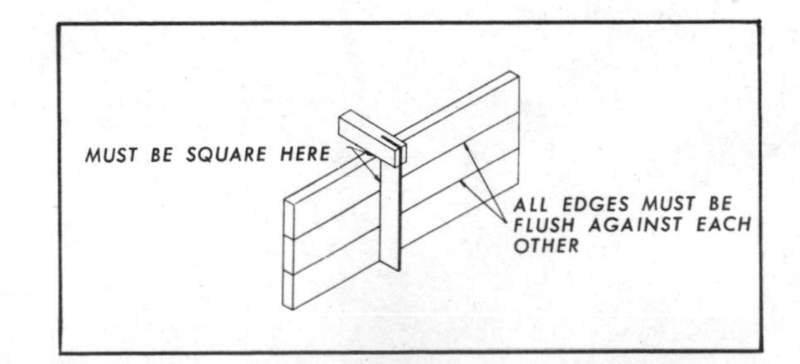

Jointed work should meet both these tests.

ATTACH TO JOINTER FENCE WITH 1" SCREWS

AUXILIARY FENCE

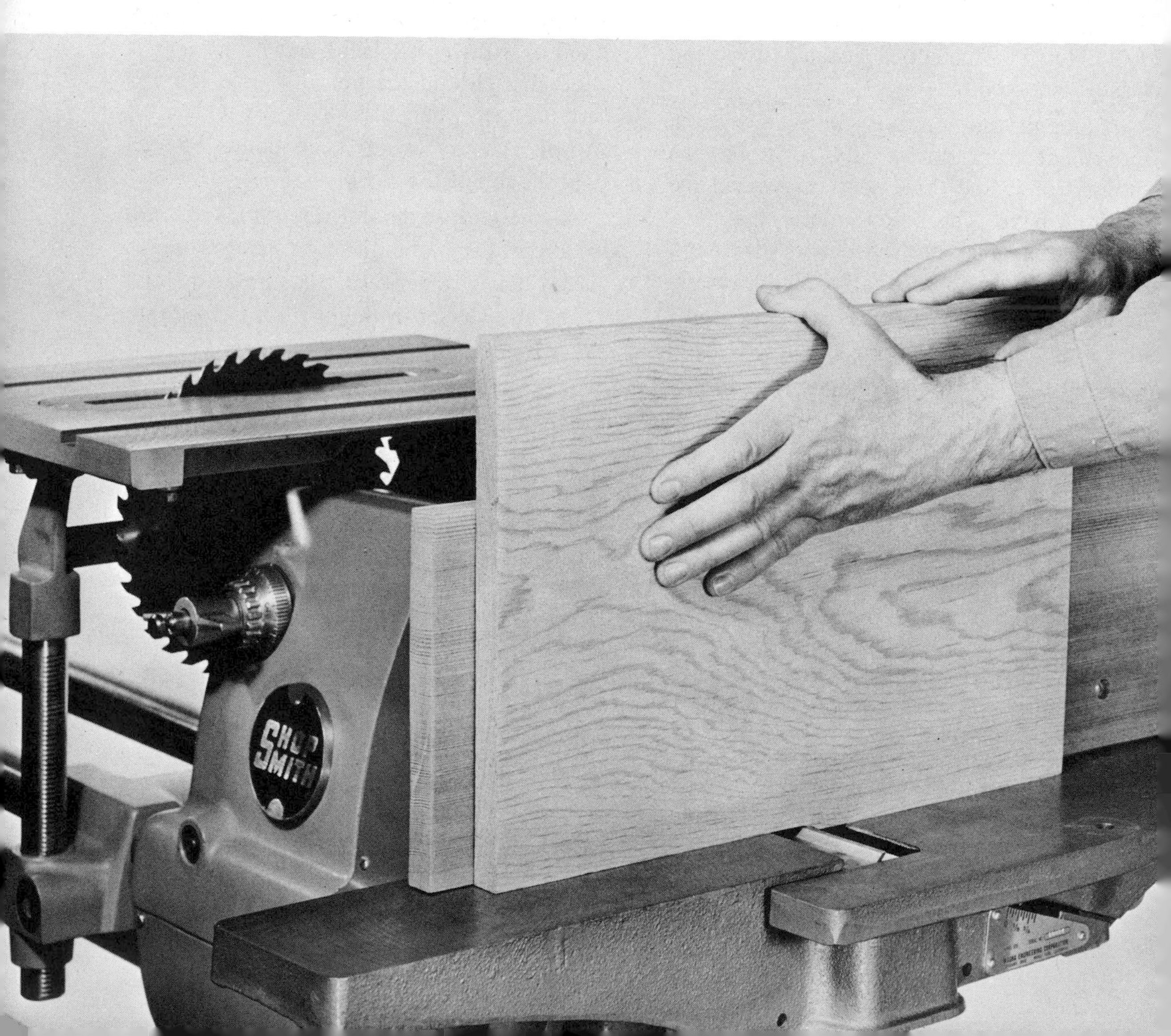

An auxiliary fence, easily attached in the manner shown in the drawing, will make it easier to joint wide boards accurately. You won't need it for most work, however.

Jointing Wide Boards (and How to Make an Auxiliary Fence)

Wide boards that project a good deal above the top of the fence require greater precaution against tilting as the pass is made. Place the left hand flat against the surface of the stock to provide greater pressure against the fence, as in the photograph on the opposite page. The right hand does the job of moving the work forward.

Two holes are provided in the jointer fence so that an extra-high auxiliary of the kind shown in the photograph may be attached when a quantity of very wide boards must be jointed. This auxiliary fence can be made of ¾″ plywood and attached with two 1″ flat-head wood screws inserted from the back of the fence. The drawing at the top of the opposite page shows how this may be done.

When jointing wide boards, hold them carefully against the fence to guard against tilting. The use of a simple, extra-high auxiliary fence like the one shown here helps.

Jointing Uneven Edges

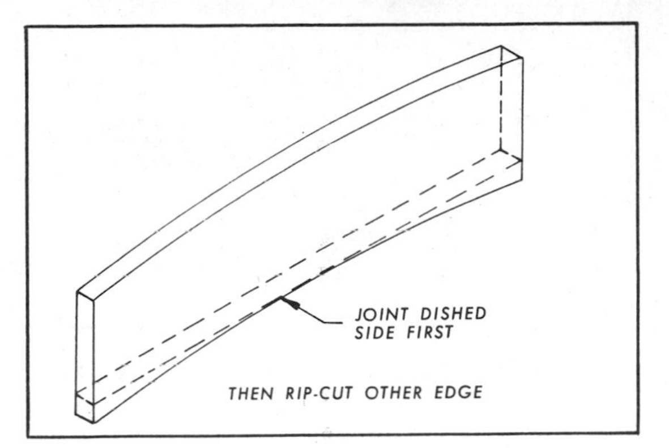
JOINT DISHED SIDE FIRST
THEN RIP-CUT OTHER EDGE

Joint dished side first on stock like this.

Whenever possible, stock that is distorted like the piece shown above should be jointed on the dished side first. This is to provide adequate bearing surface for the jointing cuts that will produce one even edge so the stock may be ripped parallel on the table saw.

Use extra care when a curved edge must be jointed, since little of the edge will bear on the table surface. The first pass will provide a flat area that will facilitate subsequent passes.

Work having one uneven side, as shown in the drawing below, is handled by jointing the one straight edge first. This rides the fence for the rip cut which will remove the uneven edge. Then the second edge is jointed.

Follow this sequence on stock like this.

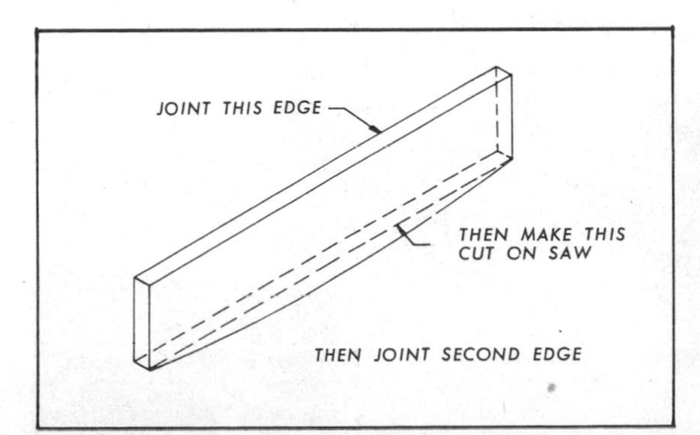
JOINT THIS EDGE
THEN MAKE THIS CUT ON SAW
THEN JOINT SECOND EDGE

Don't attempt to joint end grain in one pass.

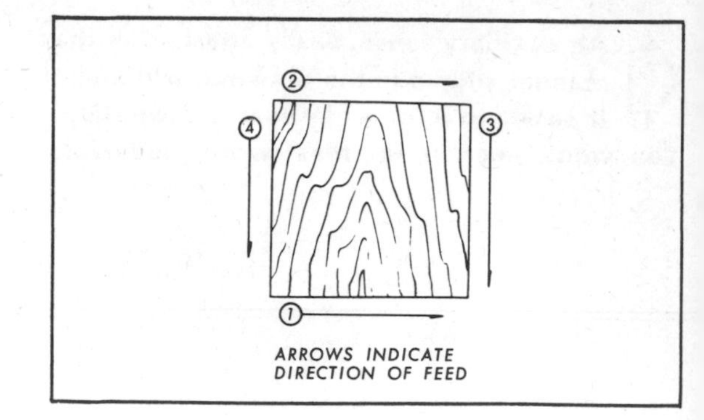

Follow this sequence to joint four edges.

Jointing End Grain

If end grain is jointed in one straight pass, the knives will split off a piece of wood at the very end of the cut in the manner shown in the drawing above of how **not** to do it. To avoid this make the cut in two passes as shown in the photographs below. For the first pass, hold the work as in jointing wide stock. Advance it over the cutter head just far enough to joint about ½″ of it. Then lift the work—don't pull it back, lift it—from the table. Reverse its position and complete the operation with a second pass.

However, when four edges of a piece of stock are to be jointed, the operation may be done as shown in the drawing above. The first and second cuts—across the grain—can be accomplished with single passes; the third and fourth cuts—with the grain—will remove the slight imperfections resulting from the first two cross-grain cuts.

With end grain, joint about ½″, then turn the work end for end and make a second pass.

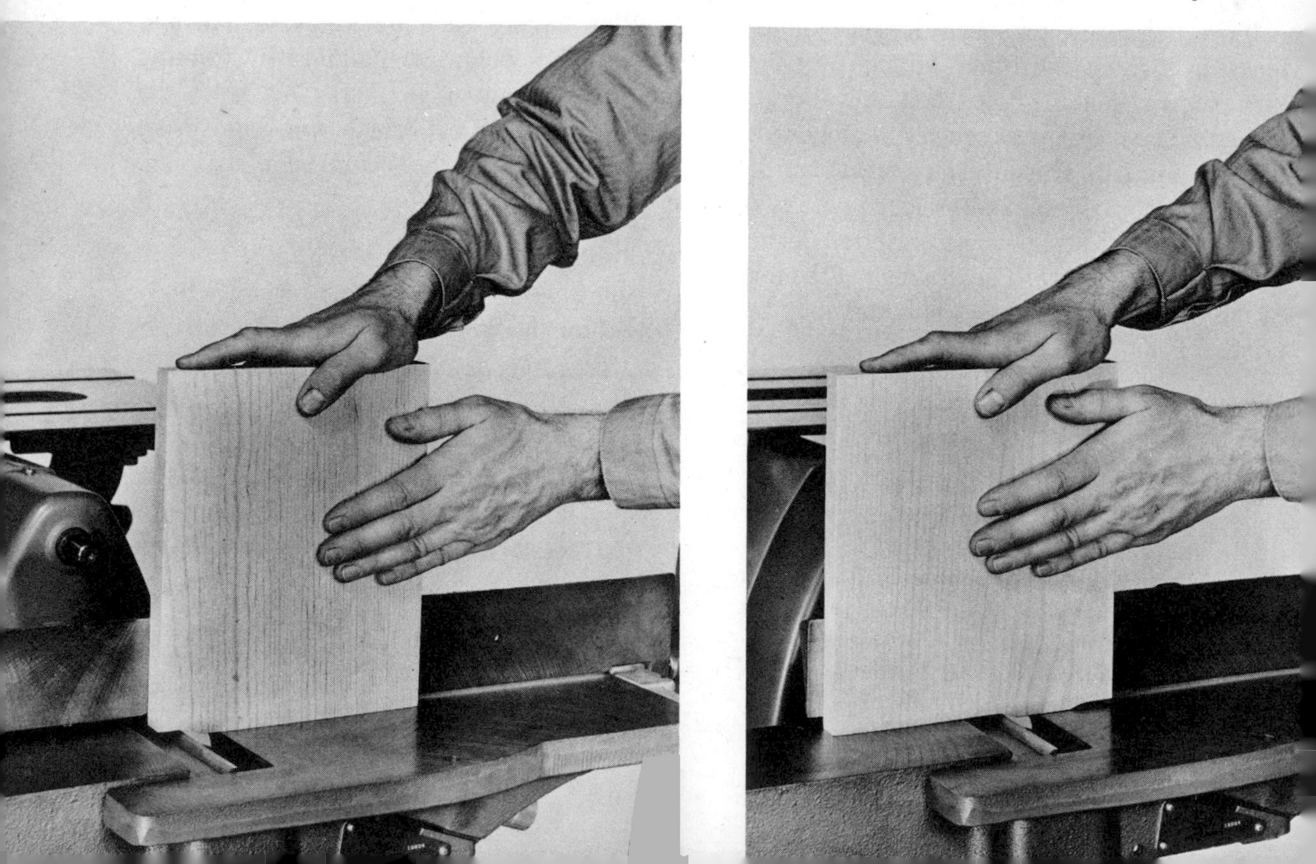

Note hand position and use of pusher-hold-down when the jointer is used for surfacing.

Surfacing

For surfacing, place the work flat on the table as in the photograph above. Then pass it over the cutter head as in edge jointing. Always use a combination pusher-hold-down—it's easy to make one like those in the drawing below—and keep the cut under 1/16". When surfacing it is a good idea not to allow either hand to pass over the knives.

Advance the work with the right hand on the pusher and the left hand flat on the top surface of the stock until enough of the board has passed over the cutter to sit firmly on the outfeed table. Then move the left hand quickly to the outfeed table.

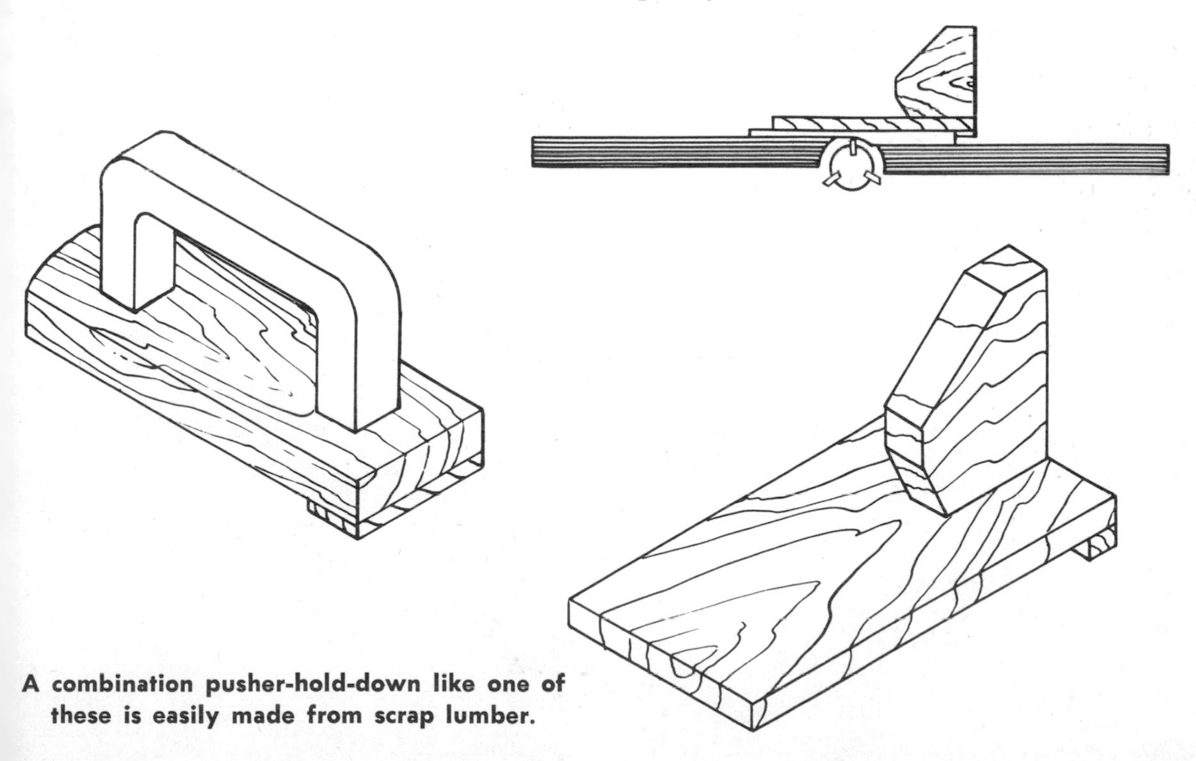

A combination pusher-hold-down like one of these is easily made from scrap lumber.

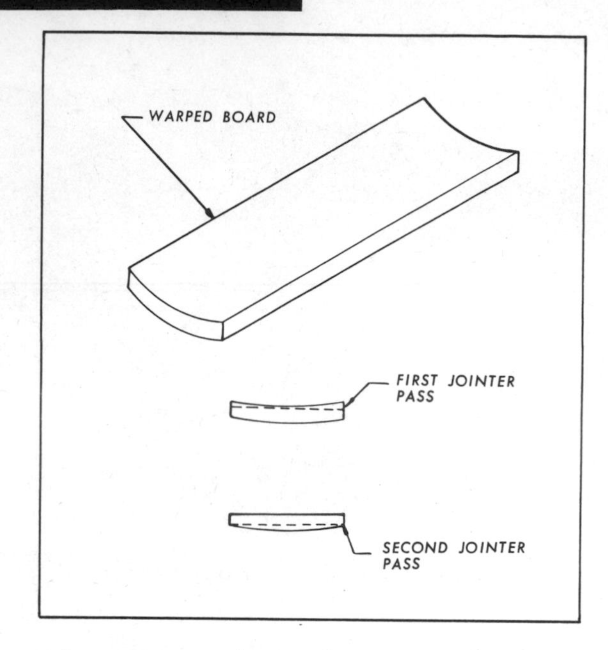
WARPED BOARD
FIRST JOINTER PASS
SECOND JOINTER PASS

Take extra care when surfacing a warped board like this one on the jointer.

Boards with defects such as warp or wind must have special attention if they are to be surfaced safely and with a minimum loss of stock. A warped board is dished across its width as sketched at left; its high points provide some bearing surface when the board is placed concave-side-down on the table.

Keep the board as level as possible during the first pass; after that it will have a "flat" on it to provide some bearing surface.

Shown below is a good procedure to use when width of stock permits: resawing after the jointer has established a flat surface for the rip fence. This will roughly surface the second side parallel to the first one. Saw marks can then be removed with a light surfacing cut.

With narrow stock, surface concave side first, then resaw to produce parallel surfaces.

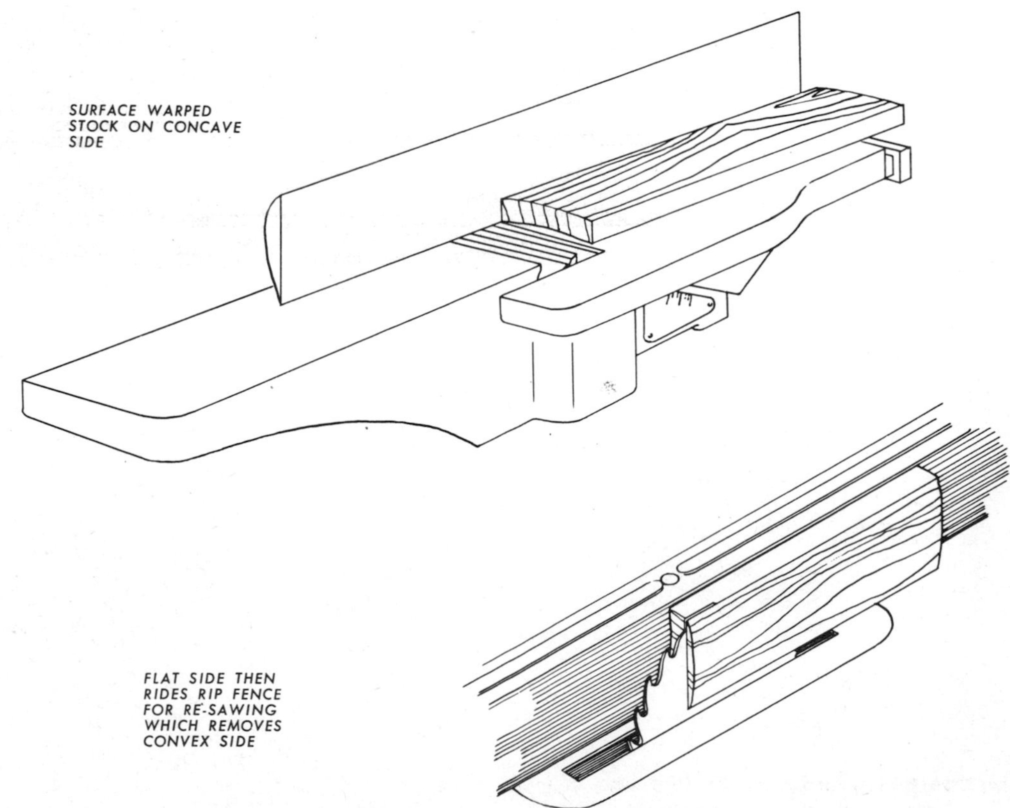
SURFACE WARPED STOCK ON CONCAVE SIDE
FLAT SIDE THEN RIDES RIP FENCE FOR RE-SAWING WHICH REMOVES CONVEX SIDE

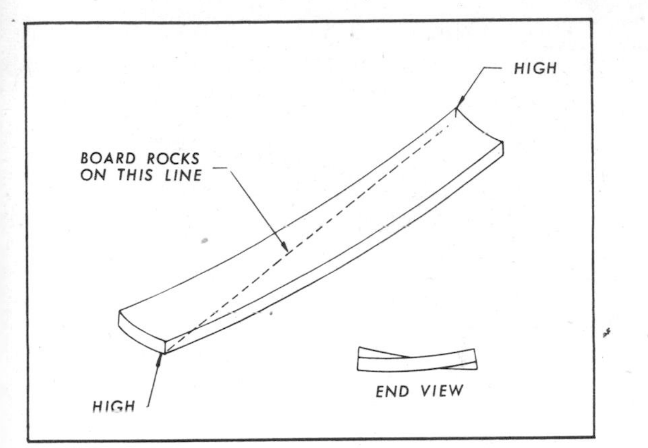

Boards in wind look like this.

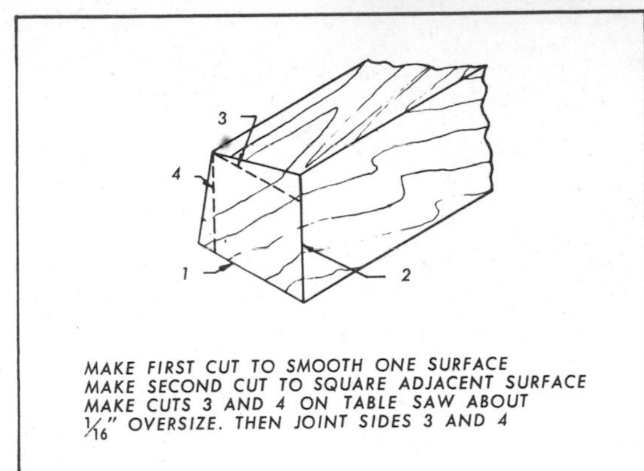

3
4
1
2
MAKE FIRST CUT TO SMOOTH ONE SURFACE
MAKE SECOND CUT TO SQUARE ADJACENT SURFACE
MAKE CUTS 3 AND 4 ON TABLE SAW ABOUT
1/16" OVERSIZE. THEN JOINT SIDES 3 AND 4

Follow this sequence to surface four sides.

Boards in wind (drawing above) have a twist the length of the stock. Best bet for leveling such a piece is to mark the high spots and remove them in the first pass, creating flat spots on which the board can rest.

Heavy pieces of stock that must be surfaced into squareness are handled as shown at upper right. Pick the best surface (1) and smooth it on the jointer. Then place the jointed side against the fence and make the pass—or passes—to square the adjacent side (2), keeping the stock snug against the fence. The third and fourth sides are cut square, and about 1/16″ oversize, on the table saw, then jointed.

When surfacing short boards—and particularly short, thin ones—always use a pusher-hold-down.

Width of a rabbet cut is gauged by fence position, depth by depth-of-cut scale.

Rabbeting

When cutting a rabbet (photograph above) the fence is set for width of cut and the infeed table for depth. In rabbeting, the guard cannot be used in its normal position on the infeed table; it should be placed on the outfeed table behind the fence where it will cover the part of the cutter now exposed. Be sure your hands are firmly placed. Make the pass slowly. Use more than one pass for deep cuts.

Rabbets may be cut with the stock held on edge, as shown in the photograph below. The drawing at left on opposite page indicates how rabbeting is used to form a tongue.

End rabbets should be handled as shown in the photograph at bottom of opposite page. Use a pusher-hold-down to keep the work square and to advance it across the knives. Just as rabbeting is used to form a tongue, so may it be used to make a tenon (drawing at far right).

When the rabbet is cut on the edge, its width is limited by maximum depth of cut of machine.

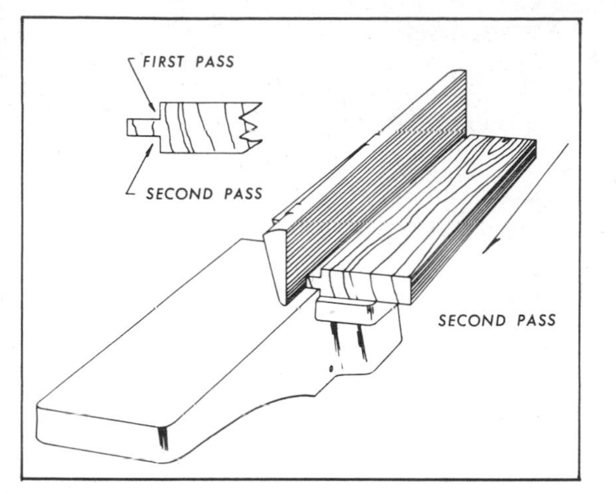

A tongue is formed by making two rabbet cuts, the stock being turned over, or around, between cuts. These cuts may be made with the stock in the position shown or with it on edge.

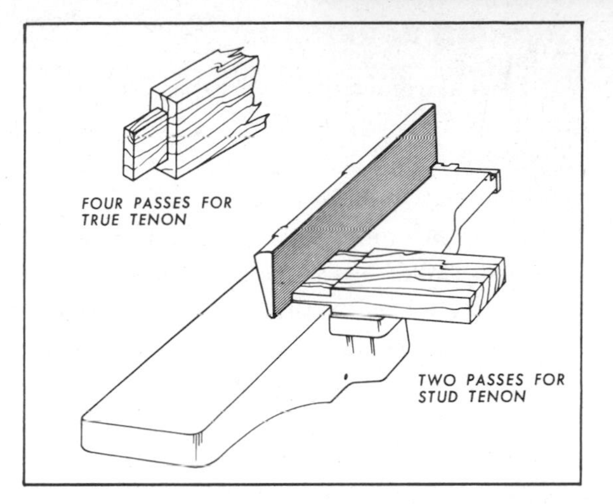

Tenons may be cut on the jointer by using two or four passes. As shown here, two passes produce what is known as a stud tenon, four passes produce a full tenon.

Always use a pusher-hold-down like this when cutting rabbets across end grain.

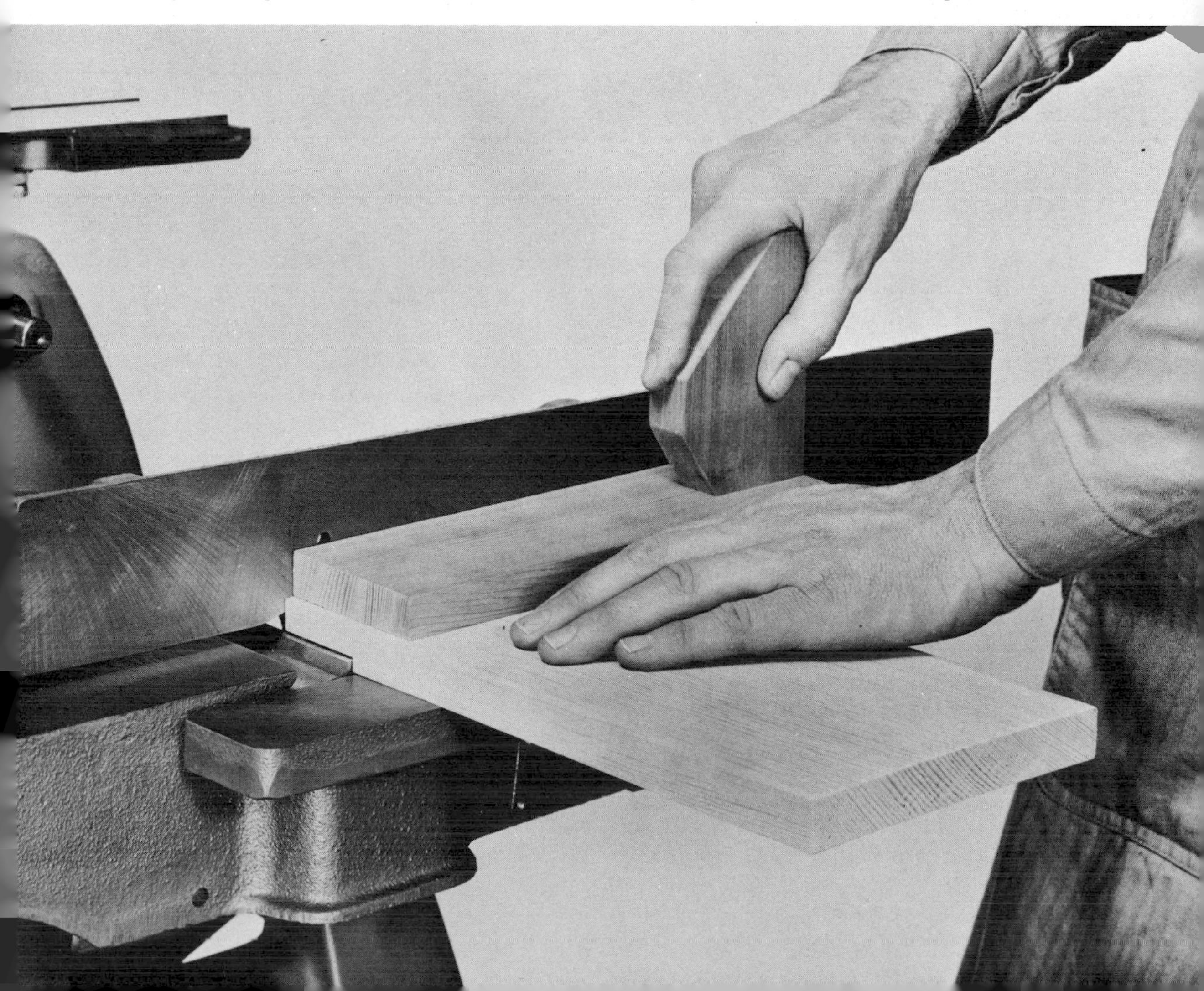

Making Bevel Cuts

To make bevel cuts, tilt the fence to the angle desired (photograph below) and pass the work across the knives while maintaining full contact with the fence.

Whenever possible, tilt the fence so it forms a **closed** angle (one that is less than a right angle) with the tables. Photograph shows open angle only so cut may be seen. The closed angle is safer.

When the size of the work makes it necessary to tilt the fence back, use extreme care to prevent the work's sliding out from under your hands. Usually it is necessary to make more than one pass before the full bevel is shaped.

Stopped bevels, formed for decorative reasons, are made by using stop blocks clamped to the fence to control the length of the bevel. Place the work against the forward block and drop it over the cutter head. Then advance the work until it hits the second block.

To cut bevel, tilt fence—set to closed angle if possible instead of open angle shown.

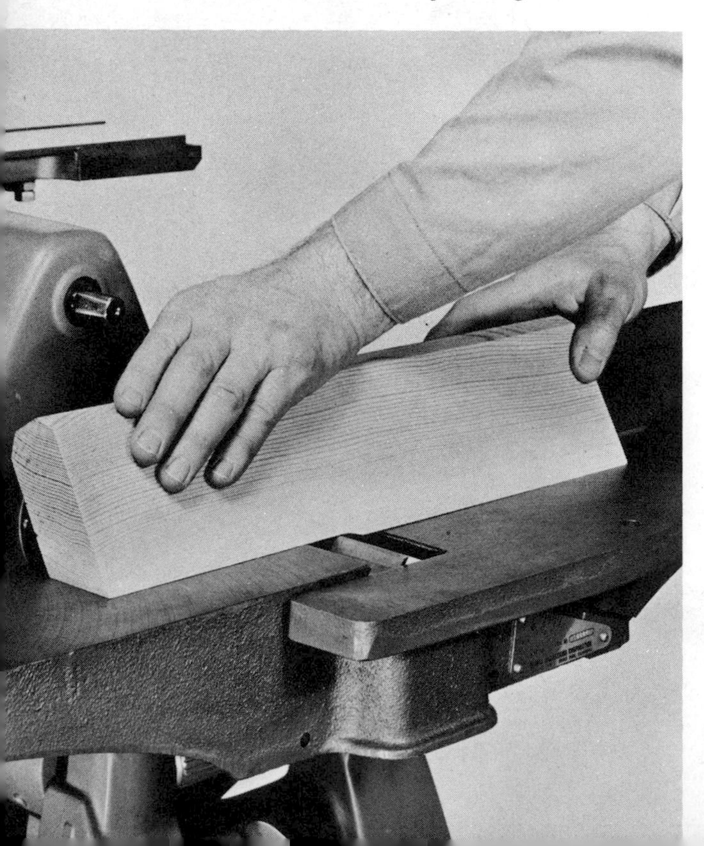

Tapering

Set the infeed table to the amount of taper required and position the work over the cutter head where the taper is to begin (top photograph on opposite page). If, for example, the taper is 10″ long and ¼″ deep, set the infeed table for a ¼″ cut and mark off the stock so you can place it over the blades 10″ from its end. If more than one piece is needed, clamp a stop block to position the work at the start of the cut. Lower the work with its end butting against the stop block until contact with the outfeed table is made. Then advance the work to cut the taper.

Work that's longer than the infeed table must be handled differently. If, for example, the taper is 20″ long and ¼″ deep, mark the stock into two 10″ divisions and set depth of cut at ⅛″. Place the stock so the line marking the first 10″ division is at the forward edge of the outfeed table to make the first cut. This forms a taper 10″ long and ⅛″ deep. Then place the stock at the 20″ mark and make a second pass along its entire length. The second cut produces the required taper 20″ long and ¼″ deep.

When tapering is to be done on four sides, as for many styles of table legs, work from side to side until all four surfaces are tapered.

To make the fancy legs shown in the middle photograph, first cut a four-sided taper. Then use stop blocks on both tables to gauge beginning and end of cut. Make four passes.

Handle short tapers as shown in bottom photograph. Mark length of taper on the stock and set the mark on the front edge of the outfeed table. Since this lifts the back end of the work off the table, use a block to maintain its height while the pass is being made.

The photograph shows the height block clamped to the jointer table. To make a true, flat taper, tack the height block to the work so that it moves along with it as the pass is being made.

The stop block gauges length of taper cut and also provides support at the start of cut.

Two stop blocks and two sets of tapering operations produce fancy table legs like this.

Here's the setup for short tapers. For a true straight taper, fasten stop block to work.

FIRST PASS *SECOND PASS*

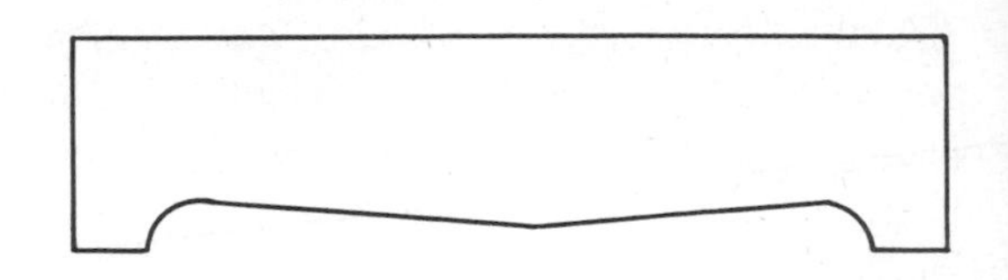

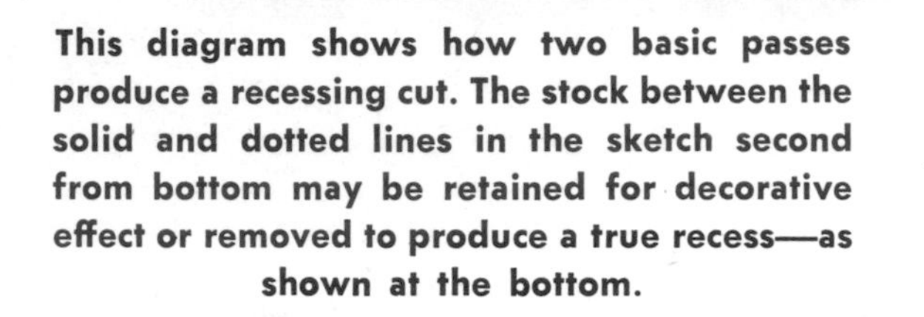

This diagram shows how two basic passes produce a recessing cut. The stock between the solid and dotted lines in the sketch second from bottom may be retained for decorative effect or removed to produce a true recess—as shown at the bottom.

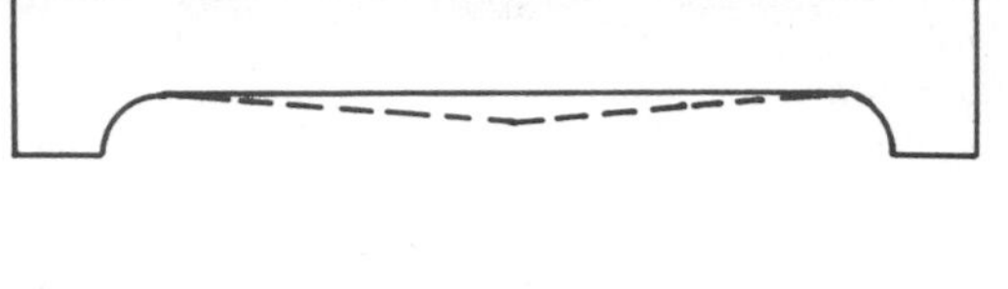

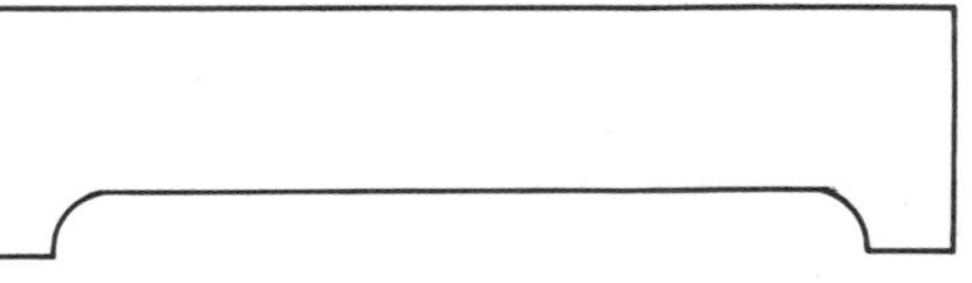

For recessing cut, stop blocks are set up like this and first pass is made as shown here.

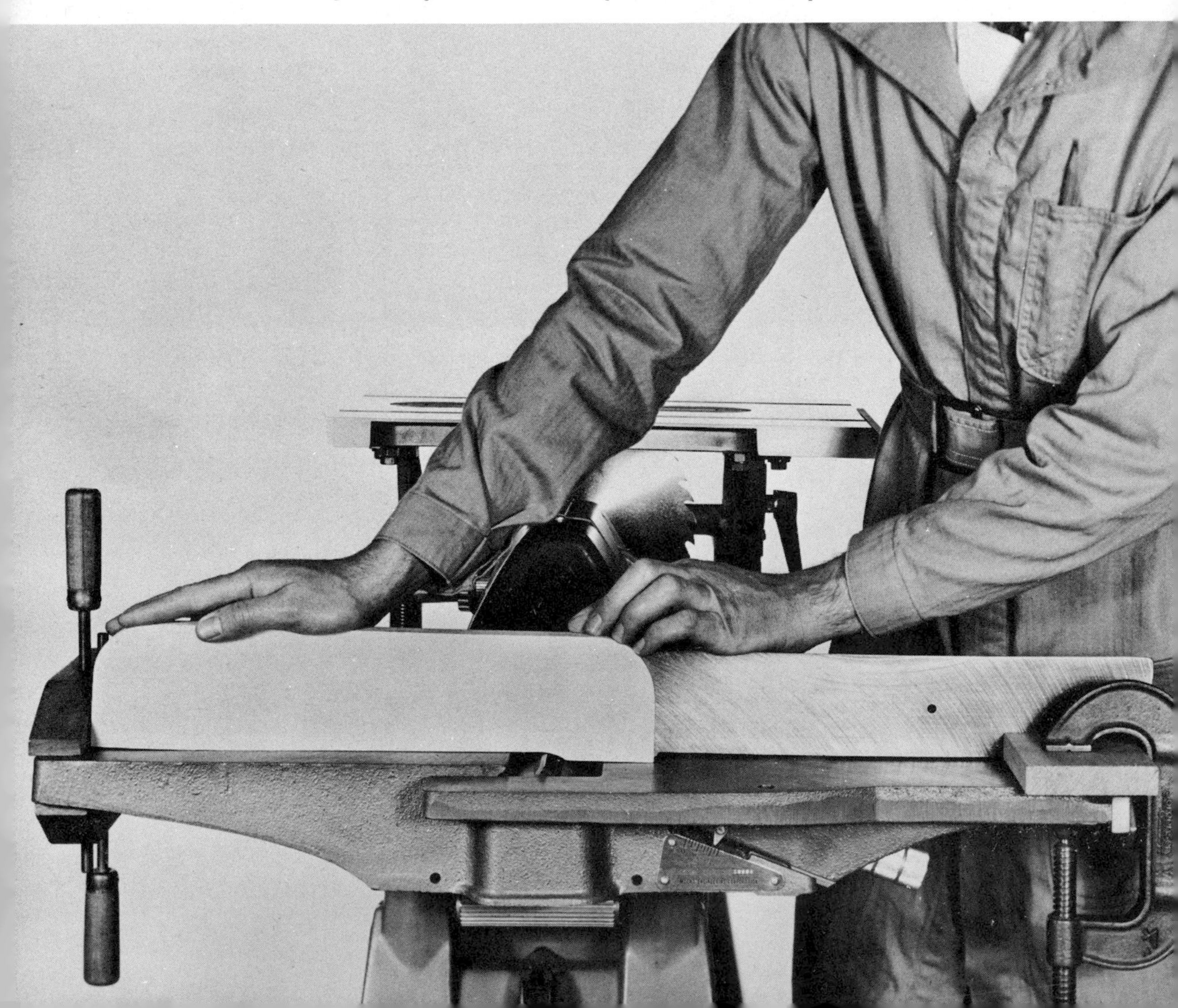

Chamfering

A chamfer is a bevel cut that does not remove the entire edge of the stock. Accomplish it by setting the fence to the angle desired—as you would for a bevel cut—and then making the number of passes required to shape the chamfer.

The cut shown in the drawing on the opposite page is often referred to as a stopped chamfer. Actually it is a recessing cut, seen most often on base members and bottoms of table and stand legs.

The true stopped chamfer is made with the fence tilted and with stop blocks to limit length of cut.

When the jointer has a fixed outfeed table, make the recessing cut in two passes. Use stop blocks to gauge start and end of cut. Place the work against the front block. Drop it down over the cutter, and advance it to meet the rear block as in the photograph on the opposite page. Then turn the work end for end and make a second pass (photograph below).

The slightly raised area left in the center may be removed, or it may be allowed to remain as a decorative detail.

Second pass of the recessing cut finishes in this position, with stop blocks remaining exactly as for first cut. Raised area in center is then removed—unless it is wanted.

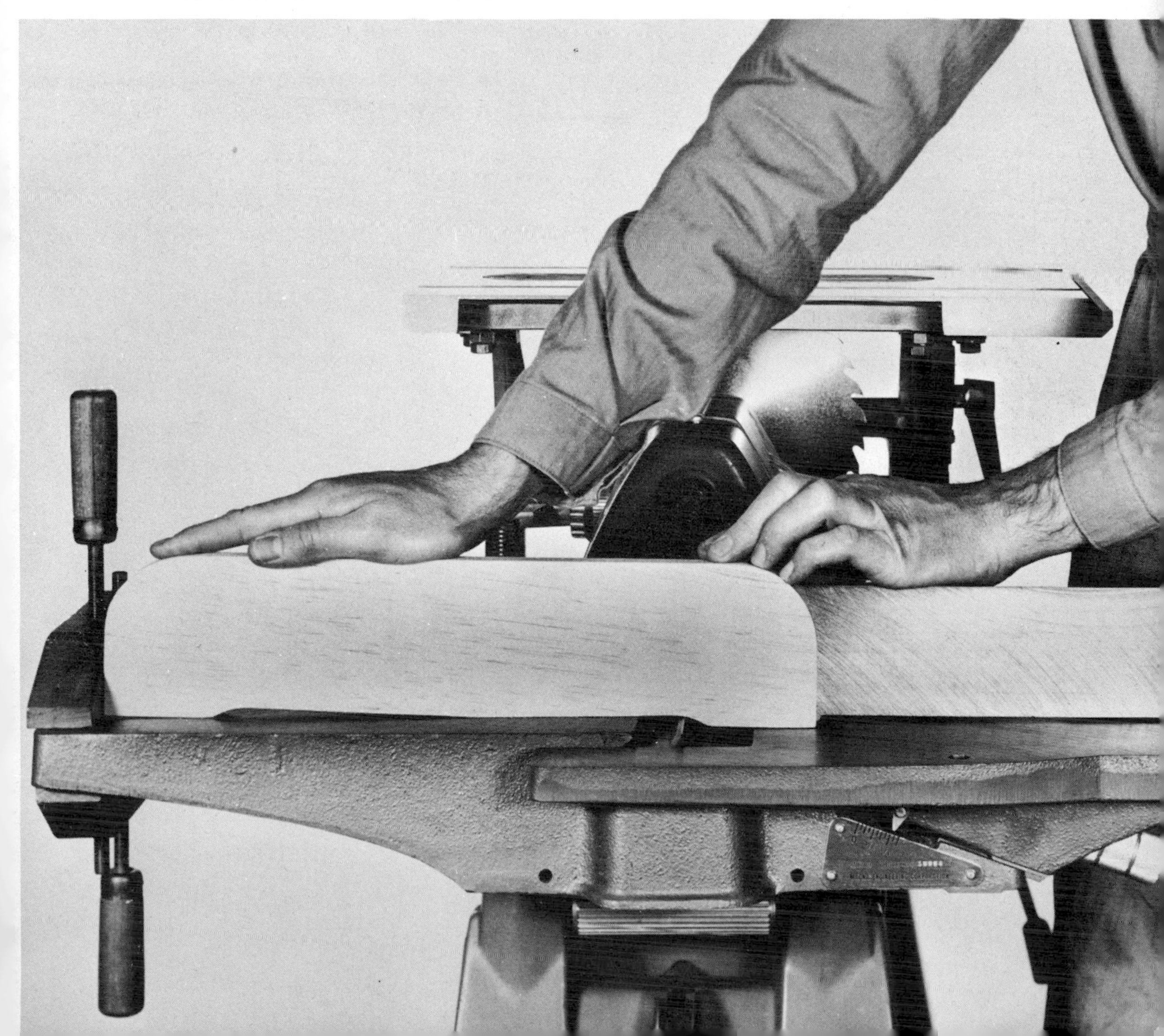

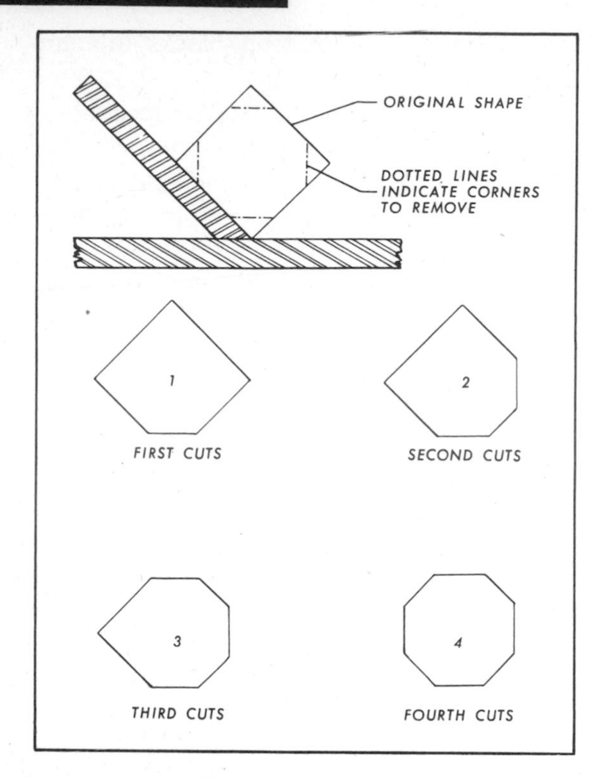

Making Octagonal Shapes

Shown in the photograph below is a piece octagonal in section. To make such a shape, begin with a piece of stock that has been accurately squared.

Set the jointer fence at a 45° angle. Make the passes as diagrammed below to remove the corners of the square and form four new faces. For a regular octagon, make the same number of passes on each surface.

To shape an octagon from square stock, use the jointer in this way, fence set at 45°.

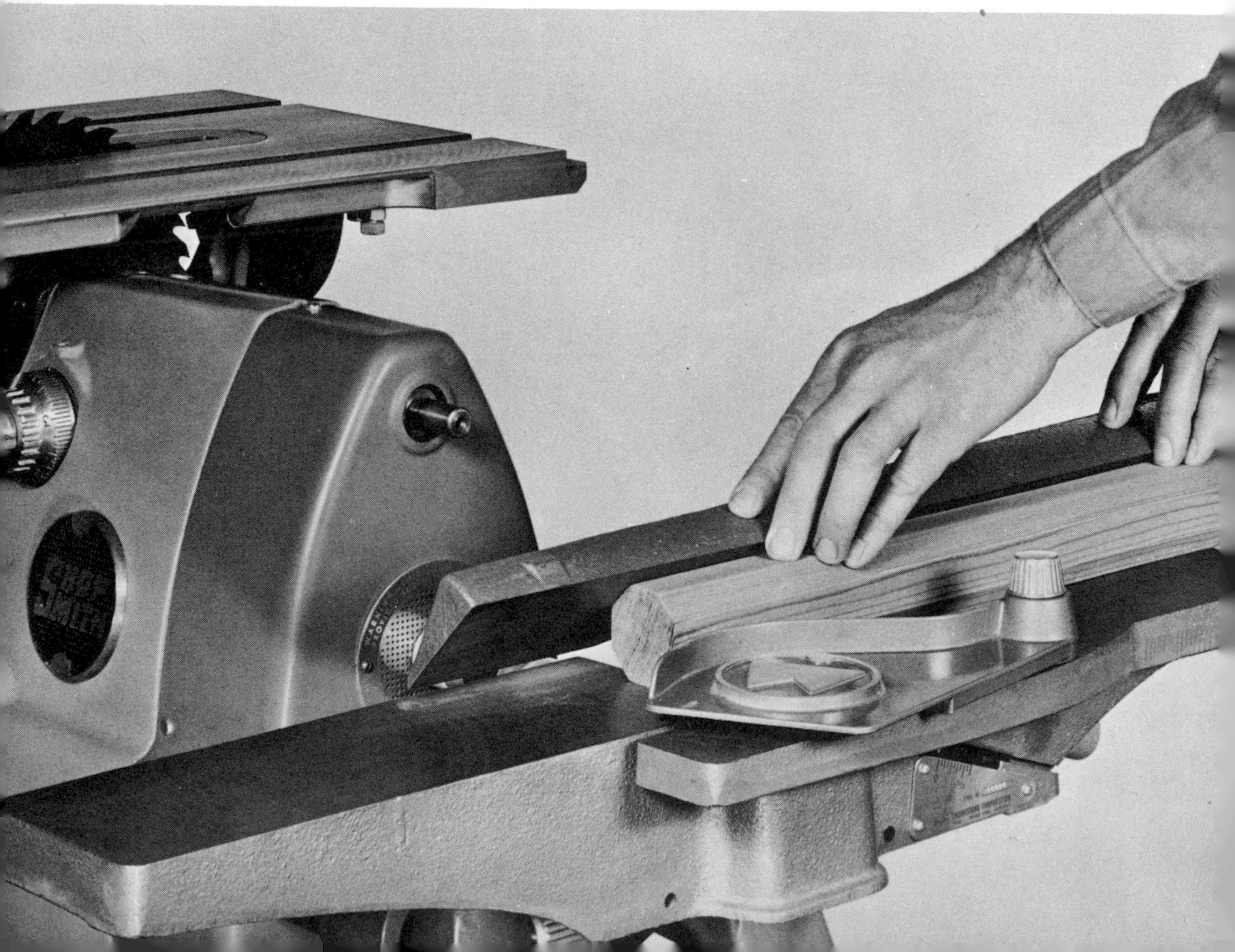

TROUBLE-SHOOTING CHART FOR THE JOINTER

	THE TROUBLE	POSSIBLE CAUSES	THE CURE	SEE PAGE
JOINTING AND SURFACING	JOINTED EDGE NOT SQUARE TO SURFACE OF STOCK	fence not 90° to tables	adjust "0" setting auto-stop	81
		work tilted during pass	hold stock snug against fence throughout pass	82
	STOCK STRIKES EDGE OF OUTFEED TABLE	knives are too low	reset knives for alignment with outfeed table	78, 79
	STOCK DROPS AT FINISH OF CUT AND GOUGES END	knives are too high		
	ROUGH OR CHIPPED CUT	working against grain	turn stock end for end and make another pass	83
	CUT UNIFORMLY RIPPLED	pass made too fast	slower feed always produces smoother cut	83
		low rpm	adjust to correct speed	—
		only one knife cutting	reset knives	78
		stock vibrating	keep uniform pressure down on tables throughout pass	83
	RAISED LINE RUNS ALONG LENGTH OF CUT	nicked cutting edge on knives	regrind and sharpen; meanwhile joint with fence reset to avoid nick	327
	DEPTH OF CUT INACCURATE	misalignment	check and reset depth-of-cut scale and indicator	80
RABBETING	CUT IS WIDER AT ONE END	excessive pressure against fence during pass	use fence as guide only	90
	WORK HITS OUTFEED TABLE	lateral knife setting is incorrect	adjust knives laterally so cut will clear outfeed table	79
	DEPTH OF CUT IS UNEVEN	work allowed to rise during pass	keep uniform pressure down on work during pass	90
BEVELING	CUT DOES NOT MATCH WITH ANGLE SETTING	misalignment	check fence adjustments	81
		work slipped	hold work snug against fence throughout pass	92
	BEVEL CUT HAS SLIGHT TAPER	pass made incorrectly	down pressure should be uniform throughout pass	92

3 THE DRILL PRESS

How it works • the tools • layout
work support • drilling to exact depth
screw holes • concentric holes • angles
heavy work • joinery • dovetails • doweling
routing • drilling moldings
jigs • indexing • extra-large holes
metal layout, drilling, tapping, and surfacing
finishing and polishing • drilling glass • trouble shooting

FROM its original limited applications in metal drilling, the drill press has become one of the most versatile machine tools for home-workshop use.

This is especially true of the drill press on the multi-purpose tool because of its "bonus" feature, the use of the drill press in a horizontal position. Horizontal boring and mortising machines are commonplace in industry, but only recently have home craftsmen been introduced to their convenience and accuracy.

No attempt is made in this chapter to distinguish between horizontal and vertical tools. Some standard operations are especially applicable to the horizontal or to the vertical drill press. Others, though shown here in the conventional vertical position, can be done as well in the horizontal.

Ordinarily you can make the choice between these positions on the basis of convenience. But there are some instances, of which drilling for dowel holes is often one, where the choice is a matter of greater accuracy and more professional results.

How the Drill Press Works

The basic mechanism of the drill press is a power-driven steel rod, called a spindle, with a holding device at the free end to grip cutting tools securely and rotate them. Usually a key-operated three-jaw chuck is used to secure the tool, but side thrust (developed by tools such as router bits and dovetail cutters) often makes it wise to use another kind of chuck.

Side thrust is illustrated by a moving automobile. The area of the wheel that comes in contact with the road develops a thrust against the axle which moves the car forward. The same principle applies to a tool that has a side cutting action. With such a tool, use a router chuck.

Drill chucks, router chucks, arbors, and other attachments are fastened with a set screw which seats against the tapered flat on the spindle.

The drill press on the multi-purpose tool is shown at the right. The headstock can be locked at any point along the tubes. Because of its weight, the head is easier to move when the tool is in a horizontal position. Chuck-to-table adjustments are made by moving the table up or down, as on all presses.

The quill (the sleeve in which the spindle rotates) has a feed of 4¼″ and is returned to its starting position by a coil spring enclosed in the headstock. This factory-set spring can be adjusted to strengthen or weaken the pull with which it returns the quill. Normally, it should return smoothly and without shock. To adjust it, follow this procedure:

1. Use Allen wrench to loosen screw on top of headstock (forward end).

The drill press is shown here with fence and miter gauge, both of which are very useful on many drill-press operations.

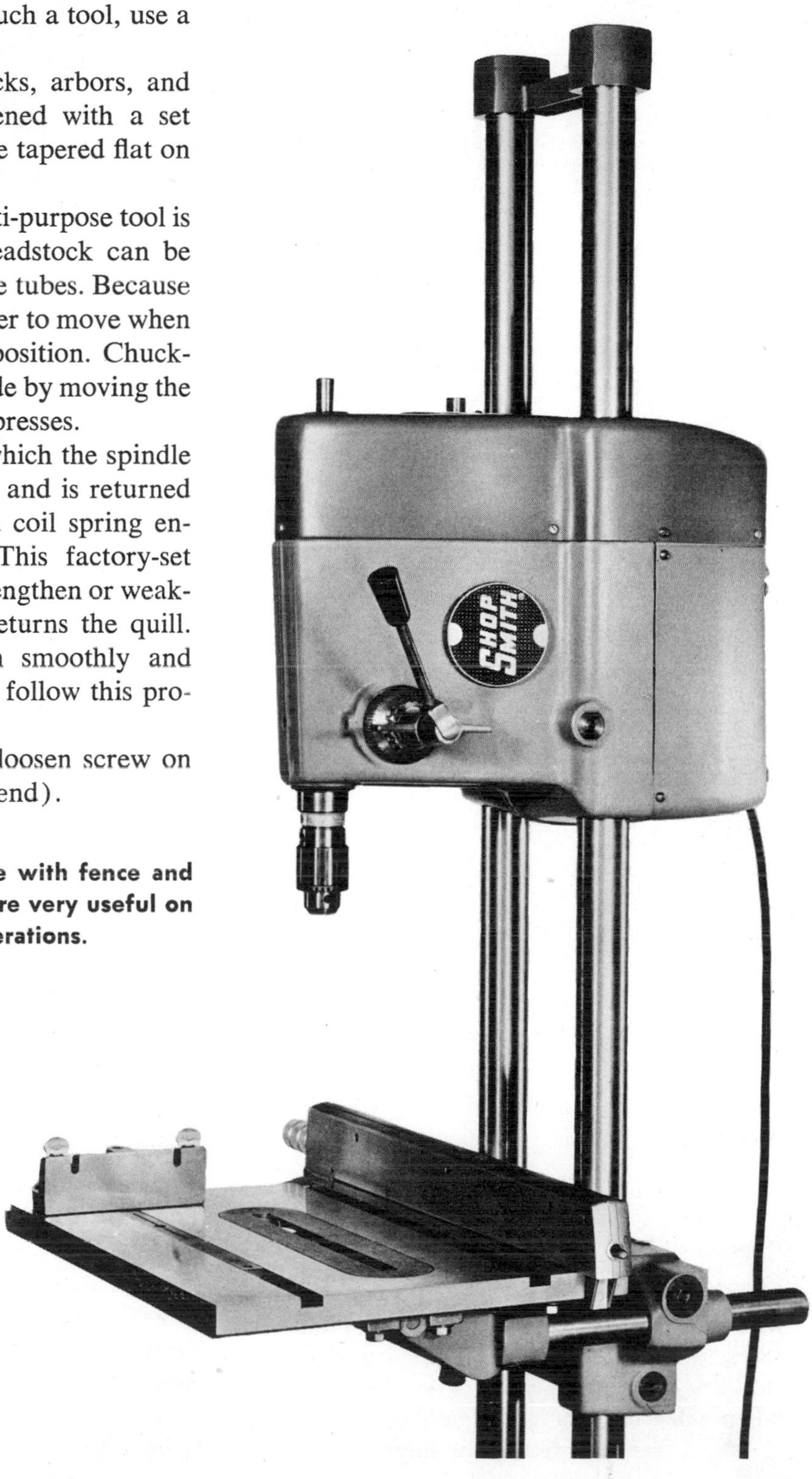

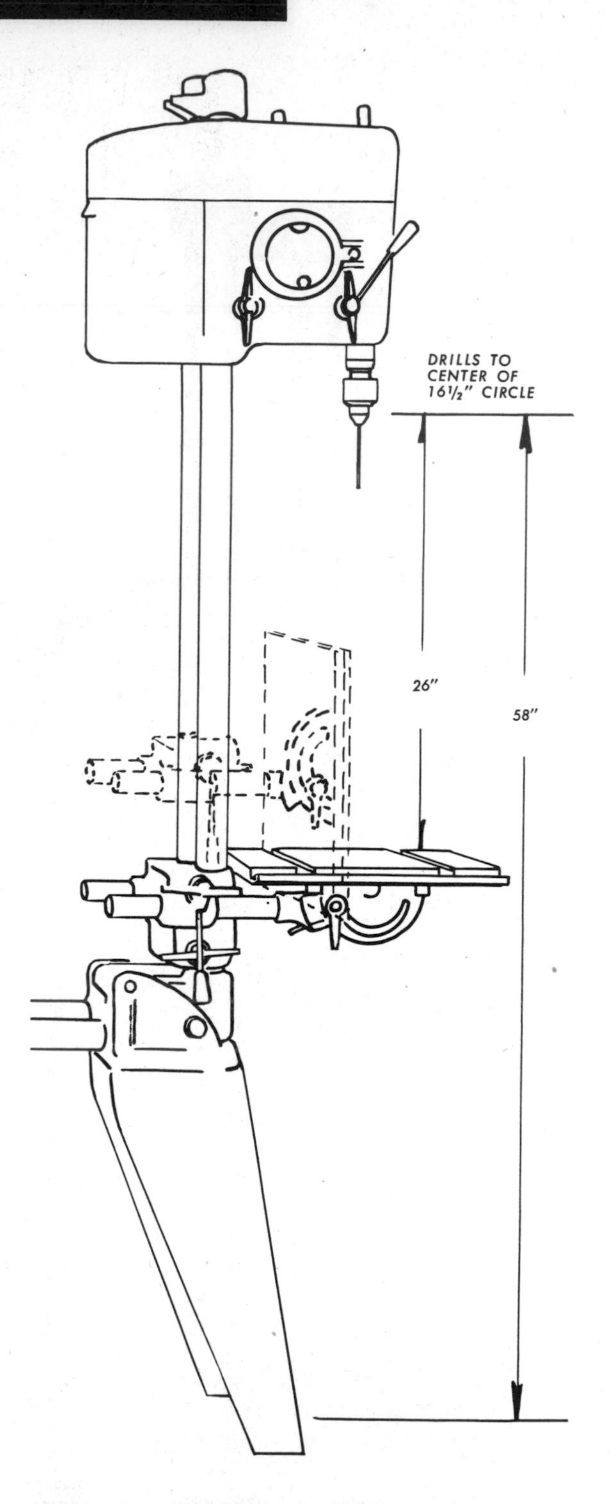

Drill-press capacities are figured in terms of distance from column to spindle and from chuck to table. Dotted line shows position in which table may be locked to align work that is supported by the floor.

2. Extend quill until it disengages from pinion gear.

3. To increase tension, continue turning quill feed lever in same direction while quill is disengaged. To decrease tension, turn the quill feed lever a small amount in the opposite direction.

4. Holding the spring tension with the quill feed lever, push the quill back until the rack teeth engage with the pinion shaft gear. (Be sure that keyway on top of quill is aligned with screw in top of headstock).

5. Bring quill back to non-extended position and retighten set screw in top of headstock. This set screw should not be locked, but merely turned sufficiently to engage the keyway in the quill. **Overtightening will cause the quill to bind.**

The quill assembly is moved downward by a feed lever that actuates the rack-and-pinion gear. The feed lever can be used on either side of the headstock and positions radially merely by unscrewing it a few turns, setting where desired, and then retightening it. A little more than one complete revolution extends the quill the maximum 4¼". The quill lock will secure the quill in any extended position.

The stroke may be set for a predetermined depth by using the depth-control dial on the side of the headstock. Direct readings may be taken from the dial.

Drill-press capacities are figured as distance from column to spindle and from chuck to table. With the multi-purpose tool, you can drill in the center of a 16½" circle and have a variable adjustment (by moving the table up or down) up to 26 inches between chuck and table. However, when the table is used in the position shown in the drawing at the left, the drill press may be used as a floor model with the table providing a vertical plane against which work may be clamped and aligned with the spindle center.

In the horizontal position, the machine has advantages that include unlimited capacity in length and width of work that can be handled; the extension table provides extra support for larger-than-average work.

Since the saw table is used as the drill-press table, the operator can utilize the locking miter gauge, rip fence, and hold-downs as stops, supports, jigs, V-blocks, straightedges, and for many other applications.

Before lifting the machine to its vertical position, be sure the headstock and carriage are securely locked. If it is necessary to raise the headstock after the initial adjustment has been made:

1. Bring the table up so the chuck or spindle end rests on a wood block placed on the table.
2. Lock the carriage and loosen the headstock lock handle.
3. Lift the headstock by using the quill feed lever as if you were drilling.
4. With the quill extended, lock the headstock.

And if it is necessary to lower the headstock:

1. Feed the quill out the maximum 4¼″ and lock it.
2. Bring the table up so the spindle end touches the wood block.
3. Lock the table carriage and loosen the headstock, while holding the quill feed lever.
4. Lower the headstock by using the feed lever.

Follow the general safety rules applicable to all phases of woodworking. Keep your sleeves buttoned at the wrists. Do not wear a loose-hanging tie. Avoid wearing rings. Women should not wear bracelets and should take the precaution of confining long hair with a scarf or bandanna. Keep hands clear of the cutting tools and operate the drill press at recommended speeds.

The horizontal drill press has unlimited capacity in length and width of work.

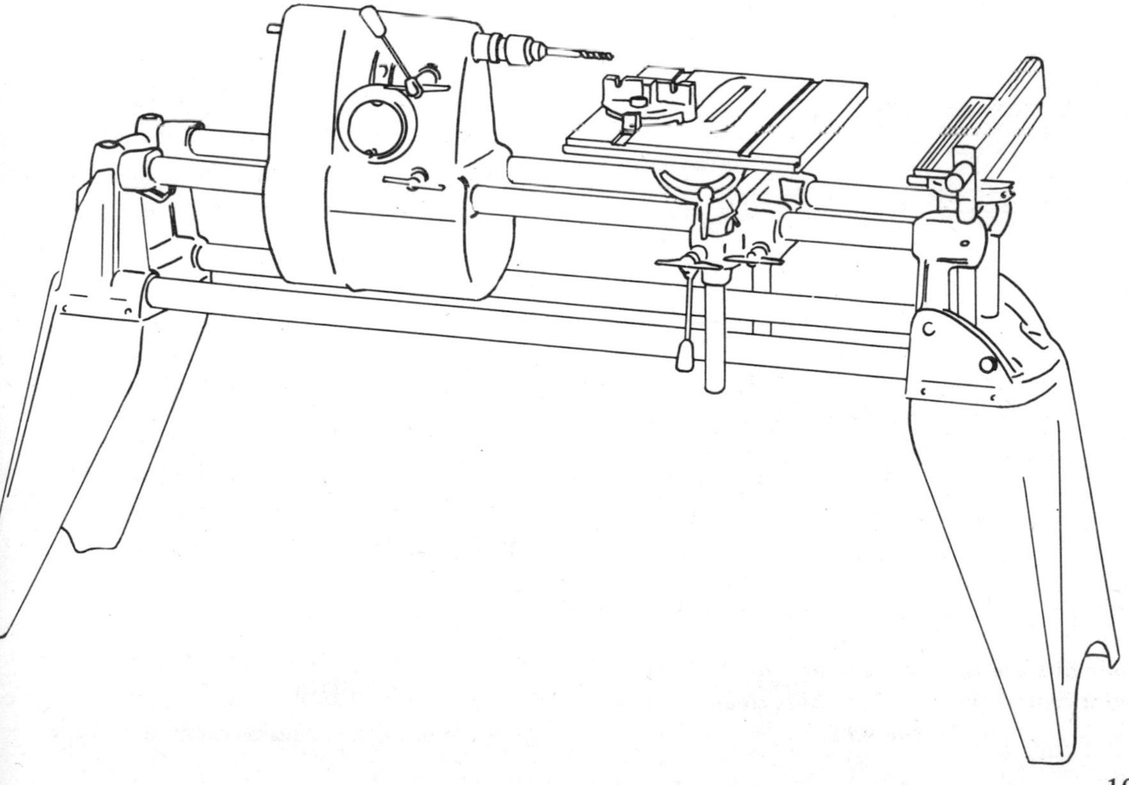

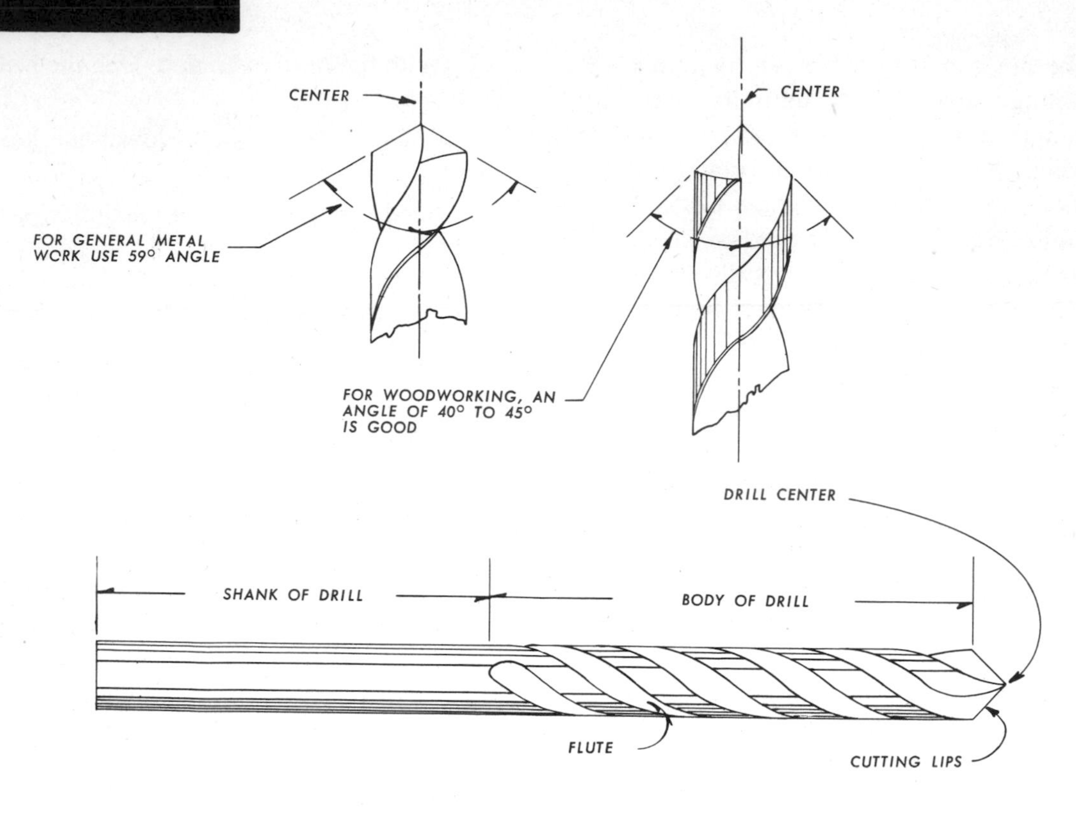

Above are shown the twist drill and the preferred cutting angles for its lips.

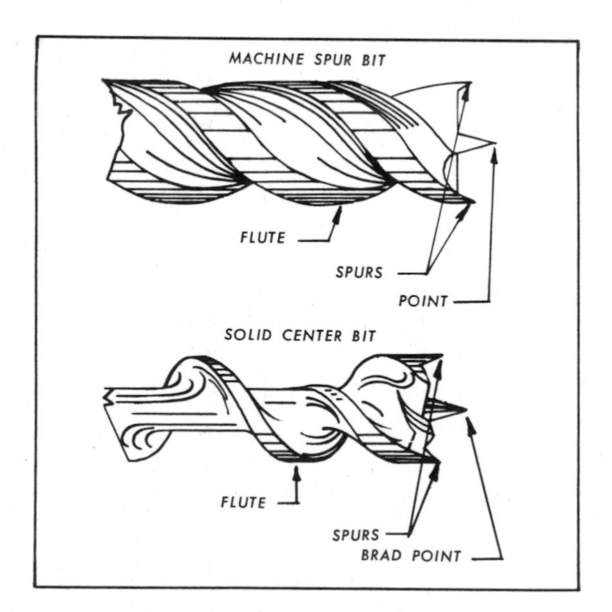

Spur bits are best for drilling wood. The brad point centers the drill. The spurs cleanly outline the hole.

Typical Drill-Press Tools

Most of the common drill-press tools are shown on the opposite page. The two tools you will be using most for straight drilling operations are the twist drill (above) and the machine spur bit and solid center bit (at left). The twist drill, usually associated with metal drilling, can be used to make holes in hard or soft woods but the hole it cuts is rough. The spurs on a spur bit will cut through the wood fibers cleanly, making a hole which is clean, smooth, and to exact size. Another advantage of the spur bit is the point; it keeps the drill centered and clears away wood not removed by the cutting edges.

Flutes in a drill provide channels for chip removal. Never allow a drill to penetrate so far that the flute ends are buried. On most jobs it's well to pull the cutting tool out frequently to cool it and to clear the chips.

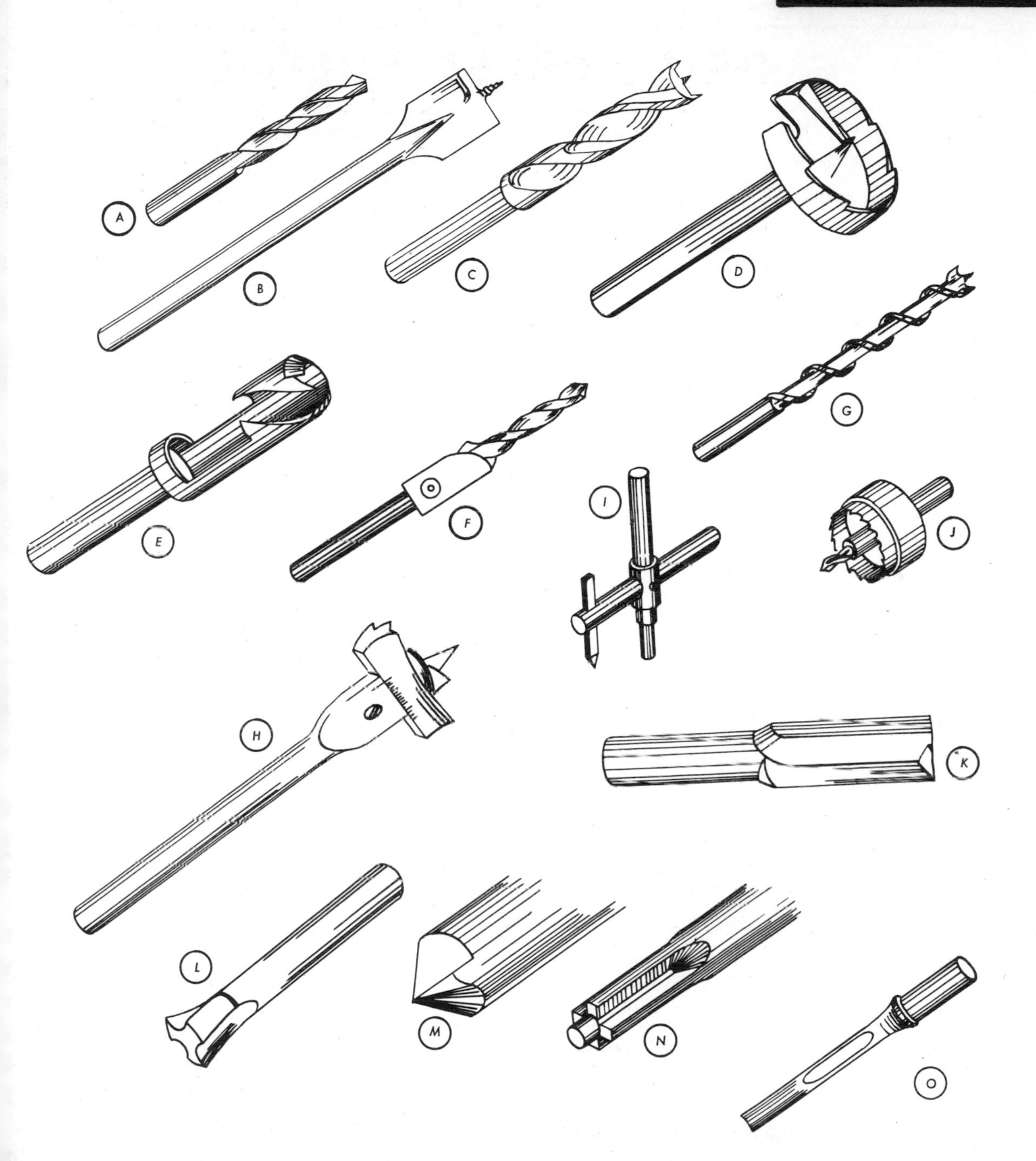

Shown above and listed below are most of the common tools used in the drill press:

A. twist drill
B. power auger bit
C. spur machine drill
D. multi-spur machine bit
E. plug cutter
F. adjustable countersink attachment
G. solid-center bit
H. expansive bit
I. fly cutter (hole cutter)
J. hole saw
K. router bit
L. dovetail cutter
M. countersink
N. counterbore (with center pilot)
O. hollow chisel

DRILL PRESS SPEEDS

MATERIAL	OPERATION	SPEED (rpm)	SPEED-DIAL SETTING
wood	drilling—up to ¼″	3,800	S
wood	drilling—¼″ to ½″	3,100	P
wood	drilling—½″ to ¾″	2,300	M
wood	drilling—¾″ to 1″	2,000	K
wood	drilling—over 1″	700	Slow
wood	using expansion or multi-spur bit	700	Slow
wood	routing	4,000-5,000	Rout-Shape
wood	cutting plugs or short dowels	3,300	Q
wood	carving	4,000-5,000	Rout-Shape
wood	using fly-cutter	700	Slow
wood	using dowel-cutter	1,800	J
hardwood	mortising	2,200	L
softwood	mortising	3,300	Q
metal	fine wire-brushing	3,300	Q
metal	coarse wire-brushing	1,000	D
wood	coarse wire-brushing	2,200	L
soft metals	buffing (cloth wheel)	3,800	S
hard metals	buffing (cloth wheel)	4,700	U
plastics	buffing (cloth wheel)	2,300	M
metal	using fly-cutter	700	Slow
metal	grinding—3″-4″ cup wheel	3,100	P
glass	drilling with metal tube	700	Slow

Speeds for Typical Operations

Excessive speeds on some tools cause overheating. A slow speed on some materials causes the cutting edges of the tool to take too deep a bite; this may stop the motor or cause breakage at the cutting edges. The correct drill speeds (charted above) have been devised with consideration of the operation, the material, and the tool. When it isn't possible to run the machine at recommended speeds, try to keep as close to them as possible.

Feed—the amount of pressure you apply and the speed with which you allow the cutting edge to penetrate the work—will vary with the operation. The best general rule to follow is to keep the tool cutting, taking a small bite, evenly and without strain.

Laying Out the Work

Work carefully and slowly when measuring and scribing lines. If you use a pencil, select one at least as hard as 3H and keep it sharp.

The simplest and most accurate method of marking a hole location is to draw two lines that intersect at the center of the hole. A combination square is a good tool to have, since it is used to draw lines square with the edge of the work and as an edge-marking gauge. Dividers work best when it is necessary to transfer a measurement from one piece to another or to mark off a line into a number of equal spaces.

Other methods may be utilized according to the job and the number of pieces to be drilled. Templates may be made of illustration board, Masonite, plywood, or metal, depending on how long they will be used. Some pieces of hardware are their own templates; a hinge, for example, or a drawer pull.

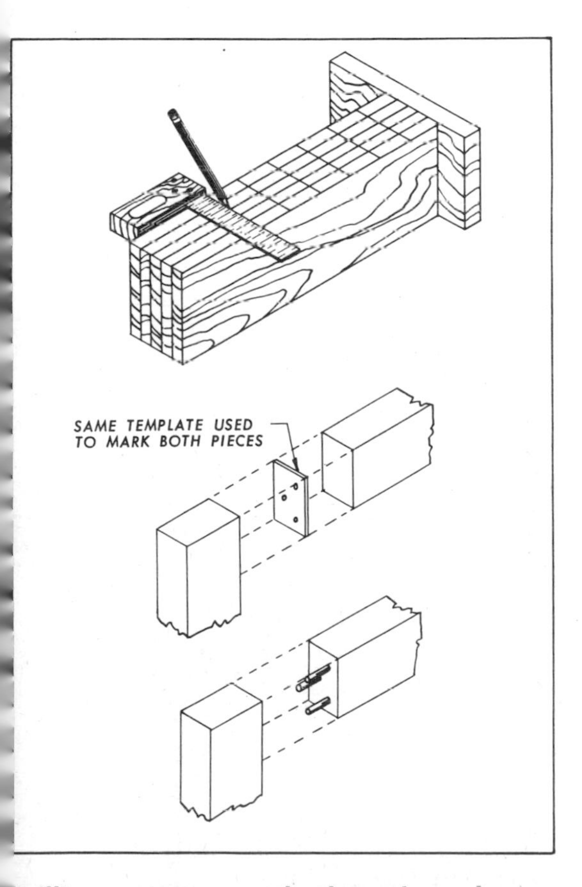

Drilling accuracy greatly depends on layout. Use a template when marking many pieces.

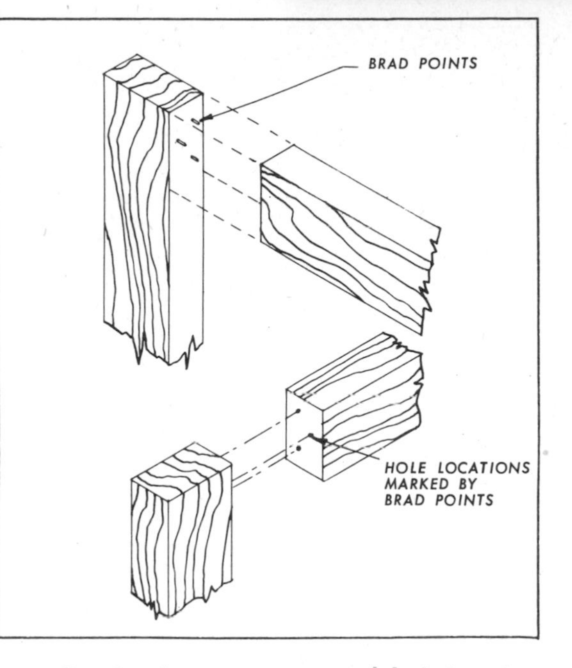

Headless brads in one piece mark hole locations in the other when parts are pressed together.

One little trick that should be remembered for use on mating pieces, when ordinary layout may be impractical or time-consuming, is to insert headless nails in small holes drilled in one of the pieces (drawing above). Let the points protrude about 1/16″ and then press the piece against the mating part. The nail points will mark the hole locations on the second piece. Pull the nails with a pair of pliers and open up the holes to full size.

The top sketch in the drawing at left illustrates a method of marking hole locations when boards are to be joined edge to edge by doweling. The pieces are marked by running a pencil along the blade of a square. Center lines are not needed when the holes are drilled with the machine in the horizontal position.

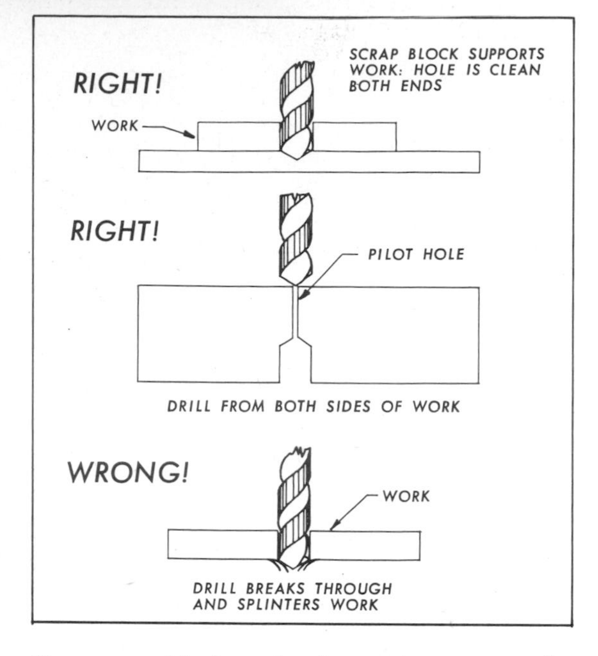
RIGHT!
SCRAP BLOCK SUPPORTS WORK: HOLE IS CLEAN BOTH ENDS
WORK
RIGHT!
PILOT HOLE
DRILL FROM BOTH SIDES OF WORK
WRONG!
WORK
DRILL BREAKS THROUGH AND SPLINTERS WORK

Use a scrap block under the work to protect the table and to assure a clean hole when the drill breaks through.

Supporting the Work

Always keep a scrap block between the work and the table. This protects the table and lets the drill point cut through into the scrap block so that it does not splinter the under surface of the work as it emerges.

When you are drilling in wood or metal, the work should usually be clamped to the table. A drill may grab in the hole and jerk the work out of your hands, particularly when the drill point is about to break out. Use of the rip fence as a guide and support will lessen the need for clamping. When work being drilled is held against the fence, the twisting force exerted by the drill is taken by the fence and not by your hands.

Stubborn grain on some woods, such as fir, may pull a drill off center. When this happens, try clamping the work, drilling a small pilot hole, and then enlarging the hole to full size by drilling halfway through from each side.

Drilling to Exact Depth

Many times it is necessary to drill one o a series of holes to a predetermined depth This is easily done by using the Depth Control Dial in one of two ways.

Method One:

1. Set the work on the table and feed ou the quill until the drill point just touches th work (photograph below). Secure quill lock

2. Turn the Depth Control Dial until i

In using the first method for drilling to exac depth, begin by feeding out the quill unti the drill point just touches the work. Secur the quill lock. Turn the depth control until i reads "0" and then . . .

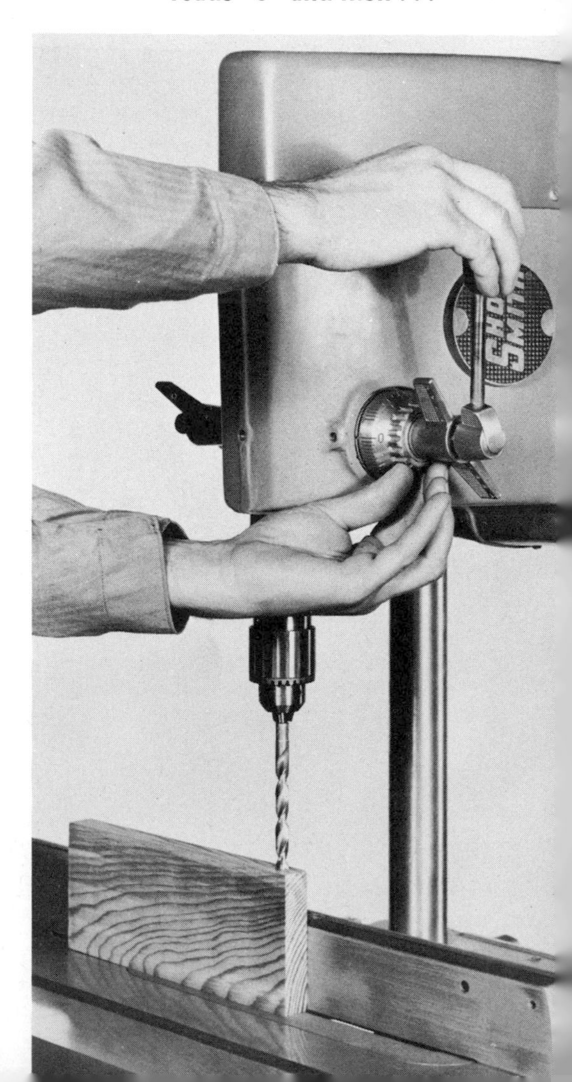

reads "0"; then back it off and lock it at the depth of hole required.

3. Unlock the quill, place the work in position and proceed with the drilling (photograph below).

Method Two:

1. Extend and lock the quill so the drill point lines up with a mark on the edge of the work that indicates the depth desired.

2. With the quill locked in this extended position, turn and lock the Depth Control Dial at "0", as in photograph at right below.

3. Unlock the quill and proceed with the drilling.

These photographs show how the fence is used to provide a guide for parallel drilling. Any number of holes may be drilled with the fence maintaining the distance from the edge of the work to the centers of the holes.

When adjusting the fence, lock it in an approximate position and then use the table height lever as a forward feed mechanism to make the final adjustment.

. . . back it off and lock it according to the depth of hole wanted. Then unlock the quill and place the work in position. Proceed with the drilling. All the holes will be of accurate and uniform depth automatically.

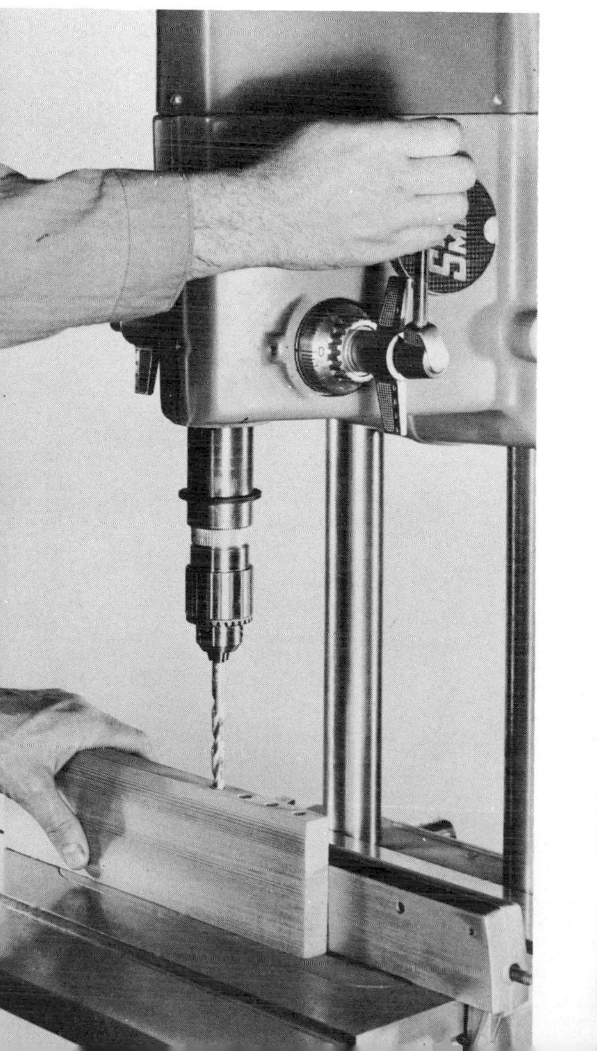

Another method (*Method Two* described in text) of using the dial calls for setting the drill to the required depth, then locking the depth dial on "0". Note the use of the fence as a guide for parallel drilling.

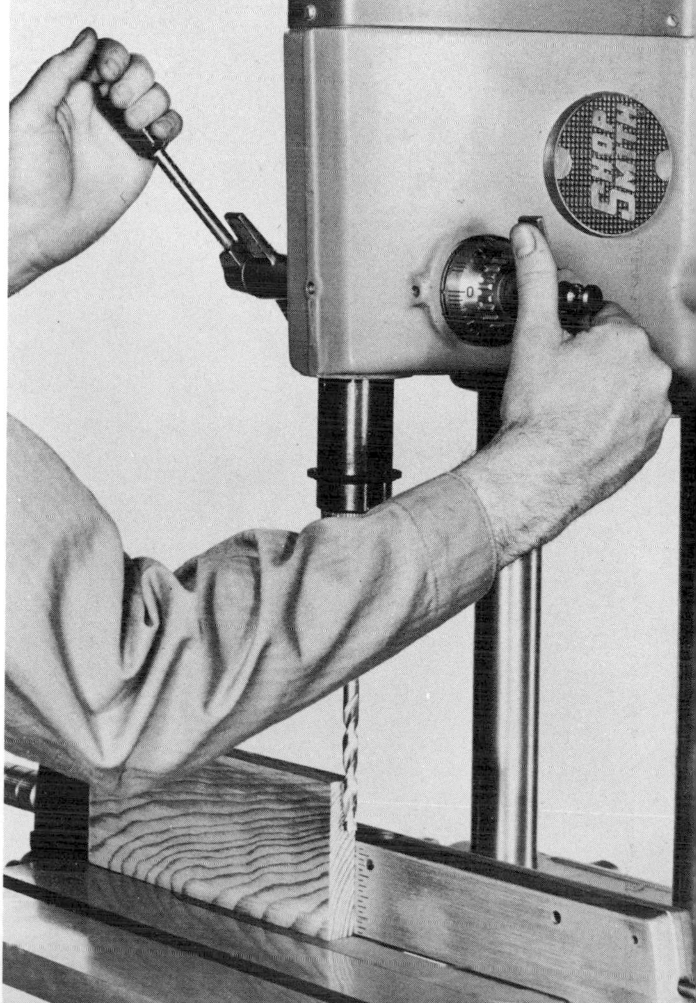

A screw usually requires a body hole for the shank and a lead hole for the thread. Body hole should equal gauge of screw and go through the first piece. Lead hole should be half the length of the threaded portion of the screw. Largest diameter of countersink should equal diameter of screw head. Counterbore should be at least equal to diameter of screw head.

BODY HOLE

LEAD HOLE

COUNTERSINK

COUNTERBORE

Cutters are available that form screw-hole plugs to exact size required.

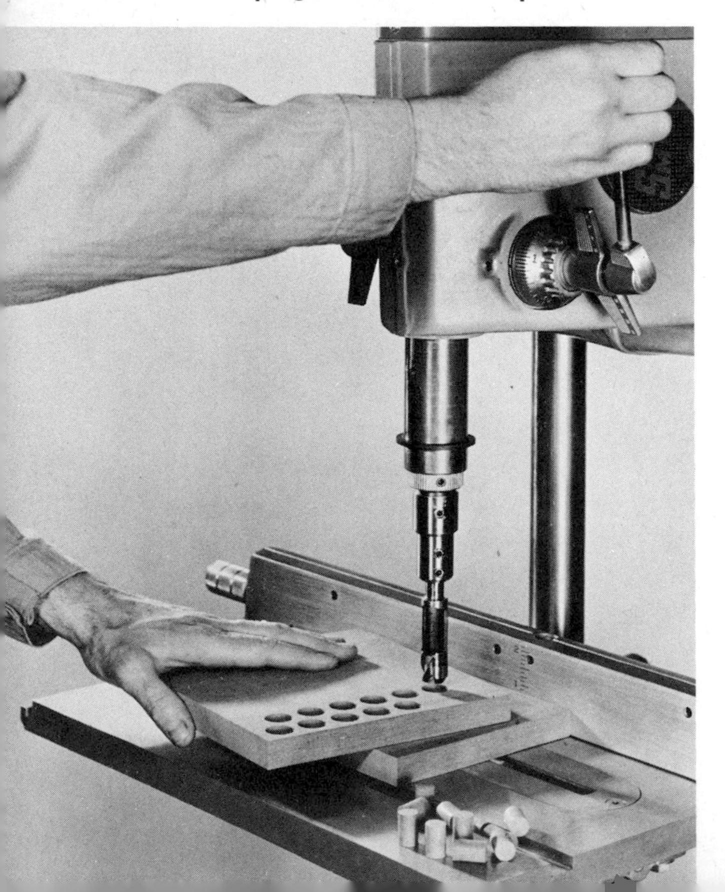

HOLE SIZES FOR WOOD SCREWS

SCREW GAUGE	BODY HOLE	LEAD HOLE	SCREW GAUGE IN INCHES
0	53	—	.060
1	49	—	.073
2	44	56*	.086
3	40	52*	.099
4	33	51*	.112
5	⅛	49*	.125
6	28	47	.138
7	24	46	.151
8	19	42	.164
9	15	41	.177
10	10	38	.190
11	5	37	.203
12	7/32	36	.216
14	D	31	.242
16	I	28	.268
18	19/64	23	.294
*In hardwoods only.			

Drilling Screw Holes

If screws are to drive easily and hold with maximum strength, holes for them must be drilled carefully and to size. Usually the two holes shown at left are needed: the body hole, which equals the gauge of the screw, and a smaller lead hole, which allows the screw end to penetrate the wood.

The easiest procedure is to drill the lead hole first. This establishes a pilot hole as a guide for the body hole. Countersinking, which can be controlled by using the depth control dial, is done on the larger hole to establish a seat for the head of the screw when it must be flush with the surface of the work. In soft woods or when the head of the screw is small enough, countersinking may be eliminated since the screw head will form its own seat as it is turned into the wood.

Screw and bolt holes are counterbored when it is desirable for the fastener head to be set beneath the surface of the wood. Counterbores usually have removable pilots, so one may be selected that will fit the hole to be enlarged. The size of the counterbore and the depth of the cut are determined by the size of the head on the fastener.

Counterbored holes are often sealed with plugs cut from the same type of wood. These may be set flush with the surface of the work and glued in place so the grains match—or they can protrude slightly to provide a decorative touch. This is seen quite often on Early American furniture.

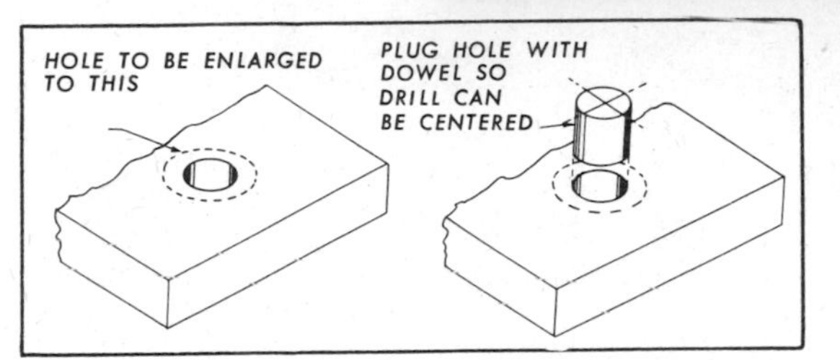

A drilled hole may be enlarged by sealing it with a plug to permit centering the drill.

Enlarging holes already drilled may be accomplished by the method shown above. The plug provides a solid center for the drill point to ride in.

When a job calls for drilling a series of equally spaced holes, a good deal of layout can be eliminated by using a simple guide (below). The auxiliary fence is clamped to the regular fence and positioned to provide the spacing required. The dowel, which slips into a hole in the guide block, engages the hole drilled in the work and positions it for the next hole to be drilled. If you use a small dowel or metal pin and drill pilot holes, you can use the guide for drilling all hole sizes. The pilot hole marks the location and can be enlarged to the size needed.

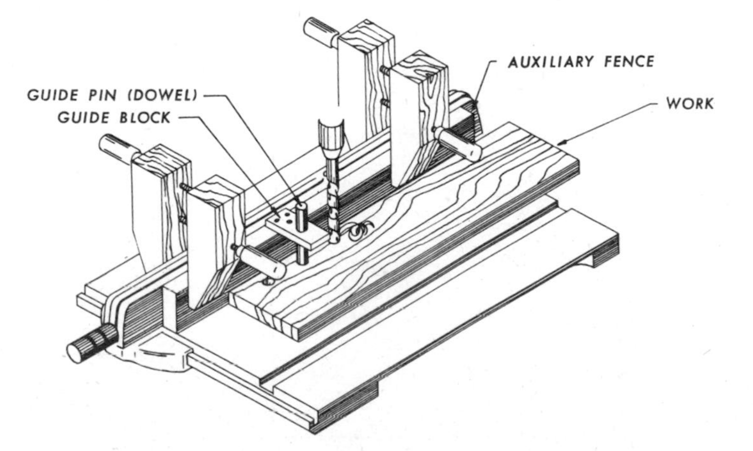

An easily-made jig may be utilized to control automatically the distance between holes.

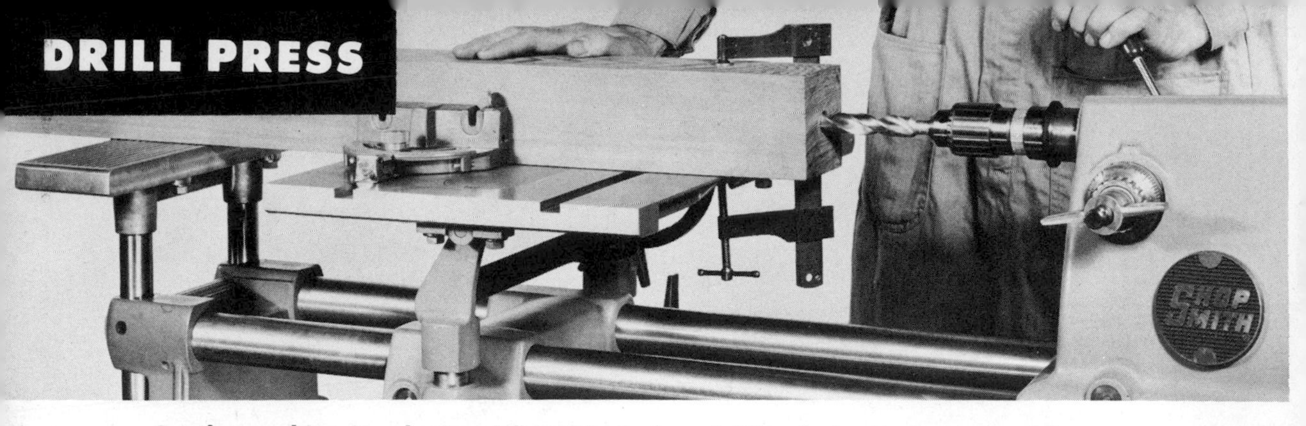

Set the machine in a horizontal position when drilling holes in the ends of heavy posts. Use the extension table for additional support and the miter gauge for alignment.

Drilling Concentric Holes

Since most drill presses have a stroke of 4″, which is about the length of the common bit, it is apparent that the maximum depth of any hole that can be bored in one operation is 4″. Deeper holes may be bored with longer drills by first drilling a 4″ hole in the conventional manner. Retract the bit and slide the table carriage toward the headstock until the drill tip touches the bottom of the hole. Then lock the carriage and repeat the drilling operation. With an 8″ drill, this would give you a hole 8″ deep.

Concentric holes in round stock can be handled with a V-block clamped to the table (drawing at lower left). The fence is used as a stop. Work is hand-held; and it is turned end for end if the hole is to be through.

Another method is to eliminate the V-block and use the miter gauge as a guide (below). In this case, the workpiece must be held firmly against the miter-gauge head or clamped to the table.

A V-block with an extension (top of drawing at lower left) is a good fixture for handling long stock. It will handle short stock, as shown at the top of the next page, yet it also provides maximum support for longer pieces. Notice that auxiliary V's are used to grip pieces of small diameter and that the miter gauge is used as a guide to position the block.

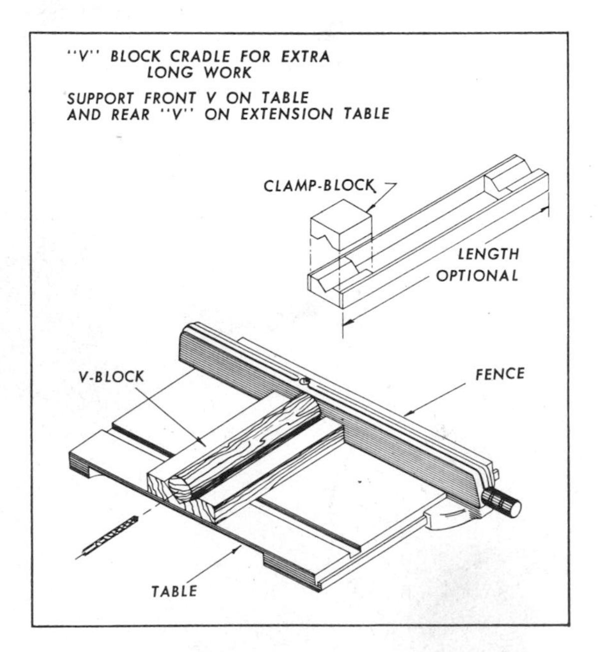

Use a V-block, as at left, to cradle work for concentric drilling. A locked miter gauge, as shown below, may also be used.

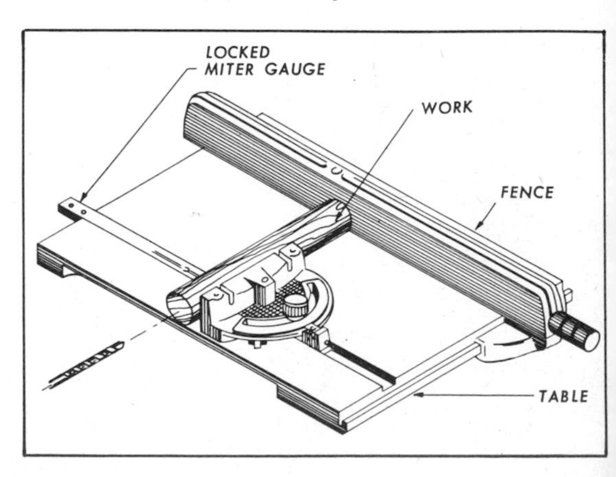

Auxiliary V's are used, as above, when small-diameter rods must be locked in the V-block. Used with clamp and miter gauge (below) the extension V-block easily handles long pieces.

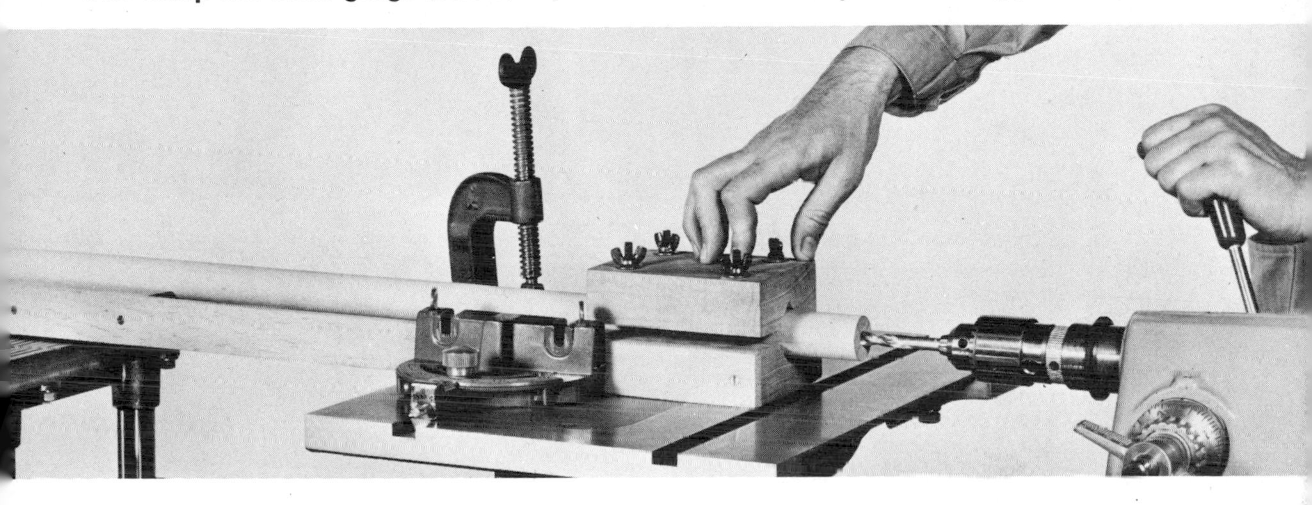

Use this setup with an extension drill to make a deep concentric hole. Retract drill frequently to clear chips from the hole.

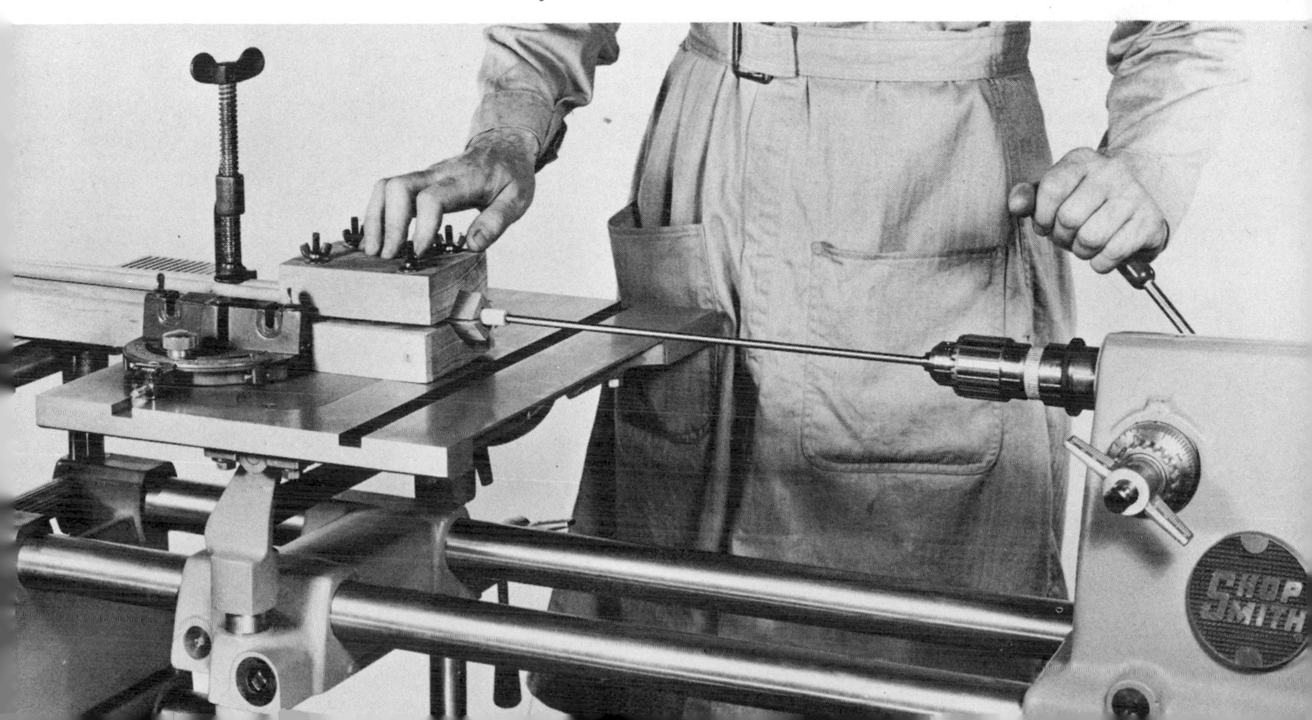

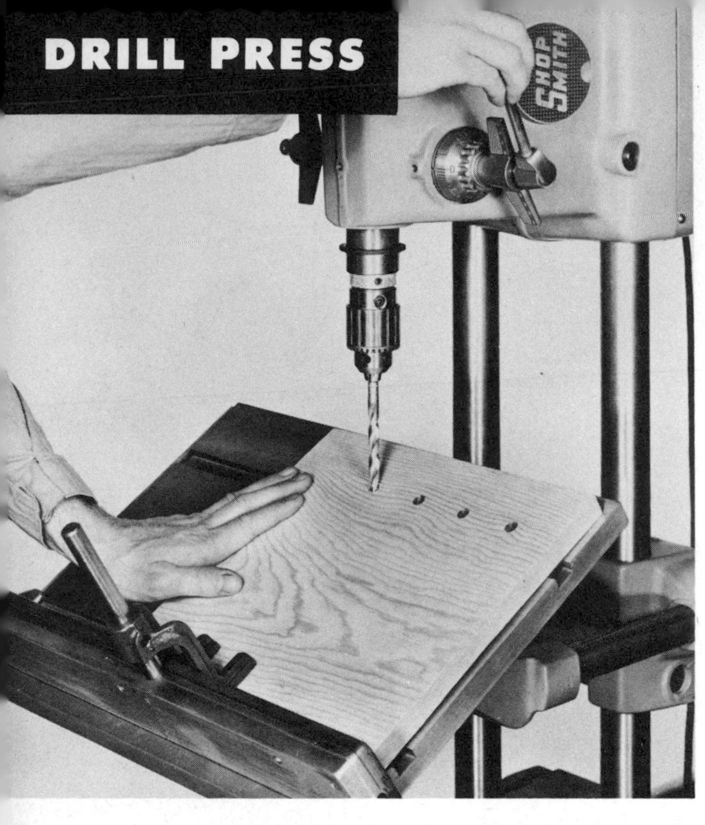

A simple angular hole is drilled by tilting the table to the angle required. The fence, used as a stop, also assures alignment.

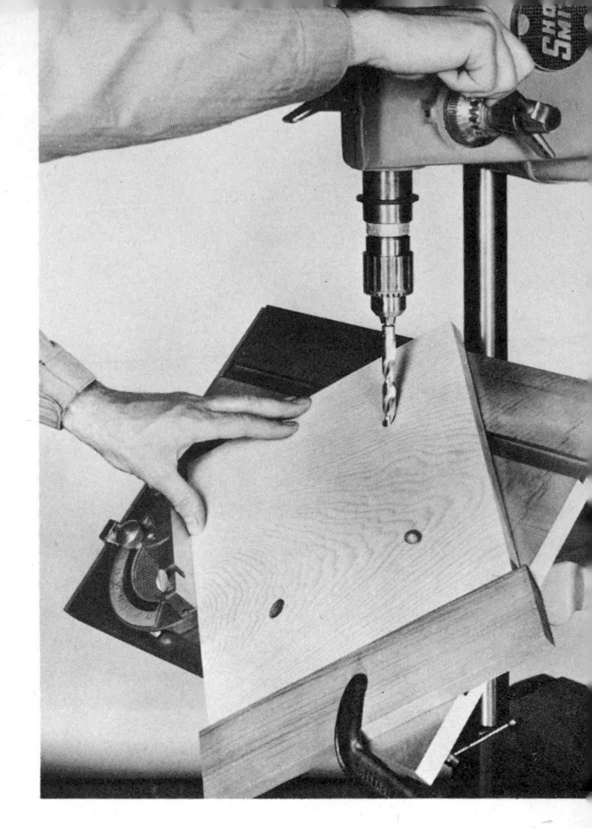

V is used when equal compound-angle holes are drilled. Miter gauge provides one side of V; clamped scrap block provides the other.

Angular Drilling

There are three kinds of angular holes:

1. **simple angle:** A chair leg fitted at a simple angle tilts in one direction. If it tilts to the side, angle is obvious when viewed from front.

2. **equal compound angle:** Here leg tilts in two directions, with amount of tilt equal both ways. Angle is the same when viewed from front or side.

3. **unequal compound angle:** Here the chair leg tilts two ways, but more in one direction. Angle viewed from front differs from angle viewed from the side of the chair.

Simple angles are drilled by tilting the table (above) and using the fence as a guide.

Most used of the compound angles is the equal compound. This is accomplished best with a V-block. When the work is too large to be cradled as shown at upper right, it may be positioned with the miter gauge and clamped in place.

Angular holes in round work require an arrangement that permits the work to be turned while the hole locations are maintained on a common center line. The distance from the holes to the center of the workpiece must be constant. V-blocks are usually used, clamped into position on the table so the work may be turned within the V, as shown on the opposite page. Here the miter gauge is used to locate and maintain the work position. The second leg of the V—which is just a scrap block—is clamped to the table.

Unequal compound angles also require a table tilt, but the position of the work determines the direction in which the greater tilt will occur.

The V-block arrangement is also used to drill angular holes in circular work.

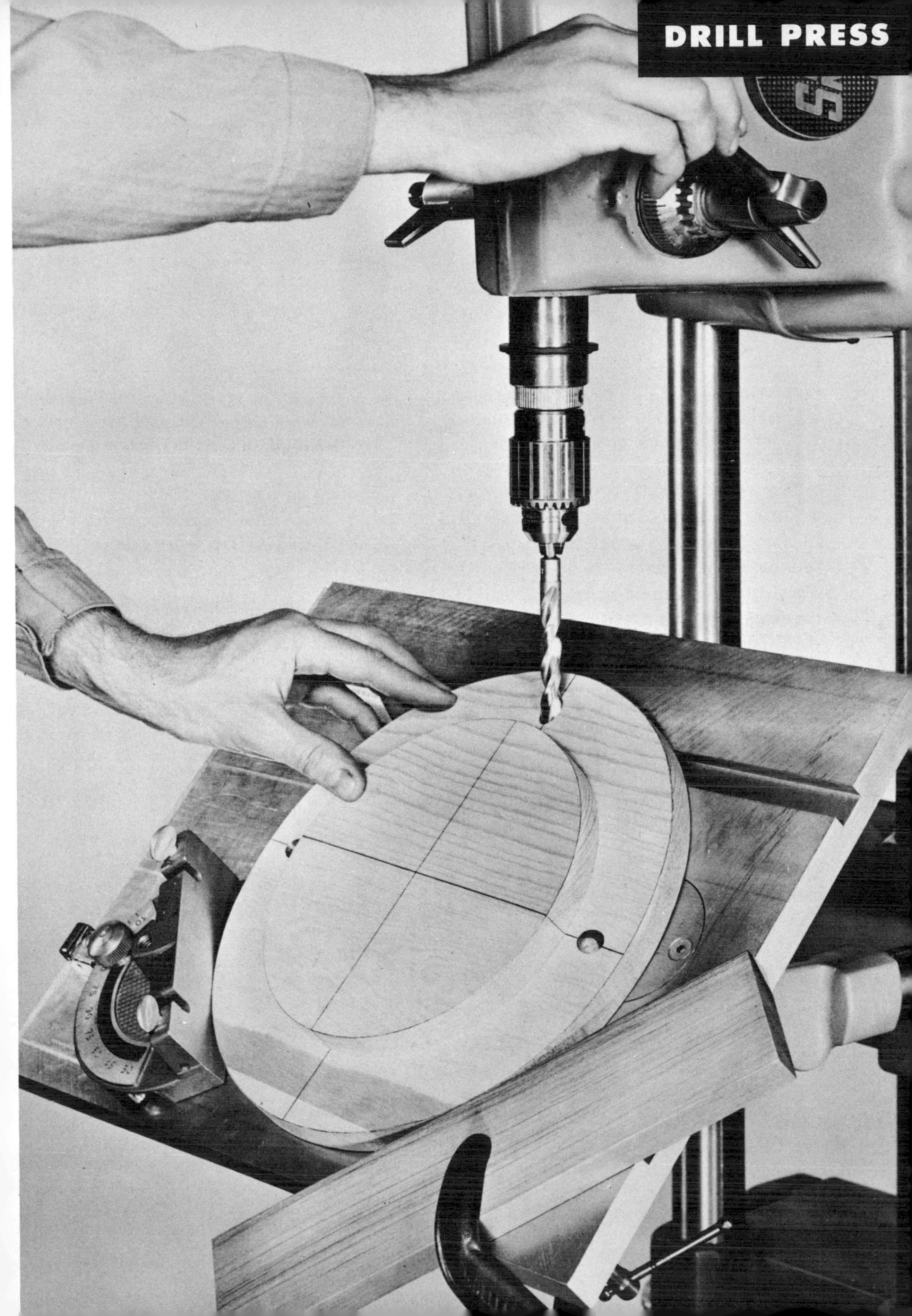

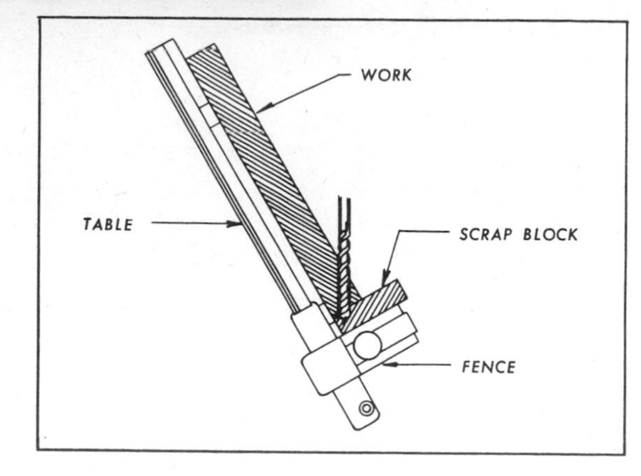

Screw-hole pockets are a form of angular drilling needed when rails or frames are attached to the underside of a top surface.

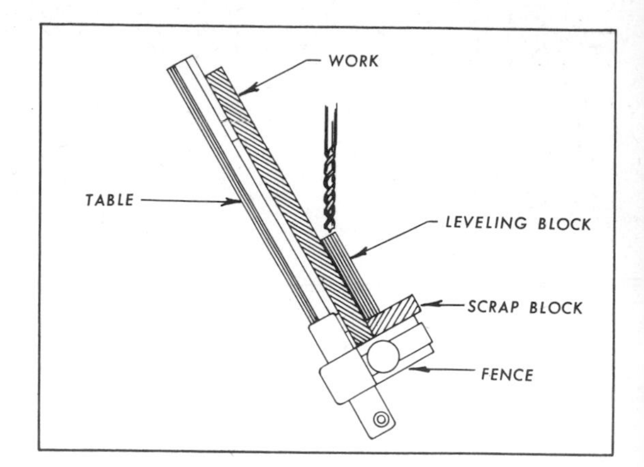

On an extreme angle, the side of the drill will meet the work before the point does. Use a leveling block to keep the drill centered.

Screw-hole pockets (above) are a form of angular drilling needed when, for example, rails or frames are attached to the underside of a top surface, perhaps of a table or desk. They usually require a sharp angle, causing the side of the drill to touch the work before the center does. Since this can result in the bit's walking off center, use a scrap block as a leveling device. With the block in place, the center of the hole is located before the bit touches the work. The result can be seen at lower right. Use of the fence provides a stop as well as a guide, which makes positioning the holes on a common center line automatic. If the holes are to go through the work, protect the table with scrap material.

The leveling block shown here assures accuracy on extreme angular drilling.

The action of the drill and its results on extreme angular holes can be seen here.

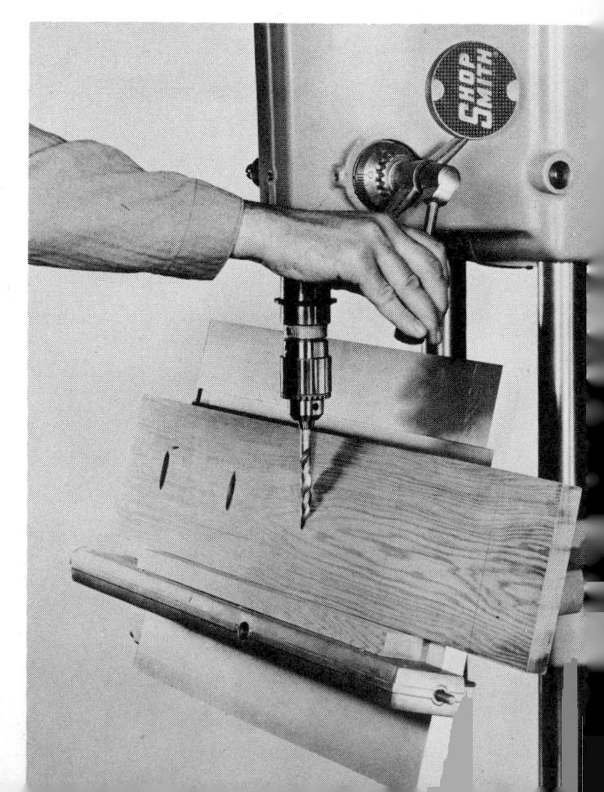

Drilling Through Heavy Work

Another useful idea is shown at the right. A scrap block, with a peg the same size as the hole being drilled, is centered on the table after the hole has been drilled in one end of the work. The work is then seated over the peg, which positions it for drilling from the other end.

Another method, shown below, is to modify a no-slot table insert to take a pin that will be concentric with the spindle center. This pin should be small (about 1/8″) to permit its use in making pilot holes. The pilot hole, drilled through the stock, can then be enlarged to the size required.

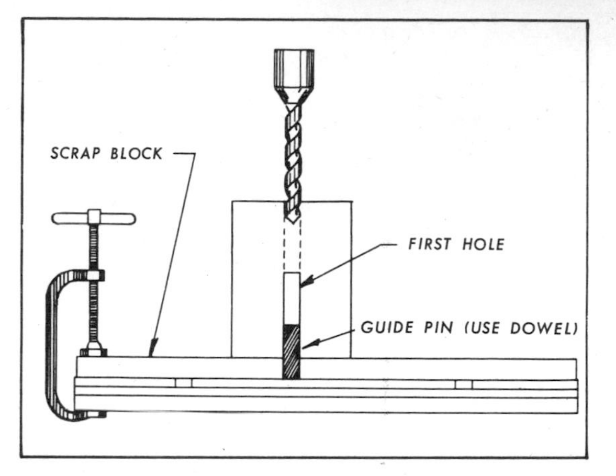

Use a scrap block with a guide pin to drill accurately through both sides of heavy stock (above). Or modify a no-slot insert to provide the guide pin, as diagrammed below.

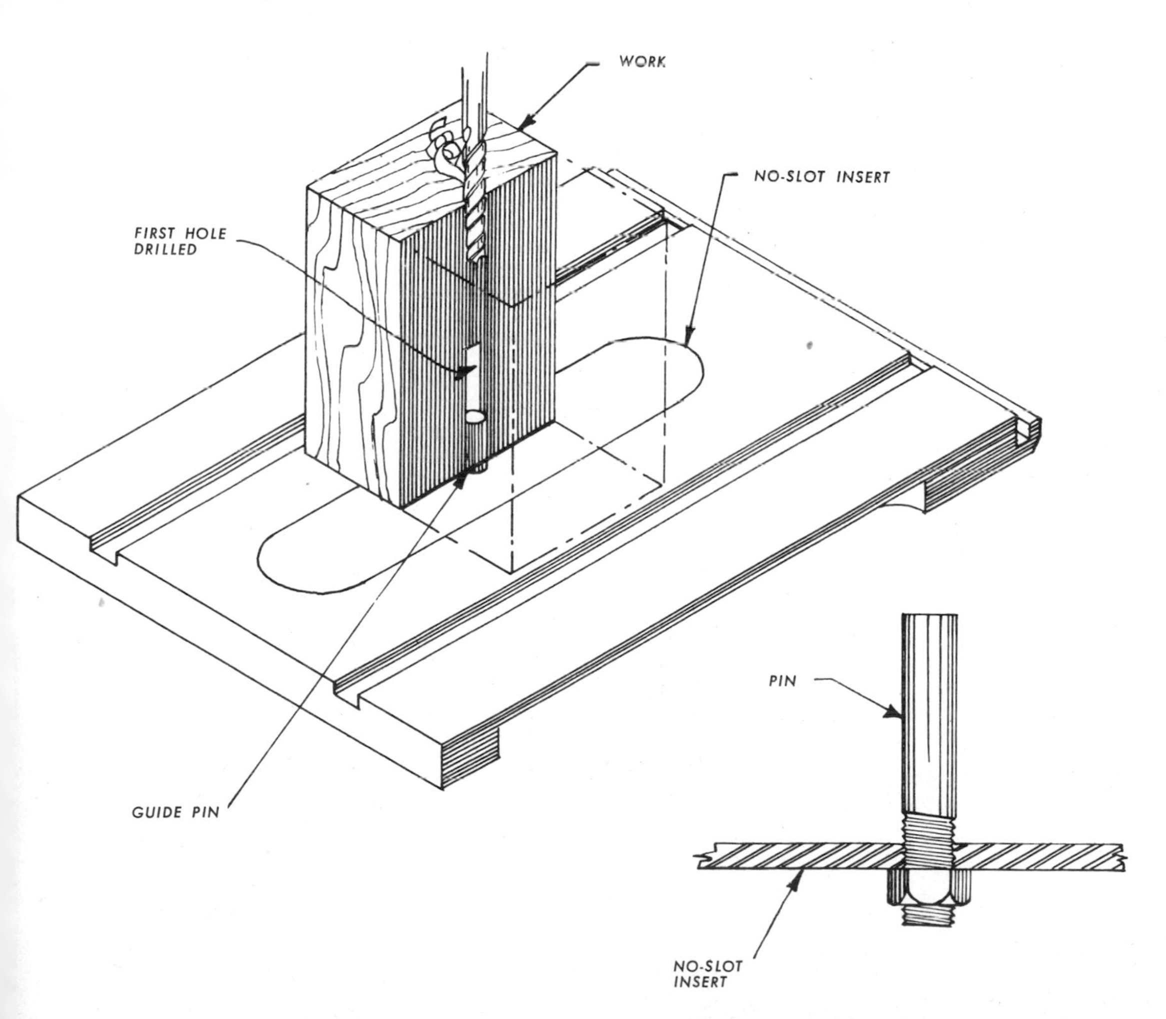

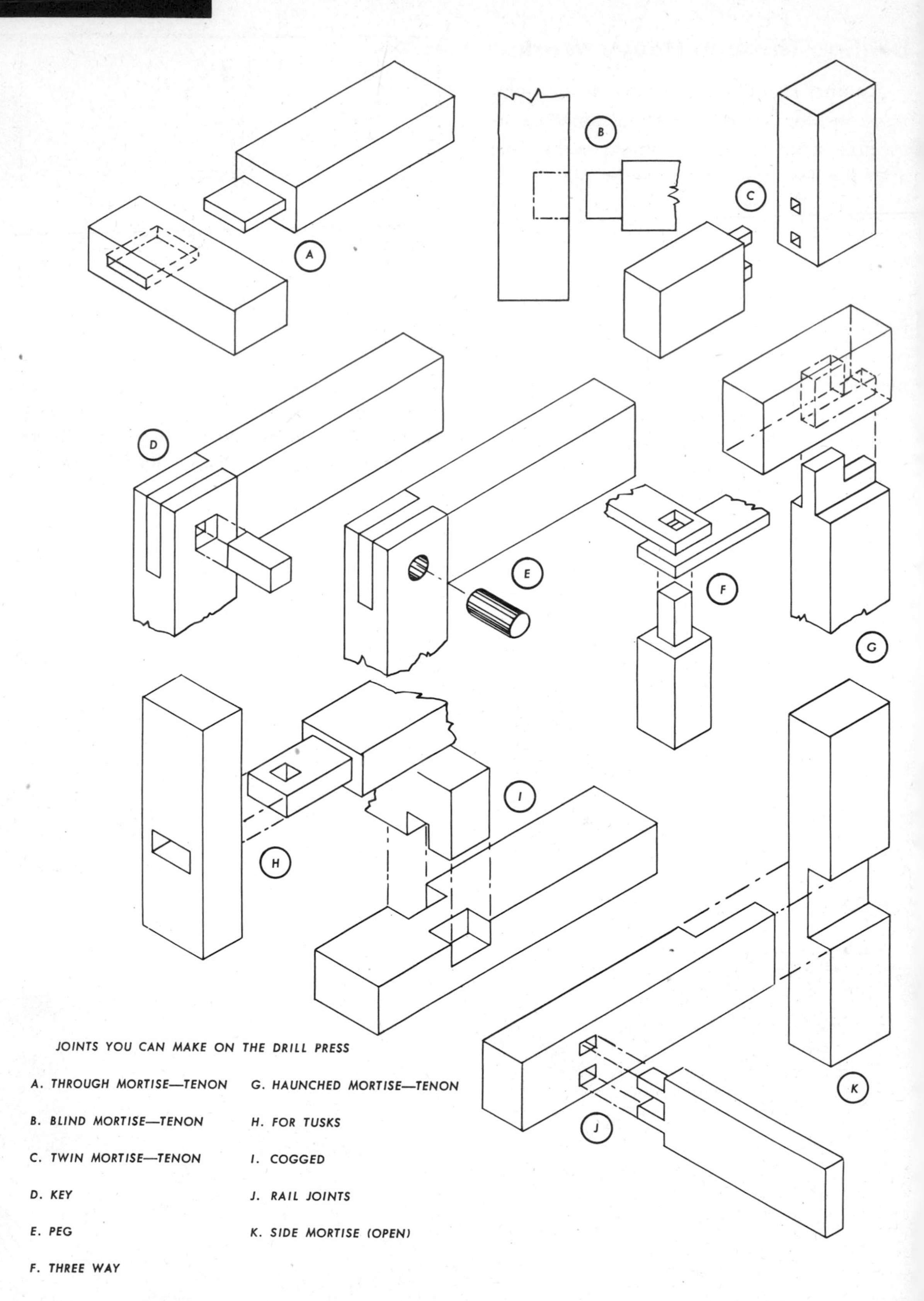

JOINTS YOU CAN MAKE ON THE DRILL PRESS

A. THROUGH MORTISE—TENON
B. BLIND MORTISE—TENON
C. TWIN MORTISE—TENON
D. KEY
E. PEG
F. THREE WAY
G. HAUNCHED MORTISE—TENON
H. FOR TUSKS
I. COGGED
J. RAIL JOINTS
K. SIDE MORTISE (OPEN)

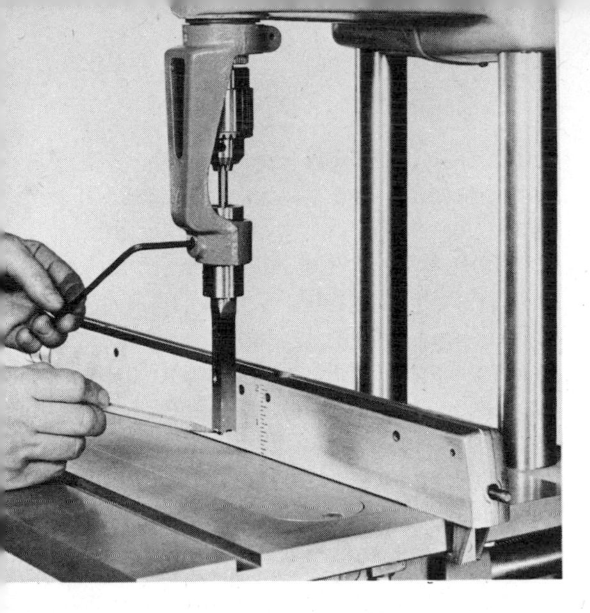

Drill Press Joinery: Mortising

All the joints shown on the left-hand page, except the peg (E), require the use of a mortising bit and chisel. This is a special attachment that eliminates tedious hand work when forming mortises for mortise-and-tenon joints and other joints calling for a square cavity.

The mortising attachment is slipped over the collar on the quill and secured with an Allen set screw. To secure the chuck, turn the spindle by hand so the tapered flat faces forward and set the chuck in place in the usual manner. One caution: the chuck must be secured while the arm of the attachment faces the tubes. After the chuck is in place, turn the attachment to suit the work. Insert the hollow chisel in the adjustable sleeve and secure it with the set screw. Insert the bit through the chisel and into the chuck and lock with the chuck key. The adjustable sleeve is positioned in the casting so there is a gap of between 1/32″ and 1/16″ between the cutting edge of the bit and the chisel.

Since the fence is used as a guide for the work, the chisel must be squared to it. Place the head of a square against the fence and the blade against the side of the chisel (photograph at upper right). Make the adjustment by turning the adjustable sleeve; then secure it in position with the set screw.

The mortising hold-down, which sits in a hole in the fence, should be used to keep the

Always allow a gap of 1/32″ to 1/16″ between the cutting bit and the edge of the hollow chisel, as photograph at upper left shows.

The side of the hollow chisel should be located at right angles to the fence. Check it with a square, as illustrated at upper right.

Below: the mortising hold-down prevents work from being lifted off the table when the cutting tool is retracted.

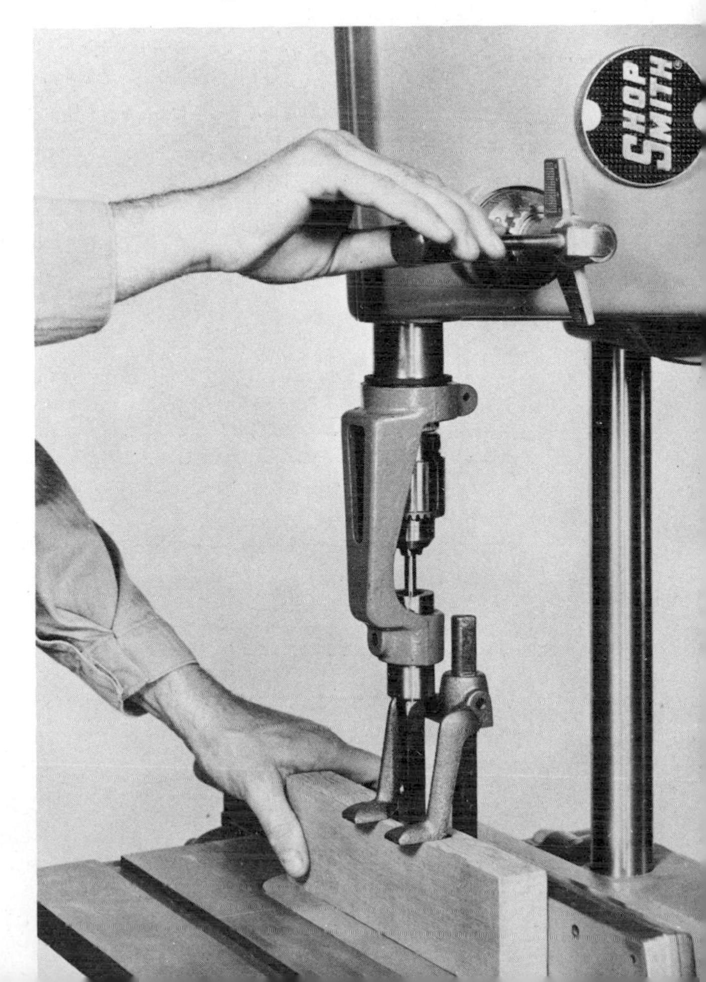

work from pulling up when the quill is retracted.

The final step is to adjust the depth dial for the depth of cut needed. If the cut is to go through the work, use a scrap block to protect the table.

After the workpiece has been located on the table, it is simply a matter of depressing the chisel to do the cutting. Pressure required will vary with the size of the chisel and the hardness of the wood. Softwoods such as pine cut easily, while hardwoods such as maple require considerably more pressure. Excessive pressures are never necessary. If you can't make the cut without exertion, it is probably because the edges on the bit or the hollow chisel are dull.

Two factors which tend to spoil a mortise are illustrated below. To eliminate these, cuts should be made as shown in the order given in the second detail of the drawing. The general rule is: always make the end cuts first and clean out the stock between by making successive cuts, never less than three-quarters

For a perfect mortise, watch the factors covered below and the speed you use. For chisels up to ½", use speed of 1,750 to 3,500 rpm in softwoods, 1,750 to 2,000 in hardwoods. The larger the chisel, the slower the speed. Correct speed will produce a chip fine enough to pass through the chisel without binding, clogging, or over-heating.

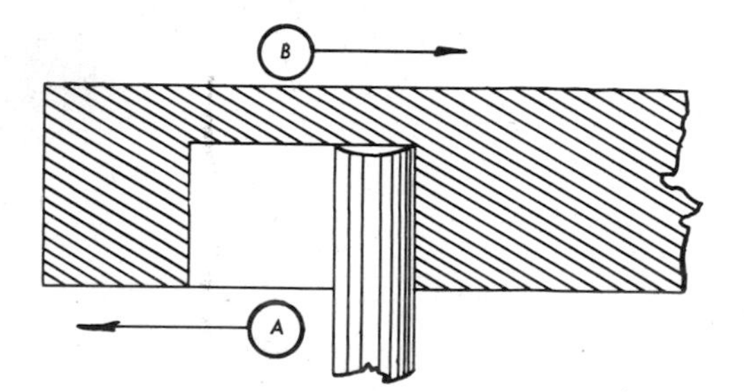

TWO FACTORS THAT MAY SPOIL A MORTISE

A. CHISEL TENDS TO LEAD OFF TOWARD THE CAVITY ALREADY FORMED.

B. WORK TENDS TO CREEP AWAY FROM THE CHISEL AS THE CUT IS BEING MADE.

ALWAYS MAKE END CUTS FIRST. OVERLAP CUTS SO THAT CHISEL ALWAYS MAKES A CUT THAT IS AT LEAST ¾ SIZE.

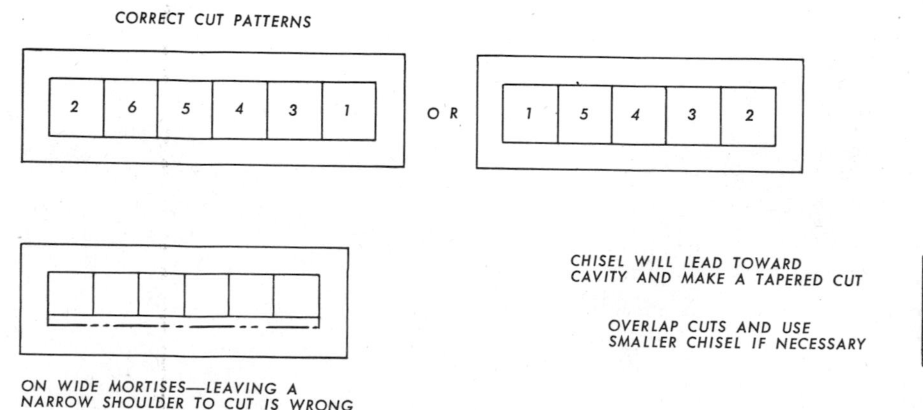

ON WIDE MORTISES—LEAVING A NARROW SHOULDER TO CUT IS WRONG

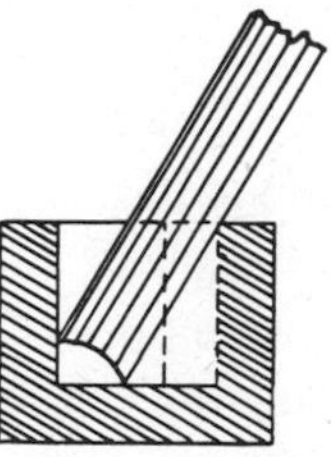

CHISEL WILL LEAD TOWARD CAVITY AND MAKE A TAPERED CUT

OVERLAP CUTS AND USE SMALLER CHISEL IF NECESSARY

of the full width of the chisel. That may not be possible on the last cut, but keep as close to it as you can.

Avoid narrow shoulders. The chisel will creep away, leaving a tapered side. Many pieces of work split because tenons are forced into mortises with sloping sides. If necessary, use a smaller chisel.

When cutting a side mortise (photograph below) use a scrap piece between the work and the fence to provide support for the chisel.

Drills may be used to cut mortises, but the ends of the slot will be round unless cleaned out with a hand chisel. The procedure is to drill one hole at each end of the mortise, as diagrammed below. Then clean out the waste material between by boring successive overlapping holes. After all the holes are drilled, the slot is cleaned out by moving the work back and forth while the drill is turning.

When cutting a side mortise, be sure to use a scrap block between the work and the fence, as shown here. If necessary, clamp the two pieces firmly together.

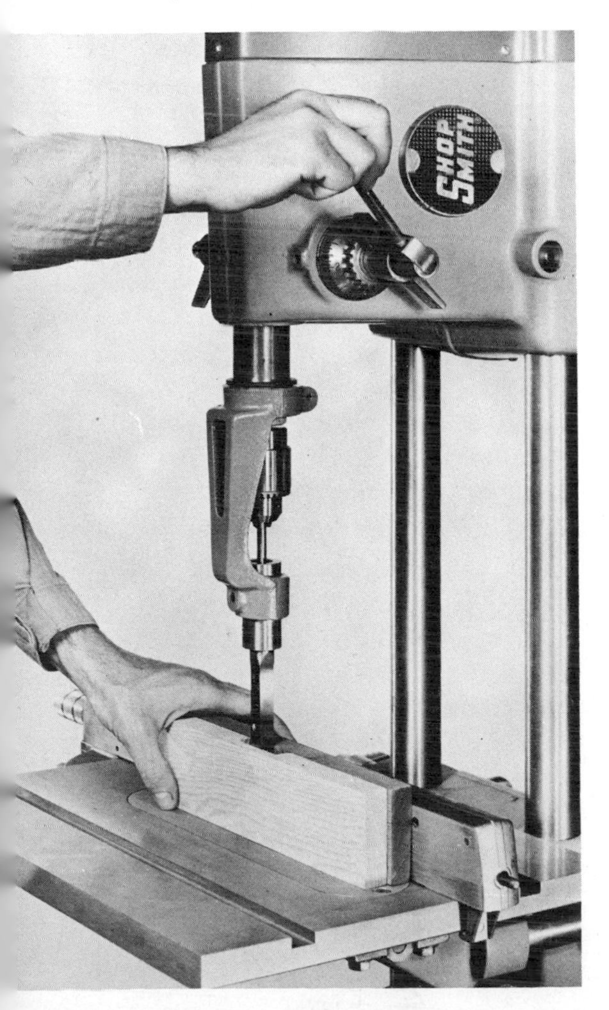
SHOP SMITH

A drill may be used to form a mortise. However the tenon must be rounded off to fit the semi-circular ends of the mortise, as the diagram below shows.

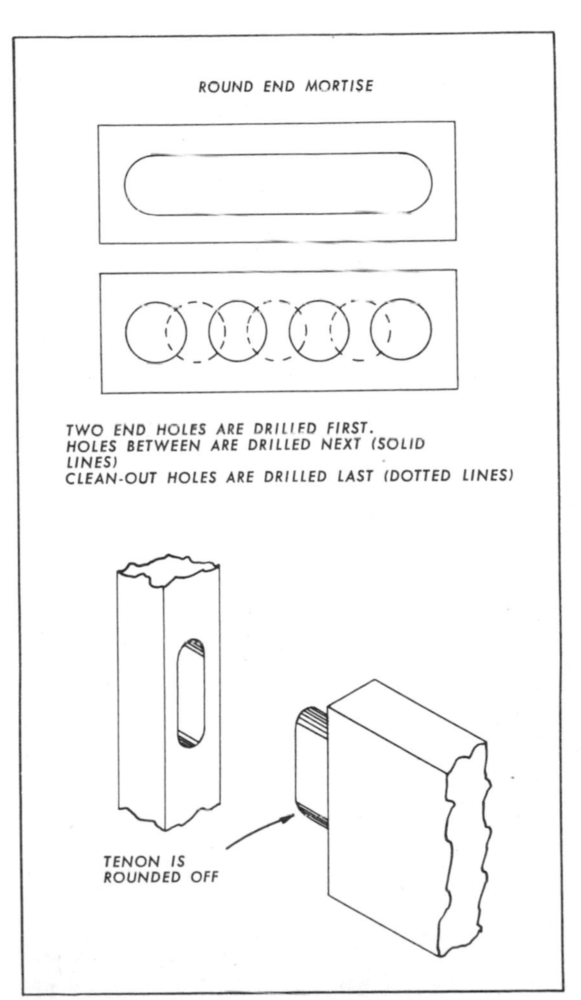
ROUND END MORTISE
TWO END HOLES ARE DRILLED FIRST.
HOLES BETWEEN ARE DRILLED NEXT (SOLID LINES)
CLEAN-OUT HOLES ARE DRILLED LAST (DOTTED LINES)
TENON IS ROUNDED OFF

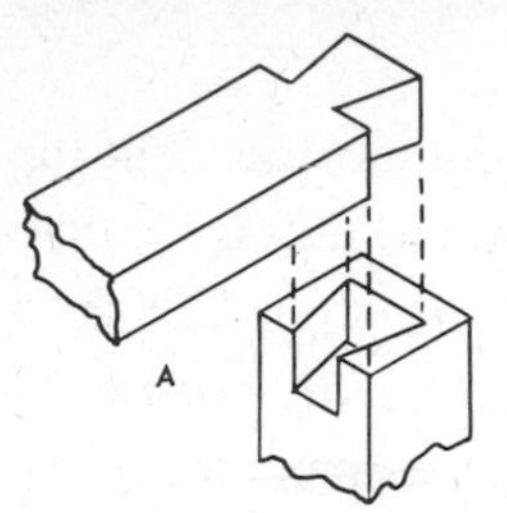

B

C

A—SINGLE HALF-BLIND DOVETAIL

B—MULTIPLE HALF-BLIND DOVETAIL

C—THROUGH MULTIPLE DOVETAIL

How to Make Dovetail Joints

Much antique furniture has exposed dovetails, probably because they were achieved with painstaking layout and craftsmanship and were considered a mark of quality.

A dovetail is one of the strongest joints in woodworking because it will resist a pulling strain in every direction but the one from which the tenons are inserted.

Two of the most common applications are sketched above.

The use of a dovetail cutter makes it possible to do dovetailing on the drill press. The same cutter is used to form the dovetail and the key, or tenon. Mating the parts is a matter of positioning the cuts in proper relationship to each other.

On the multi-purpose tool, single or multiple dovetails are cut with the table in a position parallel to the ways, using the table height lever as a forward feed mechanism (top of opposite page). Spacing of the cuts is determined by the size of the cutter and the design of the joint. One method is to mark the workpiece and align each cut with the cutting tool. Another method is to pencil-mark the table so that the edge of the workpiece can be moved forward to a new mark after each cut. When you mark the table, first determine the center line of the spindle and then mark the cut lines by measuring toward the table edges, front and rear. It will prove useful to obtain some measuring tape which has a gummed side. This may be placed on the table and then removed when not in use.

To position the work, first adjust the table to provide the workpiece with maximum support near the cutting tool. Use the quill feed lever to obtain the exact depth of cut. Whenever possible, use the fence as a platform for the work. Use the miter gauge to square the work to the spindle. When feeding the work forward against the cutter, move the table slowly, and be sure the work is clamped securely in place. When the cut is made, stop the motor and return the table to the starting position. Place the work for the next cut and repeat the procedure.

The single half-blind dovetail is often found on toprail and leg construction in cabinetwork, where the holding power of the joint combats pulling strain. The multiple half-blind dovetail is used to attach drawer sides to fronts since it resists the strain when the drawer is pulled out.

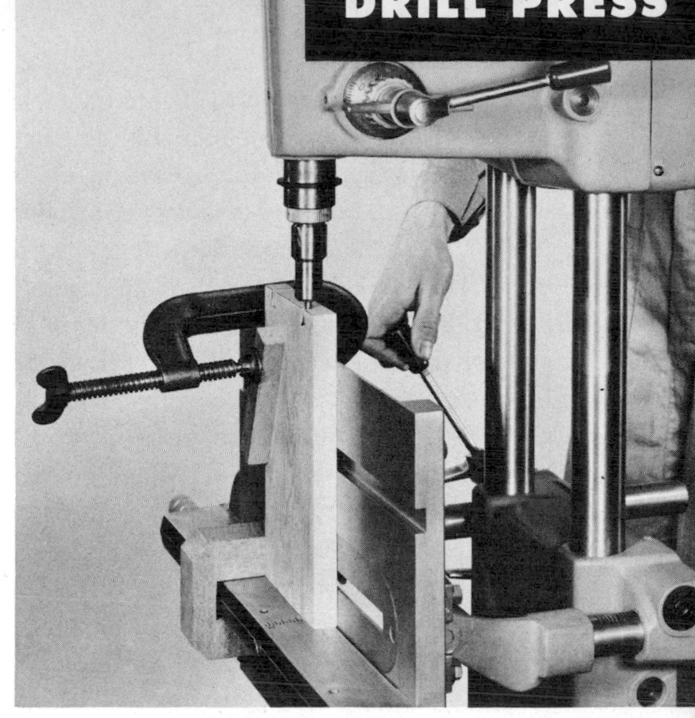

Single or multiple dovetails can be formed as shown at right. Fence and stop block are used to position work, which is firmly clamped to table. Table-height lever is used as forward feed mechanism.

Make slots with fence and block to control position, quill extended and locked for depth.

The mating cuts are formed with the table in the horizontal position and with the fence used as a guide. The table is brought up as close to the cutting tool as possible, and the final adjustment is made by extending the quill. The work is fed forward against the cutting tool. A stop is used on the fence to control the length of cut. For spacing, the fence can be moved for each new cut or the table can be advanced—again by using the table-height lever as a forward feed device. When feeding the work against the cutter, hold it firmly on the table and push it slowly. If the cut is for a through dovetail, use a scrap block between the work and the table. Always keep hands clear of the cutting tool.

The advantage in making the cuts as described is that you can space them to suit the application, combining the latitude of handwork (on a joint of this type) with the labor-saving advantages of machine practice. The system may be used for uniform multiple dovetailing or for a single dovetail.

The tenon on a single, wide dovetail is formed by making two cuts, one on each end of the stock. The mating part is formed the same way, with the waste stock cut away by running the work across the cutter within limits set by two end cuts. Care must be exercised in positioning the pieces for successive cuts, but testing in scrap wood before cutting will make this easier.

Dovetailing need not be confined to drawer, corner, and rail joints. By using the setups shown in the photographs below, you can use the joint to join boards edge to edge or to provide a sliding arrangement that is occasionally called for in woodworking.

Cut the slot in one pass by placing the table as shown and adjusting it so the cut is made directly down the center line of the board. Depth of cut is set by lowering the quill and locking it in position. Feed the work slowly and keep it flat against the table. Do not force the work.

The tenon requires two passes. The work is positioned so the cutter forms the tenon on one side of the board. Then the work is turned and the second pass made; thus the cutter completes the forming of the tenon on the

This long dovetail slot might be required for a sliding assembly. Note position of table and fence and use of mortising hold-down.

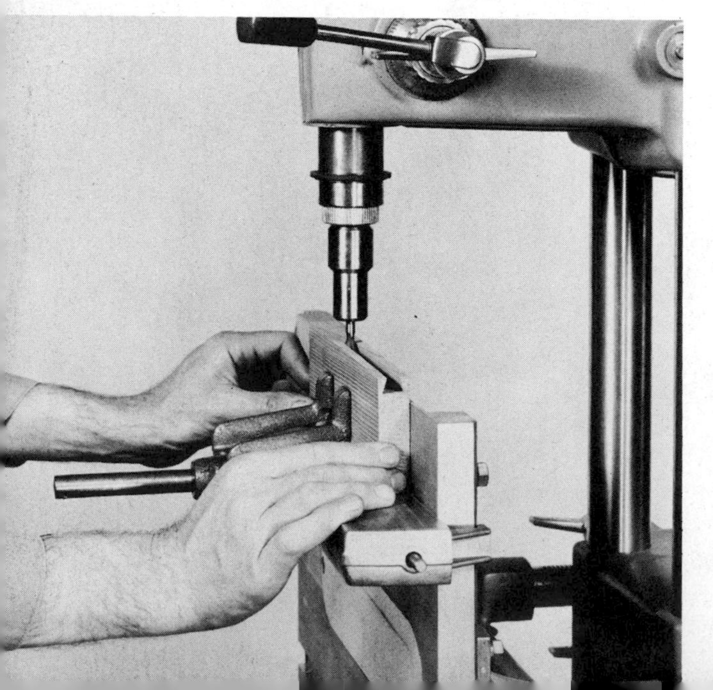

A dovetail tenon is formed in a similar manner except that two passes are required, one on each edge of the stock.

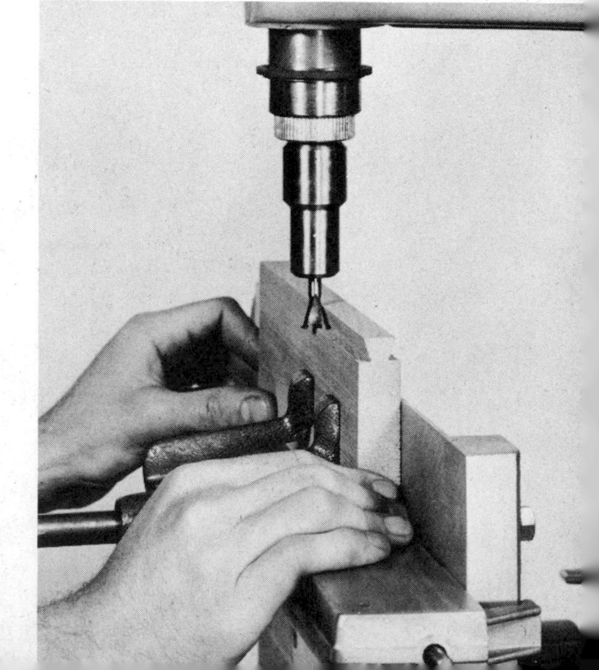

opposite surface of the board. Here, even more than elsewhere, be sure the work is held firmly and flat against the table.

You can cut a dovetail slot much as you would form a groove on the table saw, except that the cutter is above the work (photograph below). The slot may be through or blind. The blind dovetail requires a tenon that does not run clear across the edge of the board. When forming the tenon, first cut it across the board and then remove the unwanted section on the table saw.

Dovetail cutters should be secured in a router chuck or special adapter and operated at high speeds. Keep hands clear of the work at all times and, when possible, use a guard similar to the simple arrangement shown at the right. This is a short piece of tubing, 2″ outside diameter, with a ⅜-inch section of it cut away lengthwise so it can be secured to the quill with a common hose clamp. The bottom end is shaped to act as a shield between the cutting tool and the operator's fingers. A piece of plastic tube can be used instead.

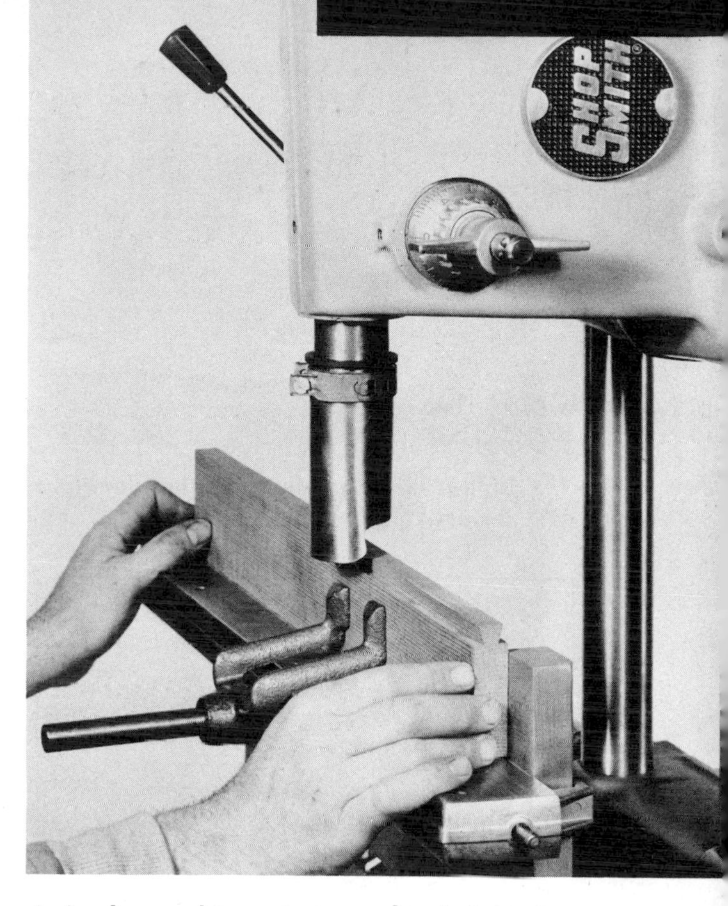

A simple guard to protect your hands from the cutting tool can be made of aluminum tubing and locked over the quill with a hose clamp.

Dovetail slots may be formed in the surface of the stock also. Hold work firmly down on the table and feed it very slowly against the cutting tool.

The sliding table greatly simplifies cutting a dovetail slot in an extra-wide piece.

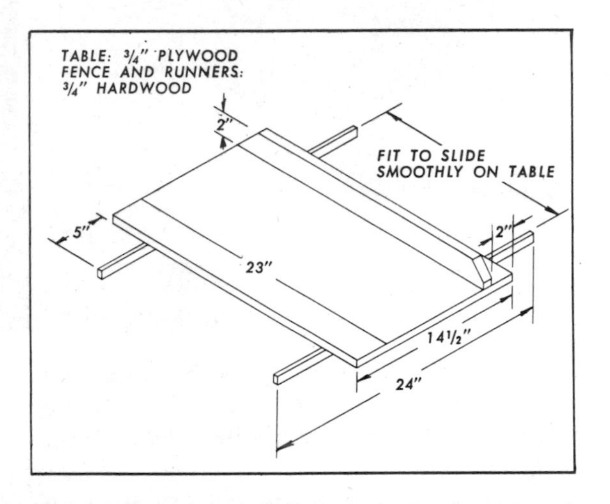

Make the sliding table like this. Runners should fit snugly against the edges of the table.

Two passes are needed on extra-wide work. Be sure to align cutter accurately.

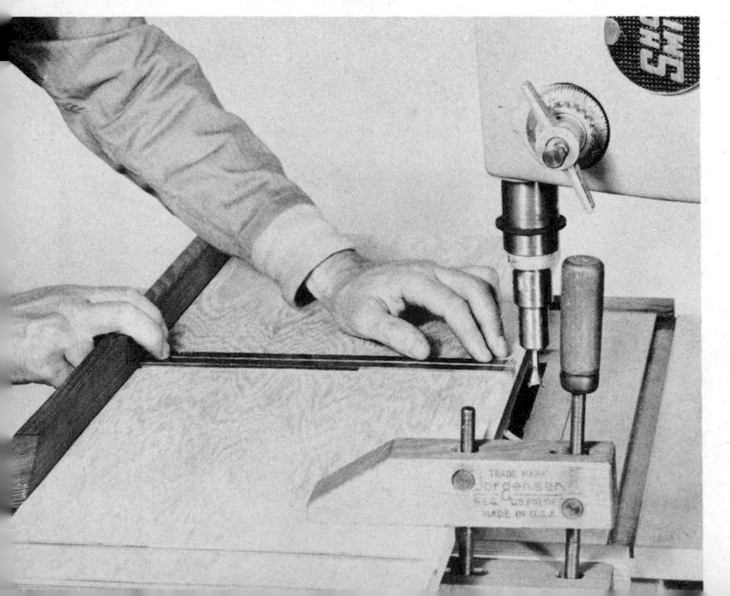

Long stock that must be grooved cross-grain requires a sliding table arrangement to which the work can be clamped (left). The fixture is constructed as shown in the drawing, with the runners situated so the platform will slide smoothly on the table. The table is raised to an approximate position and the final adjustment for depth of cut made by using the quill feed lever.

With this arrangement the length of cut is limited to the distance from spindle to tubes. On narrow boards the groove can be completed in one pass by using another board between the work and the fence. Wide boards require two cuts from opposite sides of the board on a common center line. Alignment is important. Locate the spindle center by pencil-marking a line on the fence of the sliding table. Mark lines on the work to locate the center lines of the grooves. Align these with the mark on the fence. Since the first half-cut (on wide boards) removes the line, it is necessary to use a straightedge as at lower left to re-align the work with the mark on the fence before completing the cut. This method is not limited to dovetail grooves; those with straight sides are cut with router bits, and the procedure is exactly the same.

Jigs are available for cutting multiple dovetails on mating pieces simultaneously (opposite page). The operator moves the work against the cutter, using the comb as a guide to form the slots and tenons in one operation. Use of the jig calls for a special table, which is clamped to the drill-press table to provide a platform on which the jig can slide as it is moved against the cutter. The table and work are placed in approximately correct positions; the final adjustment for depth of cut is made by using the quill feed lever.

Various types of dovetail joints cut by the methods described in this section are shown at the right.

Auxiliary table clamped to the regular table permits use of a commercial dovetailing jig.

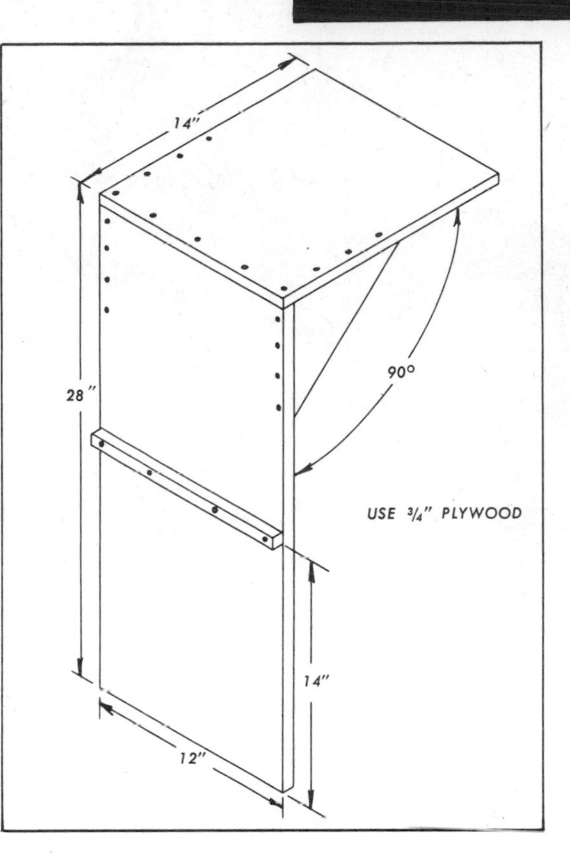

Construction details of the dovetailing table are shown in the drawing above.

These sample dovetail joints were formed by methods described in this section.

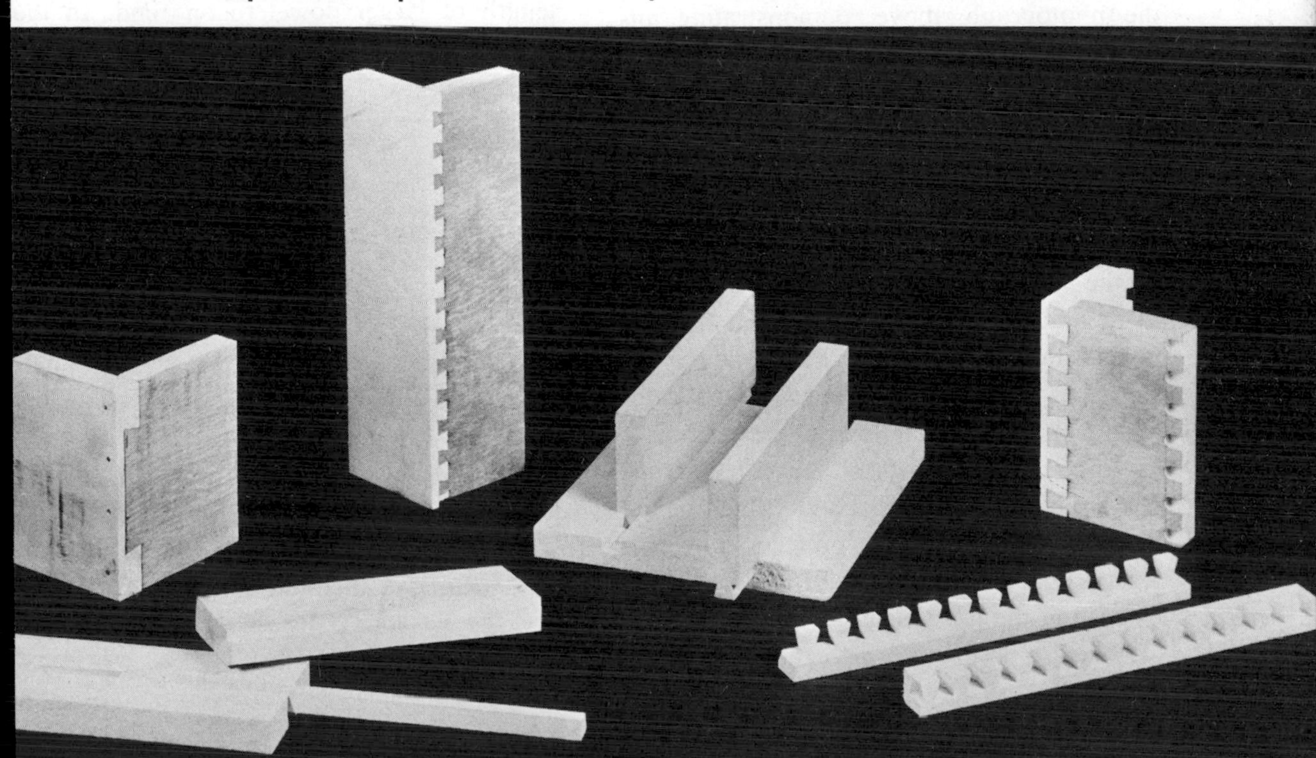

If pieces are drilled face down on table, dowel holes need not be exactly centered in edge.

Doweling

The dowel joint is easy to make and is often a suitable substitute for a mortise-and-tenon joint. One of its most common applications is in joining boards edge to edge to form a wide surface. The combination of table surface, rip fence, and depth-control dial makes the operation a mechanical one, as in the photograph above, demonstrating another advantage of a horizontal boring machine. To equalize the hole spacing, the boards can be stacked and marked with a square (see sketch on page 105).

Hole spacing can be an automatic operation if a spacing jig similar to the one shown on the next page is used. The jig is fastened to the ways. A dowel peg engages the first hole drilled and positions the work for the next hole. The series of holes drilled in the upright member of the fixture makes it possible to space holes from 2″ to 7″ apart. The important part of the construction is getting the dowel guide holes exactly on a common center line with the spindle. This is accomplished by resting the upright on the part it is to be attached to and pressing it against a drill secured in the chuck. Make a second mark at the other end of the piece and connect the two with a straight line. This is the center line of the ¼″ holes that are drilled for the dowel guide.

If several dowel guides are made, the same setup can be utilized for any hole size. Use ¼″ dowel in each case and attach a short length of larger dowel to one end. In the photograph at upper right the guide being

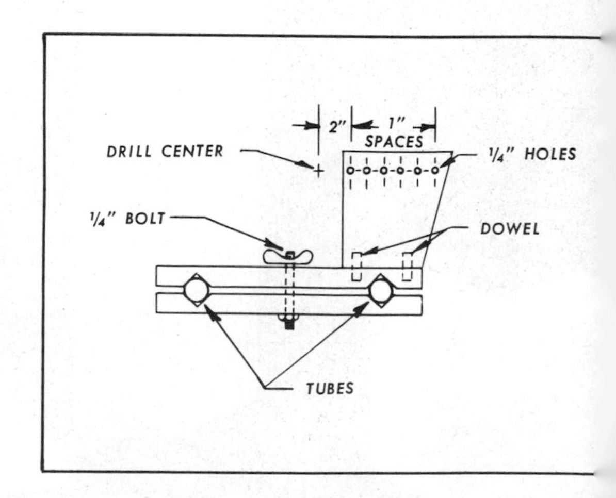

In constructing this hole-spacing jig, be sure that the V's are cut for the exact distance between the tubes.

This simple jig spaces holes automatically, a useful thing when many similar holes are to be drilled.

used has a short length of ½″ dowel attached to one end. Therefore the same pin can be used to space ¼″ and ½″ holes. Make additional pins to engage ⅜″, ⅝″, ¾″ and 1″ holes.

Dowel joints should be formed so that the

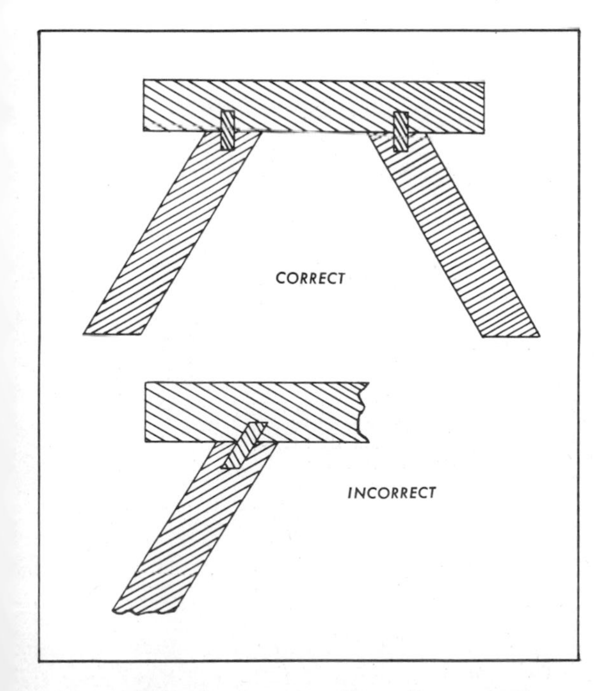

Dowels should enter at right angles to surfaces.

Varied guides adapt jig to holes of any size.

pins enter at right angles to the mating surfaces (sketch at lower left).

Miter joints are often strengthened with dowels. Here the work can be positioned on the table with the miter gauge. When the work is short enough, as with small picture frames, the fence and a stop block can be used to set the work for drilling, which elimi-

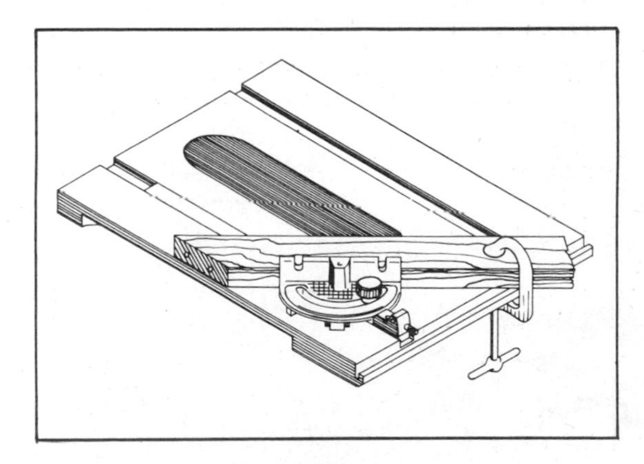

When drilling dowel holes in a miter cut, use miter gauge to position work and a clamp to hold the work firmly on the table.

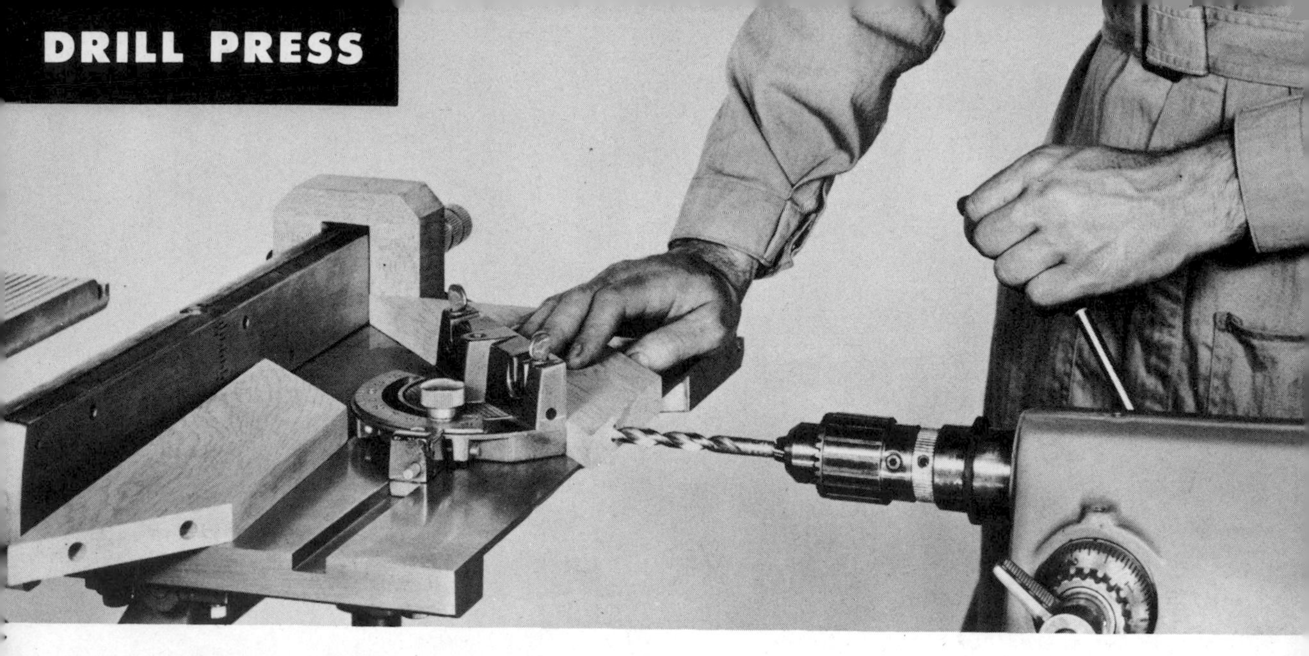

If stock is small enough, you can use the miter gauge, the rip fence, and a stop block to create a setup like this. It puts each piece automatically into position for drilling.

The pegged joint detailed at the right is an excellent drawer joint. It has the strength of the dovetail but is much easier to make.

Curved segments can also be joined by doweling. For accurate drilling they require a special setup like the one sketched here. It uses a block shaped to fit the segment.

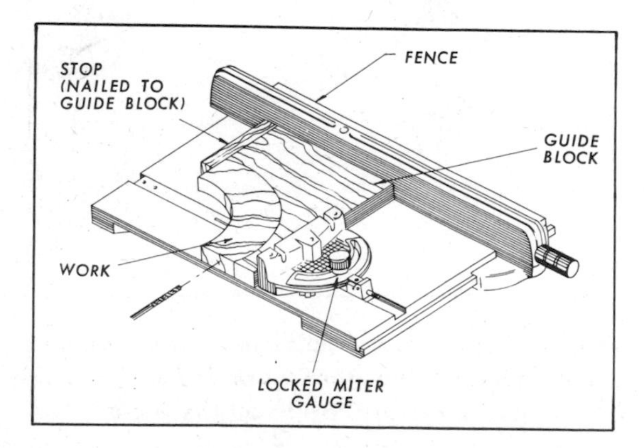

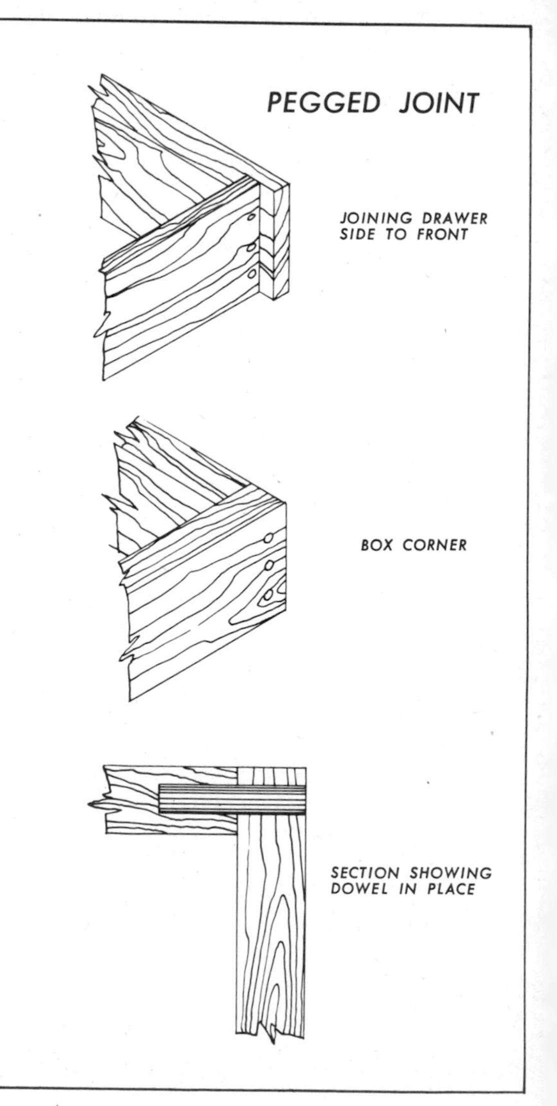

nates the need to clamp the work (as pictured at left).

Curved segments are drilled in a similar manner, as shown at lower left on opposite page, but require a block shaped to fit the part. If the block is clamped to the table, the work is automatically positioned and held for drilling and may be turned end for end—if holes are needed in each end of the piece.

The pegged joint (left) is an excellent drawer joint with the strength characteristics of the dovetail, but much easier to make. It is made with the multi-purpose tool in its horizontal position.

The drawer front, positioned by the miter gauge and backed up by the rip fence, is placed face down on the table. Table height is adjusted for hole edge distance. The setup thus created automatically locates all holes drilled on a common center line. Therefore it is unnecessary to drill exactly in the center of the stock. Depth of hole is controlled by predetermining quill extension and setting the automatic stops. Hold the side of the drawer in place and drill a hole through both pieces at once. Slip a dowel peg in the drilled hole to hold parts together for subsequent drilling. The photographs at the right show these steps.

When a drawer is pulled out, its entire weight and that of its contents place a heavy strain where the sides of the drawer are

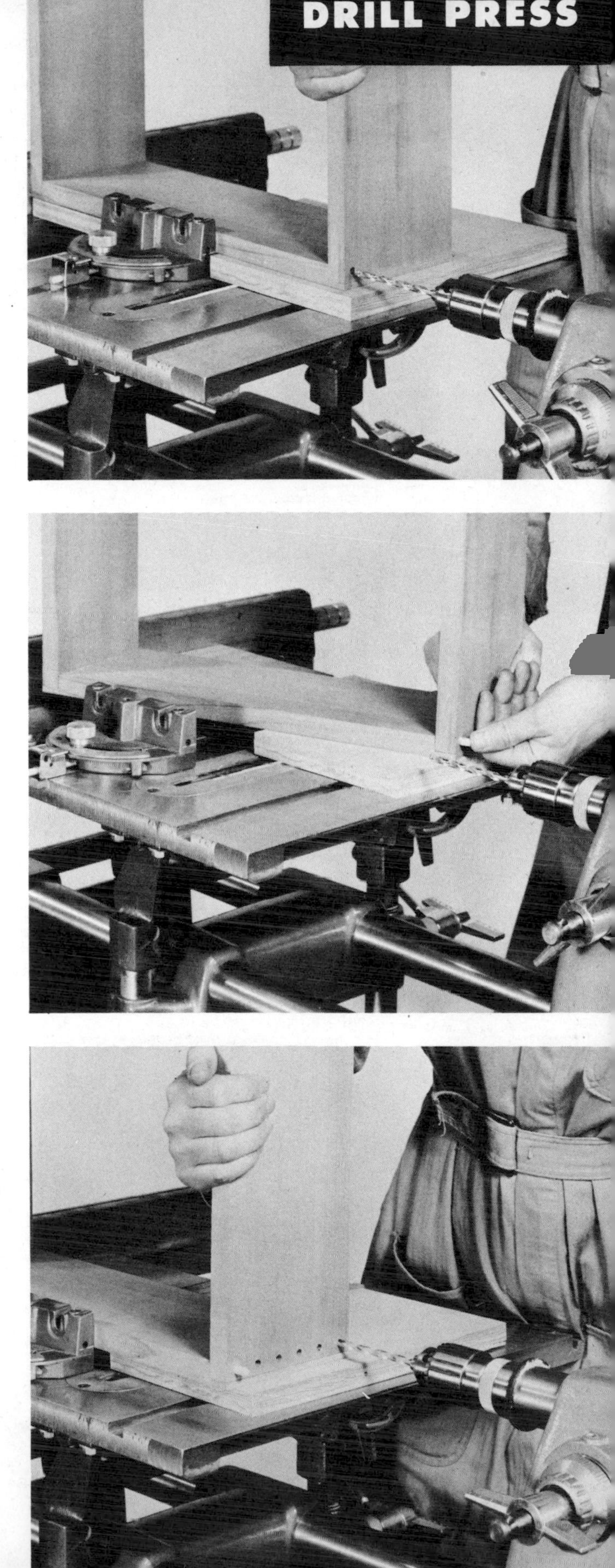

To make a pegged joint in a drawer front, begin (top photograph) by holding the side of the drawer against the drawer front, which is down on the table. Then drill the first hole.

Middle photograph: Insert a dowel in the first hole drilled, so pieces will be held in correct alignment for subsequent drilling.

Then continue the drilling with accuracy assured (photograph at bottom right).

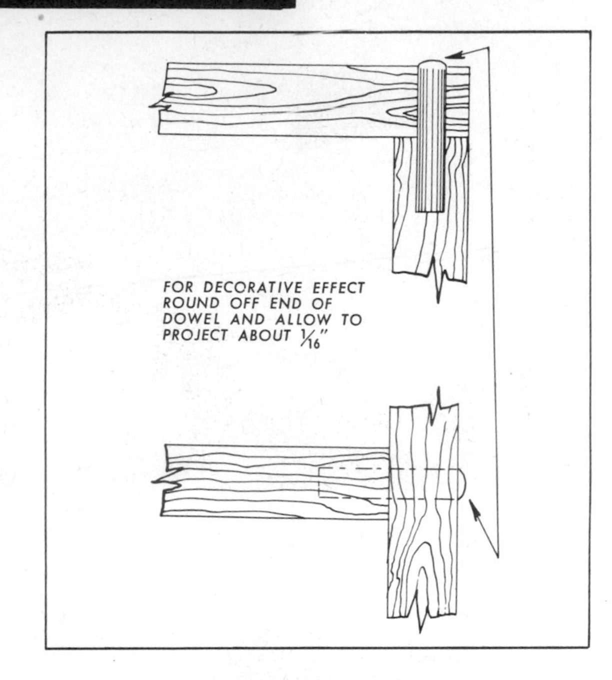

To use dowel pegs as a design detail, round them off and let them project slightly. Or sand them flush with surface of work.

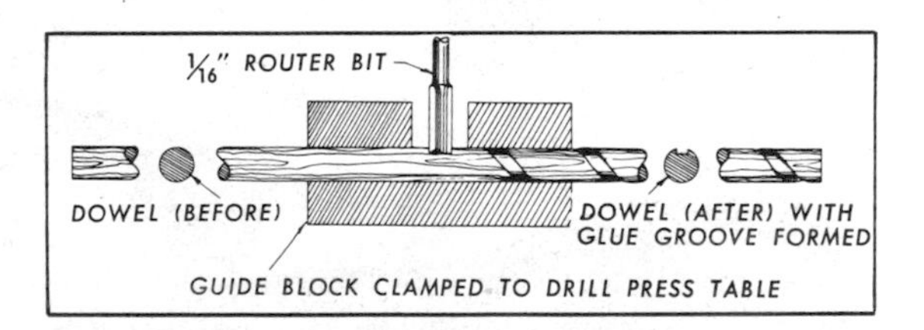

You can form spiral grooves in dowels as shown in the detail above and photograph below.

joined to the front. The pegged joint, like the dovetail, is ideal for this use, since it provides the strength needed. Naturally, pegged joints need not be limited to drawer fronts. They are applicable on any box structure. Exposed dowel pegs (left) can be used as a design detail. For further emphasis, make them of a contrasting wood.

If dowels are to hold with maximum strength, they must be a press fit in the holes. This makes it necessary to allow room for the glue used in the joint and to provide an escape route for excess glue. If the dowel is a tight fit and no provision is made for the glue, the work might split when the dowel is driven into the hole or when the work is clamped together. Sometimes excess glue is forced through the grain of the wood until it emerges on the surface of the work. Therefore glue grooves are formed in the dowel before it is cut up into the lengths required.

A simple setup for forming the grooves is shown at left and below. The block is drilled to fit the dowel being grooved, and another hole is drilled for the router bit. This hole should be larger than the bit to provide for chip clearance. Run the drill at high speed

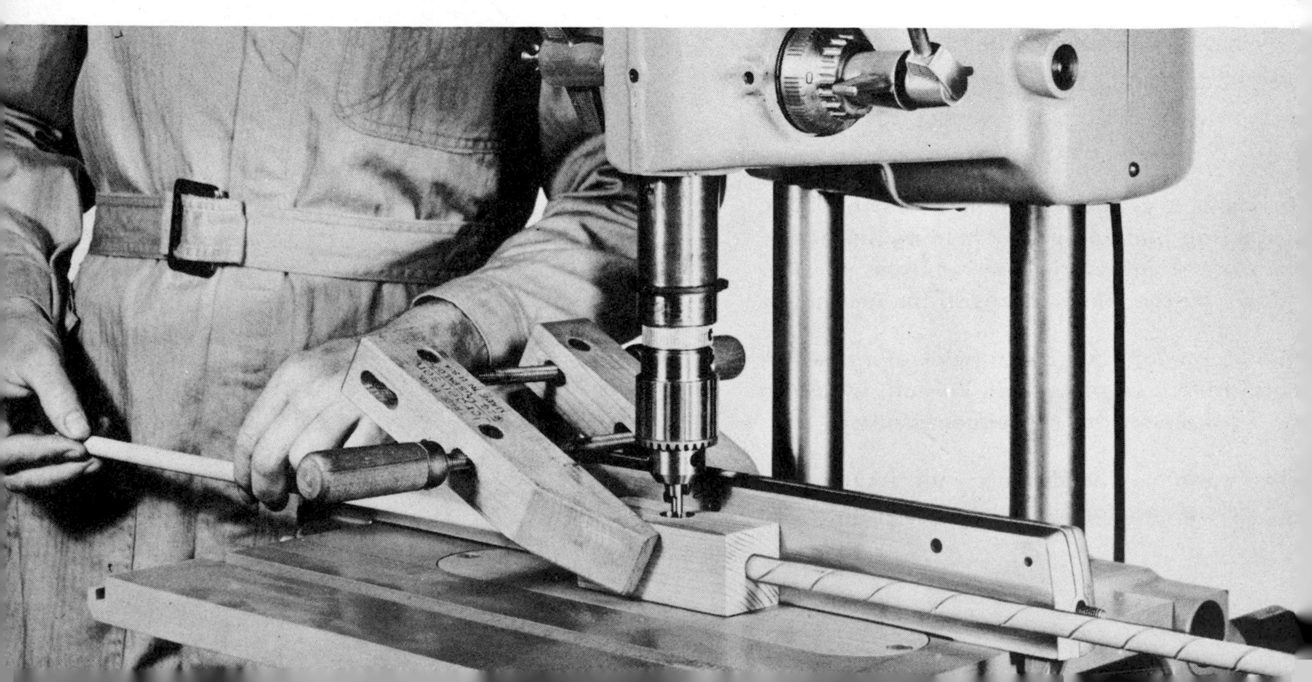

and rotate the dowel as you push it slowly through the block. Dowel pins should be about 1/16" shorter than the full depth of the hole and should be chamfered at both ends.

The plug cutter can be used to form dowels to lengths within the capacities of the tool. The grain of the wood has to be parallel to the length of the dowel, as in the photograph at the right. After the dowels are formed they are cut free on the table saw. In this way dowel pins can often be cut to the exact size needed. It's a good use for scrap blocks.

One other type of dowel joint widely used by commercial furniture manufacturers is the integrate dowel, formed at the ends of round or square bracing members.

With the setup shown below, the operation is simple, fast, and accurate. The ends of the workpieces are first shaped on the table saw to form tenons. These are shaped into dowels by the plug cutter.

On small work, kerfs are cut on the four sides of the work to match the depth of cut needed to form the dowel. The plug cutter then forms the dowel and removes waste material at the same time.

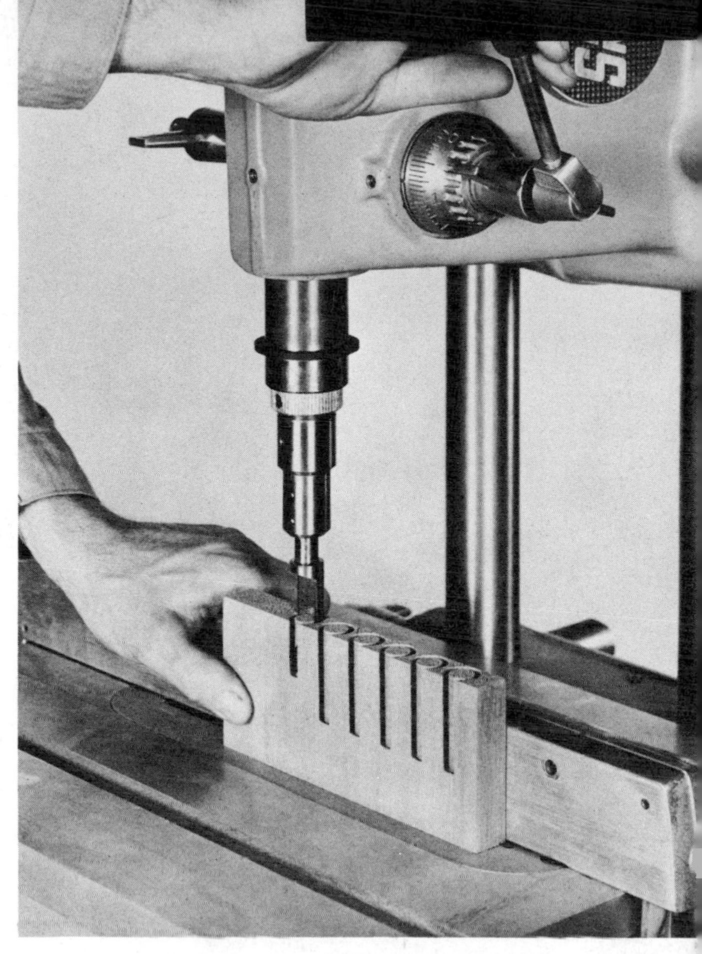

The plug-cutter can be used to form dowel to lengths within the capacity of the tool; this is useful when you need pegs of a wood not readily available in dowel form.

Pictures below show how plug cutter is used to form integrate dowel at end of stock.

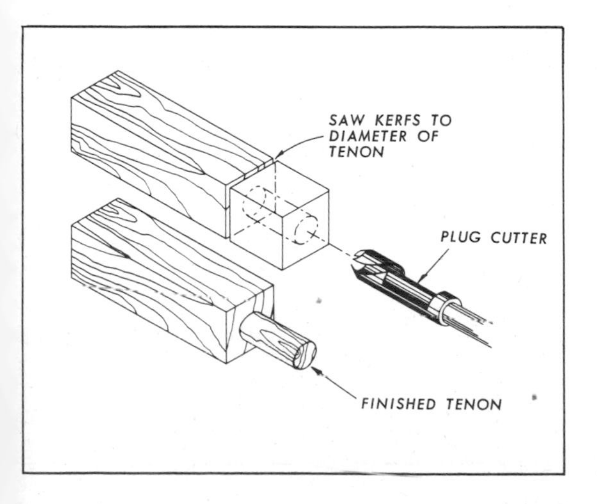

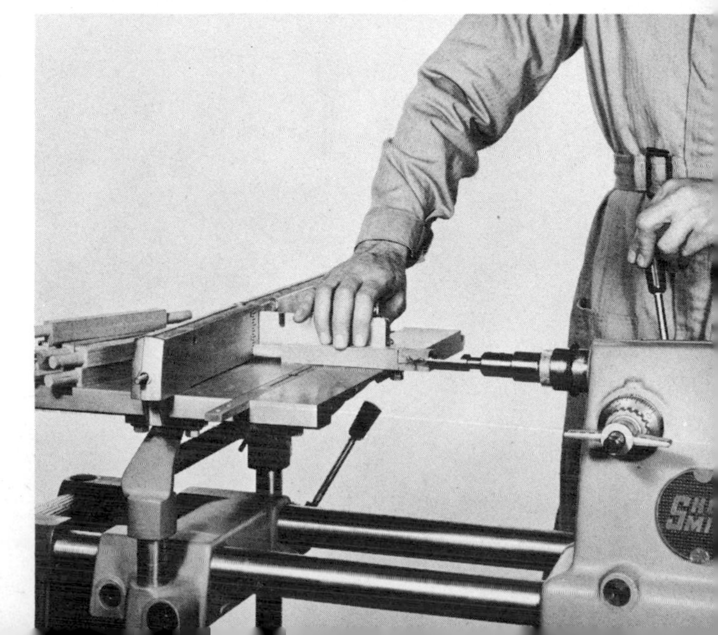

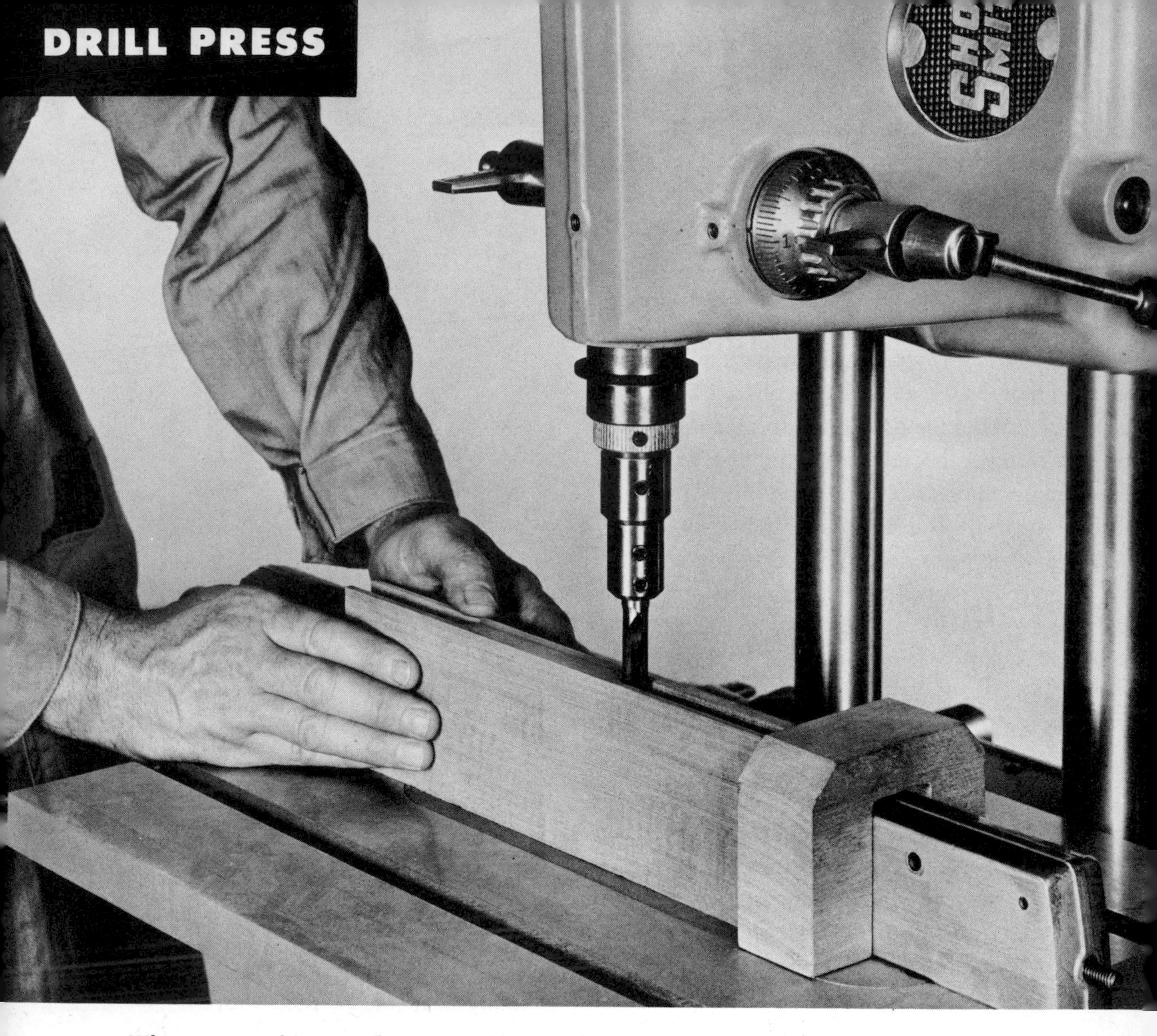

A round-end mortise may be cut with a router bit. If it's deep, take several passes.

When a router bit is used to cut a rabbet on the edge of a board, as below, use an auxiliary fence between the work and the regular fence.

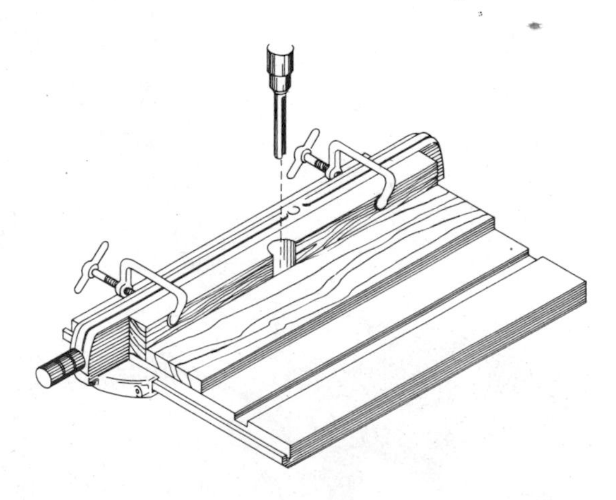

Edge grooves in short or long stock can be formed with a router bit. Diagram shows machine in horizontal position.

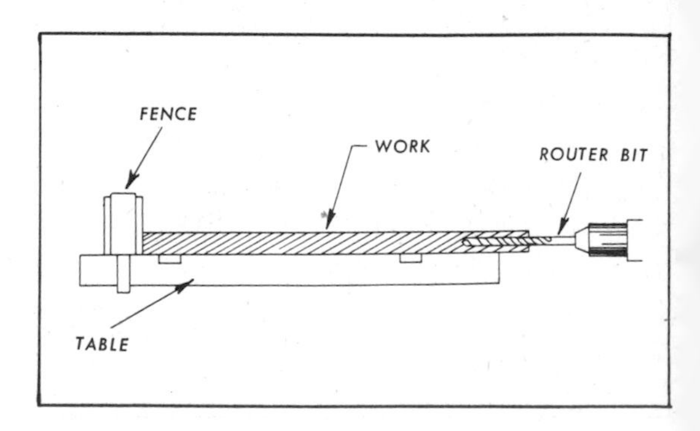

Routing

Routing is done with router bits secured to the spindle with special chucks. It is done at high speeds and always with the pass against the direction of rotation of the bit.

One example of the use of router bits is shown in the photograph at the left. Here a round-end mortise, previously described as being formed with ordinary drills, is being cut to take a round-end tenon. The fence is used as a guide, with a stop block clamped to it to control the length of the slot. The quill is locked to maintain the depth of cut. Deep cuts should be made in several passes, depressing the quill after each pass until the full depth of cut has been attained.

Router bits are often used to cut rabbets on board edges. This operation calls for the auxiliary fence sketched at lower left. The cutout permits the tool to rotate outside the edge of the workpiece. The fence is adjusted for the width of the cut, while the depth control dial is set and the quill locked in position to maintain the depth of the cut.

Always keep the work pressed firmly against the fence and move it slowly against the cutting tool.

When using fences, it is a good idea to remember that when the fence is behind the tool, the pass is made from left to right; if the fence is in front of the tool, the pass is made from right to left.

Edge grooves in long or short work are formed by the methods described for cutting dovetails or by using the machine in the horizontal position. This is diagrammed at lower right on the opposite page.

Some methods of routing grooves in curved or round work are shown on this page. In each case a guide block is clamped to the table and positioned to make the cut where needed. If the work is jigsawed carefully, the waste stock frequently can be used as the guide for the work.

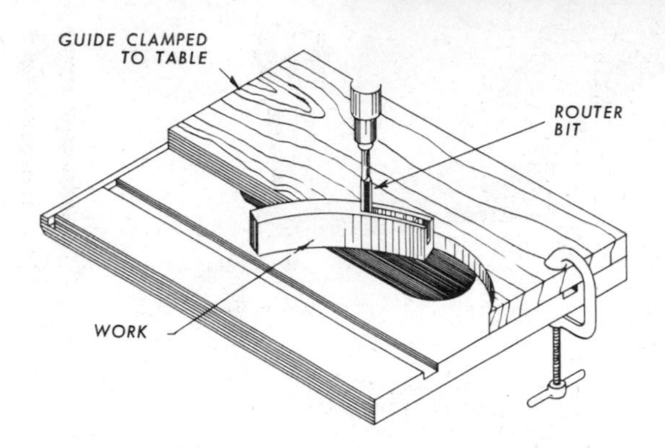

With template to guide cut, you can use router bit to cut groove in a curved segment.

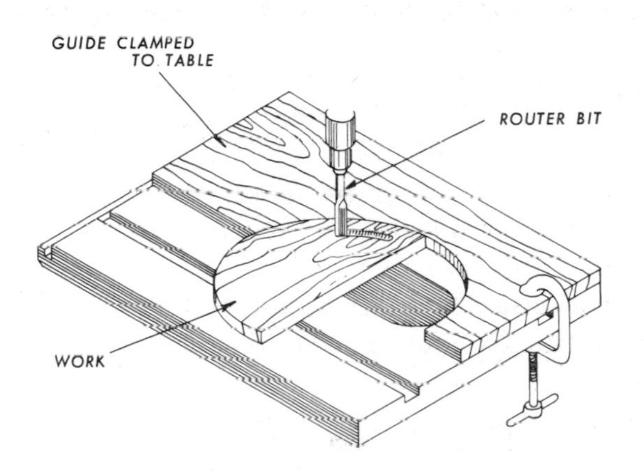

Surface grooves in circular or curved work call for a template clamped to the table.

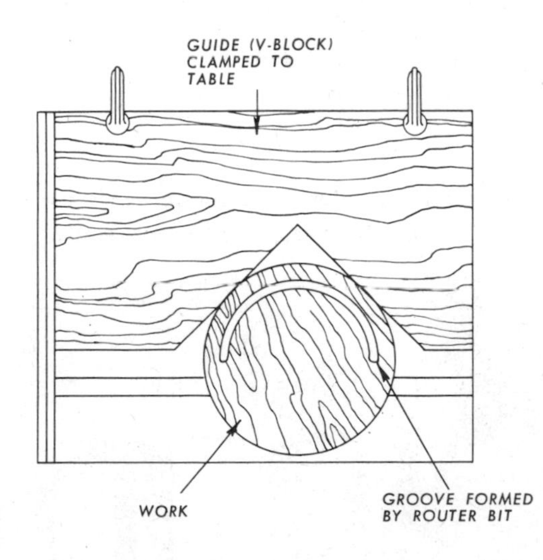

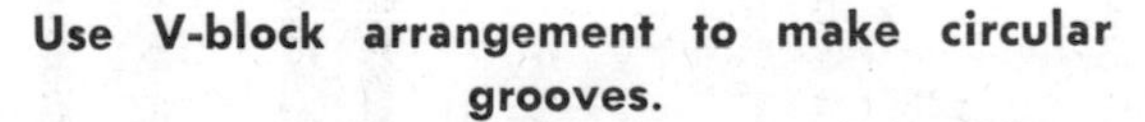

Use V-block arrangement to make circular grooves.

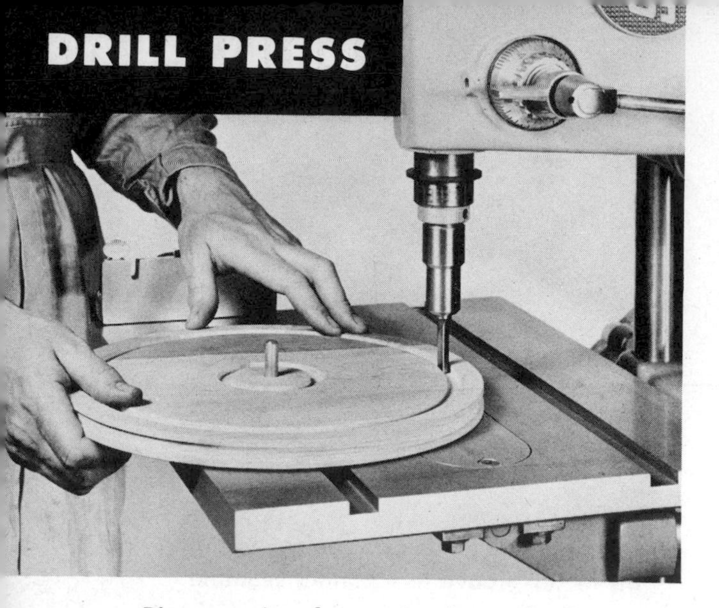

Pivot routing forms circular surface grooves.

A simple setup for routing grooves in circular work uses the miter gauge as a pivot. A hole for a pin is drilled and tapped in the free end of the miter gauge; or if a hole is already available (the miter gauge of the multi-purpose tool provides a hole for the Universal Hold Down) a suitable pin can be drilled and tapped and held in place with the countersunk screw used to hold the vertical post on the hold-down. The work is then held through a center hole and rotated under the cutting tool, as shown at left. If the work does not have a center hole, use a short pin in the miter-gauge bar and a shallow hole in the underside of the work.

An easily made guard that can be used when routing is shown in the photograph at lower left, which also illustrates the use of the pivot when routing grooves of small diameter. The miter gauge is used in the slot closer to the ways. The distance from the center of the work to the groove being cut can be adjusted by moving the table or by fixing the position of the miter gauge in relation to the spindle center.

Edge grooves in circular work are formed by using the machine in either a vertical (below) or a horizontal position. In either case, the work is positioned by adjusting the table. Keep the work flat against the table and revolve it clockwise against the cutting tool.

Pattern routing is shown and described on the opposite page.

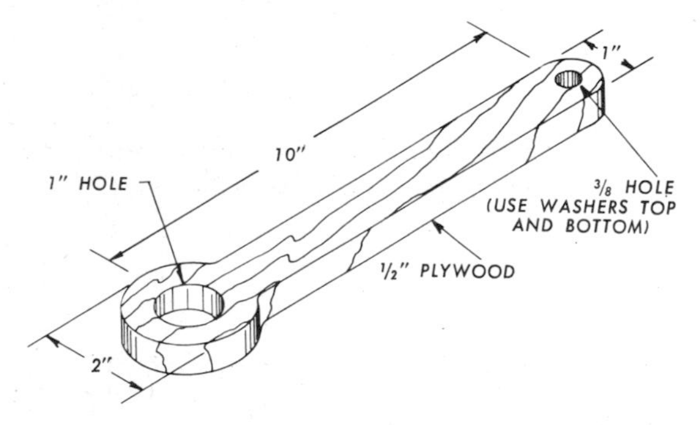

This guard is held by a longer bolt used in place of the table-positioning screw.

The pivot arrangement can be used to form edge grooves in circular pieces.

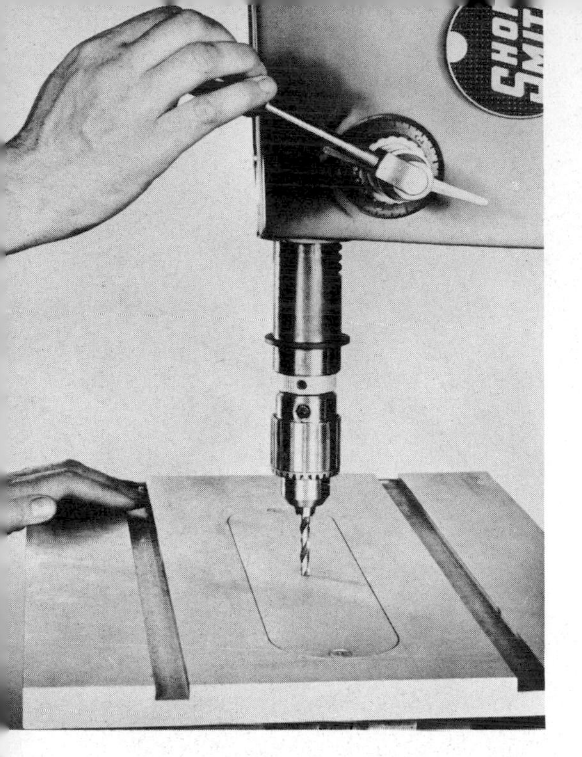

Pattern routing is a way of cutting through a piece, or recessing its surface, by attaching a pattern to its underside. The pattern rides a guide pin fitted into a hole made in a no-slot insert by drilling it in the press as in the photograph above.

As shown at upper right, this method insures perfect alignment with the router bit.

The drawing at the right shows how the system works. Diameter of the insert guide pin should match that of the router bit used.

The patterns—of plywood or hardboard—may be attached to the work with short flathead wood screws. Or screws may be put into the pattern so they stick up just enough (about 1/16") to provide points onto which the work may be pressed and held. Photograph below shows the underside of such an arrangement . . .

. . . and the picture at the lower right shows the completion of a routing job in which this pattern is being used.

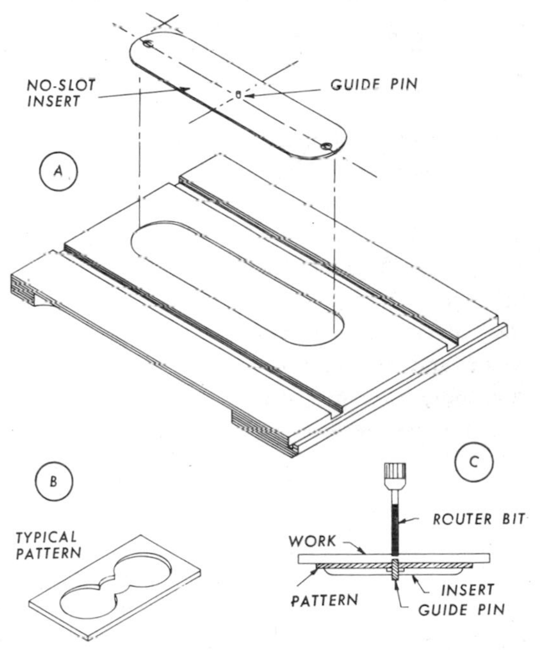

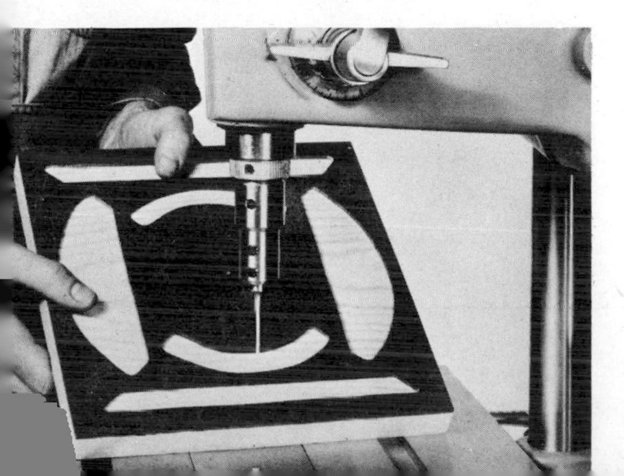

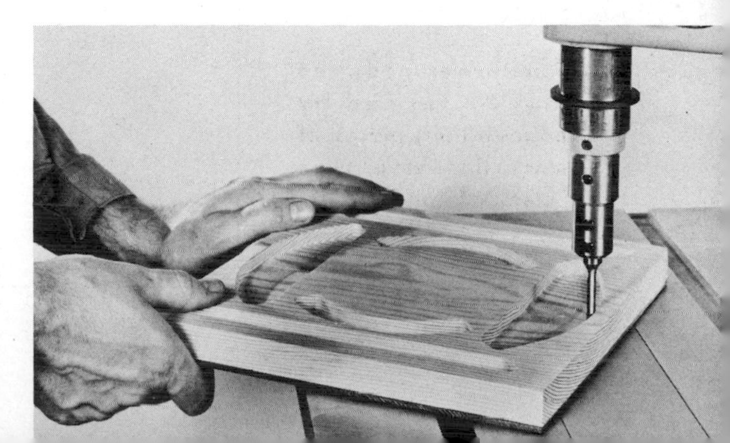

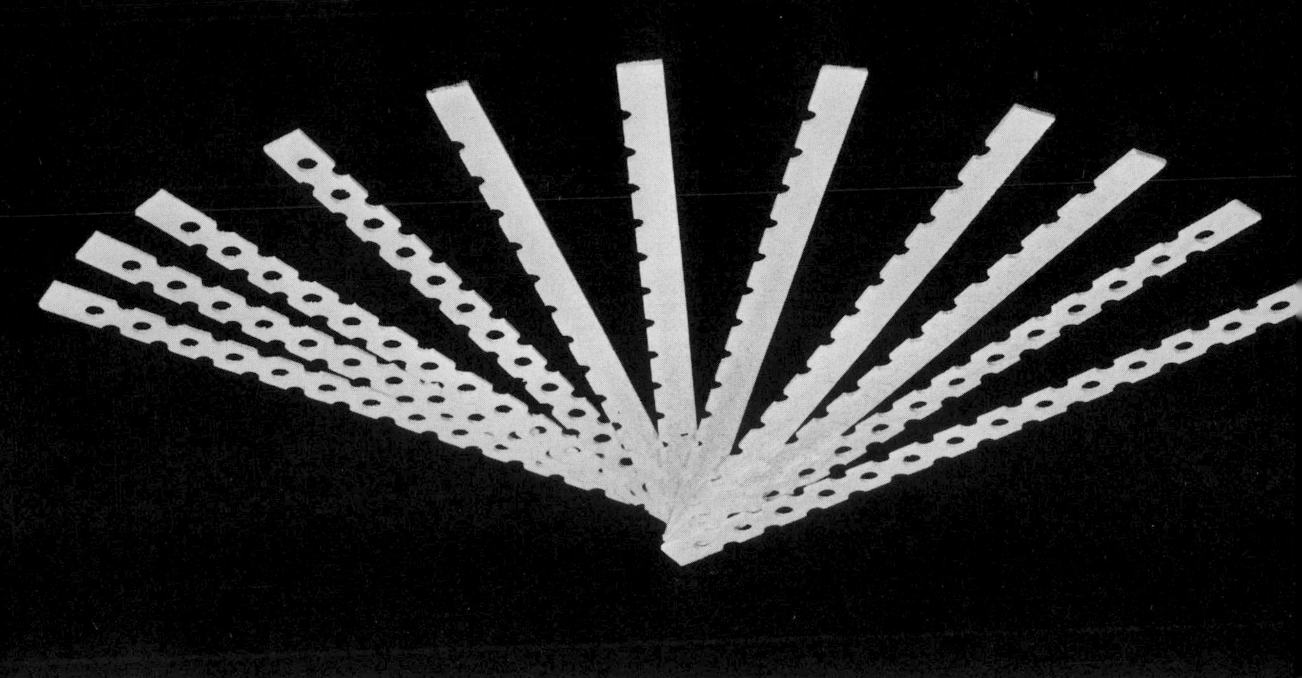

Drilling Moldings

Special moldings of the sort shown above can be made by edge-drilling pieces clamped together as indicated at the right. After drilling, the pieces are separated and strip-cut on the table saw to form the moldings.

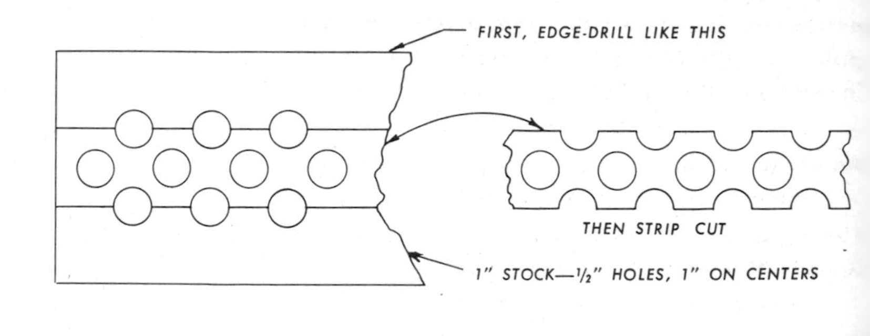
FIRST, EDGE-DRILL LIKE THIS
THEN STRIP CUT
1" STOCK—½" HOLES, 1" ON CENTERS

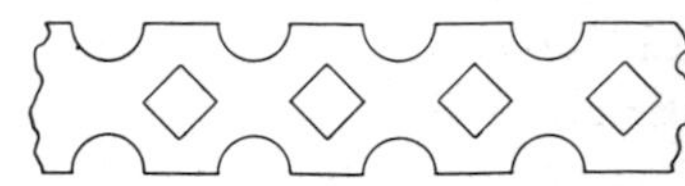

VARIATIONS USING MORTISING CHISELS AND BITS

NOTE:
DESIGNS ARE VARIED BY DRILLING DIFFERENT SIZE HOLES AND USING DIFFERENT SPACING.

Semicircular grooves may be formed by edge-drilling pieces of stock that have been clamped together.

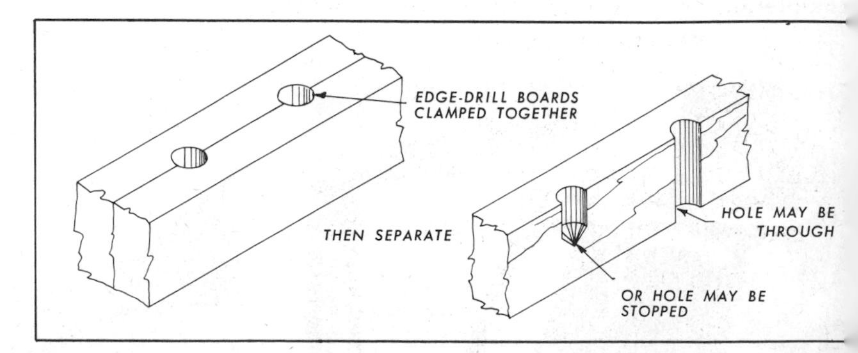
EDGE-DRILL BOARDS CLAMPED TOGETHER
THEN SEPARATE
HOLE MAY BE THROUGH
OR HOLE MAY BE STOPPED

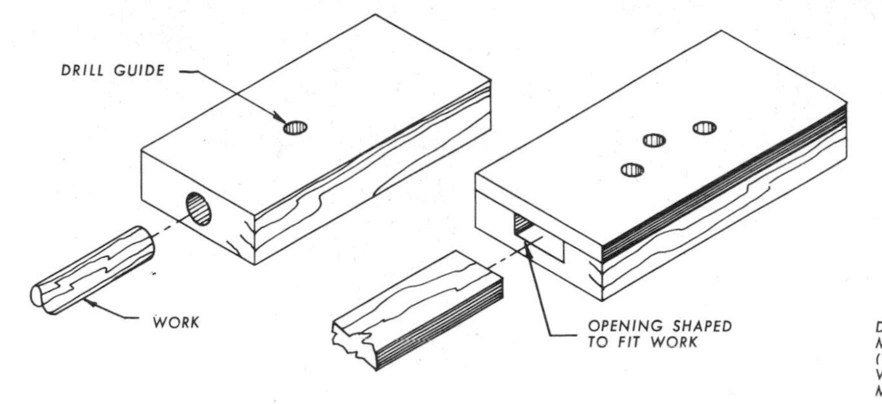

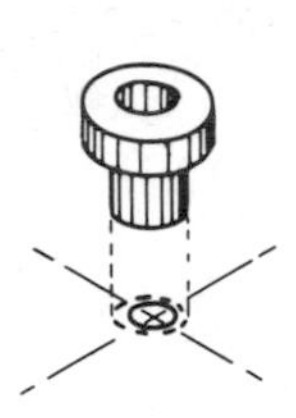

Simple jigs like these will assure accuracy of holes drilled in duplicate pieces.

Drill Jigs

Home craftsmen who manufacture projects in quantity can utilize simple drill jigs of the sort sketched above to speed production and increase the accuracy of hole locations in similar pieces. The jigs must be designed to fit the problem at hand. Quite often it is possible to use the miter gauge, fence, and stop blocks to form drill fixtures. When drill blocks are used, they should be clamped firmly to the fence. Once the setup is made, any number of similar pieces can be drilled accurately and fast as illustrated below.

Once the setup is made, any number of similar pieces can be drilled accurately and fast.

SHOP SMITH

A pivot arrangement simplifies drilling holes around a circumference.

An indexing device positions the work for drilling radial and surface holes.

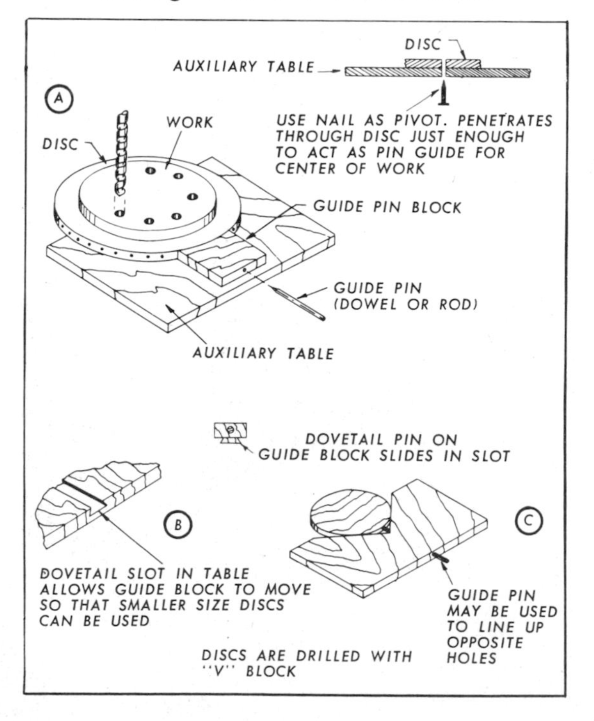
DISC
AUXILIARY TABLE
A
WORK
DISC
USE NAIL AS PIVOT. PENETRATES THROUGH DISC JUST ENOUGH TO ACT AS PIN GUIDE FOR CENTER OF WORK
GUIDE PIN BLOCK
GUIDE PIN (DOWEL OR ROD)
AUXILIARY TABLE
DOVETAIL PIN ON GUIDE BLOCK SLIDES IN SLOT
B
C
DOVETAIL SLOT IN TABLE ALLOWS GUIDE BLOCK TO MOVE SO THAT SMALLER SIZE DISCS CAN BE USED
GUIDE PIN MAY BE USED TO LINE UP OPPOSITE HOLES
DISCS ARE DRILLED WITH "V" BLOCK

Indexing

When radial holes or surface holes must be drilled around a circumference, the miter-gauge arrangement above is often used. The pin may extend through the work or merely be seated in a shallow hole drilled in the underside of it. This method locates the holes in relation to the center of the work, but spacing them equally is a matter of hand layout which requires time and care.

A better way is to make the indexing device sketched at the left. It can be used to hold the work and automatically space the holes.

If the work will vary enough in size to warrant it, the guide-pin block can be made variable by using the dovetail-slot arrangement shown at B. This will permit using various-size wheels, within limits set by the size of the platform.

The holes in the wheel must be drilled accurately. You can use the pivot idea, centering the holes with lines drawn on the surface of the stock, or you can use a V-block and pin (C) to line up opposite holes.

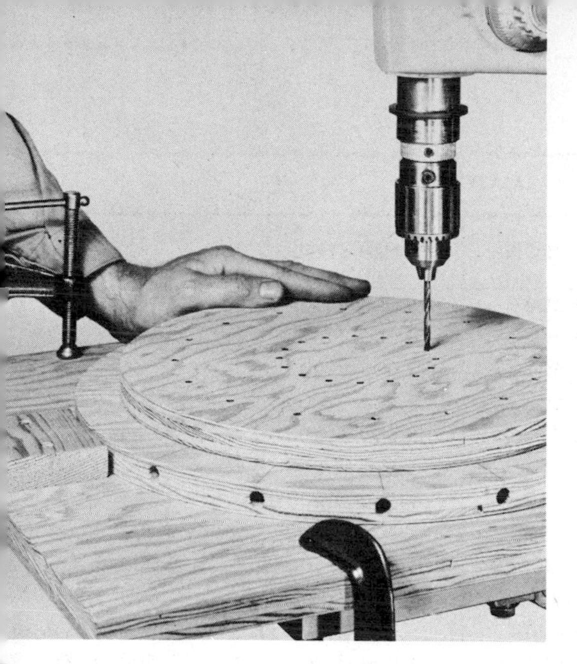

Indexing device may be used vertically for drilling surface holes on a circumference . . .

Use of the indexing device for drilling surface holes and radial holes is shown above and below. Depth of holes is controlled by the depth dial.

When surface holes must be made through the workpiece, use the indexing device to locate pilot holes, which are drilled halfway through the work. Then remove the work from the indexing wheel and open up the pilot holes to full size.

. . or in a horizontal position, for drilling radial holes around a circumference.

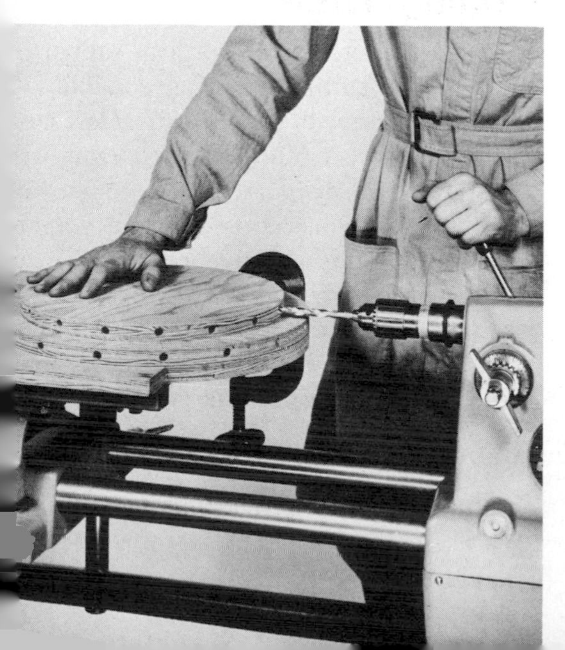

Drilling Large Holes

When extra-large holes are needed that are beyond the capacity of non-adjustable cutters, a fly cutter is usually used. One is shown in the photograph below. Such a cutter is operated at slow speeds and always with the work clamped securely to the drill-press table. Keep hands clear and feed the tool slowly. Excessive pressure on the feed lever will cause the cutting edge of the bit to bind in the groove and the chuck may spin on the shank of the tool.

Most cutters of this type require a center hole to position the tool. If a blank is to be cut which does not call for a center hole, the cutting tool may be fixed to strike the work before the pilot does. Here, especially, the speed must be slow, and the pressure on the feed lever very light.

Use a fly cutter to make extra-large holes. Be sure speed is correct, work firmly clamped.

DRILL SIZE, INCHES	MATERIAL			
	SOFT METALS	SOFT CAST IRON	MILD STEEL	PLASTICS AND HARD RUBBER
1/16	6,000–6,500	6,000–6,500	5,000–6,500	6,000–6,500
3/32	6,000–6,500	4,500–5,500	4,000–5,000	6,000–6,500
1/8	6,000–6,500	3,500–4,500	3,000–4,000	5,000–6,000
5/32	5,000–6,000	3,000–3,500	2,500–3,000	4,000–5,000
3/16	5,000–6,000	2,500–3,000	2,000–2,500	3,500–4,000
7/32	4,500–5,000	2,000–2,500	2,000–2,500	3,000–3,500
1/4	4,500–5,000	2,000–2,500	1,500–2,000	3,000–3,500
9/32	4,000–4,500	1,500–2,000	1,500–2,000	2,500–3,000
5/16	3,500–4,000	1,500–2,000	1,000–1,500	2,000–2,500
11/32	3,000–3,500	1,500–2,000	1,000–1,500	2,000–2,500
3/8	3,000–3,500	1,500–2,000	1,000–1,500	1,500–2,000
13/32	2,500–3,000	1,500–2,000	1,000–1,500	1,500–2,000
7/16	2,500–3,000	1,000–1,500	400–1,000	1,500–2,000
15/32	2,000–2,500	1,000–1,500	400–1,000	1,500–2,000
1/2	2,000–2,500	1,000–1,500	400–1,000	1,000–1,500
9/16	1,500–2,000			1,000–1,500
5/8	1,500–2,000			1,000–1,500
11/16	1,500–2,000			1,000–1,500
3/4	1,500–2,000			400–1,000
FEED	Medium	Medium	Heavy	Light
LUBRICANT	Dry or paraffin oil	Dry	Lard oil	Dry

Stay as close as possible to these speeds whe[n] drilling metals with high-speed drills. Redu[ce] speeds about 40 per cent for carbon-ste[el] drills.

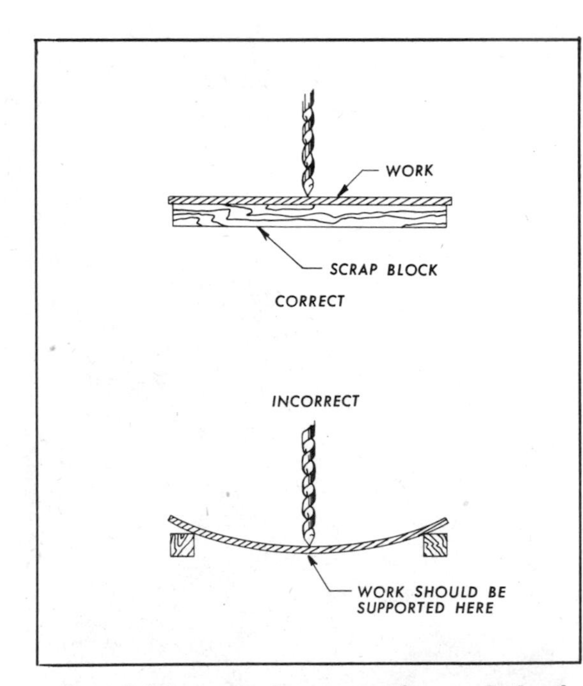

When drilling metal support the work firmly and as close as possible to the cutting tool.

Drilling Metals

Metal drilling requires a firm support, close to the cutting point as possible. T "right" technique in the drawing at left sho the scrap-block method of supporting wo on a table that does not have a center ho The "wrong" illustration shows a comm error that results in drill breakage becau of the spring created in the work by t pressure of the drill. Use of parallel suppo is good practice, but they should be plac closer together to provide support close the pressure area.

The general rule is: Keep work clamp at all times or else provide stops so the tw

FRACTION	NO.	DECIMAL	FRACTION	NO.	DECIMAL	FRACTION	NO.	DECIMAL	FRACTION	LETTER	DECIMAL
	80	.0135	3/32		.0937		5	.2055	13/32		.4062
	79	.0145		41	.0960		4	.2090		Z	.4130
1/64		.0156		40	.0980		3	.2130	27/64		.4219
	78	.0160		39	.0995	7/32		.2187	7/16		.4375
	77	.0180		38	.1015		2	.2210	29/64		.4531
	76	.0200		37	.1040		1	.2280	15/32		.4687
	75	.0210		36	.1065				31/64		.4844
	74	.0225	7/64		.1094	FRACTION	LETTER	DECIMAL	1/2		.5000
	73	.0240		35	.1100				33/64		.5156
	72	.0250		34	.1110		A	.2340	17/32		.5312
	71	.0260		33	.1130	15/64		.2344	35/64		.5469
	70	.0280		32	.1160		B	.2380	9/16		.5625
	69	.0292		31	.1200		C	.2420	37/64		.5781
	68	.0310	1/8		.1250		D	.2460	19/32		.5937
1/32		.0312		30	.1285	1/4	E	.2500	39/64		.6094
	67	.0320		29	.1360		F	.2570	5/8		.6250
	66	.0330		28	.1405		G	.2610	41/64		.6406
	65	.0350	9/64		.1406	17/64		.2656	21/32		.6562
	64	.0360		27	.1440		H	.2660	43/64		.6719
	63	.0370		26	.1470		I	.2720	11/16		.6875
	62	.0380		25	.1495		J	.2770	45/64		.7031
	61	.0390		24	.1520		K	.2810	23/32		.7187
	60	.0400		23	.1540	9/32		.2812	47/64		.7344
	59	.0410	5/32		.1562		L	.2900	3/4		.7500
	58	.0420		22	.1570		M	.2950	49/64		.7656
	57	.0430		21	.1590	19/64		.2969	25/32		.7812
	56	.0465		20	.1610		N	.3020	51/64		.7969
3/64		.0469		19	.1660	5/16		.3125	13/16		.8125
	55	.0520		18	.1695		O	.3160	53/64		.8281
	54	.0550	11/64		.1719		P	.3230	27/32		.8437
	53	.0595		17	.1730	21/64		.3281	55/64		.8594
1/16		.0625		16	.1770		Q	.3320	7/8		.8750
	52	.0635		15	.1800		R	.3390	57/64		.8906
	51	.0670		14	.1820	11/32		.3437	29/32		.9062
	50	.0700		13	.1850		S	.3480	59/64		.9219
	49	.0730	3/16		.1875		T	.3580	15/16		.9375
	48	.0760		12	.1890	23/64		.3594	61/64		.9531
5/64		.0781		11	.1910		U	.3680	31/32		.9687
	47	.0785		10	.1935	3/8		.3750	63/64		.9844
	46	.0810		9	.1960		V	.3770	1		1.0000
	45	.0820		8	.1990		W	.3860			
	44	.0860		7	.2010	25/64		.3906			
	43	.0890	13/64		.2031		X	.3970			
	42	.0935		6	.2040		Y	.4040			

This chart gives decimal equivalents of fractional, letter, or number drill sizes.

developed by the drill as it breaks through the work will not jerk the metal out of your hands.

Operating speeds vary with the type of drill, its size, and the material being worked on. The table shown on the left-hand page is satisfactory for most types of metalworking done in the home shop. When the speed recommended is not available, run the press at the closest speed possible. The "feed" refers to the amount of force used on the quill feed lever.

The chart above will be handy when you don't have the exact drill size called for in a drawing. If the plan calls for a 3/32" drill, the chart tells you that a No. 42 comes close to being the size required and will do an adequate job except when tolerances are extremely tight.

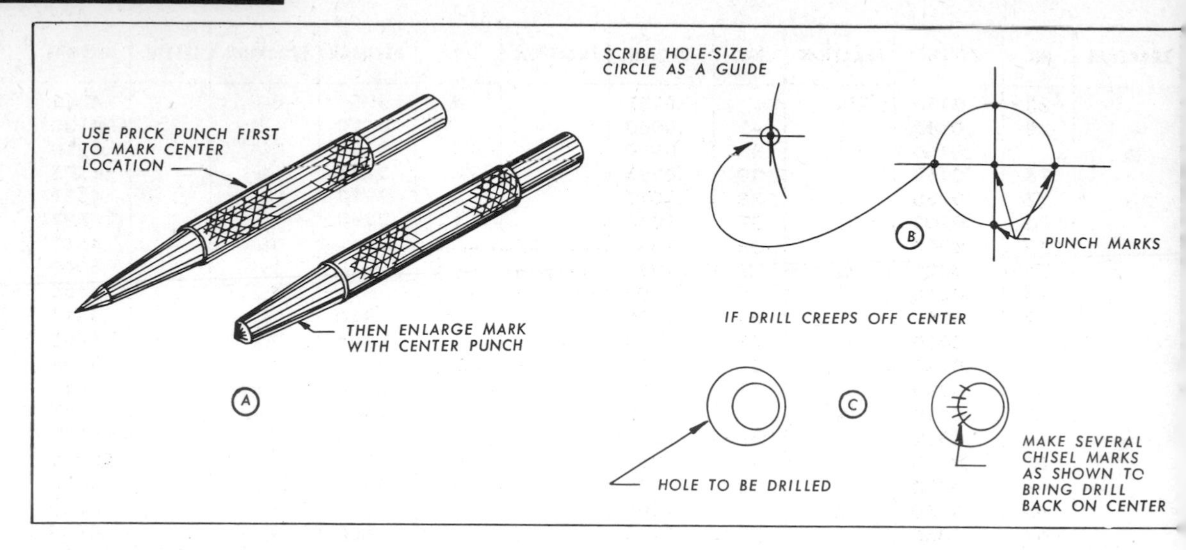
SCRIBE HOLE-SIZE
CIRCLE AS A GUIDE
USE PRICK PUNCH FIRST
TO MARK CENTER
LOCATION
PUNCH MARKS
B
THEN ENLARGE MARK
WITH CENTER PUNCH
IF DRILL CREEPS OFF CENTER
A
C
HOLE TO BE DRILLED
MAKE SEVERAL
CHISEL MARKS
AS SHOWN TO
BRING DRILL
BACK ON CENTER

Always mark hole locations with a prick punch before drilling. This will accurately locate the hole and do much to prevent the drill from "walking" off-center.

Layout for Metal Drilling

A scriber is always used when marking metals. A scribe line does not show clearly enough on some metals, and a surface coater is used as indicated below to show up the line. In cases where scribe marks could harm the surface of the metal, the scribe line can be just light enough to mark the coating (removing a tiny thread of it to reveal the metal surface beneath) without harming the metal.

After the locations have been established, a prick punch is used to mark the hole centers (above). The prick punch has a slender, sharp point which is easily placed at the exact intersection of the hole-location lines. The small spot it makes is enlarged with a center punch, which forms the well needed to keep the drill in place.

Positive accuracy, especially on large holes, is assured by using the method shown in B above. After the center has been prick-punched, a circle the same size as the hole (or a bit larger) is scribed around the center mark. The scribed circle then acts as a guide that reveals any tendency of the drill to creep off center (C). When this does happen, the drill can be drawn back to the correct posi

Surface coaters are used when preparing metal for layout work. Keep scribe marks light, just heavy enough to remove coating and leave metal surface exposed.

MATERIAL	DYE
Wood	No coating required. Patterns may be rubber-cemented directly to wood or transferred with carbon paper.
Rough Metals	White or blue chalk, rubbed on surface.
Castings	Whiting (mixture: 50-50 white lead and turpentine).
Smooth Steel	Copper sulfate (2 tablespoons in 1 cup water—crystals available at drugstore or chemical house) or layout compound (purple coating, available at hardware store).
Bright Sheet Metal	Layout compound.

Keep layout dye in discarded shoe polish bottle—one with dauber which may be used to apply the dye. Apply dye evenly and smoothly on the surface of the metal.

DON'T lay ruler flat on work when marking it. Instead, hold the scale on edge, as shown . . .

. . . above, and slide the scriber point down the graduation groove and onto the work.

tion by making a series of chisel marks or prick-punch marks as shown in the detail. Nine times out of ten this technique will draw the drill back to where it should be.

Drilling a pilot hole and then enlarging it is good shop practice. Pilot holes, however, do not always keep a drill from walking off center. A little trick that helps is this: Start the hole with the full-size drill as explained, but stop just before the hole becomes full size. **Then** drill a pilot hole, which will automatically center itself in the well started by the larger drill. After the pilot hole is drilled, switch back to the full-size drill to complete the hole.

A combination square or similar tool can be used as an edge marker or marking gauge by drawing the head along the side of the work and following the edge of the blade with a scriber, as shown at left below.

Combination square or similar tool can be used with scriber as marking gauge.

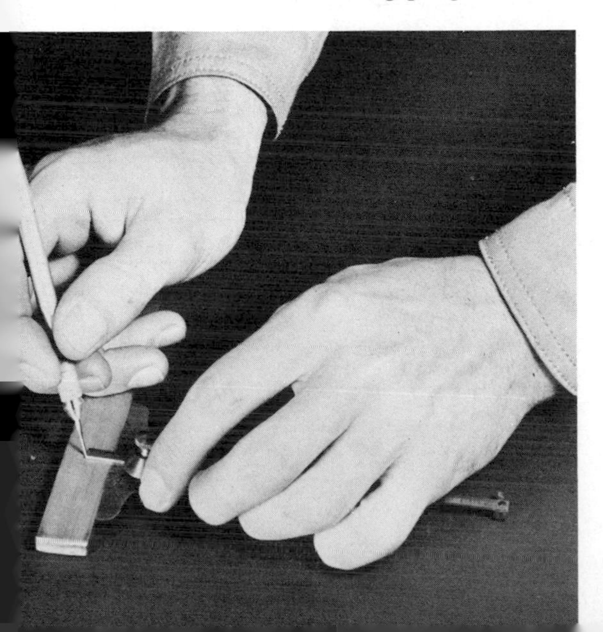

To mark for equally spaced holes, use dividers set for the required distance.

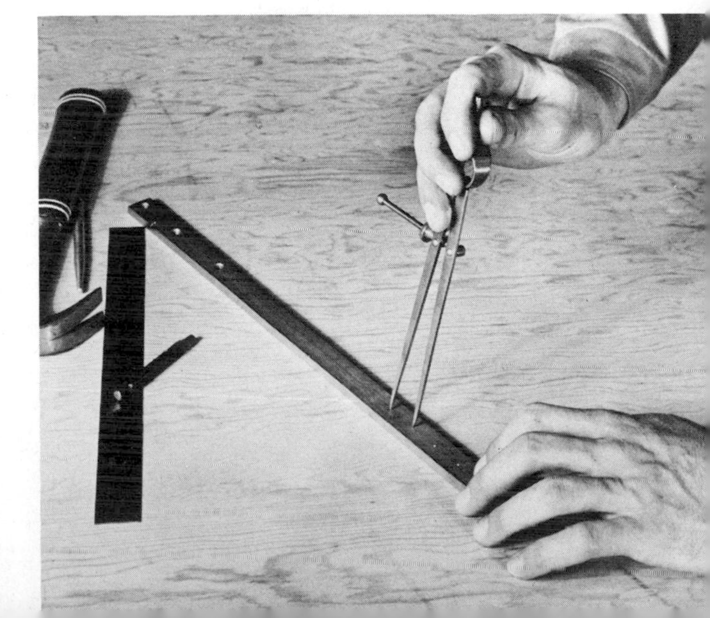

A centering pin made of sharpened drill rod will accurately locate work for drilling.

Using the Centering Pin

A sure way of locating work so the hole location is centered exactly with the drill point is to use a centering pin as shown above. The pin itself is a short piece of ⅛″ or ¼″ drill rod, sharpened to a fine point at one end. The pin is secured in the chuck and lowered so the point engages the indentation made with the prick punch. The quill is locked and the work clamped firmly to the table (below).

After the work is located the drill is locked in the chuck in place of the centering pin.

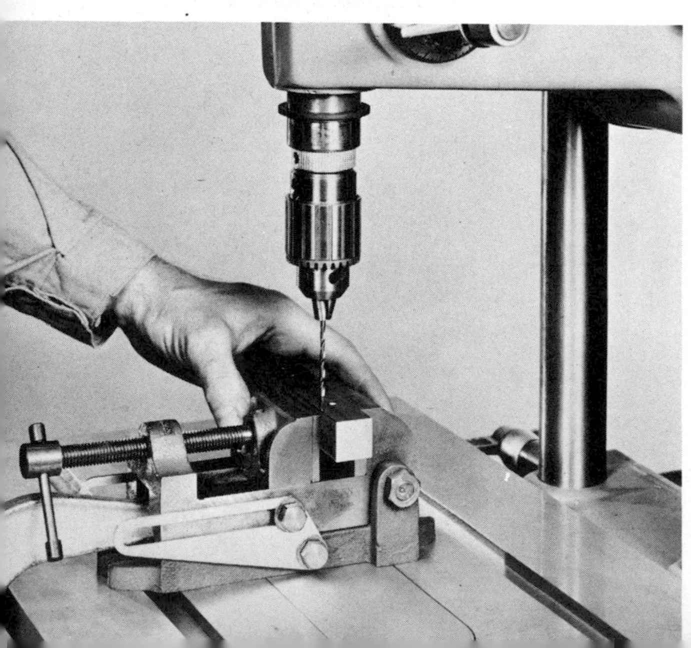

Tapping

The task of keeping a tap square to the work surface is difficult when the tapping is done by hand. The drill press can be used to overcome this difficulty. Any of the three kinds of taps, when secured in the drill chuck, will be held square to the surface of the work throughout the job.

Tap-hole sizes depend on the size of the tap and the type thread. The chart below gives this information for National Coarse and National Fine threads.

The clearance drill clears threads from a hole already tapped.

TAP			TAP DRILL		DRILL FOR CLEARANCE
NO. OR FRACTION	NC	NF	NC	NF	
0		80		3/64	51
1	64	72	53	53	47
2	56	64	50	50	42
3	48	56	47	45	37
4	40	48	43	42	31
5	40	44	38	37	29
6	32	40	36	33	26
8	32	36	29	29	17
10	24	32	25	21	8
12	24	28	16	14	1
1/4	20	28	7	3	Same as tap
5/16	18	24	F	I	Same as tap
3/8	16	24	5/16	Q	Same as tap
7/16	14	20	U	25/64	Same as tap
1/2	13	20	27/64	29/64	Same as tap
9/16	12	18	31/64	33/64	Same as tap
5/8	11	18	17/32	37/64	Same as tap
3/4	10	16	21/32	11/16	Same as tap
7/8	9	14	49/64	13/16	Same as tap
1″	8	14	7/8	15/16	Same as tap

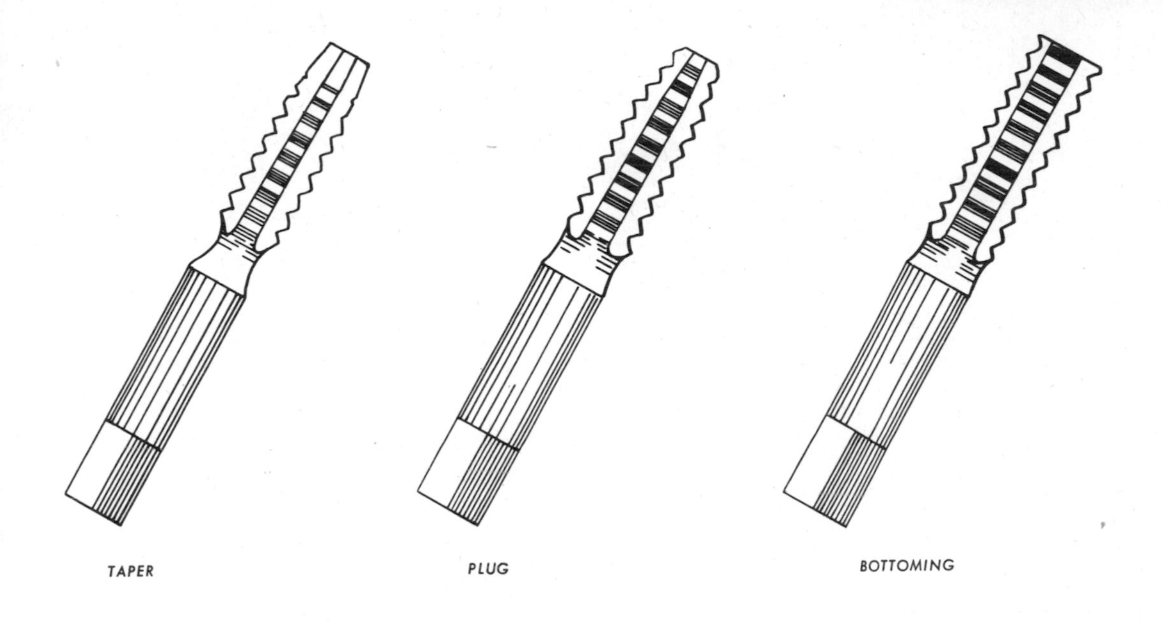

To tap hole that is clear through material, use taper or plug tap. When hole does not go through, use taper to start threads, plug to continue, bottoming tap to finish.

Drill press holds tap square to surface.

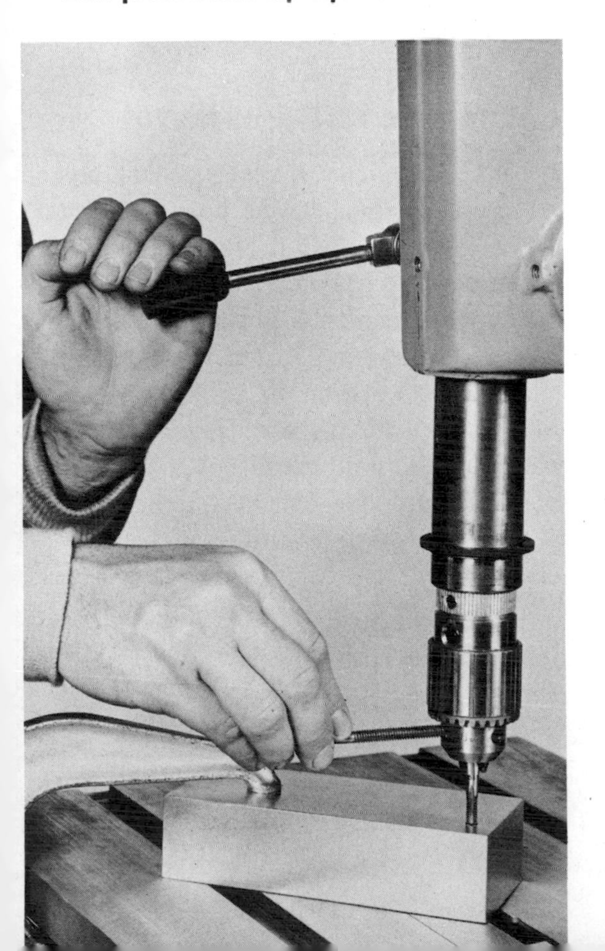

Since tapping cannot be done with normal drill-press speeds, the drill chuck must be turned by hand. A good method of doing this is to use a ¼" bolt as shown at the left. Turn the chuck with one hand and use the other to feed the tap into the work. The amount of pressure on the feed lever will vary with the size of the tap used and the thickness of the material being worked on.

When tapping, retract the tap about one-eighth turn for every half turn accomplished. This is necessary to remove material cut away when the thread is formed.

Withdraw the tap carefully when the job is complete. Keep one hand on the feed lever to prevent the pull of the quill return spring from jerking the tap from the hole and ruining the last few threads.

Thinner materials are handled in a similar manner, but pressure on the feed lever should be less. Use a very light pressure, and be very careful when withdrawing the tap to keep it from pulling from the work.

This setup is extremely useful for drilling concentric holes in long stock. Be sure that the work and the V-block are firmly clamped to the table.

A lathe faceplate can be used to hold round stock for concentric drilling.

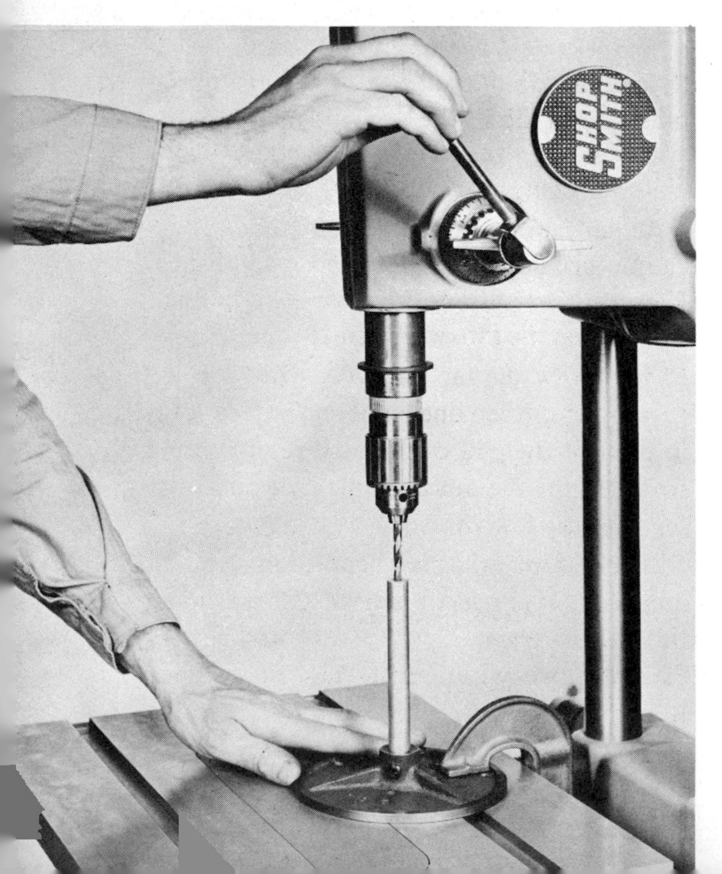

Concentric Holes in Metal

Lathe faceplates make excellent holders for rod stock that fits the hole in the plate. Although a drill vise is commonly used for holding short, round stock, a faceplate arrangement, such as is illustrated at the left, is often preferred because it automatically squares the work to the drill. The rod can be secured with the set screw that is ordinarily used to hold the faceplate to the spindle. The faceplate can be fitted to rods of various size by using bushings in the faceplate center hole.

Long work is accurately handled by using the setup shown above. Here the end of the work is held against the tailstock lathe center and supported in a V-block clamped to the table. The rod could rest on the table itself, with the miter gauge used as a guide.

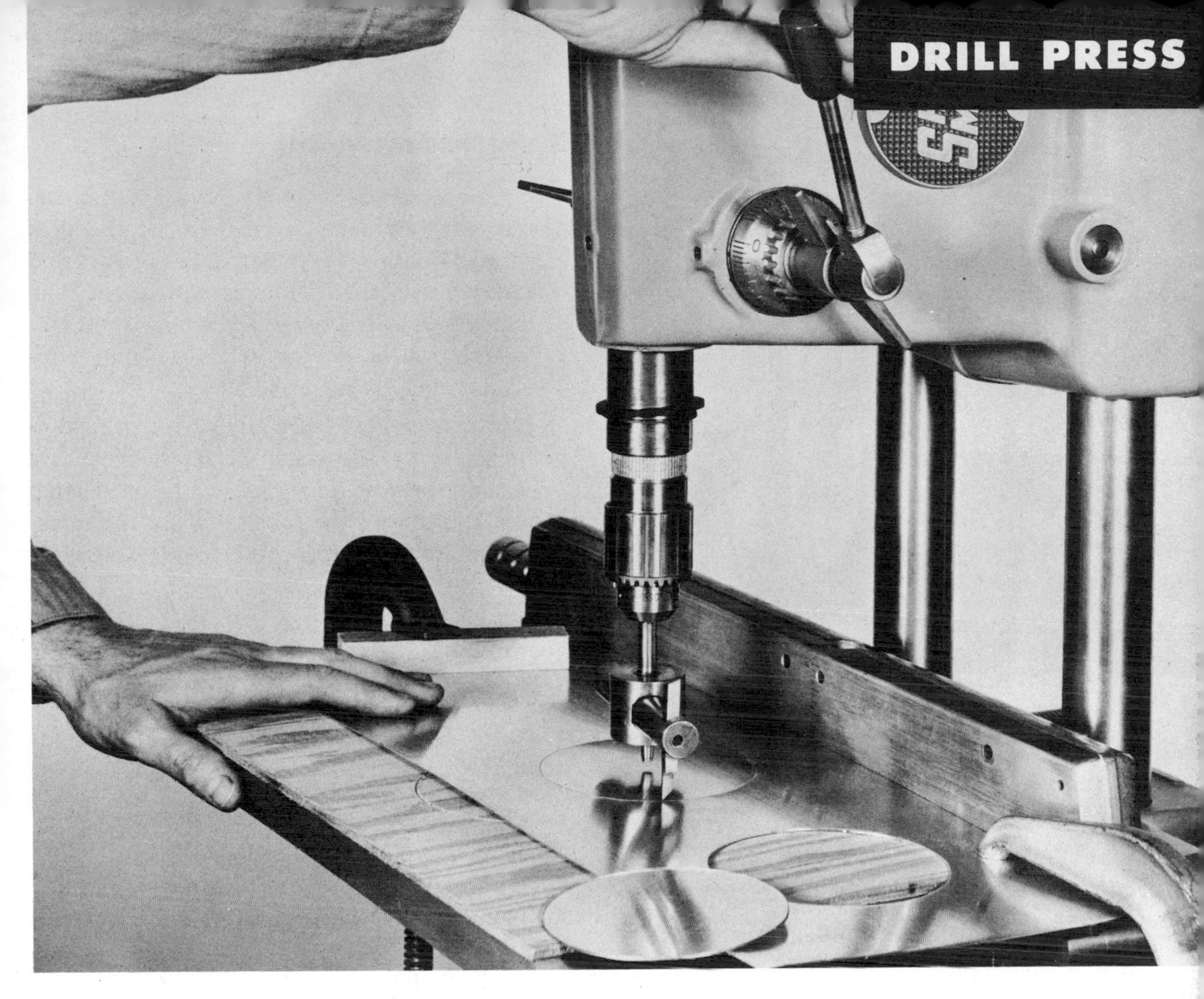

CUTTING LARGE HOLES IN METAL

Sheet-metal discs, or large holes, can be cut from thin sheets with a fly cutter. Clamp the work securely, use slow speed, and keep the feed slow and pressure light.

Table and Fence as V-Block

The combination of fence and table as a V-block works for woodworking as well as metalworking. With the table tilted 45° and the fence locked front and rear, perfect support is created for drilling round stock.

Be sure that the setup is situated under the spindle so the drill point meets the work at its highest point, which is the center line of the work. If the hole is to go through the stock, use scrap pieces under the work to protect the table and fence, or situate the insert slot directly under the drill.

When tilted, the table and fence form a V-block for drilling holes in round stock.

By using the table-height lever as a forward feed mechanism, you can do small surface-grinding jobs with a cup wheel.

Surfacing Metal

A cup wheel, shown in use at the left, can do light surfacing operations on the drill press. Depth of cut should be set to grind away a very small amount of material. The cup wheel is held on an arbor with a resilient material between the washers (thin cork sheet or gasket material).

Never run the wheel above speeds recommended by the manufacturer. These are usually printed on the paper flange. Clamp work firmly to the table and use the table-height lever as a forward feed mechanism.

Making Metal Edgings

Attractive metal edgings like those below can be made by drilling sheet metal as shown at the right. Two strips are formed at the same time by drilling holes on a center line and then cutting the strip on the line.

These are metal edgings formed by drilling sheet metal and then cutting through the center line of the holes.

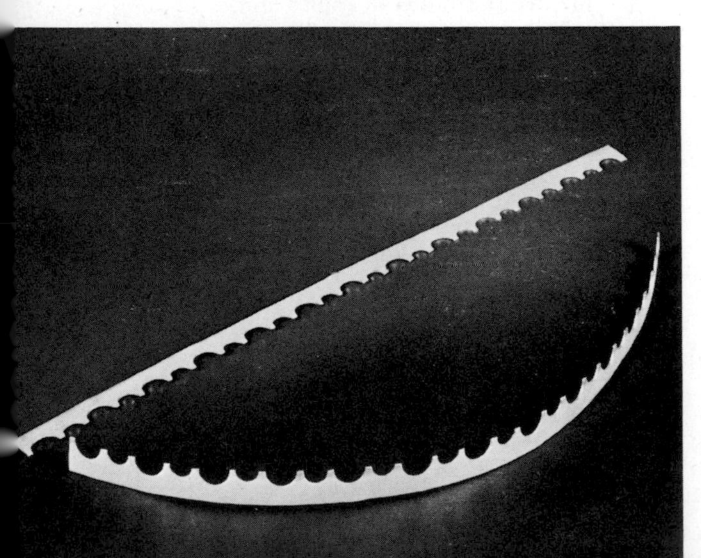

Below are typical layouts for metal edgings.

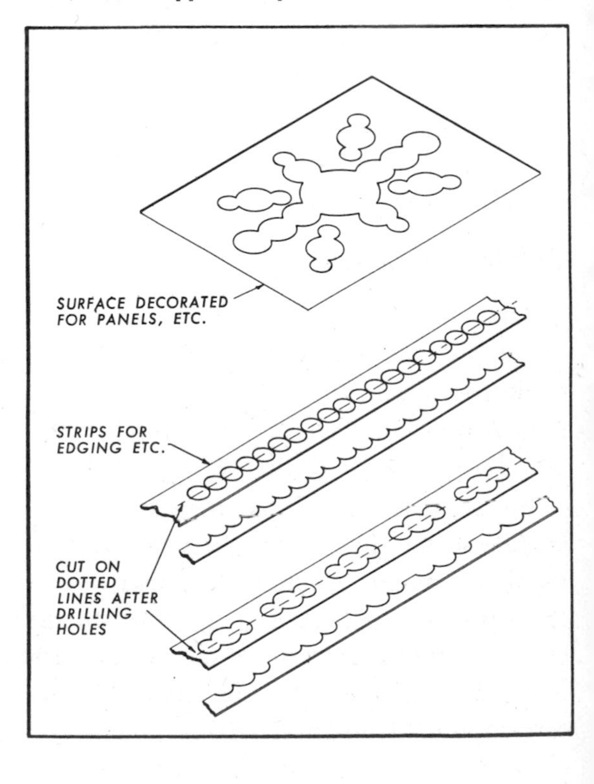

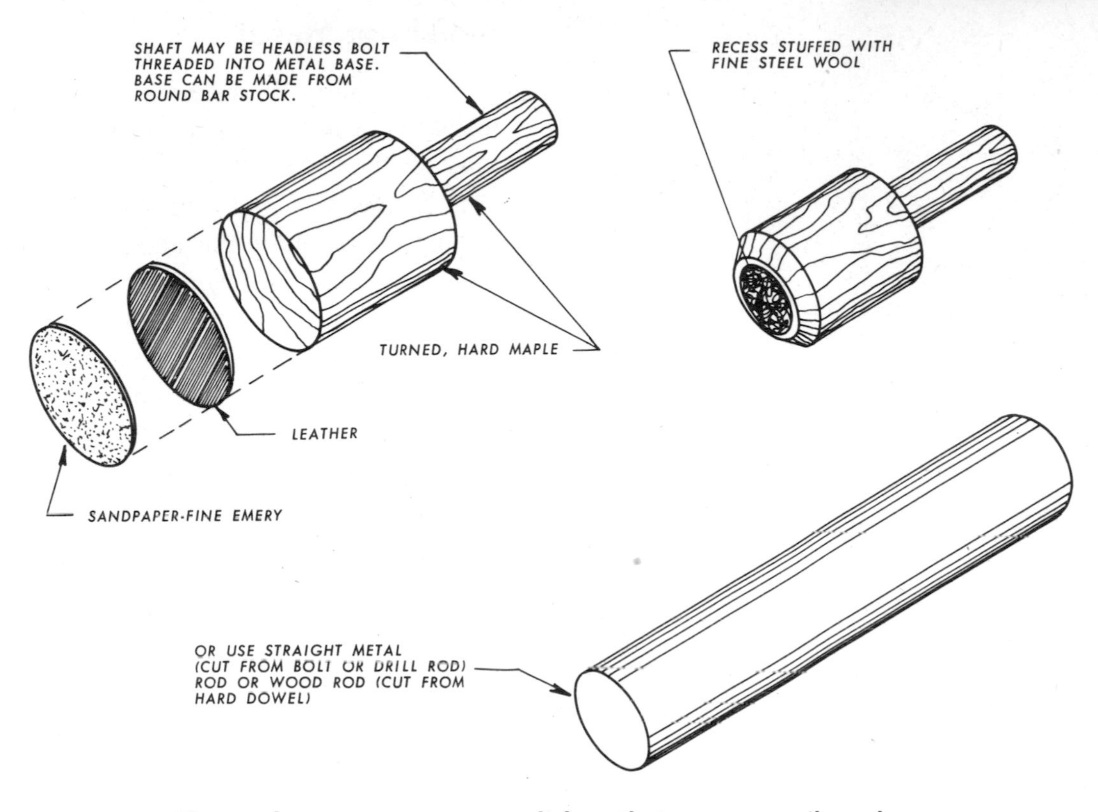
SHAFT MAY BE HEADLESS BOLT THREADED INTO METAL BASE. BASE CAN BE MADE FROM ROUND BAR STOCK.
RECESS STUFFED WITH FINE STEEL WOOL
TURNED, HARD MAPLE
LEATHER
SANDPAPER-FINE EMERY
OR USE STRAIGHT METAL (CUT FROM BOLT OR DRILL ROD) ROD OR WOOD ROD (CUT FROM HARD DOWEL)

Shown above are some spot polishers that you can easily make.

Spot Polishing

An attractive finish, easily accomplished in the home workshop on soft metals, is shown at the right.

The tool itself is made in any one of the three ways shown above.

The rip fence is used as a guide.

The spots are overlapped to form the pleasing design seen so often on commercial items.

When emery paper or steel wool is used to abrade the spots, the work is done dry. If a straight rod is used, a mixture of emery dust and light oil is used on the work, with the rod abrading the mixture into the surface of the metal.

The final appearance of the finish will depend on the uniformity of the application. Use the rip fence to keep the lines straight. Try to overlap the spots evenly.

Spot polishing, or damaskeening, provides an attractive metal finish. This work is easily done on the drill press.

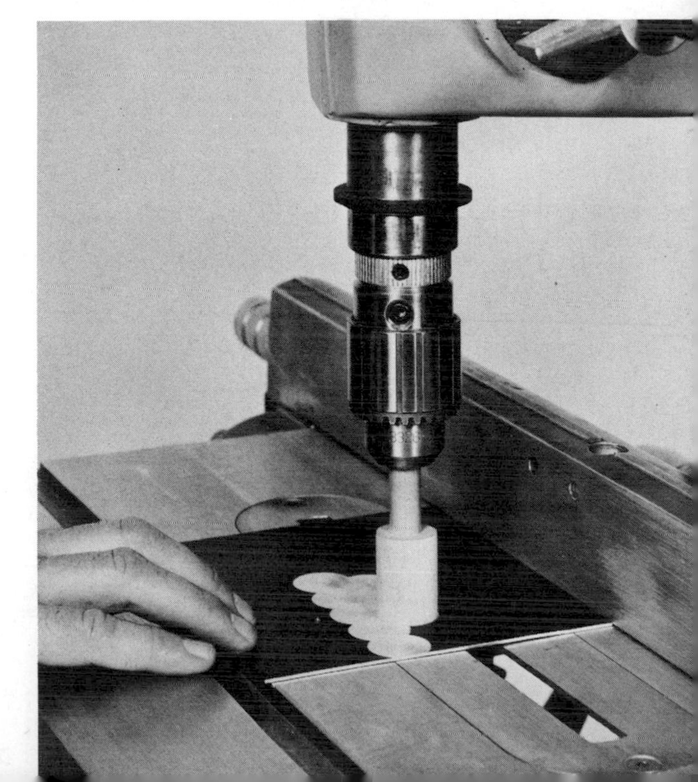

Details below show how to make the guard shown above for use with wire brushes.

Finishing Metal

A good satin finish can be given to soft metals by using wire scratch brushes of the kind shown at the left.

It is always a good idea to use a hood around the brush on this and similar operations to guard against flying dirt and particles of metal. Construction details of the guard are shown below. The same hood can be used during buffing (shown at right), which produces a high polish and a glass-smooth finish on plastics as well as metals.

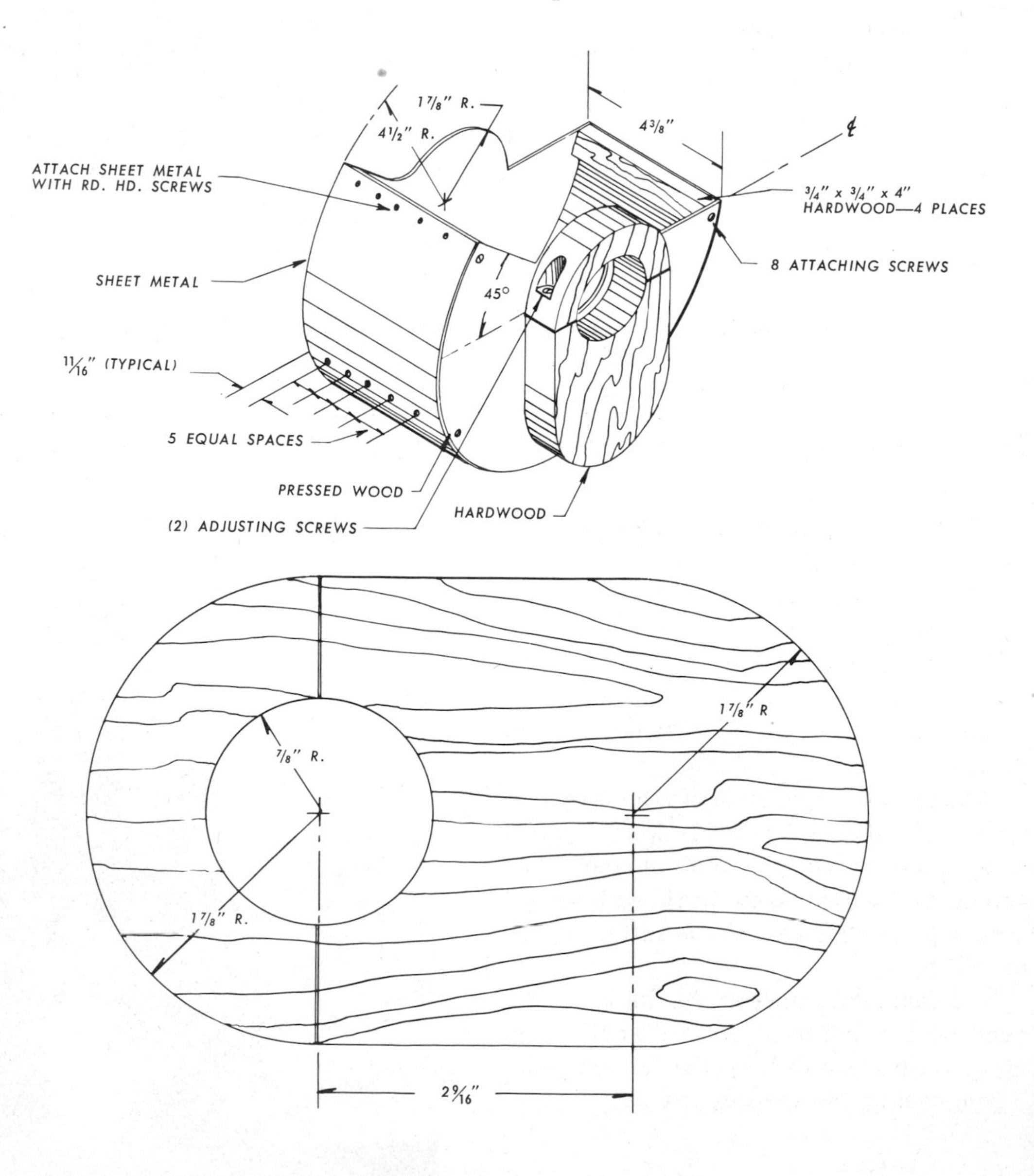

Use a buffing wheel like this to produce a high polish on plastics as well as metals.

Drilling Glass

This is an application that will interest hobbyists who like to turn bottles and jugs into lamp bases.

One method uses a triangular file sharpened at one end and employed like a drill. There's danger of catching the point in the hole and cracking the glass—or of breaking it as the point comes through.

A better method is to use a metal tube with an outside diameter equal to the size of the hole needed. A mixture of emery powder and light oil is confined around the hole location by a dam made of putty (photograph below). The end of the tube is cut square across and notched in two or three places with a hack saw. The notches should be about ⅛″ or ¼″ deep. The tube is secured in the chuck and brought down lightly to the work, which—if it is a flat sheet of glass—should be placed on a perfectly flat surface.

Frequent retractions of the tube are necessary in order for the cutting compound to flow into the circular groove being formed by the tube. Feed slowly and lightly, especially near the end.

When glass objects of irregular shape (such as bottles and jugs) are to be drilled, a cradle must be provided to hold the work. The table and fence may be used as a V-block, for example, when a small bottle is being drilled.

Use a dam of putty to contain the grinding compound when drilling holes in glass.

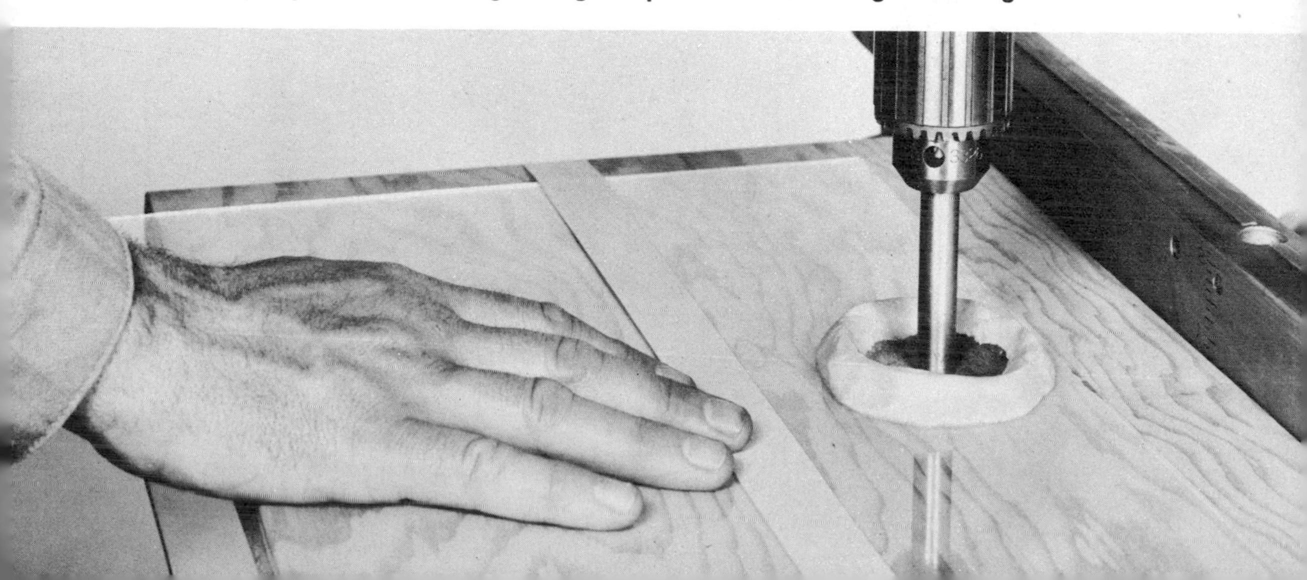

TROUBLE SHOOTING CHART FOR THE DRILL PRESS

GENERAL

THE TROUBLE	POSSIBLE CAUSES	THE CURE	SEE PAGE
DRILL OR OTHER CUTTING TOOL HEATS UP—OR—WORK BURNS	excessive speed	change to slower speed	104, 140
	chips not clearing	retract drill frequently to clear chips from hole	102
	dull drill	sharpen	331
	feeding too fast	feed just enough to keep tool cutting	104
DRILL LEADS OFF	hard grain causes drill to veer	drill pilot hole first—then enlarge	106
WORK SPLINTERS ON BREAKTHROUGH	no support	use scrap block under work	106
DRILL GRABS ON BREAKTHROUGH	feeding too fast	slow up feed on breakthrough—especially on metals	106, 140
WORK TORN FROM HANDS	incorrect procedure	clamp work to table or fence	140, 141
CUTTING EDGES OF DRILL BREAK OR QUICKLY DULL	feeding too slow	feed so tool is continuously cutting	104
TOOL ROTATES IN CHUCK	tool not locked in chuck	always use chuck key—do not depend on hand-tightening	98, 99
DEPTH OF HOLE WRONG	incorrect procedure	follow instructions for drilling to predetermined depth	106, 107
	no allowance for drill point	allow for point, especially on twist drills	102
DRILL BINDS IN WORK	work pinching drill	support work directly under, or as close to cutting area as possible	140
	excessive feed pressure	do not jam drill into work	104
ANGULAR HOLES MOVE OFF CENTER	side of drill hits before center	use leveling block	114

MORTISING	SERRATED EDGE ON MORTISE	misalignment	be sure chisel is square to fence before cutting	117
	OVERHEATING	misalignment	be sure of 1/32″ to 1/16″ clearance between end of bit and chisel	117
		chips piling up in cut or chisel	retract to aid chip clearance—be sure chip clearance hole in chisel is not buried	118
		incorrect rpm	reset to correct speed	104, 118
		dull chisel and/or bit	sharpen	332
	WALL OF MORTISE TAPERED	chisel leading off into existing cavity	keep cuts to ¾ width of chisel if possible	118
		work creeping	always clamp work firmly	117, 119
	EXCESSIVE PRESSURE REQUIRED	usually dull tools	sharpen	118
		very hard wood	drill relief holes first	—
	WORK PULLS UP WHEN CHISEL RETRACTED	incorrect procedure	always use hold down	117
ROUTING	ROUGH CUTTING ACTION—CHATTER	speed too slow	high speeds produce smoother cuts	104, 133
		excessively deep cut	achieve full depth of cut by making successive passes	132
		vibration	be sure to hold work firmly throughout pass—use hold downs when possible	133
		incorrect procedure	whenever possible make pass against direction of rotation of tool	133

4 THE LATHE

**Lathe capacities • tool rest • adjusting • speed
the chisels and their three actions • gouge • skew • roundnos
parting tool • squarenose • spear point • the importance of desig
spindle turning • faceplate turning • large wor
glued sections • split turnings • center hole
thin faceplate work • making an indexing hea
dowel steady rest • fluting and reeding • turning spira
wooden chucks • how to turn: box with fitted cove
rings • ball shapes • ovals • offsets (tapers) • special leg shape
trouble shootin**

The modern lathe is shown here with a spindle turning mounted between the centers.

A LATHE is a machine with two adjustable centers on a common longitudinal axis, one powered and the other dead, between which material can be held and rotated.

The lathe has not changed in principle since it was a primitive, bow-powered tool that is said to have been invented in ancient Egypt. It remains a means of turning work at controlled speeds so sharp tools may be pressed against it, shaping it symmetrically.

Electric motors have replaced the various hand- or foot-powered devices originally used, but the quality of the output still depends on the operator's skill in manipulating the chisels used to do the forming.

The modern lathe is designed to provide great latitude in size of work and variety of treatment, as illustrated by the photographs of turnings on this page.

The skill required to manipulate the turning tools effectively may be gained through time and practice, so anyone can soon learn to produce professional turnings. Once you know the techniques of using the lathe chisels, you can apply them to turning out anything from the wheel hub for a scale-model car to a good-sized Lazy Susan or a fluted table leg.

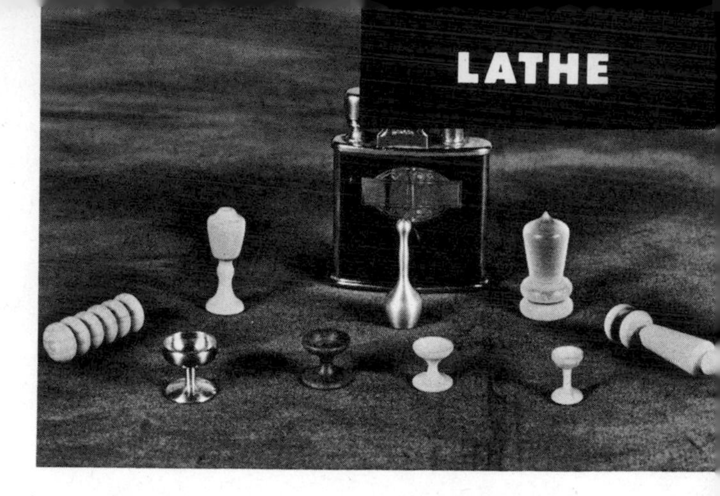

Even tiny scale-model parts are easily turned. Compare size with cigarette lighter.

Complete projects may be accomplished on the lathe alone. Many craftsmen, fascinated by the transformation of rough stock into a smooth cylinder, design or select projects that are strictly lathe jobs. They need little urging to acquire skill through practice.

Others regard the lathe simply as an accessory tool and begrudge the time it takes to turn a part for a project. Either way, true craftsmanship demands a knowledge of the lathe and what it can do.

The modern lathe can handle work having a tremendous variety in size and treatment.

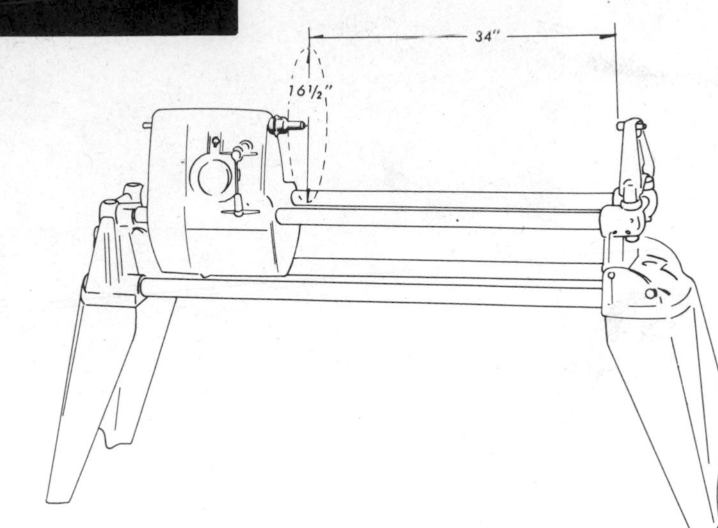

Lathe capacities for normal operations are determined by two things. One is the distance between centers, which is the maximum length of stock that can be mounted for spindle turning. The other is swing, twice the distance from spindle center to lathe bed, which is the maximum diameter of work the lathe can handle.

Adjusting the Lathe

The one major adjustment on the lathe is lining up the dead center with the powered one, which is mounted on the spindle and is not adjustable. The tailstock is fitted with an eccentric cup-center mount, which is locked with an Allen set screw. For normal operation this is locked in zero position. To align the centers:

1. Slide headstock toward tailstock as far as it will go.

2. Mount the spur-center on the spindle, and the cup-center (photograph below) in the tailstock.

3. Use the feed lever to advance the quill until the points of the two centers meet.

4. If necessary loosen the cup-center eccentric mount and rotate it slightly (right-hand picture below) to bring points into vertical alignment. (Look **down** on points.) Then lock.

5. Raise or lower the tailstock to achieve horizontal alignment, then lock the height collars on the tailstock tubes.

Since the cup-center does not rotate, it may burn or bind the wood. Avoid this by placing a drop of oil—or some tallow, beeswax, or soap—on cup and point. Or use a tailstock live cup-center (bottom right on opposite page), a point and cup mounted in a sealed bearing and rotating with the work. In some applications, such as metal spinning, the live center is a necessity.

The tailstock center—dead cup or live—is held in its position by friction. To place it, press it into the tapered hole of the eccentric mount. To remove it tap it out with a mallet, as shown at far right, catching the center with

Friction holds tailstock center in mount.

Points in spur- and cup-center must line up.

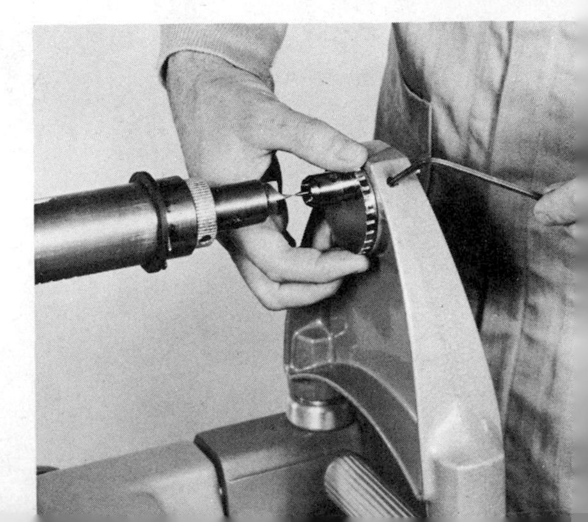

The tool rest is a horizontal arm that can be placed in proper relation to the work. On the multi-purpose tool it is mounted on the table carriage, and slides parallel to the work, saving time and trouble. With carriage locked, the rest swings in a circle, as shown. This permits working at the extreme end of a mounted spindle turning—and also behind a mounted faceplate turning. Upper sketch shows ideal position of tool rest in relation to work.

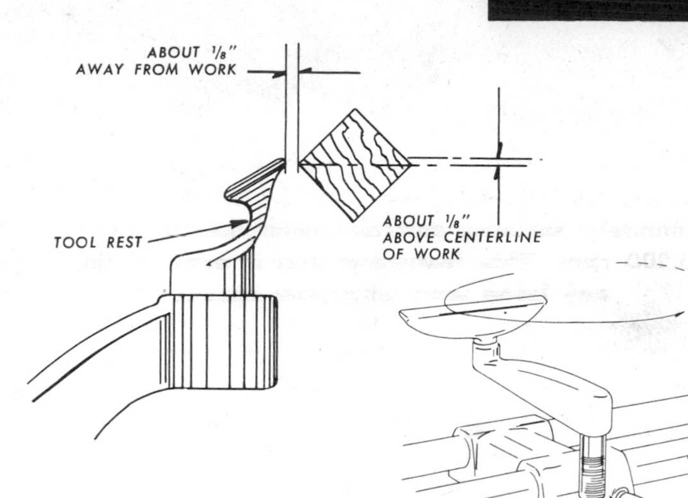

your free hand so it doesn't fall and damage the point.

On the multi-purpose tool the quill-feed lever is used to secure the work between centers for spindle turning. After locating the work centers (see page 174), hold the tailstock end of the work in place while moving the headstock to bring the spur center about 1/4" from the work. Lock the headstock. Feed the spur center forward to engage the work firmly, then back it off slightly and lock the quill.

Stationing the tool rest in relation to the work is shown in the sketch at upper right. The illustration shows the ideal condition which you should come as close to as possible. As the turning proceeds, adjust the rest to give maximum support to the lathe chisels.

Remove center from tailstock by holding securely and tapping with soft-faced mallet.

Oil on cup-center will prevent burning.

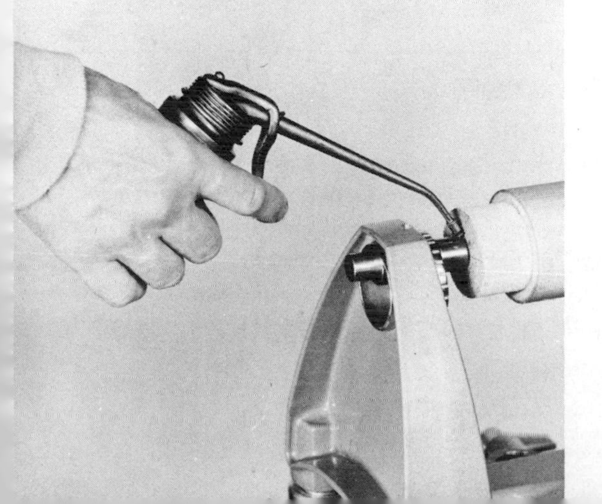

Live cup-center eliminates friction-burn.

Lathe Speeds

Diagrammed at the right, the built-in speed changer on the multi-purpose tool provides infinitely variable speeds from about 700 to 5,200 rpm. This feature makes it easy to do any lathe work at proper speed.

Generally speaking, the larger the work the slower the speed should be. Large work is dangerous when turning too fast. Use the chart below for suitable speeds. The first, or roughing, cuts are done at slow speed. Speed is increased for general cutting and shaping. Finishing begins at shaping speed, and gradually increases to maximum.

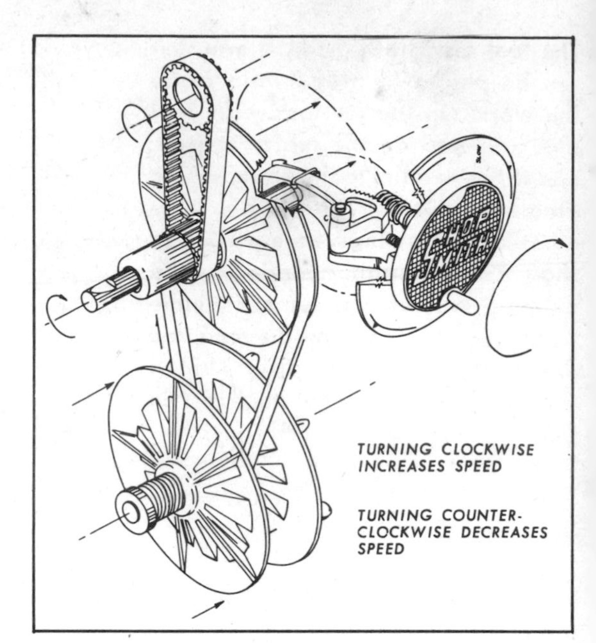
TURNING CLOCKWISE INCREASES SPEED
TURNING COUNTER-CLOCKWISE DECREASES SPEED

LATHE-SPEED GUIDE

MATERIAL AND DIAMETER	ROUGHING CUT		SHAPING CUT		FINISHING CUT	
	Speed-Dial setting	revolutions per minute	Speed-Dial setting	revolutions per minute	Speed-Dial setting	revolutions per minute
wood up to 2″	C	910	N	2,590	T	4,250
wood 2″ to 4″	B	810	M	2,375	Q	3,380
wood 4″ to 6″	SLOW	650	J	1,825	M	2,375
wood 6″ to 8″	SLOW	650	F	1,200	J	1,825
wood 8″ to 10″	SLOW	650	C	910	D	1,025
wood over 10″	SLOW	650	SLOW	650	SLOW	650
plastics up to 3″	L	2,200	P	3,125	S	3,875
plastics over 3″	D	1,025	F	1,200	I	1,680
non-ferrous metals up to 3″ (with carbide-tipped tools)	SLOW	650	G	1,300	P	3,125

Use skew for smoothing and finishing surfaces, for trimming cuts on ends and shoulders, for making V-cuts. Use squarenose, for smoothing outside contours and flat surfaces, squaring ends and shoulders. Use roundnose for cutting recesses, hollowing, coving, circular grooves in faceplate work, outside and inside contours. Use gouge for roughing-out to nearly all shapes; it can be used in almost any operation. Use parting tool for marking dimension points, separating, cutting grooves. Use spear point for finishing, touching up, squaring corners.

Lathe Chisels

A typical set of lathe chisels consists of skew, roundnose, 3/4″ gouge, 1/4″ gouge, and parting tool. Shapes of these and other lathe chisels are shown below.

An ordinary butt chisel may be used in place of the squarenose; the skew, when used on its side, will perform many of the operations usually done with the spear point.

For safety, keep tools behind you or to one side so you won't have to reach over the work. Do not wear loose-hanging ties. Keep sleeves buttoned tight. Do not check the work for roundness with your fingers. (Check by placing the blade—not the point—of the chisel on the work. Vibration of the tool will tell you whether the work is round.)

Position of hands on chisel and tool rest is shown above at right. The left hand is usually placed on the blade with the thumb on top, the back of the hand resting on the finger ledge, and the fingers placed comfortably around the tool or on the finger ledge. The right hand holds the handle of the tool and provides the movement which determines the cut. The part of the hand that rests on the finger ledge also acts as a gauge.

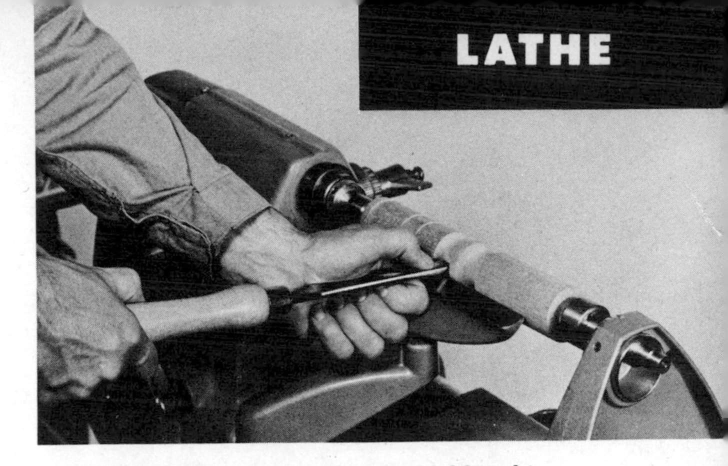

Hands should hold lathe chisel like this.

When making smoothing cuts or when roughing stock to size, the tool may be moved along the rest parallel to the work, taking a bite that remains constant because the left hand butts against the ledge and acts as a control. Consider the area of the tool rest on which the chisel sits as a pivot point, held by the thumb and fingers, and the hand on the handle as moving the cutting edge.

The feed of the chisel, which determines the amount of wood removed, should be slow and steady—never forced, never jabbed into the work. After the tool is in position, start the cut by advancing the tool slowly until it touches the wood.

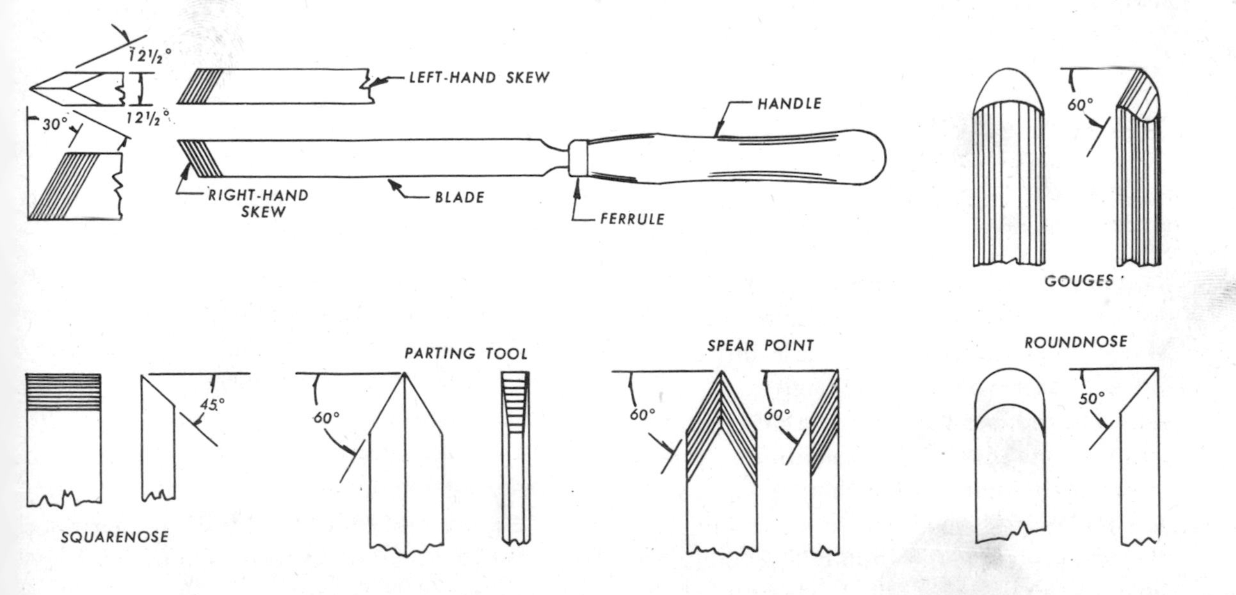

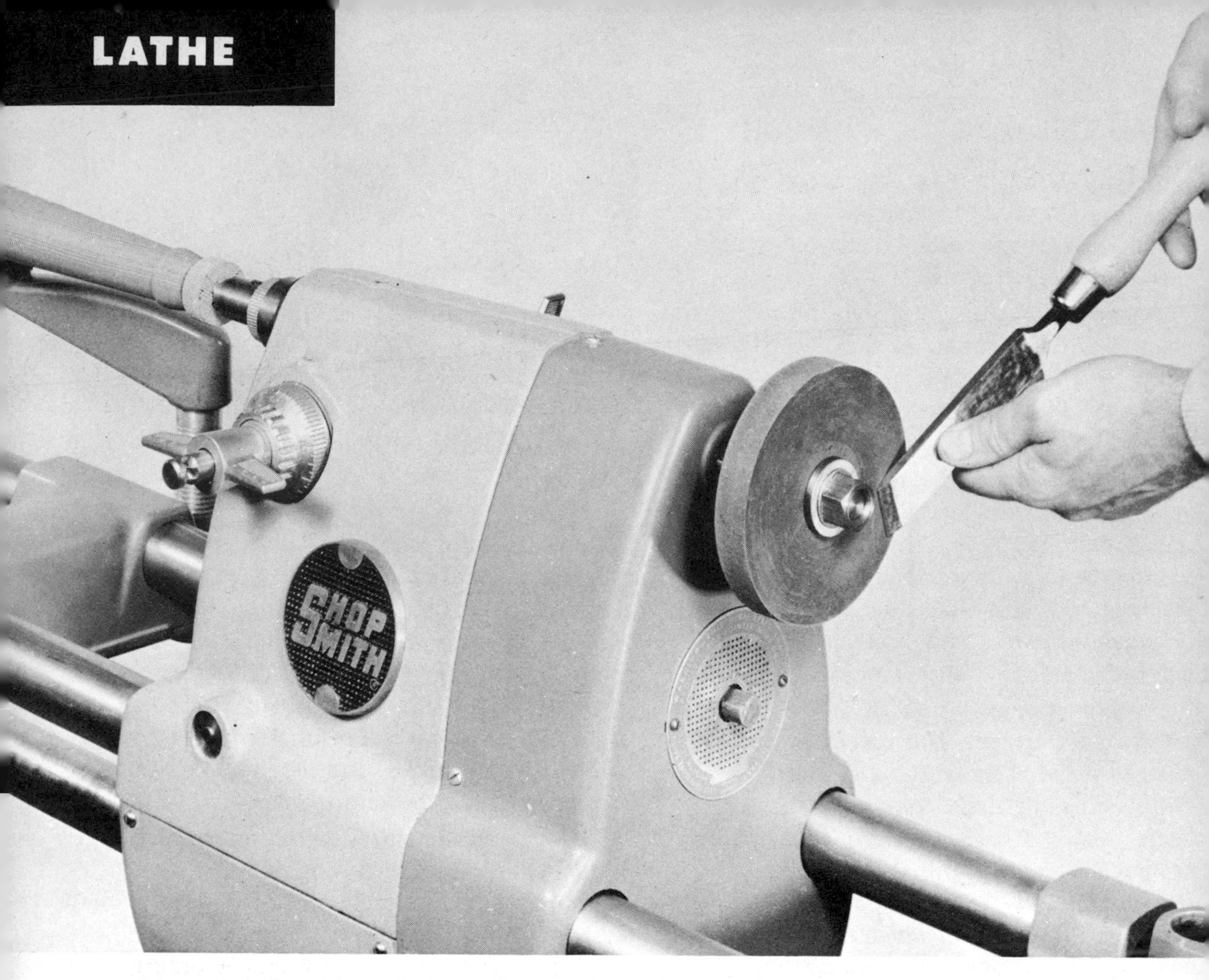

Keep the lathe chisels sharp by honing them after grinding and during the turning job. A rubber-bonded abrasive wheel handles this chore nicely; if it can be mounted for simultaneous operation with the lathe, as in this picture, so much the better. Edges may then be kept keen all the time. Chisels should be kept in a rack to protect them from nicks.

The Three Actions of the Cutting Tools

Lathe chisels act in the three ways sketched at top right, depending on how you hold them.

Scraping is the easiest and safest of the three actions and the best for the beginner to use. Many experienced operators use this action almost exclusively because it gives good results and reduces bad cuts to a minimum. A scraping action with a roundnose tool is shown at the right. Notice that the hand position has not changed except for the fingers. Placed as shown, the thumb and forefinger have a firmer hold on the blade and help to bring the edge of the chisel closer to a horizontal plane. This position is maintained while the tool is advanced to the depth of the cut and then swung slowly from side to side to increase the width of the cut if necessary. The full depth does not have to be reached at once. The chisel may be moved forward to cut into the wood slightly, then moved from side to side, maintaining the pivot point; and once more moved forward toward the center line of the work, then from side to side until the full cut is formed.

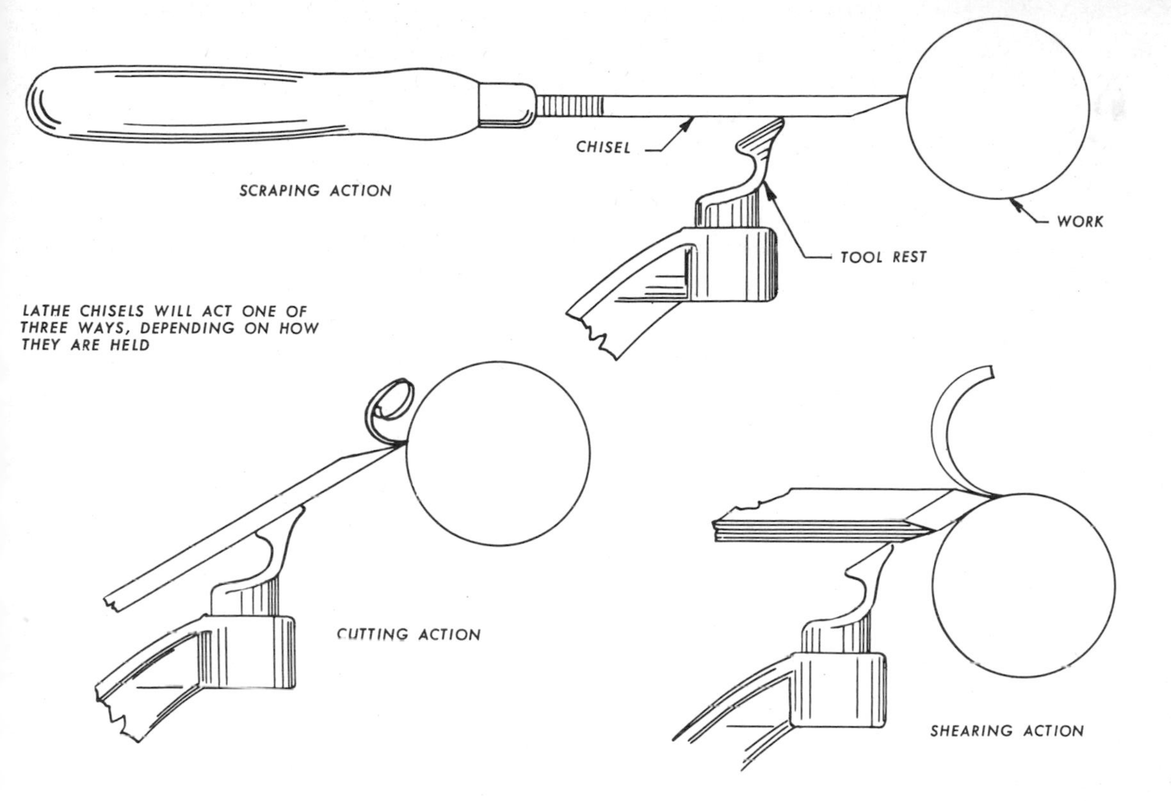

Lathe chisels may be used in these three ways. Scraping is the easiest to learn.

With a roundnose tool, a scraping action with the tool moved directly forward produces a cove equal to the size of the tool. Position of hand, rest, and tool are shown here.

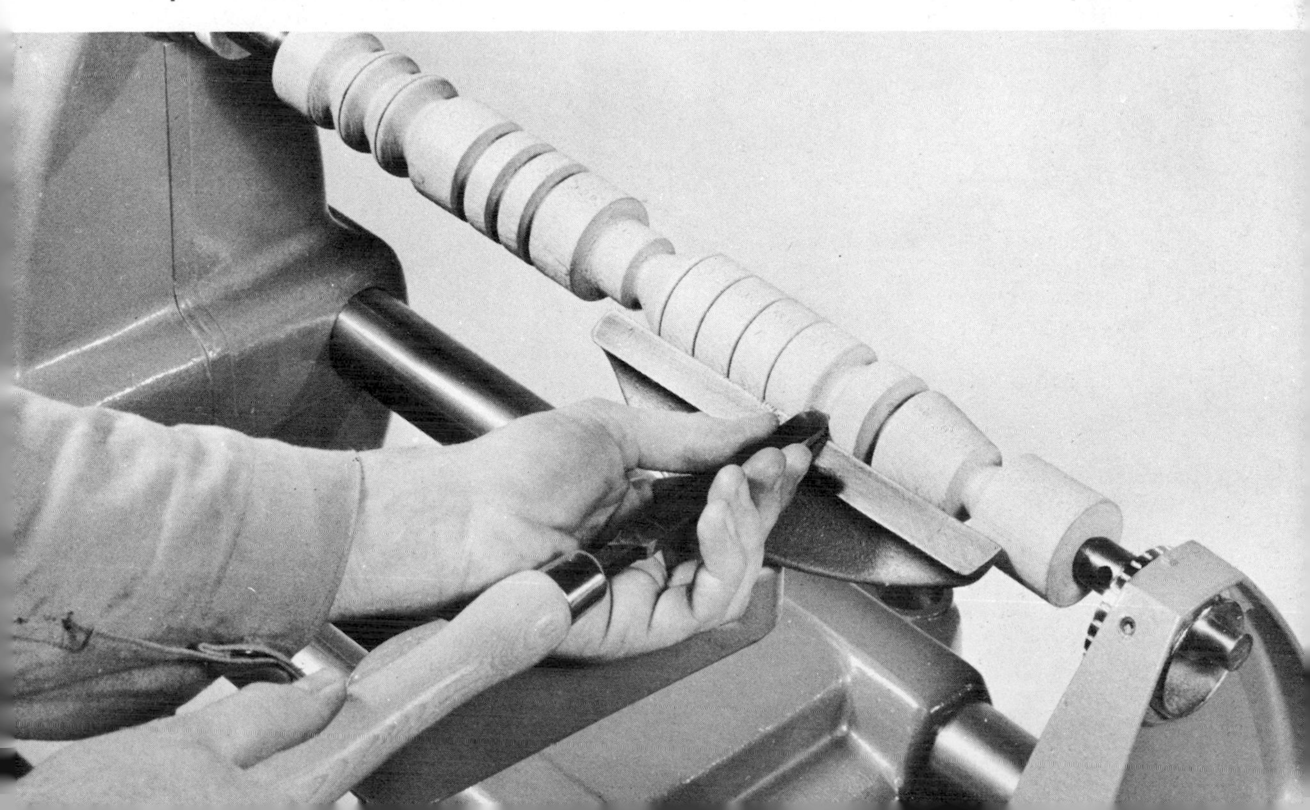

Cutting action calls for bringing the tool edge up by lowering the handle of the chisel. As shown in the drawing on the previous page, the edge of the tool cuts away the material in much the same way that a hand plane smooths the edge of a board.

Here more than elsewhere, the feed should be slow and the cut should be light. If you jab the chisel in suddenly or deeply it will be wrenched from your hands; the least that can happen is that you will ruin the work by lifting a large splinter from it.

Do not use the cutting action until you have practiced enough with the scraping action to be thoroughly familiar with each tool and what it can do.

Pictured below is a cutting action with a skew making a V-groove. Notice that the finger position has changed to accommodate the width of the blade. Once you have mastered the cutting action you will find that it leaves a surface smooth enough to finish without touch-up.

Here's a cutting action with a skew making a V-groove. Notice that the hand position has changed slightly because of the blade width. With cutting action, feed is kept slow.

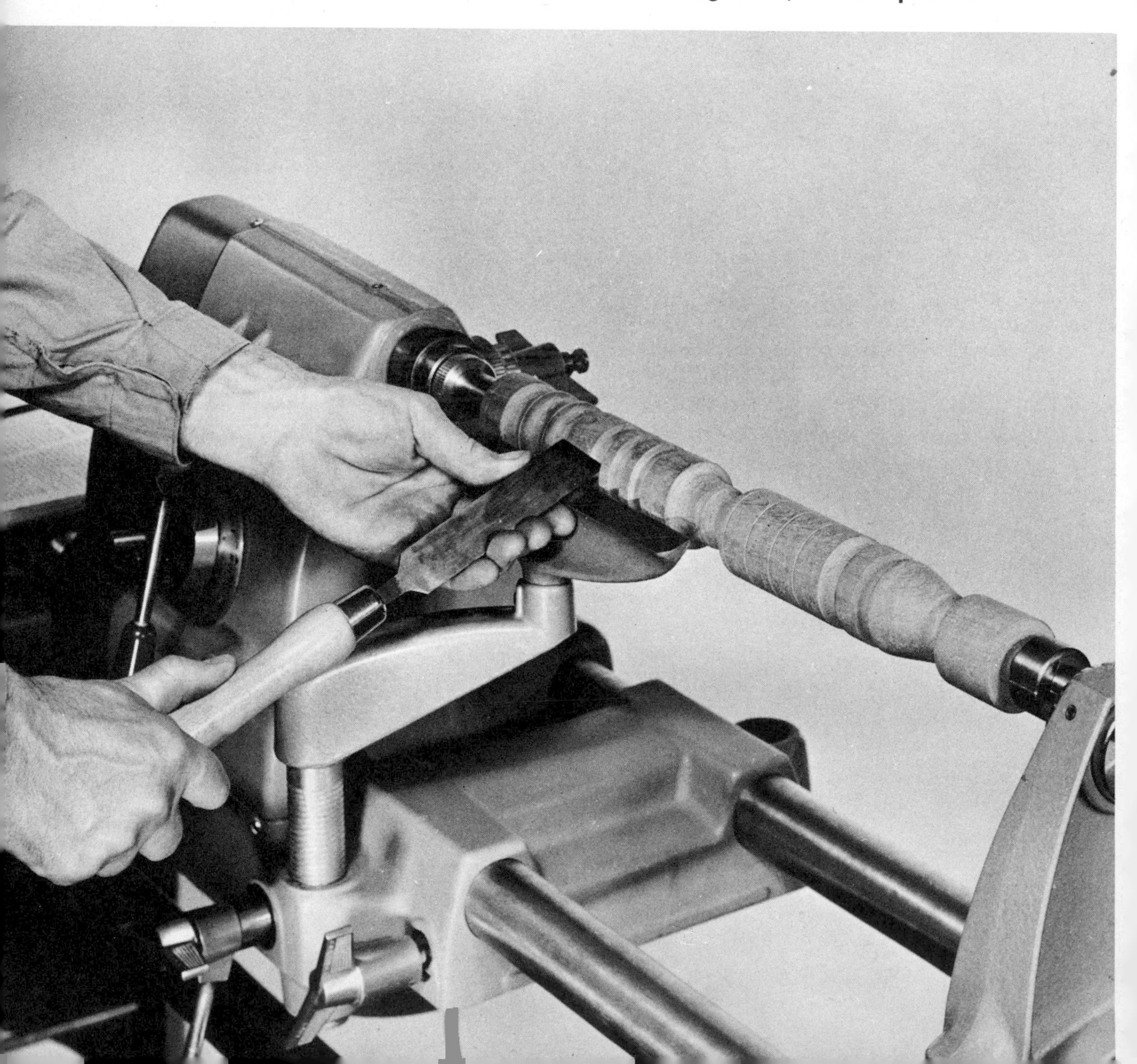

Shearing action is usually limited to skew and gouge. It is a cutting action with the tool edge moved parallel to the work, taking a constant bite, shearing away a layer of wood from the surface of the stock. A shearing action with the gouge is shown below. This is one of the easier "advanced" cuts. Since the tool is held on edge, move your thumb behind it to steady it while making the cut. When the gouge is sharp and properly held, wood is removed rapidly and the surface is left smooth.

While each of the chisels does certain operations better, the overlap is so great that no hard-and-fast limitations can be set down for each one. Each tool will cut differently, depending on the action, the angle, and the way it is moved. Practice with each chisel, duplicating the cuts illustrated, until you have the feel of each of them. When you arrive at this point, habit will take over and your use of the tools will become an individual application, standard with you.

Shown here is a typical shearing action with the gouge. The tool is held on edge, with the thumb behind it to act as a back-up while the cut is being made.

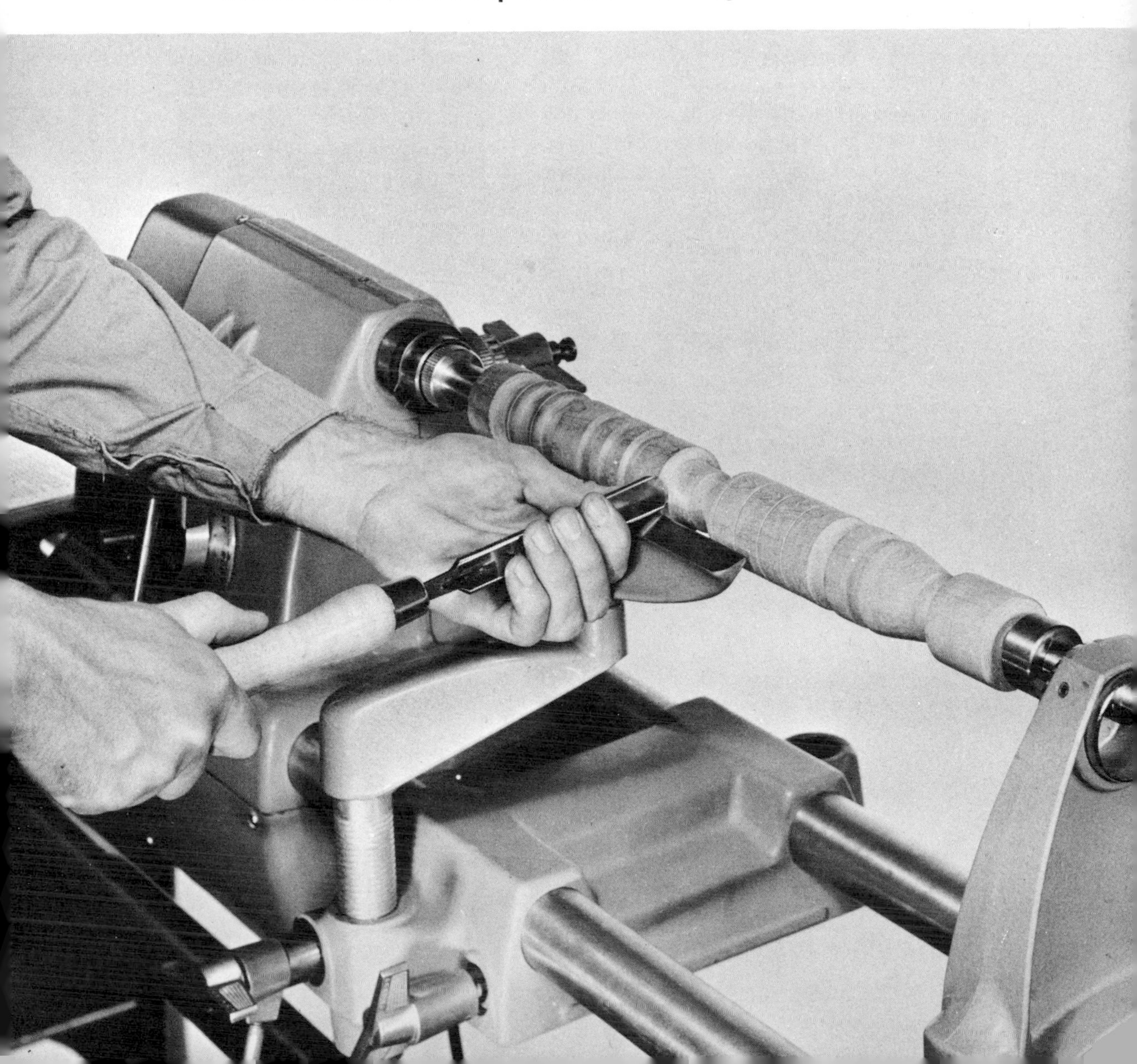

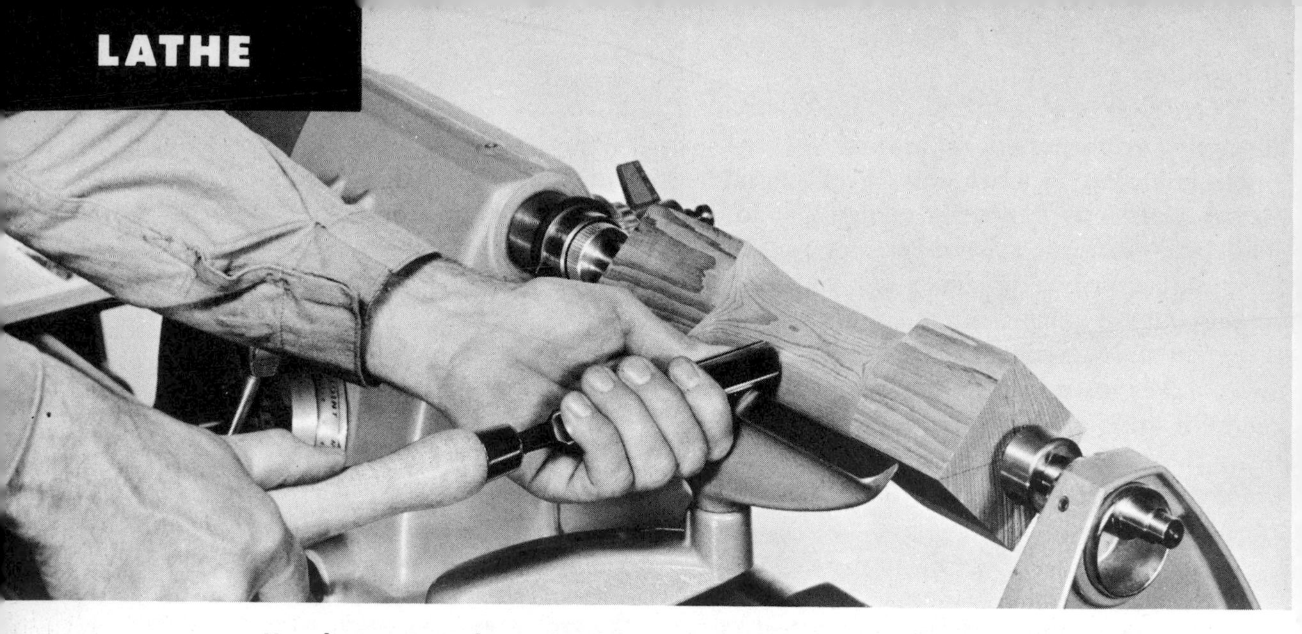

Use the gouge—shown here in a shearing cut—for all roughing operations.

Using the Gouge

The most versatile turning tool is the gouge. It may be used in any one of the three positions and at times is used so that all three cutting actions come into play.

It is the only chisel used in the roughing operation—turning the work from square to round (photograph above and drawing E below). This is a shearing cut, with the tool held on its side and moving parallel to the work. Depth of cut is maintained by the hand resting on the finger ledge.

Roughing cuts should be started somewhere along the length of the stock, with the tool being moved in the direction indicated

These are typical applications of the gouge, the most versatile of all turning tools.

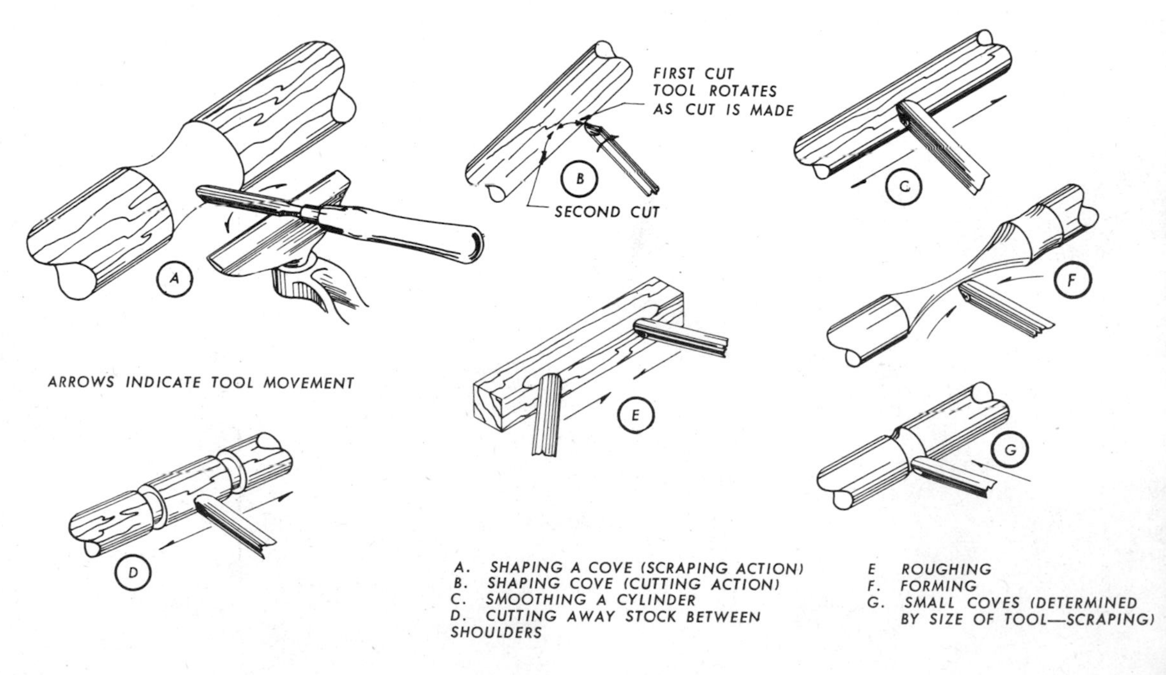

A. SHAPING A COVE (SCRAPING ACTION)
B. SHAPING COVE (CUTTING ACTION)
C. SMOOTHING A CYLINDER
D. CUTTING AWAY STOCK BETWEEN SHOULDERS
E ROUGHING
F. FORMING
G. SMALL COVES (DETERMINED BY SIZE OF TOOL—SCRAPING)

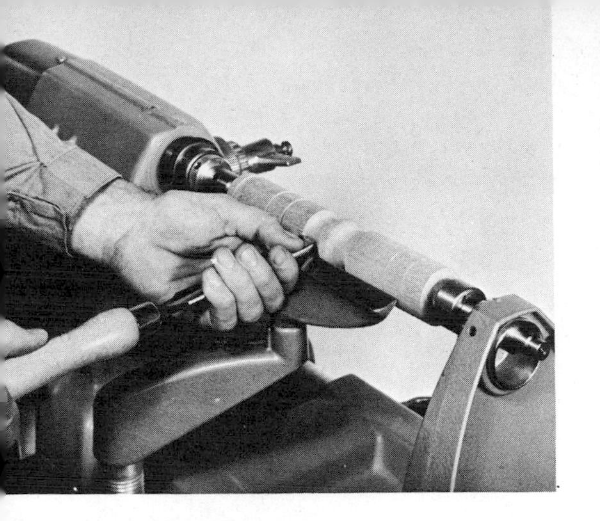

Here and in sketch G on the opposite page you see the gouge used to form a cove the size of the tool. In this scraping action the gouge is moved directly forward.

This, the two pictures below, and sketch B show a more advanced use of the gouge to form a cove. Begin with gouge on its side, feeding it forward slowly till cutting begins . . .

by the arrows in sketch E at the bottom of the opposite page. The tool rest remains in one position and the procedure is repeated.

When you need to reduce stock in a limited area, use the gouge between sizing cuts made with the parting tool. In sketch D the action is shown as a shearing cut, but the scraping action could be used. A similar procedure is shown in C—a shearing action producing a smooth finish.

The shearing action is shown again in F, in a forming operation. The cove-scraping action with the tool being moved directly forward is shown again in G.

The gouge is always used when a lot of material must be removed.

. . . and then move the tool slowly toward the center of the cove and rotate it on the tool rest. As the tool is rotated, the action changes from cutting to shearing and . . .

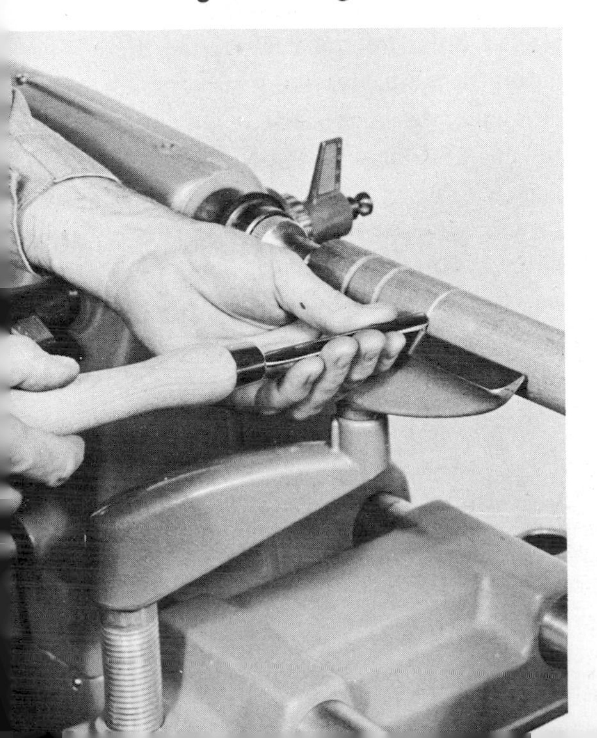

. . . becomes scraping as the final position is reached. The tool rests as shown here, and the cove is complete. On larger coves you would do this twice—once for each half.

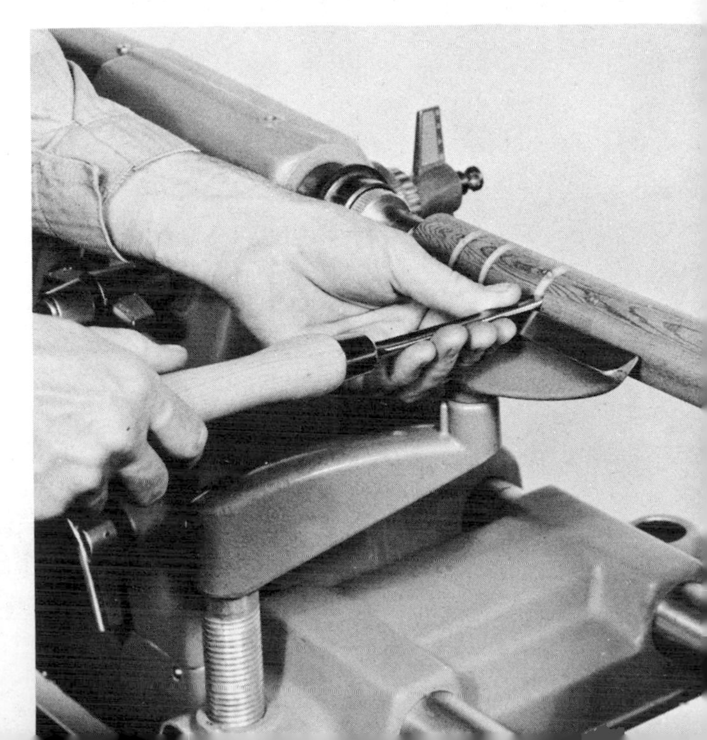

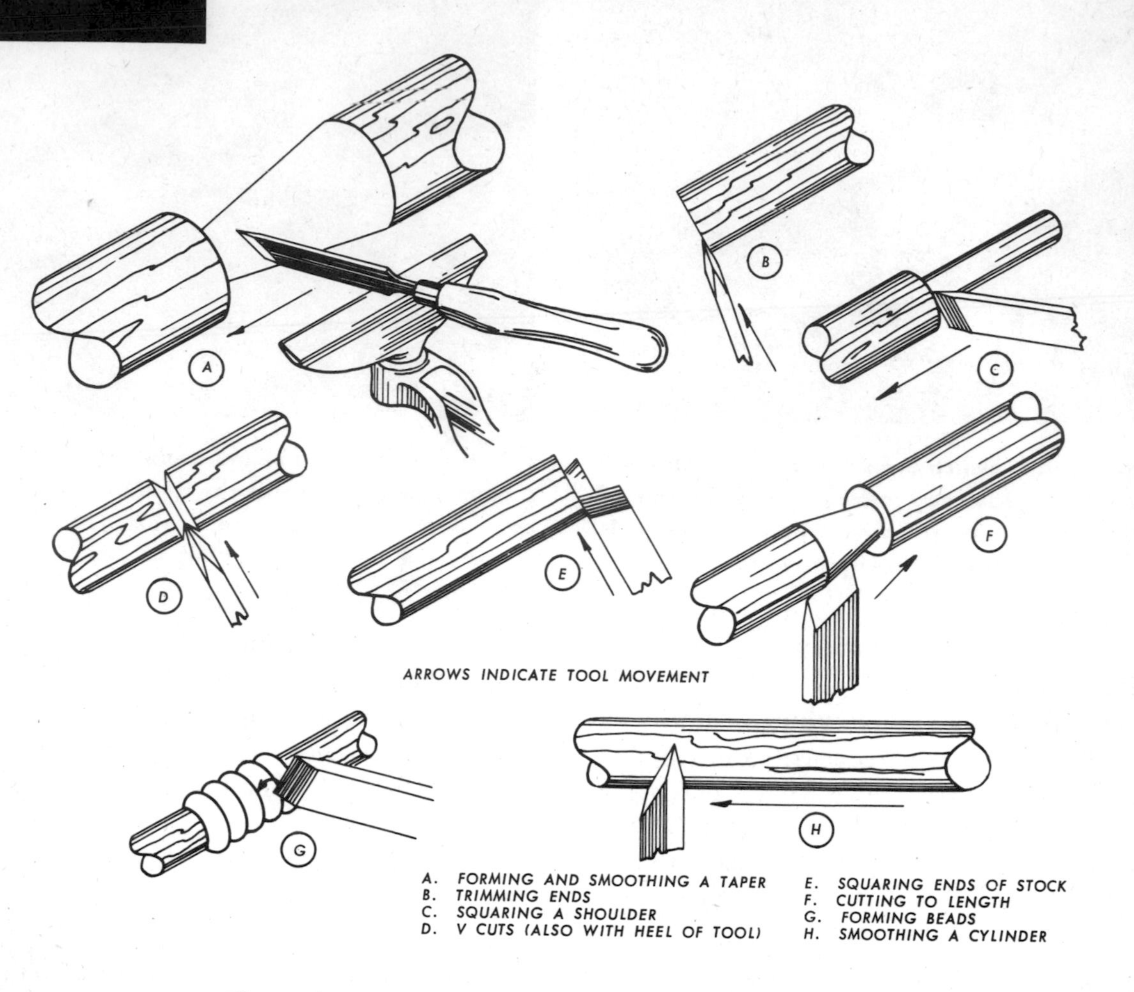

Shown here are some typical applications of the skew.

Using the Skew

Typical applications of the skew are shown above. For a scraping action hold the skew as shown in sketch E. This action may be used to square off the ends of a cylinder. The tool in this position presents a sharp point to the work, so it cuts fast, leaves a smooth finish. The same result is obtained by using the point of the skew in a cutting action (B). This may also be used for marking dimension lines or forming V-grooves (D). Form larger grooves by using the point of the skew in a cutting action on each side of a dimension line, slanting the chisel so both cuts meet at the depth of the groove.

Tapers are formed with the skew by starting the cut with the heel of the blade and ending it with the point (sketch A). To smooth a taper that has been cut with another tool, use the skew as shown at F. This may be a cutting or a scraping action: if you move the tool as shown by the arrow, the point of the tool will cut; if you place the edge of the tool parallel to the taper and move it forward, the action is scraping. The skew may also be used to clean out corners, as at C and E.

Probably the smoothest lathe-chisel surfacing cut of all is shown at H in a shearing cut to smooth down a cylinder. It requires a great deal of practice.

How to form beads with the skew is shown

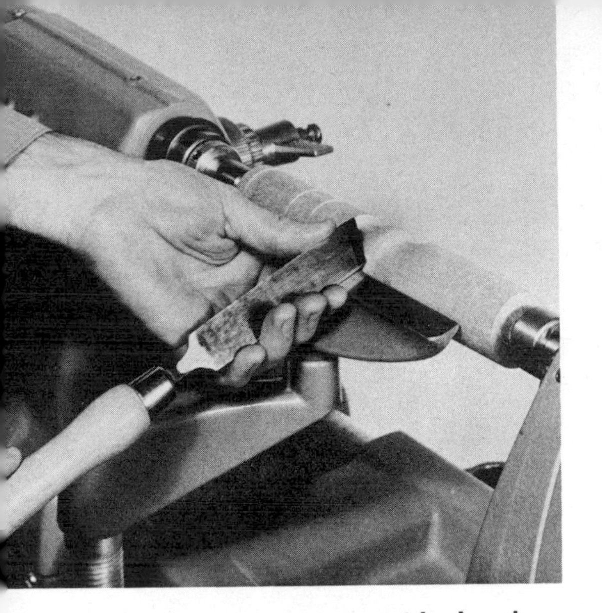

When forming a bead, start with the skew resting on the center line of the bead . . .

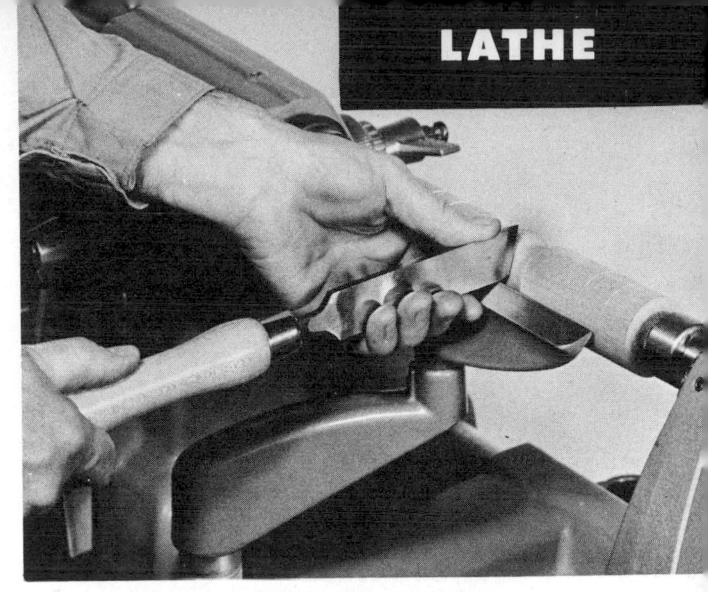

. . . and rotate the tool as if following the profile of a bead already formed.

at G. A bead, like a cove, requires three dimension lines, one on the center line of the bead and one on each of the extremities. Start the cut by placing the heel of the blade lightly on the center line (upper left photograph) with the blade edge tangent to the curve to be formed and the handle held below the cut. The heel should touch the work midway between the top of the tool rest and the top of the work. Finish the cut as shown in photograph at upper right.

Cutting off the work while it revolves is done with the skew, and always at the headstock end of the work. After using the skew to remove as much stock as you can, place it on the rest (photograph below) so the point will cut through the remaining stock. With skew firmly in left hand, hold work lightly with right hand. It will part cleanly, leaving the project in your right hand.

Remove as much material as possible before cutting off.

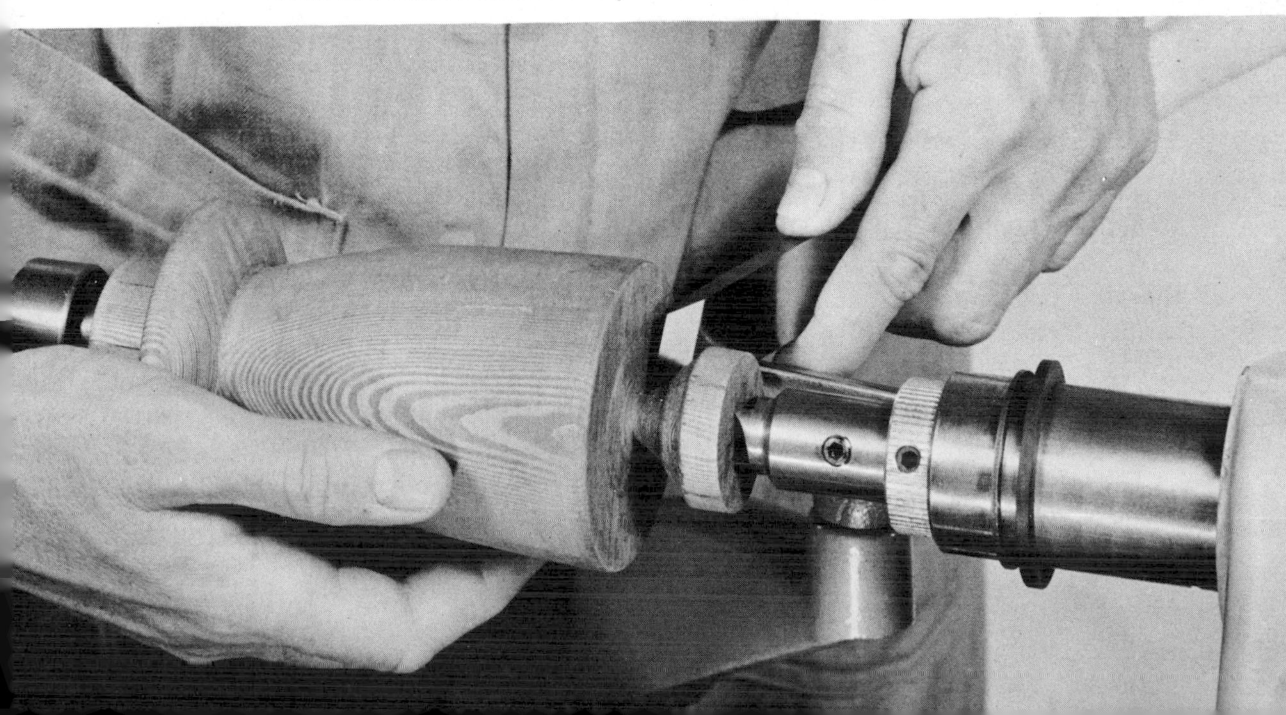

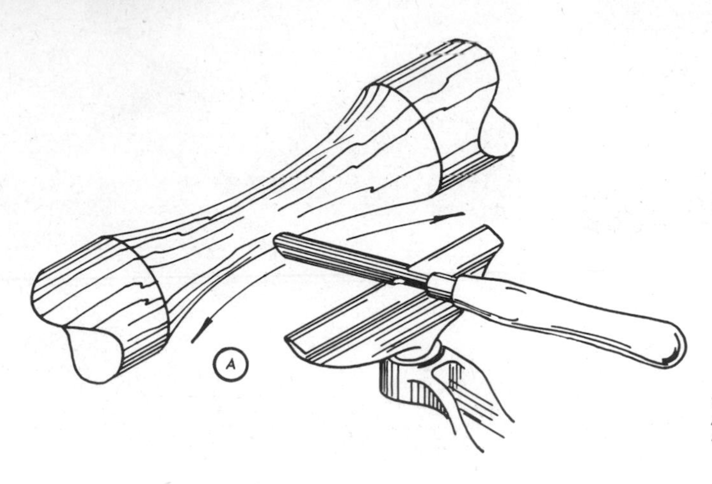
A
ARROWS INDICATE DIRECTION OF
TOOL MOVEMENT,

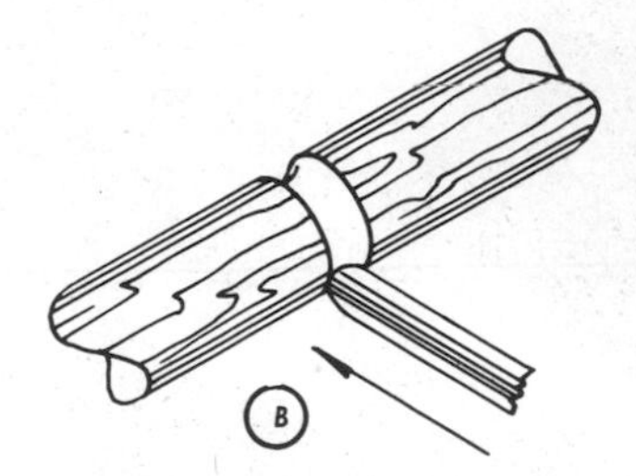
B
THE ROUND NOSE TOOL IS ALWAYS USED IN
A SCRAPING ACTION AND IS USED ON
ANY CONCAVE SHAPE

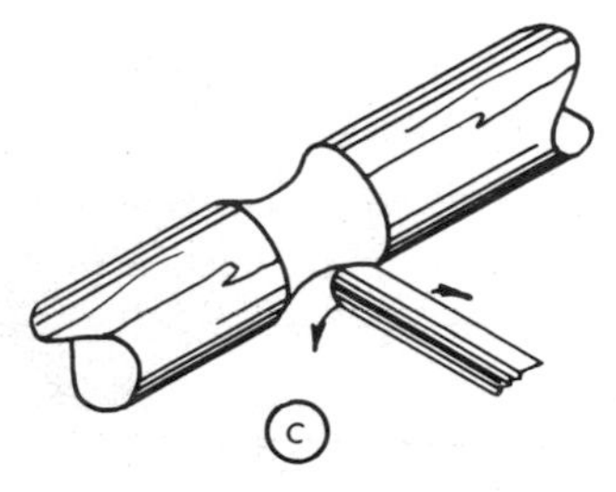
C

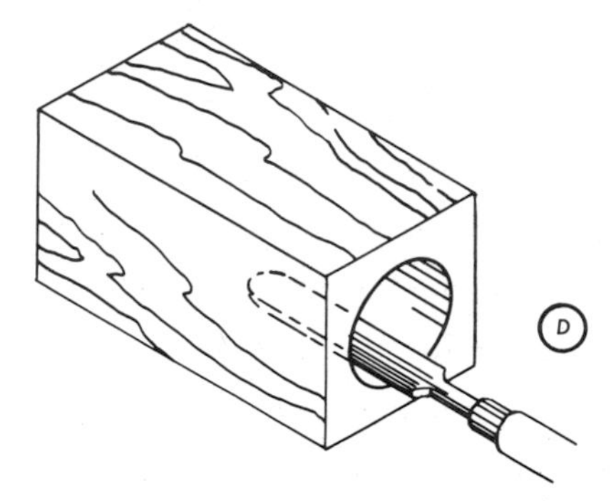
D

A. FORMING B. SMALL COVES C. LARGE COVES D. HOLLOWING

The roundnose tool, applications of which are shown here, is always used in a scraping action.

Using the Roundnose Tool

The roundnose tool is always used in a scraping action.

In the various applications shown above, the action is similar to the operations described for the gouge.

The roundnose tool is about the only chisel which will do a good, fast job in hollowing operations (D above).

The tool rest must give maximum support to the chisel, even if the rest has to be placed inside the hollow being cut.

Using the Parting Tool

The parting tool is most often used in a scraping action, blade resting on edge on tool rest and motion directly forward (top of opposite page).

To speed up the operation when making sizing cuts, place tool as shown at the right, with the handle of the tool below the tool rest. Start the cut in this position, which is a cutting action, and finish with the handle lifted so the cutting edge digs in deeper.

Use parting tool to form narrow shoulders (B on page opposite), to clean ends of stock (E), and to form small V-grooves (this is shown at C and D).

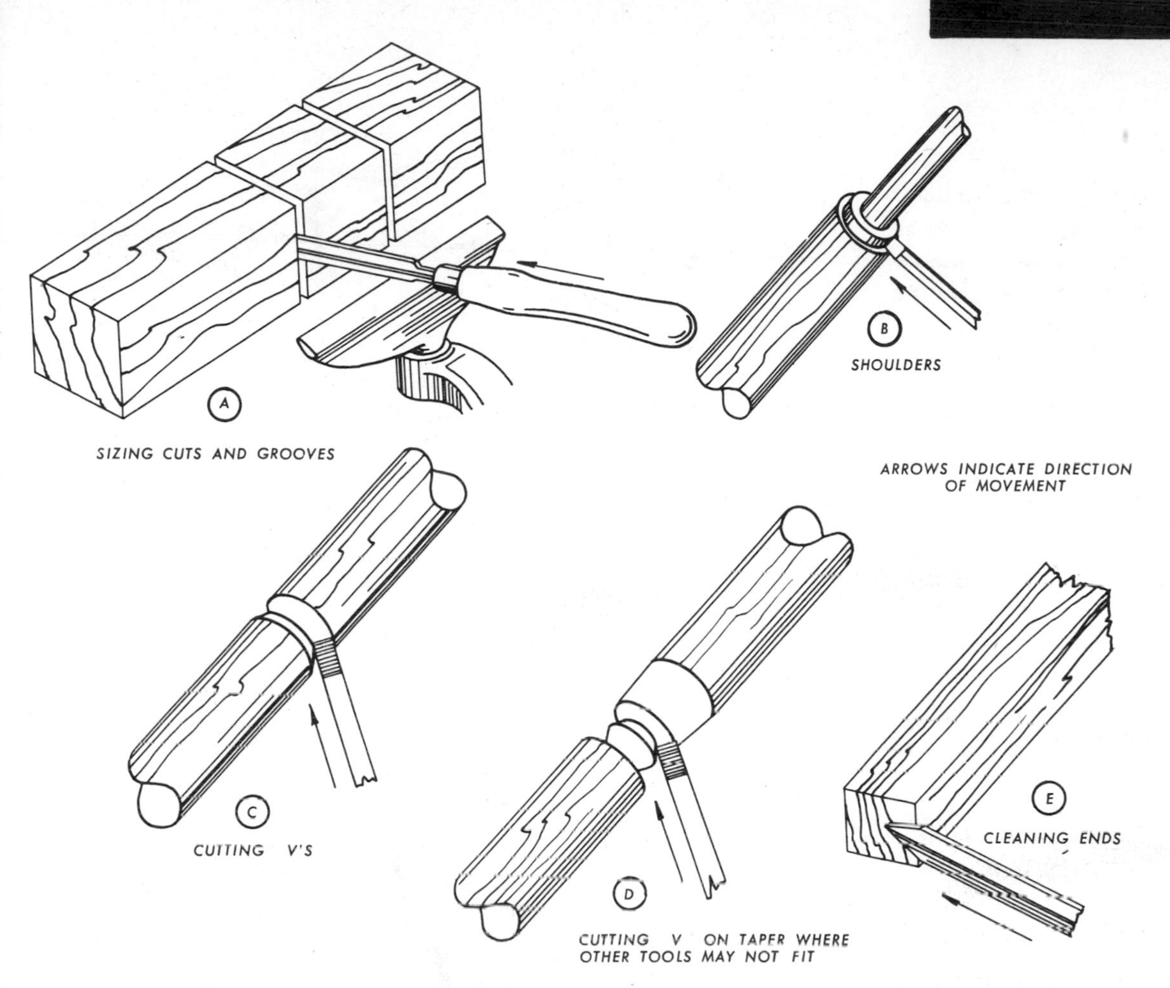

These are typical uses of the parting tool. It's most often used in a scraping action.

The diameter of the shape being turned is determined by the depth of the sizing cuts, so these cuts are important. They are easily made with the parting tool, using the technique shown here.

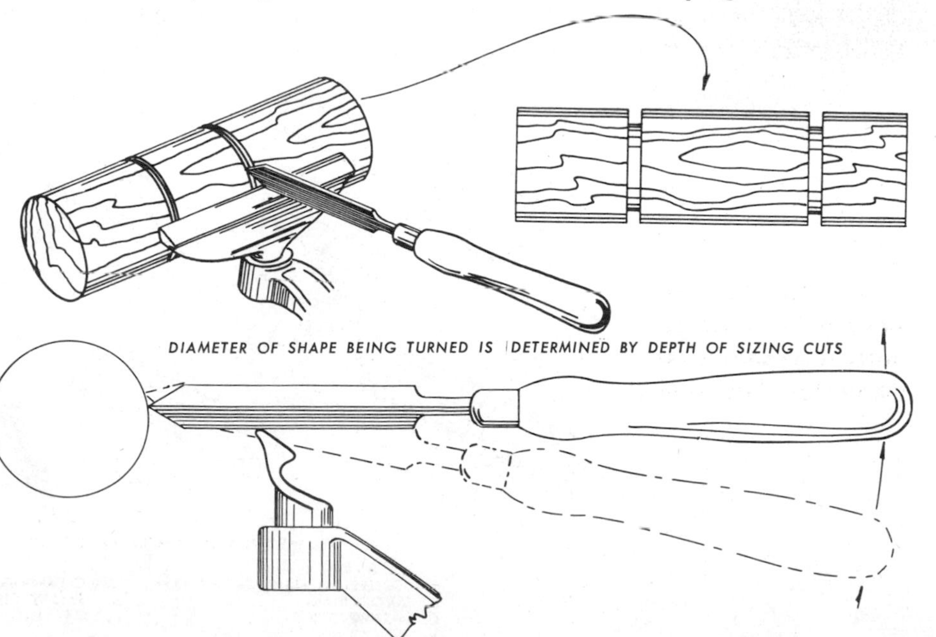

DIAMETER OF SHAPE BEING TURNED IS DETERMINED BY DEPTH OF SIZING CUTS

Though the squarenose chisel does these jobs well, ordinary butt chisels can be substituted.

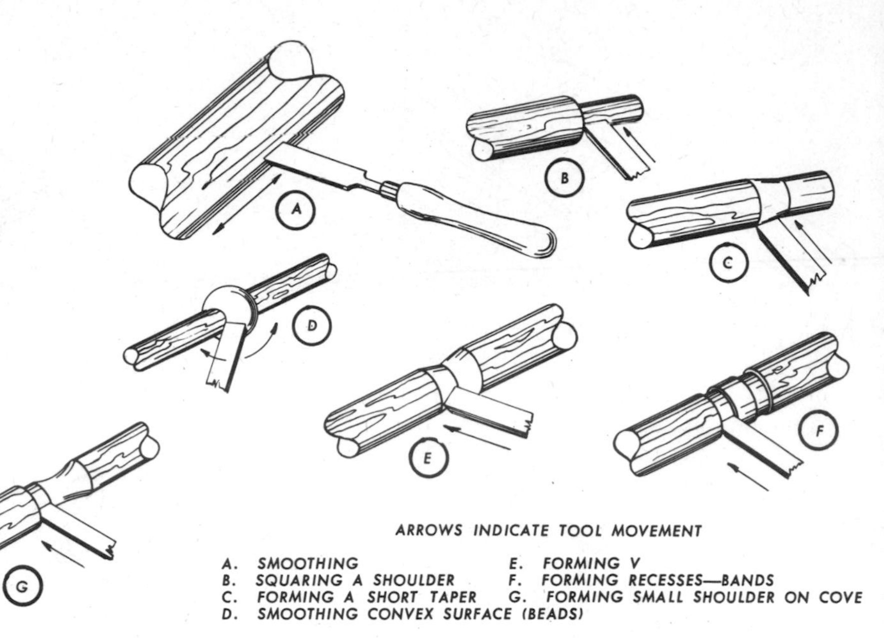

Squarenose; Spear Point

Beginners will find the squarenose tool very easy to handle. It is always used in a scraping action. When kept sharp and fed slowly and steadily it cuts smoothly and will do the variety of jobs illustrated above.

Ordinary butt chisels can be used instead, a size being selected that is particularly suited to the job; the width of the chisel in sketch F determines the width of the cut. Uniform bands are easily turned by using a chisel of the exact width.

In smoothing, the wider the chisel the faster and more even the job. Squarenose chisel, as in D above, simplifies smoothing convex surfaces.

The spear point (or diamond point) is handy because its sharp edge will cut clean lines and corners. It is used in a scraping action (sketch below) and mostly for touching up.

These are typical spear-point jobs, but other lathe chisels can do most of them well.

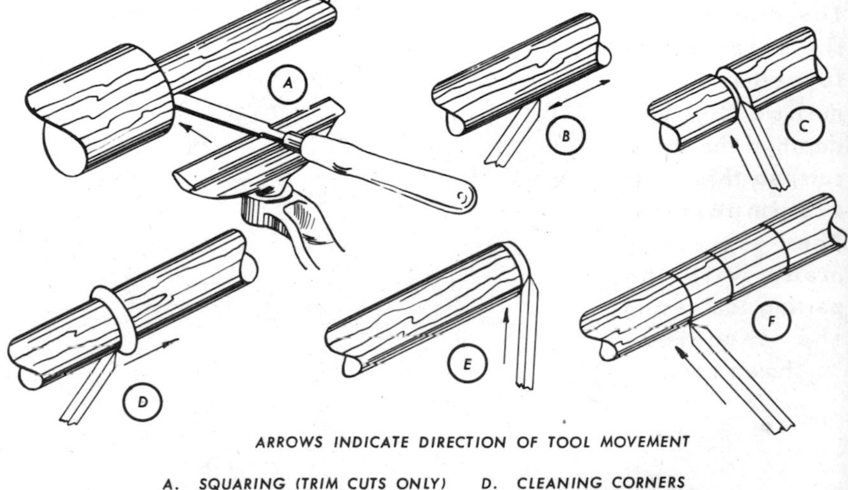

Planning the Design

It's a mistake to attempt to form a turning suitable for a project without first planning the design.

That's as bad as cutting on the table saw without a plan, thinking that somehow the pieces you cut will automatically fall together into an attractive project.

The best idea is to draw a full-size plan with the dimensions noted on it so that when the stock is in the lathe you will know exactly how you are going to cut and where.

Designing a turning is not difficult. Sketched below are some examples of classic molding forms; you will find many of these profiles used on items right in your own home —on straight moldings as well as on turned items.

It isn't necessary to limit yourself to these. If you were designing a table-lamp base about 12 inches high you could shape the base like the **cyma reversa.** From the top of the base the project could bulge out slightly in a convex form, sloping gently to a series of beads at the top and finally swelling into a full, round form which would receive the threaded sleeve holding the lamp socket.

Remember that merely covering the length of the turning with shape after shape is not likely to produce an attractive result.

You can lay out the project this way:

Draw a rectangle 4″ or 5″ by 12″. Draw a center line down its length. Break up the length into design areas by drawing horizontal lines that are proportional and pleasing. Let the base design occupy the bottom 3″; use 7″ for the transition from base to top and give the remaining beads and full round the remaining 2″.

You may shape many of these classic molding forms during your lathe-turning projects.

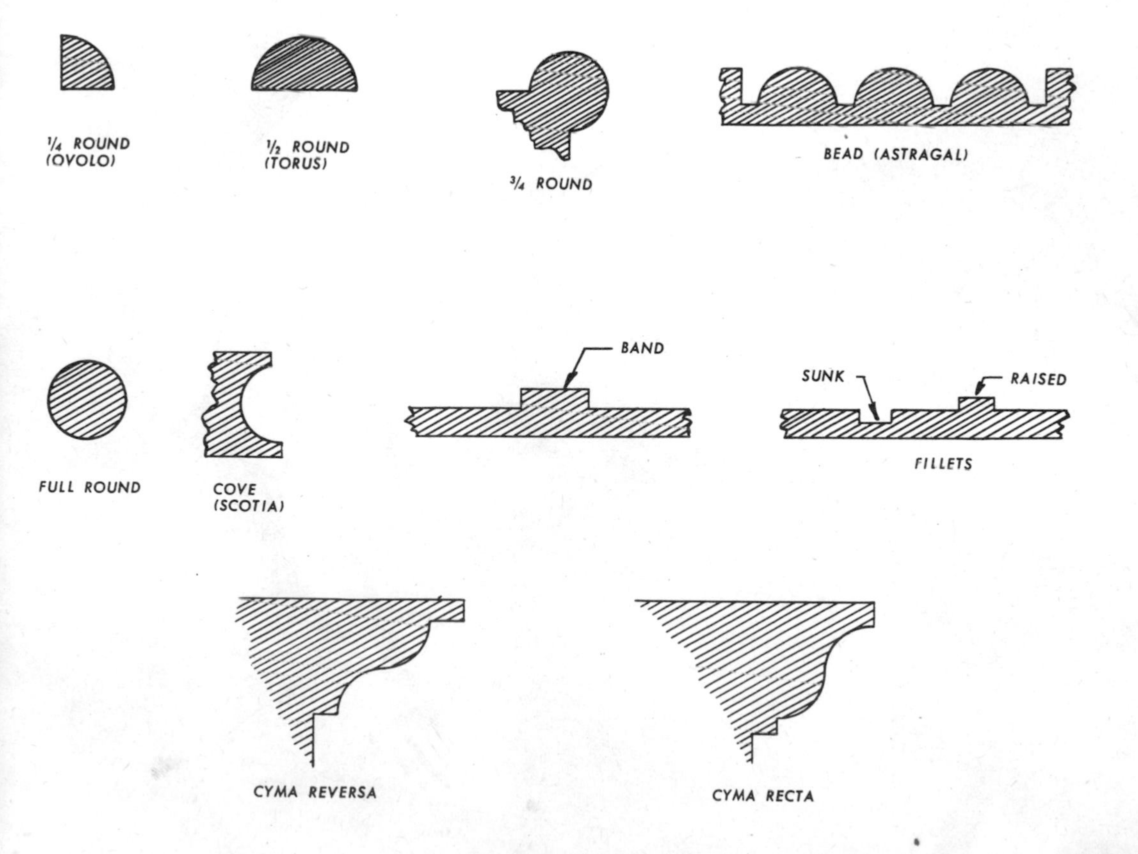

LATHE

Carbide-Tipped Tools

A carbide-tipped chisel is similar in shape to the ordinary lathe chisel but it has a tip of tungsten carbide, as shown in the drawing at the right. This is an extremely hard material which holds a sharp edge much longer than steel.

Some craftsmen have successfully substituted a few of these tools for a whole set of the ordinary steel ones.

Carbide-tipped tools can be used for free-hand turning of metals and plastics at wood-turning speeds. How the tools should be handled on various materials is shown in the pictorial chart below.

Although very hard, the carbide tip is brittle. It should be carefully protected when not in use and given maximum support during turning. Feed the tool slowly, especially on metals and plastics.

You will find that a slow speed works best, particularly on the harder materials. If the work begins to chatter it means that you are turning the work too fast, feeding the tool too fast, or taking too deep a bite.

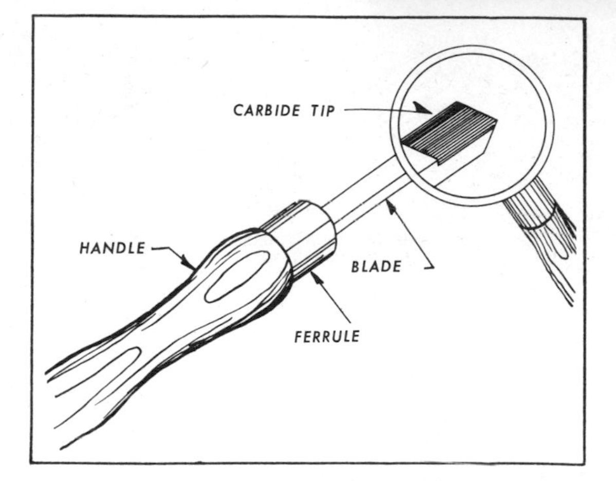

The carbide tip on tools like this is very hard and holds a sharp edge a long time.

Most woodworkers find that at one time or another they need a small metal part, such as the brass lamp-shade finial shown on the page at the left. For such projects as these alone, it is a good idea to have several of these carbide-tipped turning tools on hand and to learn how to use them.

When working with carbide-tipped turning tools, use this pictorial chart as a guide. It should give you a start toward finding the best cutting angle for each material and situation, something that must finally be determined by experiment for each.

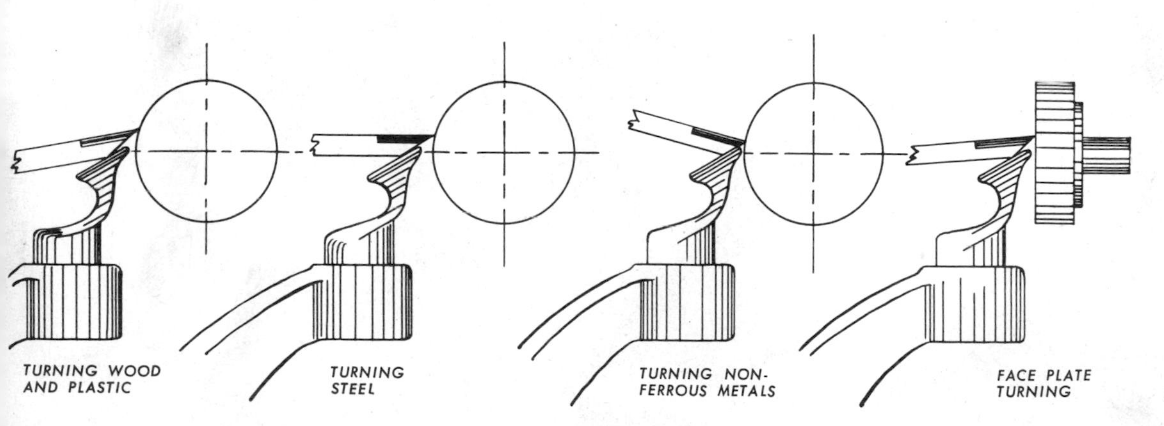

Carbide-tipped tools are especially useful for turning metal parts like this brass lamp-shade finial. It's a job you couldn't do at all with the ordinary tools made of steel.

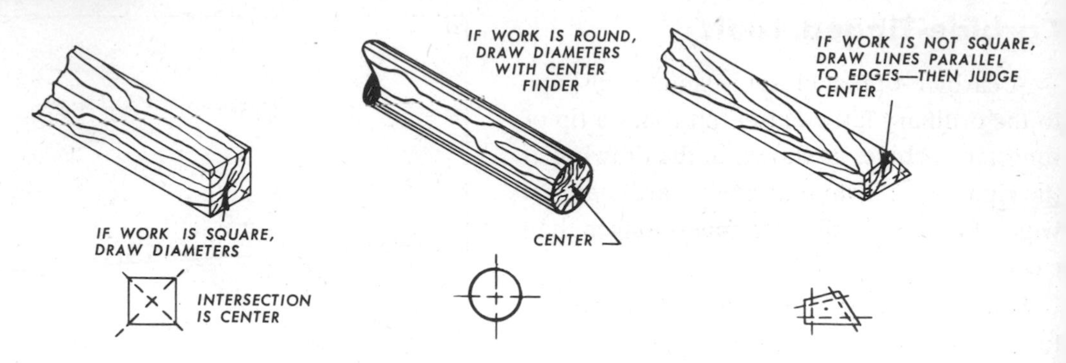
IF WORK IS ROUND, DRAW DIAMETERS WITH CENTER FINDER
IF WORK IS NOT SQUARE, DRAW LINES PARALLEL TO EDGES—THEN JUDGE CENTER
IF WORK IS SQUARE, DRAW DIAMETERS
CENTER
INTERSECTION IS CENTER

Before mounting stock, locate center at each end.

Spindle Turning

Most lathe jobs consist of mounting work between centers and forming a shape in a limited area or along the entire length of the stock. The work is marked at each end, so the points of the spur and dead center may be correctly placed on a common line running through the center of the stock. If the work is square, a straightedge may be used to draw diagonals across opposite corners at each end (see drawing above). Intersection of the diagonals will indicate the position of the

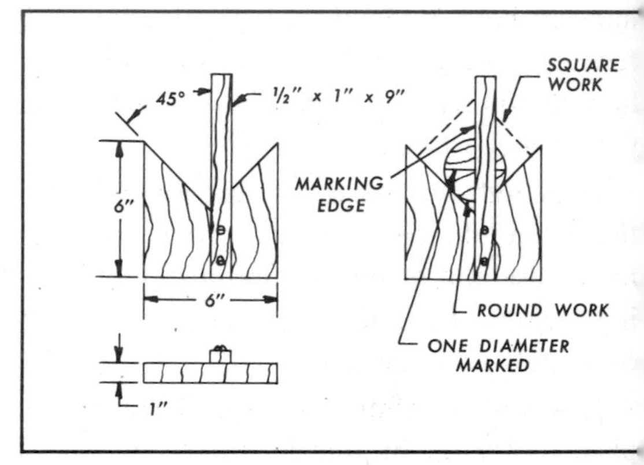
45°
½" x 1" x 9"
SQUARE WORK
6"
MARKING EDGE
6"
ROUND WORK
ONE DIAMETER MARKED
1"

This easily made tool will locate the centers at the ends of round or square stock.

To use this center-finder, place the stock in the angle of the tool and mark perpendicular diameters on the ends of the stock. The points where the lines intersect are the centers.

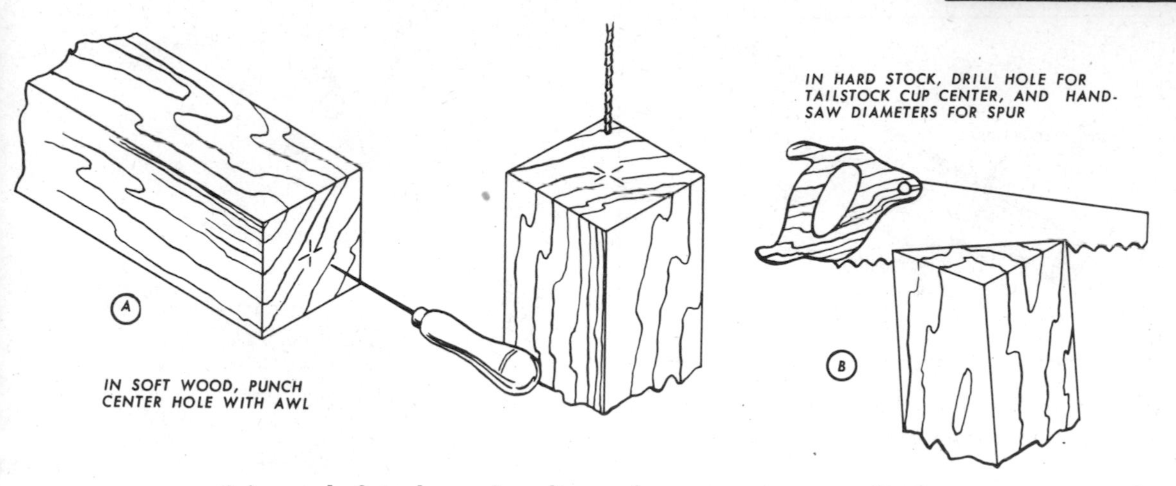
IN HARD STOCK, DRILL HOLE FOR
TAILSTOCK CUP CENTER, AND HAND-
SAW DIAMETERS FOR SPUR
A
IN SOFT WOOD, PUNCH
CENTER HOLE WITH AWL
B

Drive end of stock requires diagonals so spurs may seat firmly.

center point. If the work is not square, set a pair of dividers and draw lines parallel to the edges of the stock. The center will be confined in an area small enough so that you can judge its position with reasonable accuracy.

The center of a round piece of work is determined with the use of a center-finder. A special head which fits on the blade of a combination square will do this job; or you can make one for yourself by following the details at the left. Use maple for the parts. It's important to make it accurately.

Use the center-finder by placing the stock in the angle of the tool (photograph at lower left) and marking along the edge of the guide with a scriber, sharp awl, or sharp, hard pencil (at least 3H). The dotted lines in the drawing show how to use the center-finder to draw the diagonals on the end of a square.

When working with soft wood, use an awl to form the holes for the points on the centers (see sketch above). For the tailstock end, one hole is all that's needed. The spur-center however should be tapped into place with a mallet while the stock is out of the machine, as in photograph at right. Place the center so its point fits in the hole made by the awl and tap it down with a soft-faced or wooden mallet until the spurs are embedded in the wood.

With hard stock such as maple or birch, the procedure differs. Instead of using an awl to form the centering holes, you may find it easier to drill them (see B at top of page). Diagonals for the spur should be sawed by hand with backsaw, jig saw, or band saw.

Once the stock has been turned down to the point where you are ready for actual forming, it must be marked off to define the areas to be shaped. You can do this by turning the work at slow speed with a ruler placed on the tool rest so that it just touches the work, marking the dimensions with a pencil.

Or use a rule hooked over one end of the stock. Make the pencil lines about ½″ long. Turn on the motor and you'll be able to see the marks well enough to hold a pen-

Always set spur-center firmly before mounting stock in lathe. Use a soft-faced mallet.

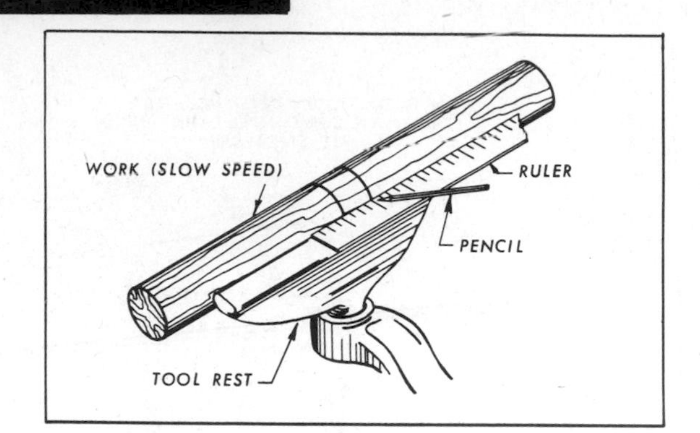

Dimension lines may be marked on a spindle by using a ruler and a pencil, like this.

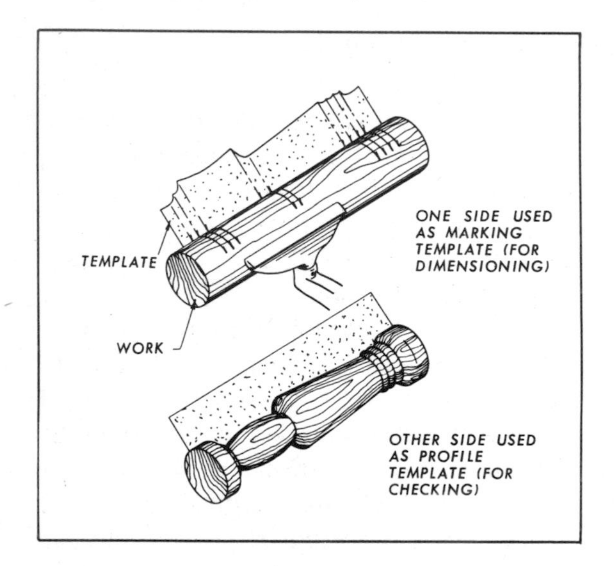

A full-scale layout of the part you wish to turn will provide a template for locating dimension points and a profile for checking.

Use these details to make the adjustable backrest shown in use at bottom of next page.

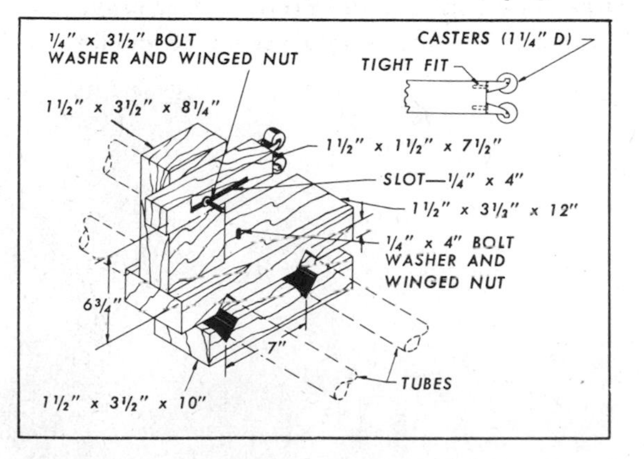

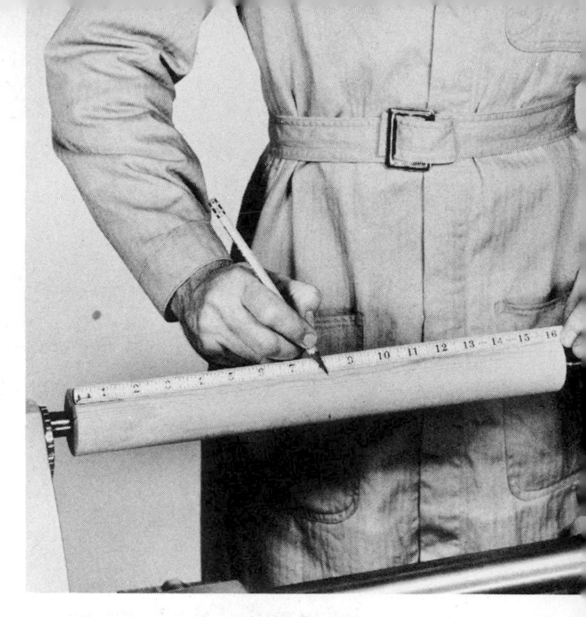

Another way to mark dimension lines is this; use a scale hooked over one end of stock.

cil against the turning stock and complete the lines.

When marking several pieces of stock—for turning similar chair or table legs, for example—it is better to make up a cardboard template as shown at left and use it in place of the other two methods. The marks will then be exactly alike on each of the turnings. Use the profile side of the template to check the work as it progresses. The template is made from a full-scale layout of the part as it will look when completed.

One important step, involving the use of the parting tool and a pair of outside calipers, is the sizing cut made after the turning has been dimensioned. Pick off from the drawing the diameter of the turning at each of the dimension points and set the calipers to match the dimension. Use the parting tool to make a slight cut on the line, then shift it to the right hand and move it against the work while the calipers, held in the left hand, ride in the cut being made and press lightly against the work as it turns. When the jaws of the calipers clear the stock the depth of cut has been reached. With the depth determined on each dimension line (this actually shows the diameter of the turning at that point), make shaping cuts until the form reaches the depth of cut set with the parting tool.

Use outside calipers and parting tool to establish diameter of stock at dimension points.

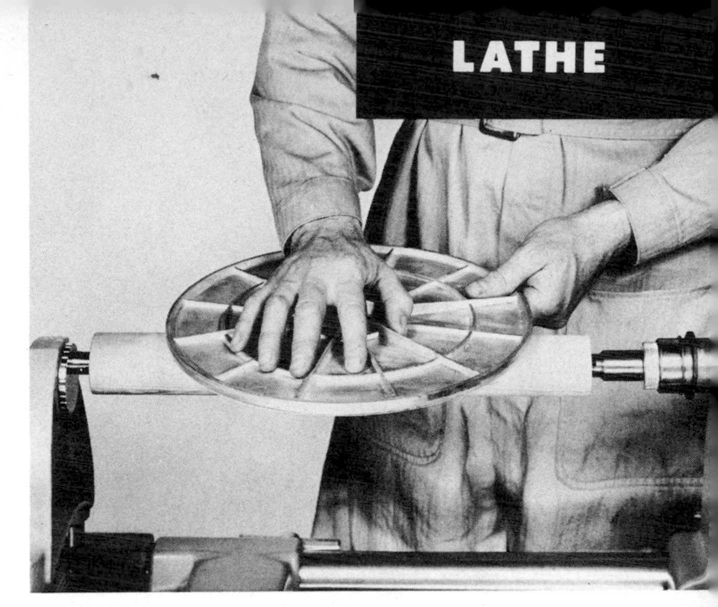

The 12″ sanding disk does a fine job of smoothing down straight cylinders and tapers.

Long, slender spindles require the support of a steady rest. The one shown below is designed to move along the ways to wherever it is needed. You can use it almost directly behind the cutting tool to provide support or away from the tool rest to overcome whip. The casters prevent marking or burning the work.

Follow the construction details at the bottom of the left-hand page and be sure that the V-grooves, which sit on the tubes, are placed correctly. Insure this by clamping the two pieces of stock together and laying out the V's on both on a common center line. With the shape marked on the wood, cut the grooves with the saw table tilted 45°.

The slot in the adjustable arm which holds the casters is made by drilling a ¼″ hole at each end of the center line of the slot, then cutting between them on the jig saw. Or drill a series of holes and then clean away the waste with a file or a chisel.

When fitting the casters, measure the diameter of the shank and drill holes slightly undersize so the shanks will fit tightly.

A backrest is essential to overcome whip that naturally develops on long, slim turnings.

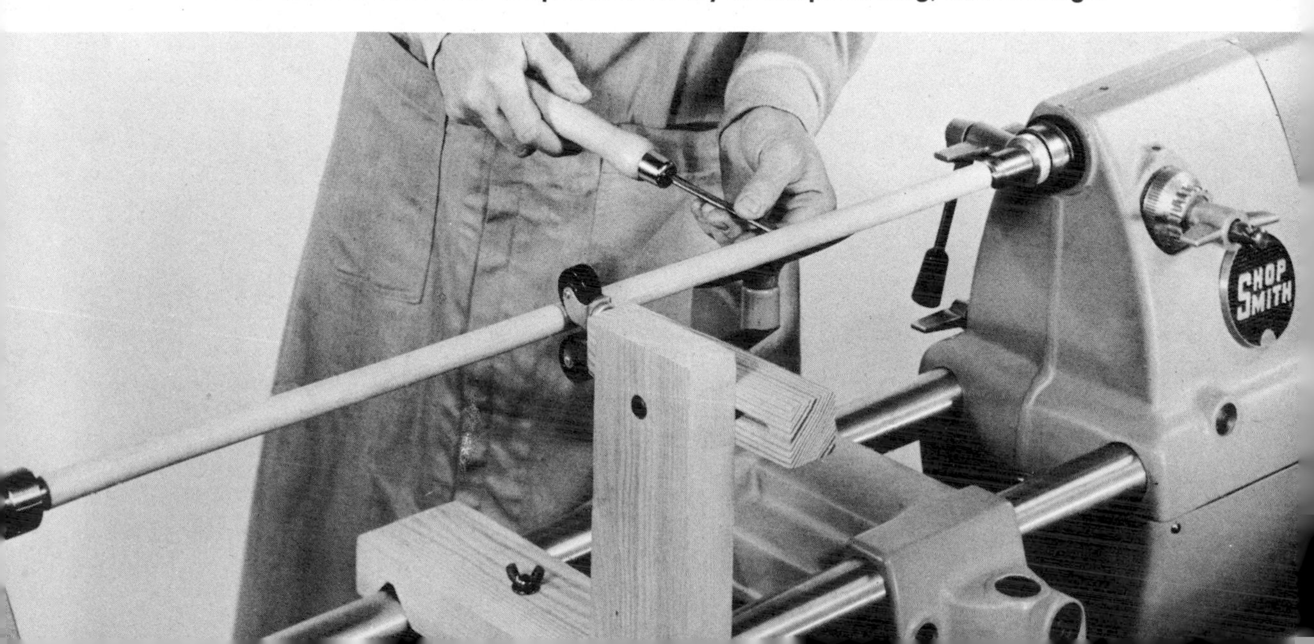

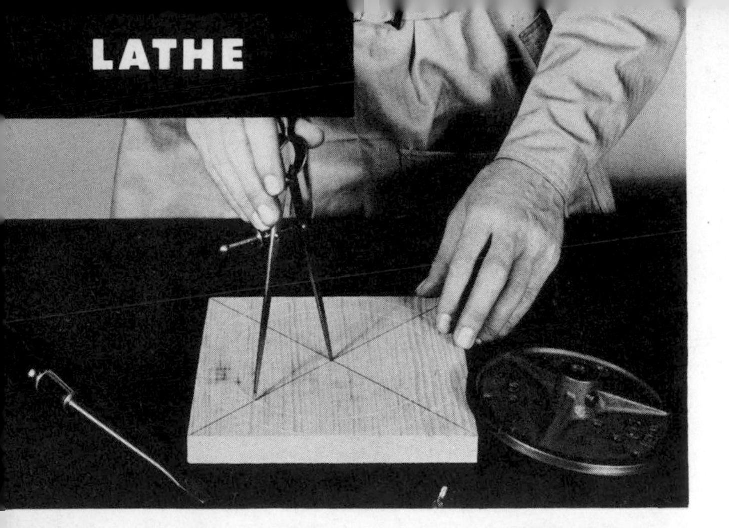

Prepare stock for mounting by scribing on it a circle slightly larger than faceplate.

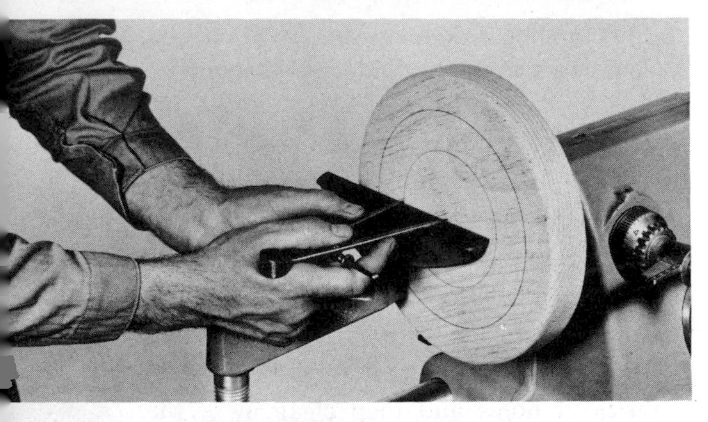

Scribe very lightly when using dividers to mark dimension lines on surface of stock.

Faceplate Turning

Not all lathe work can be mounted between centers. Such things as large lamp bases and bowls must be mounted on a faceplate.

Use screws to fasten faceplate to turning block after it has been centered. If the block to be turned is square, draw diagonals to find the center and use a pair of dividers or a pencil compass (picture at left) to scribe a circle just a bit larger than the diameter of the faceplate. Center the faceplate in the circle and mark the screw holes with an awl.

In all faceplate work note the length of the screws used so you do not shape the face of the stock deeply enough to cut into them. Cut the stock to approximate size on the jig saw or band saw before fastening it to the faceplate.

Handle the lathe chisels in faceplate work much as in spindle turning but use scraping action almost exclusively. Rotate the tool rest in its seat so it can be used on the edge of the work, and then swing it around to the front or face. Set the headstock and tool rest

A full-sized template is useful both for marking dimensions and checking profile.

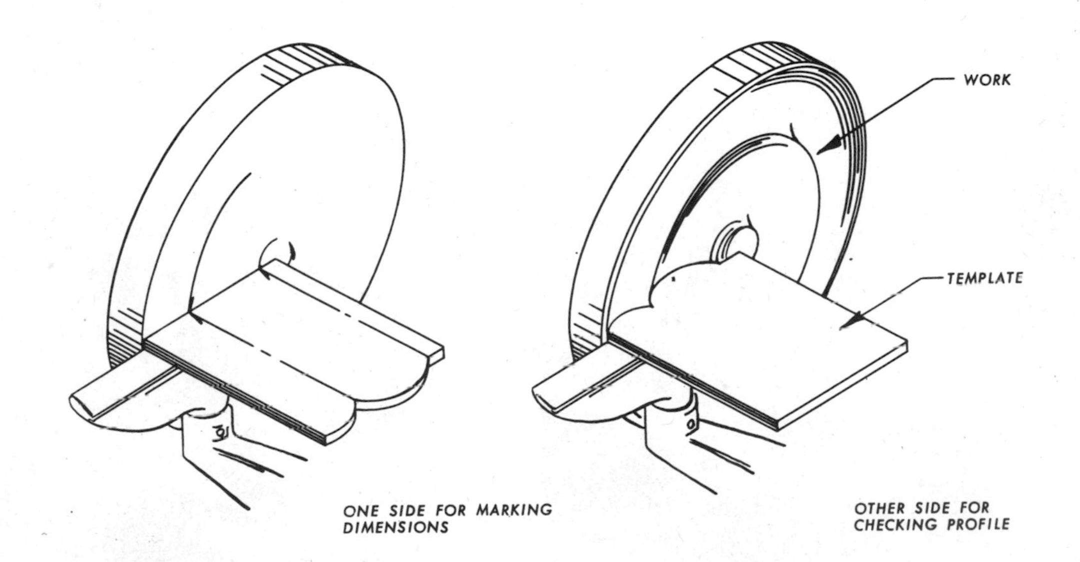

An ordinary marking gauge can be used to dimension perimeter of a faceplate turning.

at the far right end of the ways so you can face the work, a convenience in many operations.

Once the work is mounted and ready for shaping, dimension the stock to determine limits and depths of shapes. Hold a pair of dividers on the tool rest as shown at left to mark off the face of the stock. Place one point of the dividers directly in the center of the work, pressing it in just enough to form a seat for the point. Press the other point lightly against the work as it revolves, scribing the wood to mark the dimension line.

Marking templates like those described for spindle turning may be used (bottom opposite page). Profile templates are used to check the shape or to assure similarity in duplicate turnings.

Dimension lines on the edge of the stock may be marked with a woodworking marking gauge. These are usually constructed so the head can be secured at the dimension

Always place the tool rest to provide maximum support for the chisel, even if that means inserting the tool rest right into the cavity being formed, as is the case here.

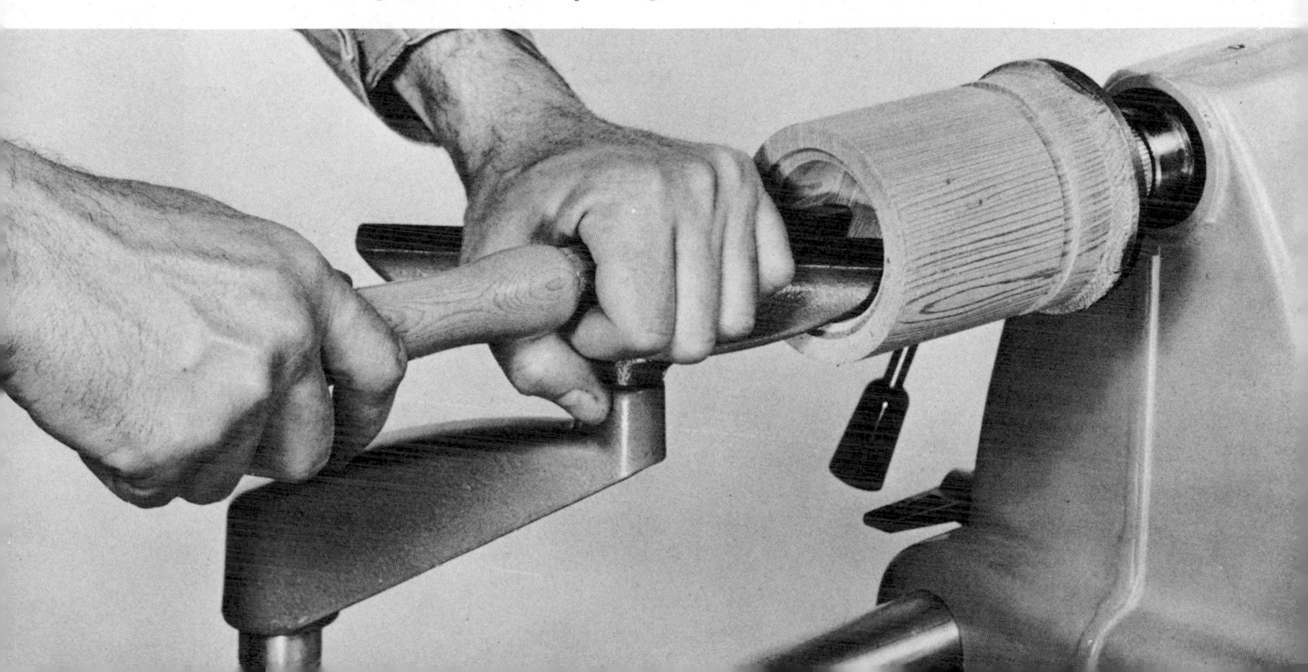

A simple homemade depth gauge is convenient for checking depth of cut.

If work can't be mounted between centers and is too small for faceplate, use screw-center.

desired. The head rides against the face of the stock and the scribe point is pressed lightly into the work.

Hollowing deep projects requires placing the tool rest so that it may be partially inserted into the cavity being formed.

The roundnose turning tool is used to remove the material, while finishing cuts and

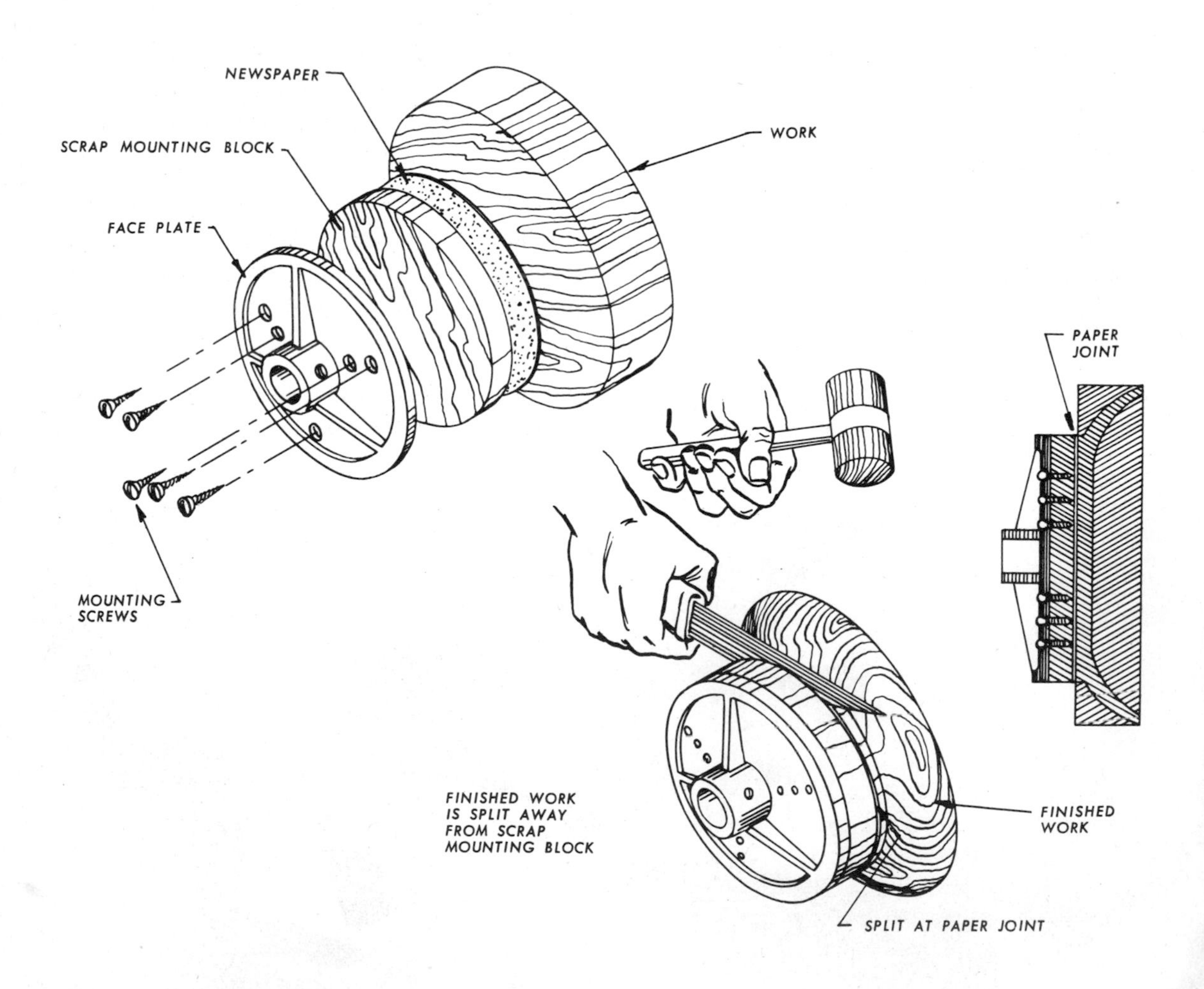

cleaning the bottom corner may be accomplished with the spear point or the skew.

A depth gauge is used as shown on opposite page to check the depth of the hollow being formed. This can also be checked by using a straightedge across the face of the work and a ruler to measure from it to bottom of hole.

Work too small to be mounted on a faceplate and not long enough to be mounted between centers is secured on a screw-center, which is then mounted on the spindle like any other attachment. The center of the work is determined by crossed diagonals if the work is square, by the center-finder if the work is round. Start a hole for the screw with an awl or by drilling. Mount the work in the screw center by threading it on (upper right on opposite page).

On many projects, holes left by faceplate mounting screws are to be avoided—or the project may require a base too thin to permit screws. In this case mount the work on a scrap block that can take the screw holes.

Coat the mating surfaces with glue (a urea resin glue works best) then clamp them together with a piece of ordinary newspaper between them. This is shown in the drawing on the opposite page.

After the glue has dried and the work has been mounted and turned, carefully split it away from the scrap mounting-block. The newspaper makes this possible and assures a clean, even separation needing little sanding.

Here's how to mount faceplate work on a scrap block. This is particularly desirable when screw holes in the bottom of the project would be unattractive—or when the project has an extremely thin base.

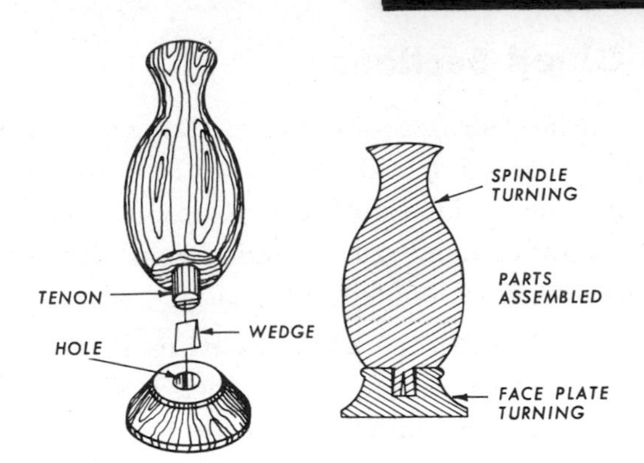

Tenon and wedge may be used to join a faceplate turning to a spindle turning.

Turning Large Work

For spindle turnings longer than the capacity of the lathe, turn the project in two or more pieces. Form a tenon on the end of one piece while it is in the lathe. Drill a hole in the mating piece. Glue the parts together. For an extremely strong joint, use the lock wedge shown in the bottom detail.

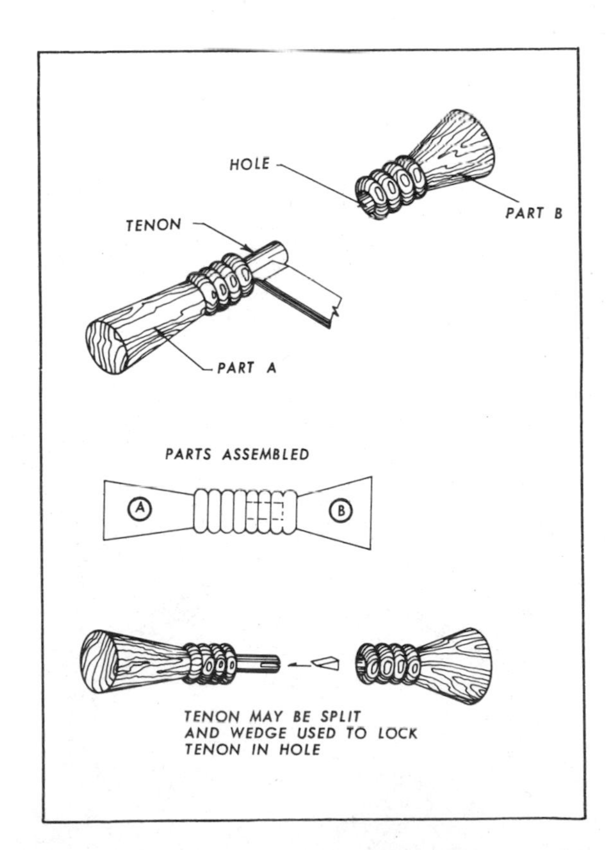

Glued Sections

Many turning jobs require a large diameter in a limited area of the work. Two methods may be used to simplify such jobs. In one, the jointer or band saw is used to remove stock before it is mounted in the lathe.

In the other, glued blocks are used to build up the limited area that requires it. The mating surfaces must be perfectly flat and true for a perfect joint if the final turning is to resemble a solid piece of wood.

When solid stock large enough for a deep bowl or similar project is not available, small blocks may be glued together. Or rough-cut rings may be glued onto a solid base. This method saves a lot of material since the cut-out disks may be used in other ways. The illustration below shows rings cut for a project that will have straight sides. If the sides are to slope or taper, the rings should vary in size. The important thing is a good glue job so the

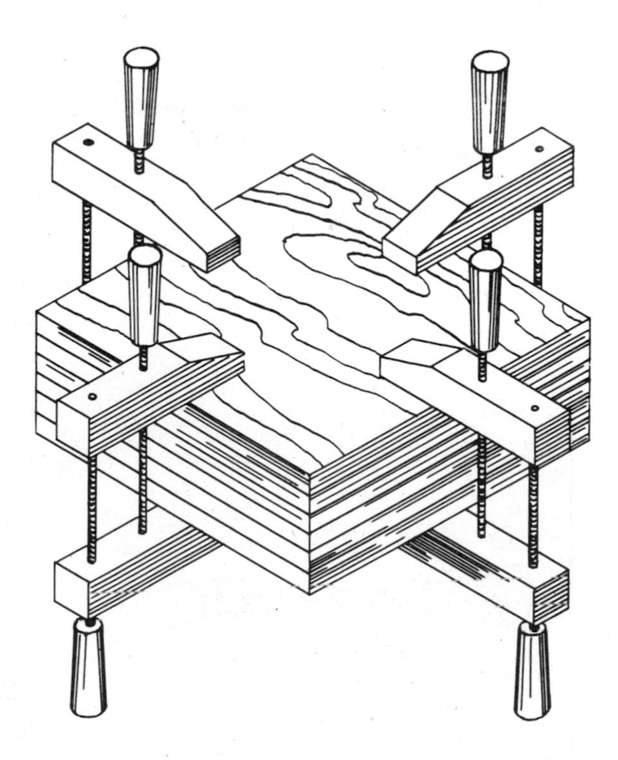

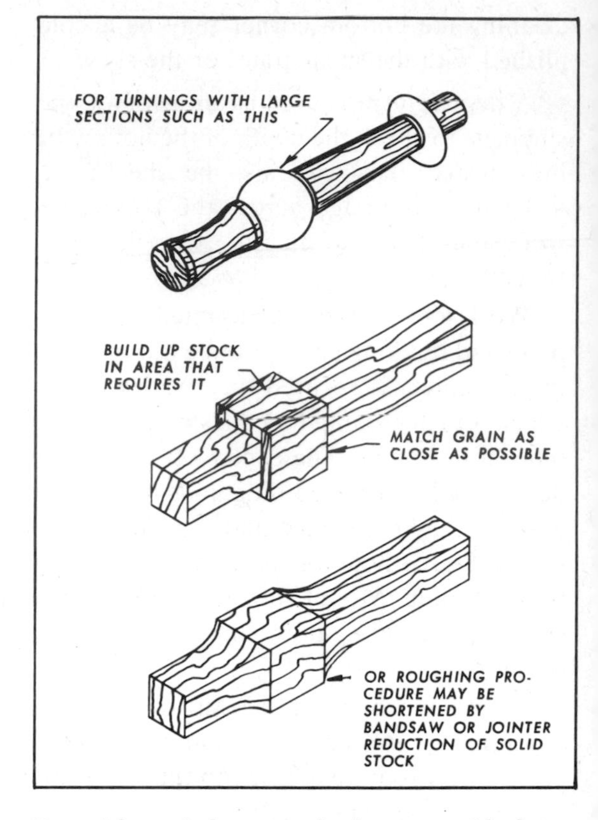

Use either of these methods to provide large diameter in a limited area of the work. Build up the stock where necessary or (bottom of drawing above) remove excess material on band saw or jointer before beginning lathe work.

Turning a deep bowl may be speeded up by rough-cutting rings and gluing them together on a solid base to make a turning block with tedious waste removal already done.

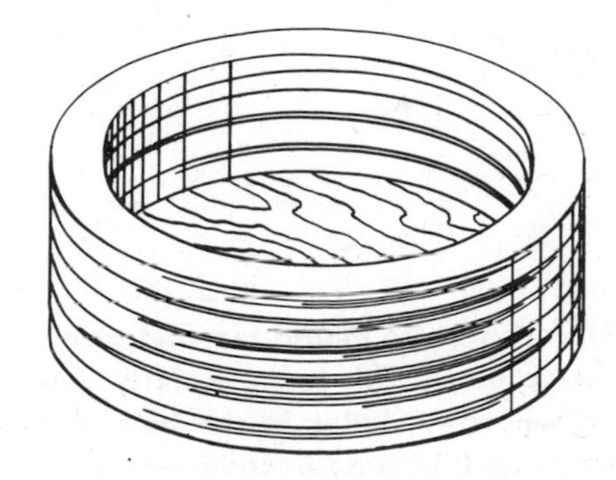

stock will hold together with just a faint line showing on the finished item.

It's an interesting lathe procedure to glue contrasting woods into squares and oblongs for turning (drawing below). The blocks may not look like much in rough form, but they are attractive "inlaid" projects when the turning is complete. Wood should be selected not only for contrast in color but for similarity in degree of hardness. Good combinations are maple with rosewood; holly or birch with cherry, walnut, or mahogany.

Create an interesting turning square by gluing together blocks of contrasting woods.

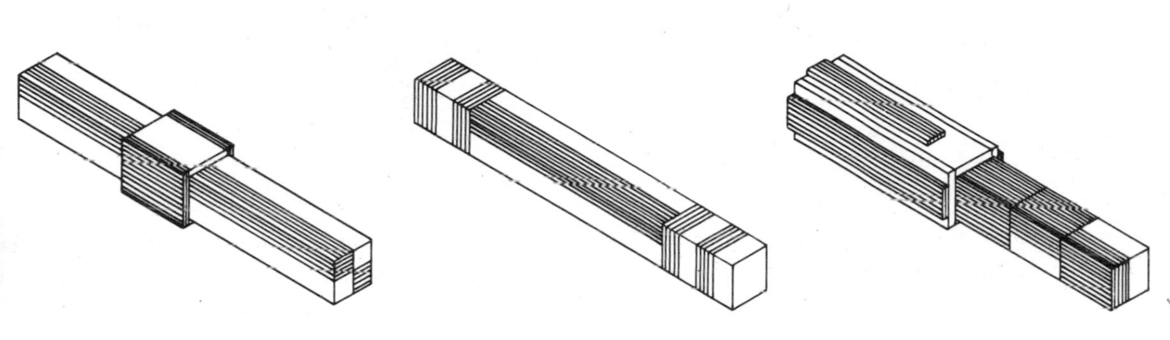

INTERESTING INLAYED EFFECTS BY TURNING GLUED-UP BLOCKS

PREDRILLING A CENTER HOLE AND MOUNTING ON DOWEL FACILITATES GLUING

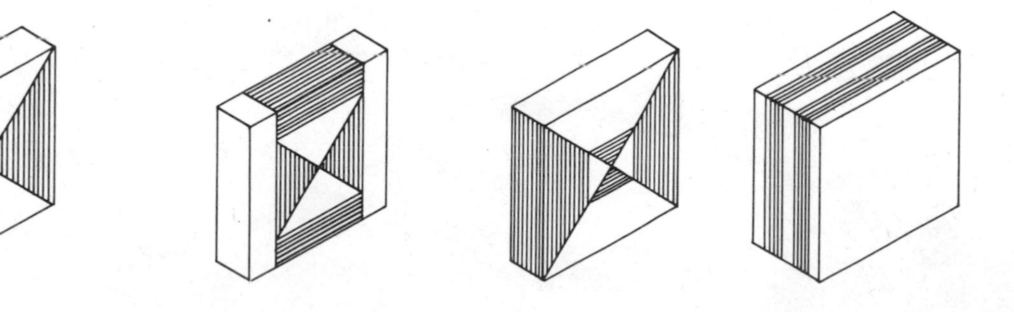

THE SAME IDEA MAY BE USED IN FACEPLATE TURNING

Make a lathe block of two identical pieces and split it apart after turning to get a pair of identica half-round moldings. One simple way of temporarily joining the pieces that form the blocks is with corrugated fasteners, as shown in the photograph below.

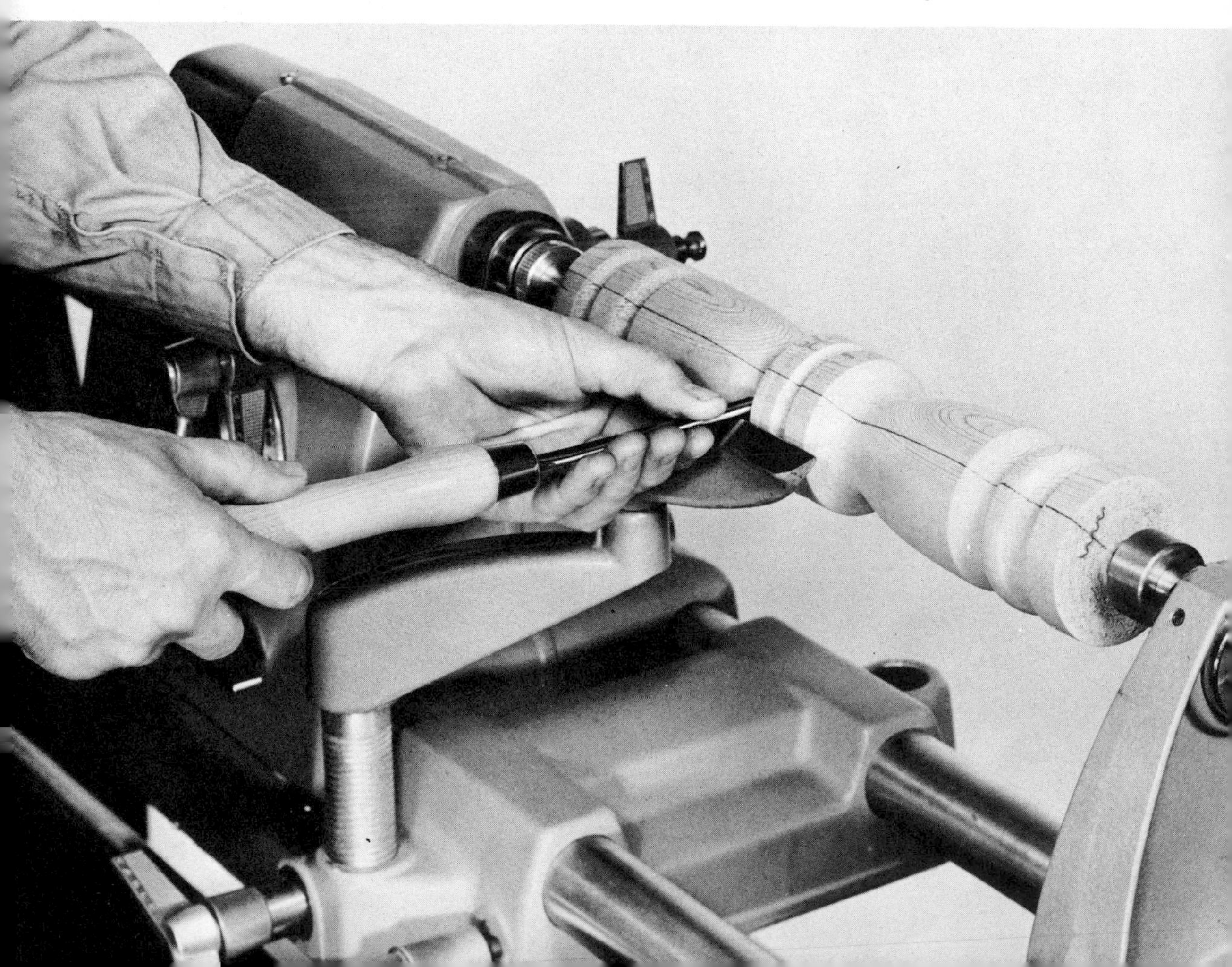

Split Turnings

Split turnings are lathe projects made to be halved (upper photograph on opposite page) or quartered. The split turning being finished in the lower photograph opposite consists of two pieces of 2″ by 4″ joined at each end by corrugated fasteners. The work is mounted and turned like any other job. When the shaping is complete, the fasteners are removed or the waste ends cut off to produce two identical half-columns.

Another method, shown at left below, uses the paper-glue joint described for faceplate turning. Glue two similar pieces together with a piece of paper sandwiched into the joint. When the joint is dry, mount and turn the work. Remove it from the lathe and split it along the joint. Use a sharp, thin-bladed knife and tap gently with a mallet until the two pieces part at the joint. The glue-coated areas may be cleaned off on the disc sander.

The upper right-hand drawing shows a method of obtaining four similar pieces of flat molding. The four outside pieces are glued to a solid core with newsprint in the joints. After the work is turned the moldings are split away from the core.

How four turning squares may be joined to obtain four identical pieces of quarter-round molding is illustrated at lower right.

Procedures like these are useful when a special molding, such as one in a fancy hardwood, is needed that cannot be obtained from the usual sources.

Turning stock every time you need a piece of ordinary molding is too time-consuming to be practical.

Shown below are some ways of making half-round, quarter-round, and flat moldings.

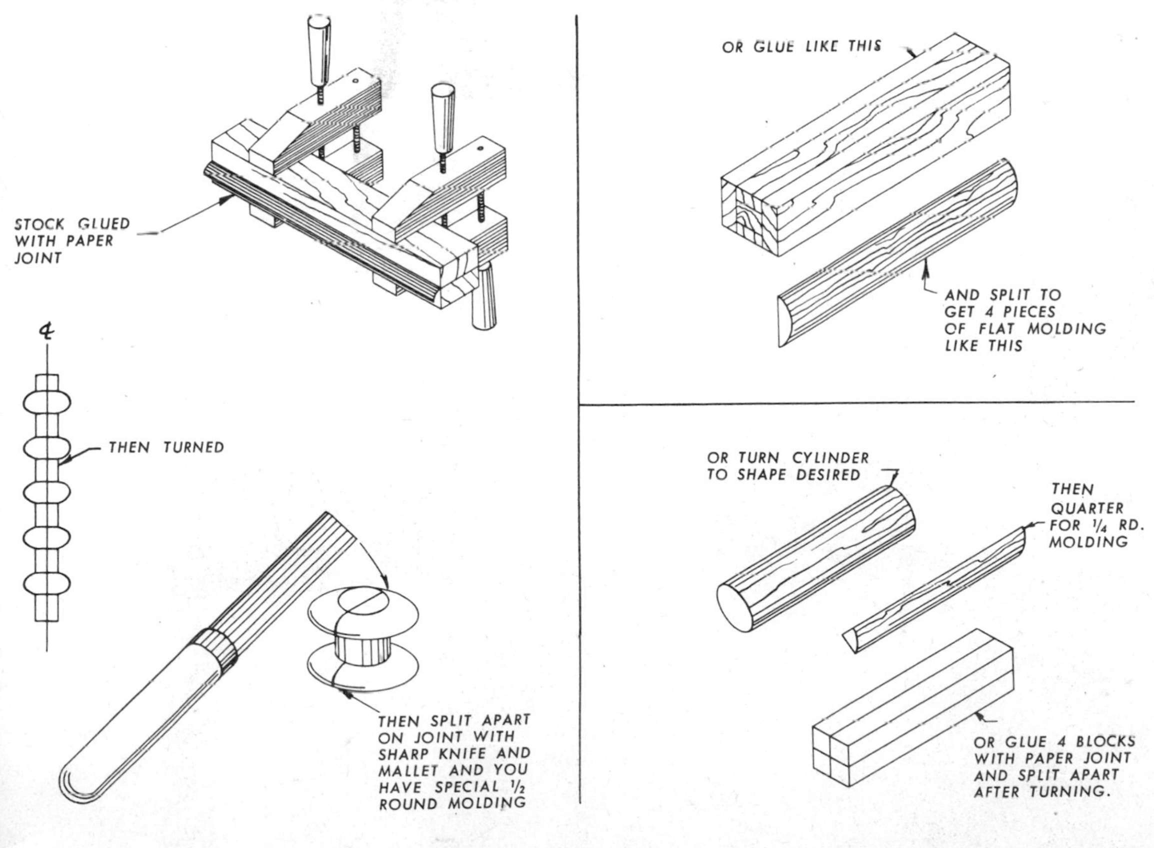
STOCK GLUED WITH PAPER JOINT
THEN TURNED
THEN SPLIT APART ON JOINT WITH SHARP KNIFE AND MALLET AND YOU HAVE SPECIAL 1/2 ROUND MOLDING
OR GLUE LIKE THIS
AND SPLIT TO GET 4 PIECES OF FLAT MOLDING LIKE THIS
OR TURN CYLINDER TO SHAPE DESIRED
THEN QUARTER FOR 1/4 RD. MOLDING
OR GLUE 4 BLOCKS WITH PAPER JOINT AND SPLIT APART AFTER TURNING.

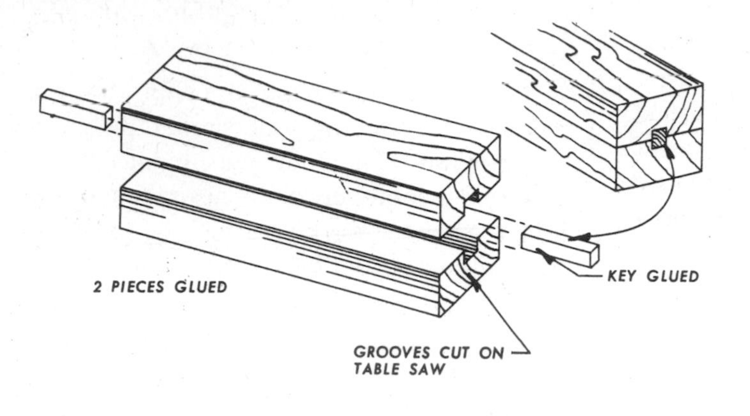
2 PIECES GLUED
KEY GLUED
GROOVES CUT ON
TABLE SAW

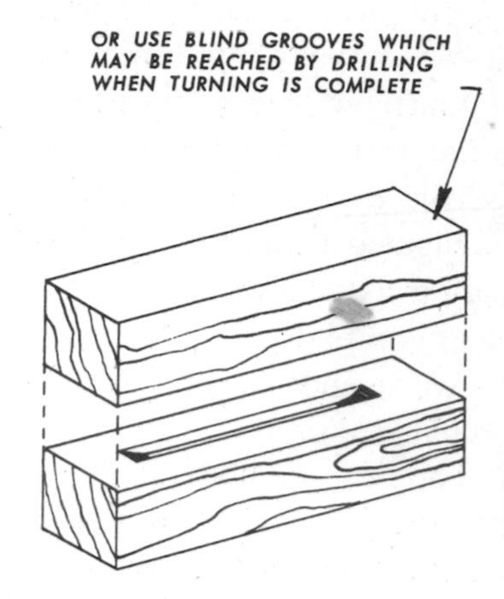
OR USE BLIND GROOVES WHICH
MAY BE REACHED BY DRILLING
WHEN TURNING IS COMPLETE

When center holes are required in a lamp base or other such long projects, use one of the two techniques sketched above. If the project is short enough, a center hole may be drilled in it right in the lathe; put a chuck in the tailstock by mounting it on a tailstock chuck arbor. Then advance the revolving work against the drill.

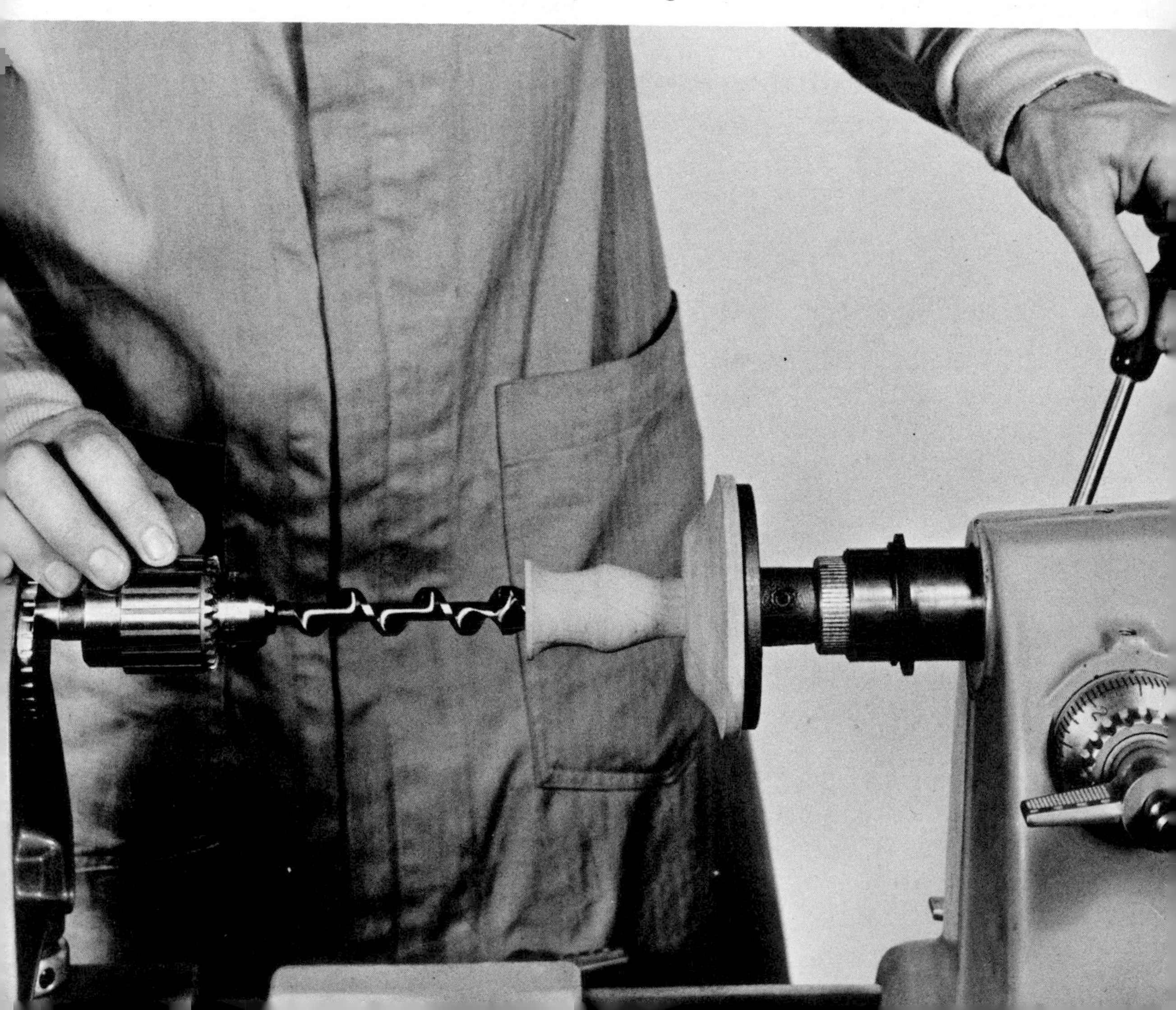

Cutting Center Holes

You can precut center holes through such lathe projects as lamp bases by using the method shown at left. Cut grooves down the center of the stock on the table saw.

(For a lamp cord, a groove about 5/16" wide by ⅛" deep in each piece will do.)

Glue the two pieces together, with keys plugging the openings at the ends. When turning is complete, carry the grooves through to the ends of the turning by boring holes to meet them.

Accurate center holes can be drilled in stock by using a chuck mounted on a tailstock chuck arbor. In the photograph at the bottom of the opposite page, a candle socket is being drilled in a candle stand. This procedure is most efficient when center holes must be drilled in stock secured to a faceplate.

Thin Faceplate Work

Work too thin to be mounted on a faceplate can be turned by mounting it, as shown below, on a nut and bolt to be gripped in the jaws of a drill chuck or router chuck mounted on the spindle in place of a conventional center. This method is good when the work requires a center hole. If not, the turning should be attached to a scrap block by gluing with the paper-joint method. The scrap block is then fastened to the faceplate in the usual manner.

Use one of these methods when turning very thin faceplate work.

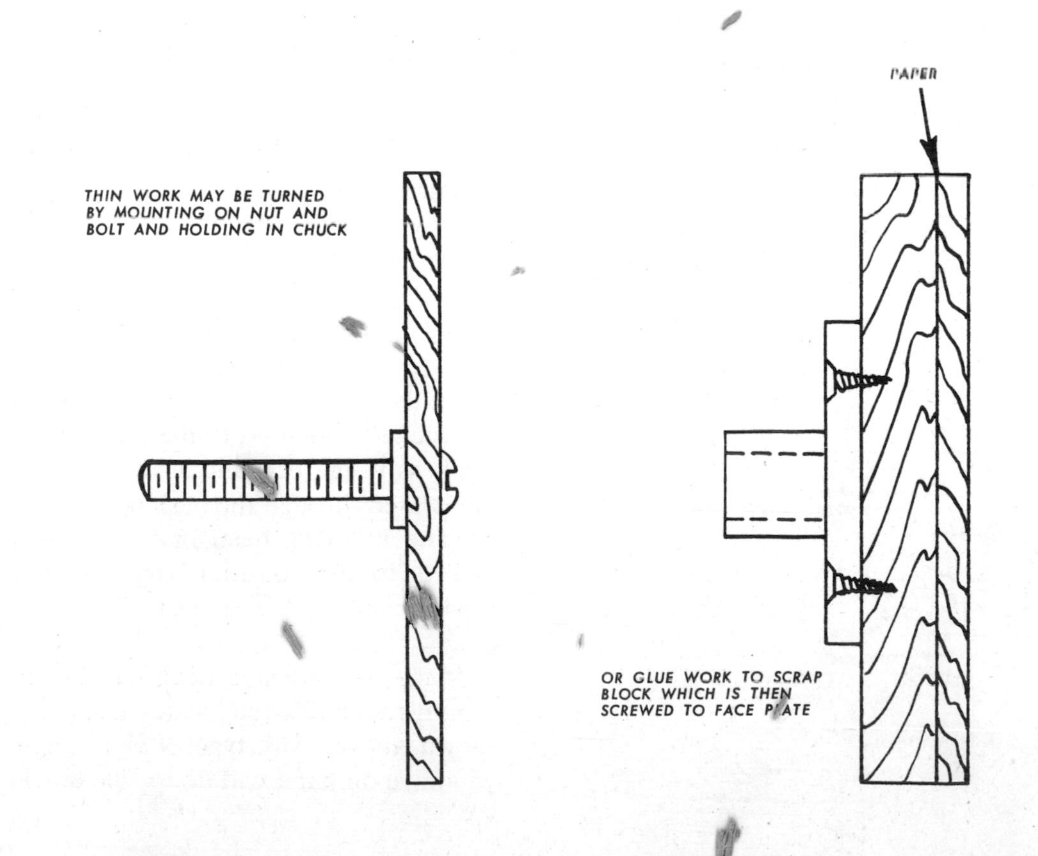
PAPER
THIN WORK MAY BE TURNED
BY MOUNTING ON NUT AND
BOLT AND HOLDING IN CHUCK
OR GLUE WORK TO SCRAP
BLOCK WHICH IS THEN
SCREWED TO FACE PLATE

This easily made indexing head can be attached to a lathe faceplate and locked on the upper auxiliary spindle of the multi-purpose tool. The extra hole for attaching the guide-pin bracket to the top of the headstock should be drilled exactly as shown—and with care.

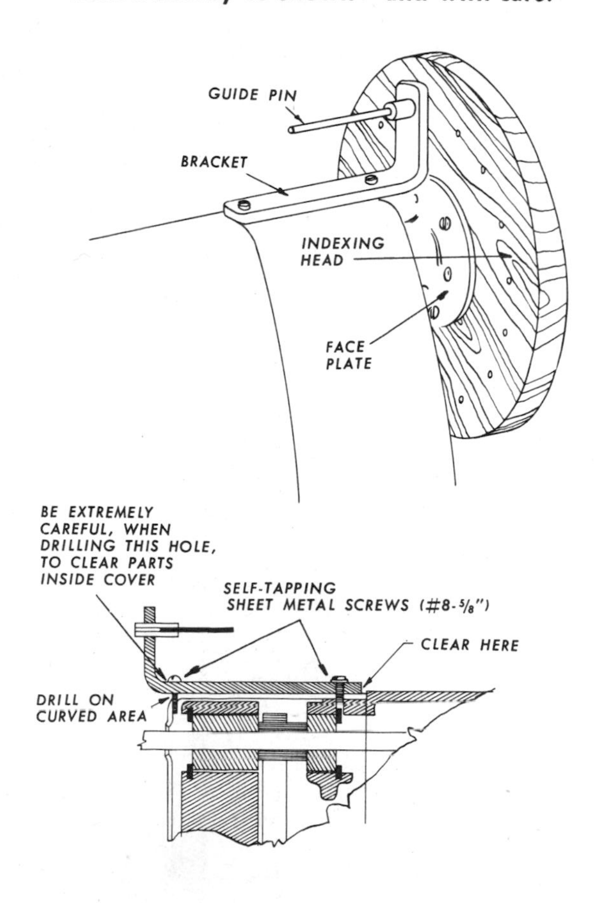

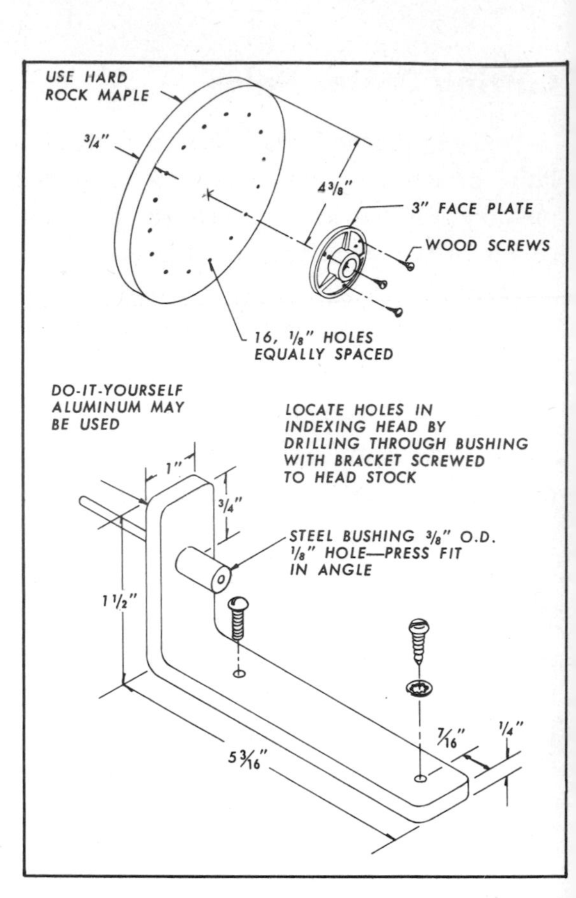

Follow the details given in the drawing above to make an indexing head.

Indexing Head

Some lathe projects require radial holes equally spaced about the circumference. These are most easily bored with the help of a spacing device known as an indexing head. An easy-to-make, improvised affair that can be mounted on the upper auxiliary spindle of the multi-purpose tool is shown at upper left. A bracket is secured to the top of the headstock as in the drawing at the left. A guide pin is used through the bushing in the bracket. The indexing head may be turned and locked in any position, thereby situating work mounted between centers or on a faceplate.

Make the indexing head and bracket assembly that holds and locates the pin guide as shown above. Any type of rigid angle that you have on hand will do for the bracket, or

Cutting Center Holes

You can precut center holes through such lathe projects as lamp bases by using the method shown at left. Cut grooves down the center of the stock on the table saw.

(For a lamp cord, a groove about 5/16″ wide by ⅛″ deep in each piece will do.)

Glue the two pieces together, with keys plugging the openings at the ends. When turning is complete, carry the grooves through to the ends of the turning by boring holes to meet them.

Accurate center holes can be drilled in stock by using a chuck mounted on a tail-stock chuck arbor. In the photograph at the bottom of the opposite page, a candle socket is being drilled in a candle stand. This procedure is most efficient when center holes must be drilled in stock secured to a face-plate.

Thin Faceplate Work

Work too thin to be mounted on a face-plate can be turned by mounting it, as shown below, on a nut and bolt to be gripped in the jaws of a drill chuck or router chuck mounted on the spindle in place of a conventional center. This method is good when the work requires a center hole. If not, the turning should be attached to a scrap block by gluing with the paper-joint method. The scrap block is then fastened to the faceplate in the usual manner.

Use one of these methods when turning very thin faceplate work.

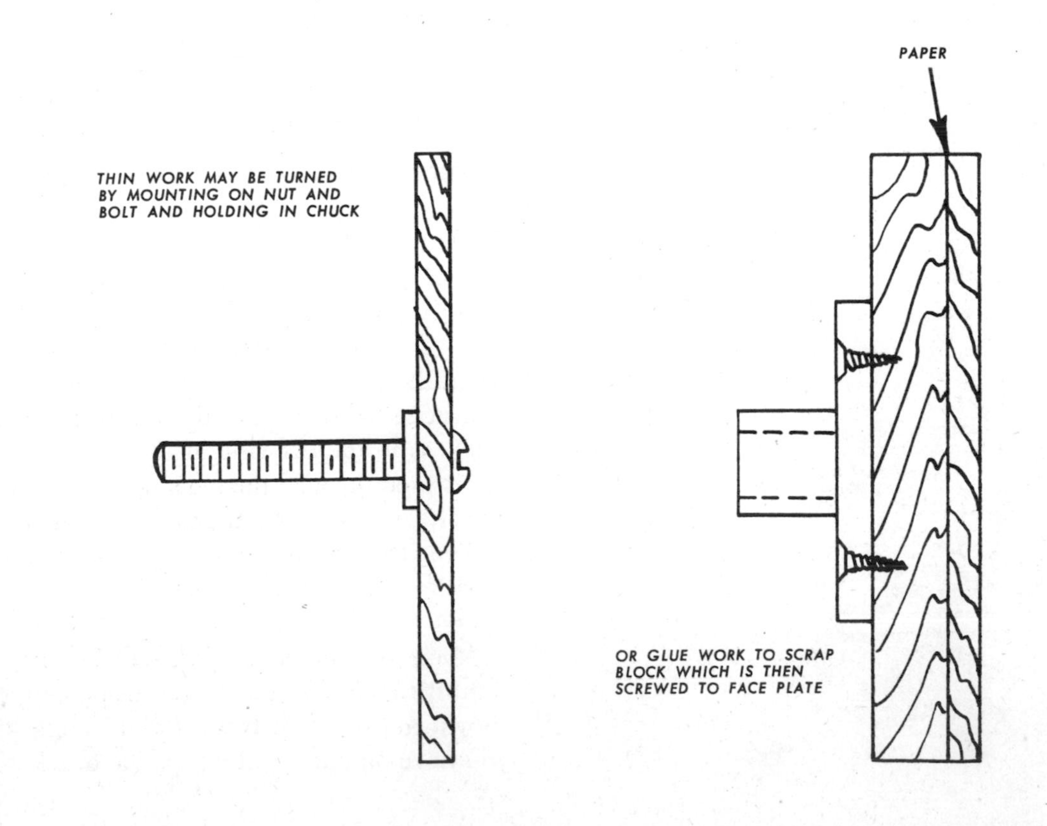
PAPER
THIN WORK MAY BE TURNED BY MOUNTING ON NUT AND BOLT AND HOLDING IN CHUCK
OR GLUE WORK TO SCRAP BLOCK WHICH IS THEN SCREWED TO FACE PLATE

This easily made indexing head can be attached to a lathe faceplate and locked on the upper auxiliary spindle of the multi-purpose tool. The extra hole for attaching the guide-pin bracket to the top of the headstock should be drilled exactly as shown—and with care.

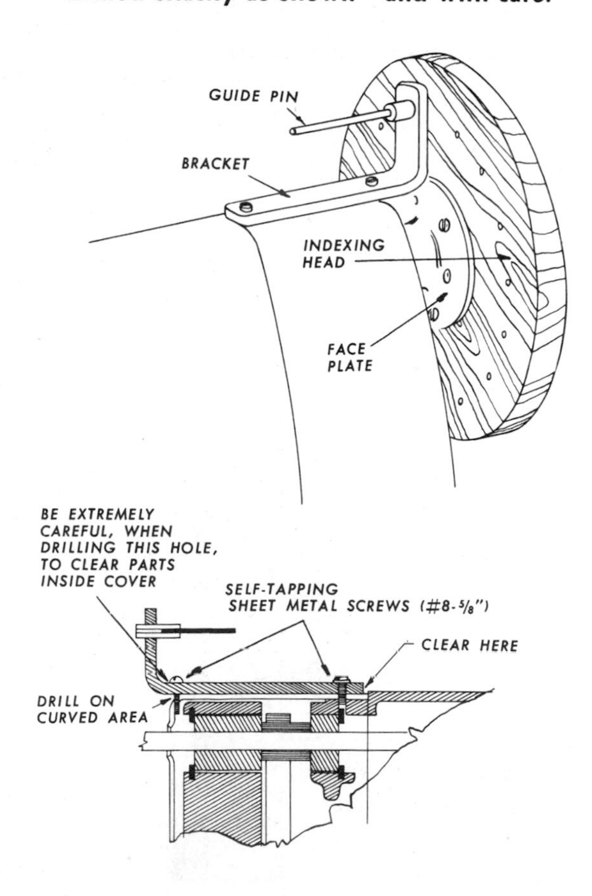

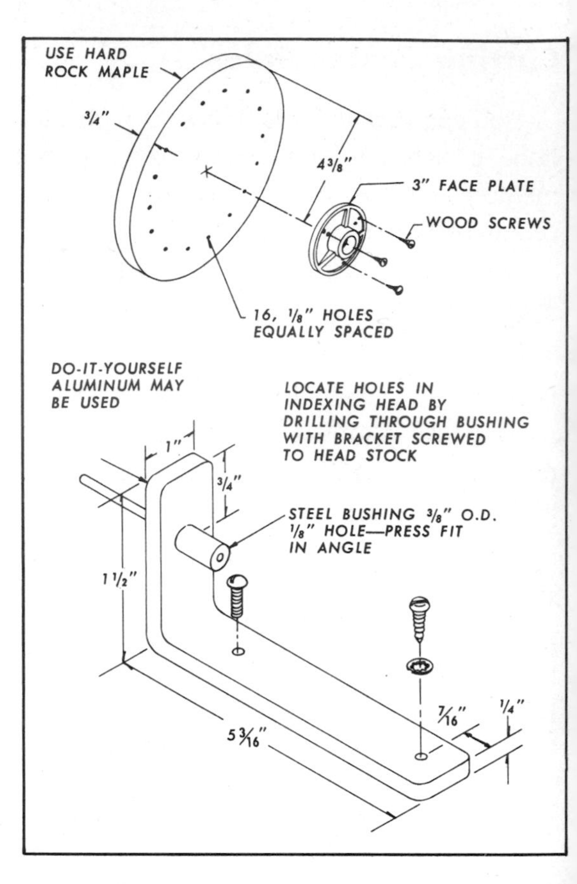

Follow the details given in the drawing above to make an indexing head.

Indexing Head

Some lathe projects require radial holes equally spaced about the circumference. These are most easily bored with the help of a spacing device known as an indexing head. An easy-to-make, improvised affair that can be mounted on the upper auxiliary spindle of the multi-purpose tool is shown at upper left. A bracket is secured to the top of the headstock as in the drawing at the left. A guide pin is used through the bushing in the bracket. The indexing head may be turned and locked in any position, thereby situating work mounted between centers or on a faceplate.

Make the indexing head and bracket assembly that holds and locates the pin guide as shown above. Any type of rigid angle that you have on hand will do for the bracket, or

The indexing head automatically positions work for drilling radial holes. In this typical procedure, the drill is being used to make holes for spokes in the hub of a wheel.

it may be bent from bar stock. Cut it to the dimensions shown and then drill the hole so it is just a bit undersize for the bushing to be used. Pressfit the bushing into place by squeezing it between the jaws of a vise.

A piece of ⅛″ drill rod, pointed at one end, is used as the lock pin by passing it through the bushing into the hole needed in the indexing head.

A typical use of the indexing head is shown in the photograph above. The hub of a wheel needed for a tea wagon is being drilled for spokes. If the wheel is to have eight spokes, use the pin to lock the indexing head at any point, and drill the first hole. Turn the indexing head 45°, lock it with the pin, and drill the second hole. Turn the indexing head 45° for each hole until all eight are drilled. If the wheel is to have four spokes, turn the head 90° for each new position.

Notice that a special guide is used in the tool-rest arm to position the drill. This guide is a hardwood block mounted on a piece of round bar stock secured in the tool-rest arm in place of the tool rest. Make it as shown in the drawing at right.

Not only does the block act as a guide, but it makes an excellent variable-depth stop. When using it, square it to the work and place it so the guide hole is level with the horizontal center line of the work. Instead of an electric drill, you could use a hand drill or a flexible shaft fitted with a drill chuck.

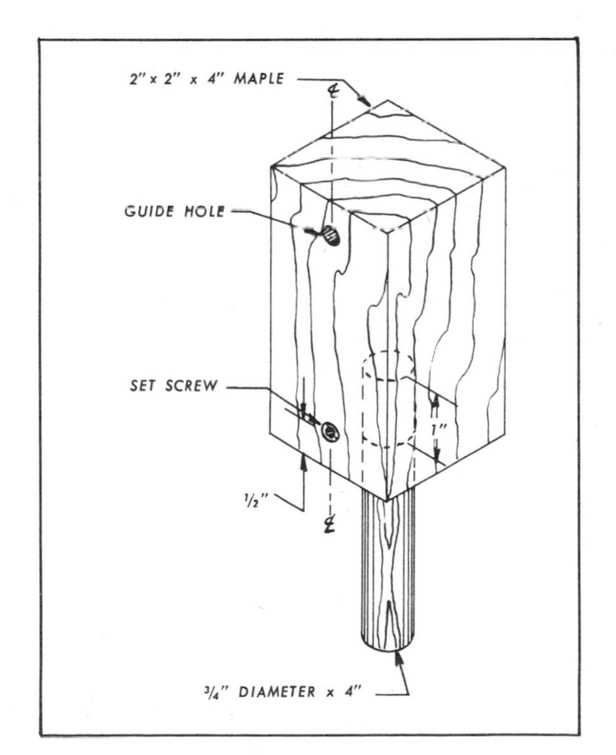

A guide like this is easily made from a hardwood block and a piece of round stock. Use it as shown in the photograph at the top of this page to position the drill and also to guide the drill square to the work.

A dowel steady rest, made as shown below, simplifies turning very tiny parts.

Dowel Steady Rest

Model workers will find a dowel steady rest almost indispensable for such small turnings as headlights, wheel hubs, rims, capstans, and deadeyes for automobile and ship models, or legs for miniature furniture.

A good feature of this rest is that it permits mounting a long piece of dowel in a drill chuck used in place of the usual center. The rest is moved for each new turning and the dowel is not cut up until all the individual parts have been formed.

The dowel steady rest above is made as shown below. After it's in position, clamp it to the table.

Coat the dowels with paste wax so they won't bind in the holes.

Accurate concentric holes may be drilled in dowel or in drill rod by using the steady rest and a chuck mounted in the tailstock. When the drill chuck is used on the tailstock the work may be held in a router chuck or the spindle or in a second drill chuck if one is available.

Use these construction details to make a dowel steady rest to be clamped to the saw table.

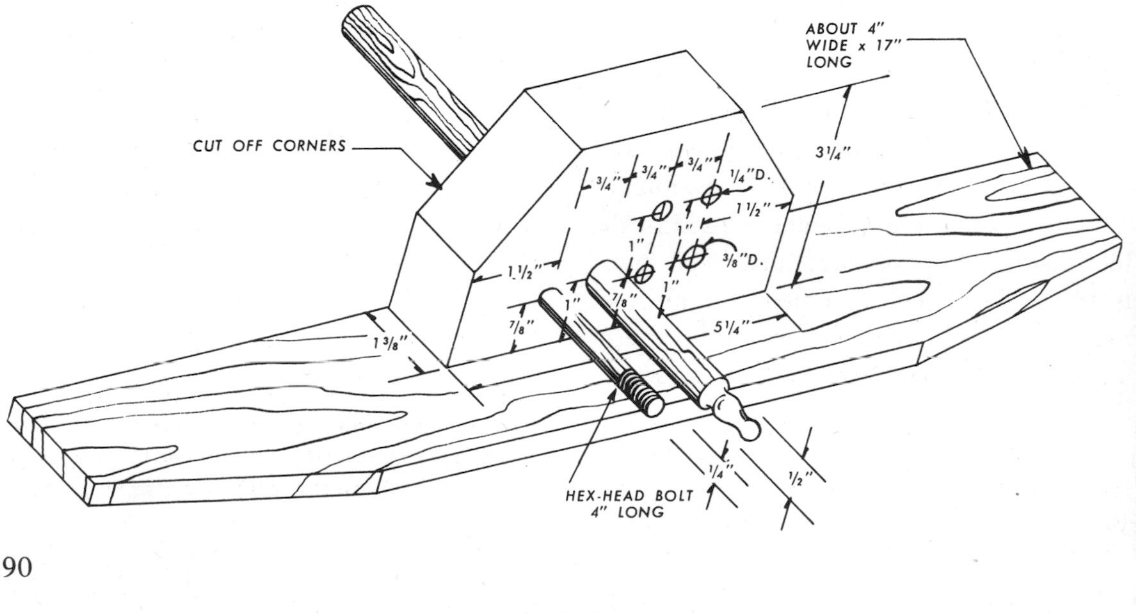

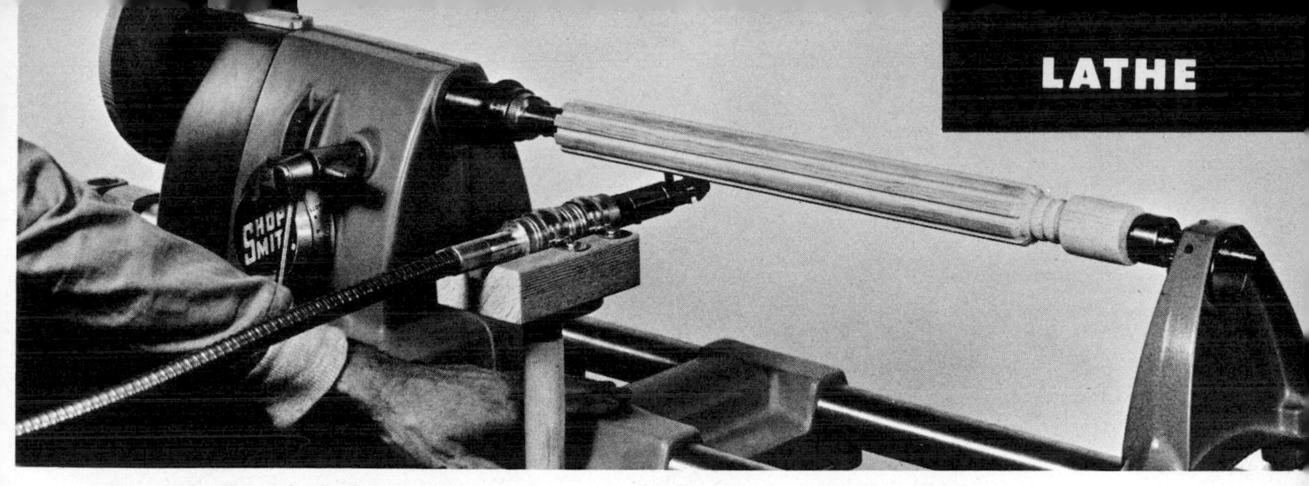
SHOP SMITH

Use a flexible shaft this way for fluting and reeding with a three-lip shaper cutter.

Fluting and Reeding

Fluting and reeding are lathe jobs that add tremendous variety and interest to your work. Once the spindle has been turned to the diameter needed, a flexible shaft is placed in a rigid position and three-lip shaper cutters do the work, as in the photograph above.

The platform for the flexible shaft is made as shown in the drawing below. The V-block is screwed to a faceplate attached to a piece of 1¼" hardwood dowel. The flexible shaft is secured with a second V-block or a half-circle pipe clamp. Place carriage flush against headstock and raise fixture to depth of cut desired. The indexing head holds the work and positions it for each new cut. A spare motor powers the flexible shaft.

Let the cutters work under the stock so the work acts as a guard. Keep the feed very slow and hold the hand supplying the feed as shown. When the cuts are very deep it is wise to make them in several passes.

To hold flexible shaft for fluting and reeding, make a clamp as shown in the drawing. At bottom of page are some of the shapes possible with the flexible-shaft technique.

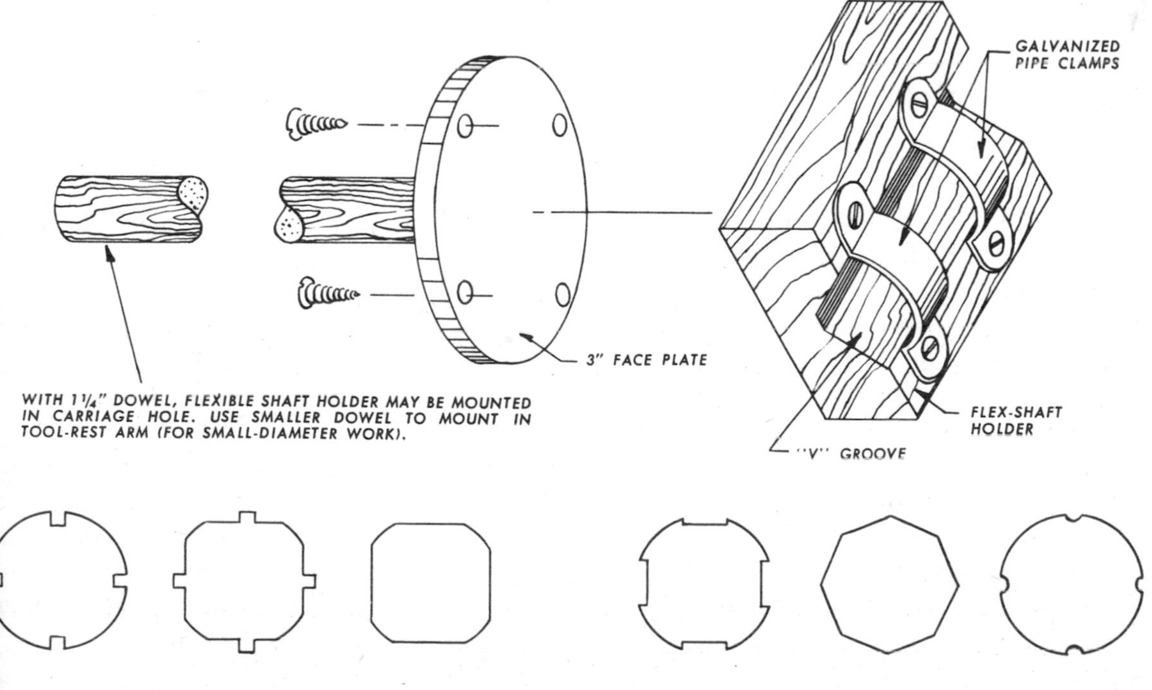
GALVANIZED PIPE CLAMPS
3" FACE PLATE
WITH 1¼" DOWEL, FLEXIBLE SHAFT HOLDER MAY BE MOUNTED IN CARRIAGE HOLE. USE SMALLER DOWEL TO MOUNT IN TOOL-REST ARM (FOR SMALL-DIAMETER WORK).
FLEX-SHAFT HOLDER
"V" GROOVE

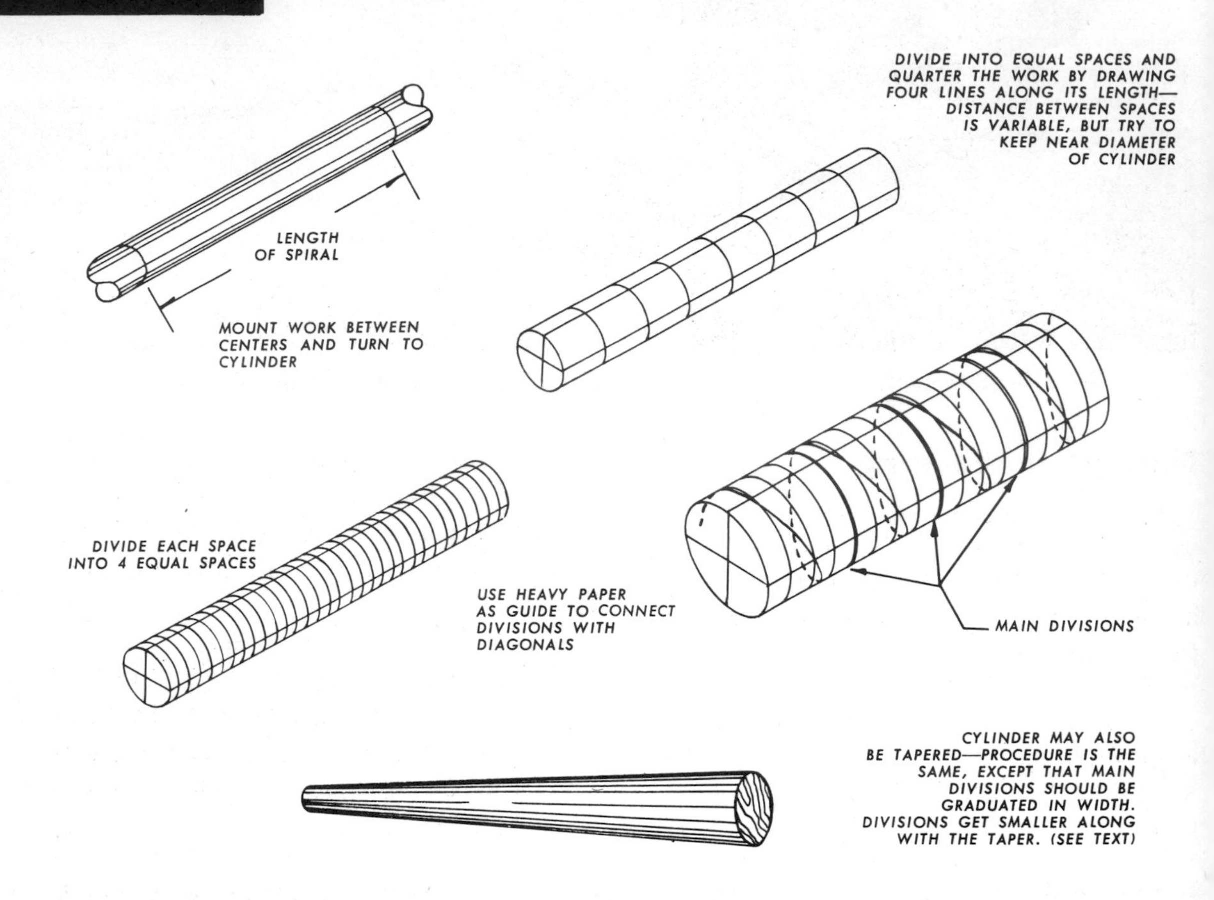
DIVIDE INTO EQUAL SPACES AND QUARTER THE WORK BY DRAWING FOUR LINES ALONG ITS LENGTH— DISTANCE BETWEEN SPACES IS VARIABLE, BUT TRY TO KEEP NEAR DIAMETER OF CYLINDER
LENGTH OF SPIRAL
MOUNT WORK BETWEEN CENTERS AND TURN TO CYLINDER
DIVIDE EACH SPACE INTO 4 EQUAL SPACES
USE HEAVY PAPER AS GUIDE TO CONNECT DIVISIONS WITH DIAGONALS
MAIN DIVISIONS
CYLINDER MAY ALSO BE TAPERED—PROCEDURE IS THE SAME, EXCEPT THAT MAIN DIVISIONS SHOULD BE GRADUATED IN WIDTH. DIVISIONS GET SMALLER ALONG WITH THE TAPER. (SEE TEXT)

The drawing above shows how to prepare cylinders for making spirals.

Turning Spirals

Spiral forming is classified as a lathe job even though most of the work is done by hand. It is started by mounting stock between centers and turning it to a round form.

Layout of the spiral divisions is shown above. First mark off the length of the spiral. Divide this into equal spaces, each approximately the diameter of the cylinder. Draw four lines along the length of the stock, connecting common perpendicular diameters at each end. Now divide each space into four equal parts and, with a heavy piece of paper as a guide, pencil-mark diagonal lines across each one as shown in the last detail above.

Now follow the sequence of photographs on the opposite page. Use a handsaw to cut along the spiral line to the depth needed. This depth is easily controlled if a keyhole saw is used. If a backsaw is used, clamp a block of wood to it to act as a depth guide.

Next use a round file to form a groove to the depth of the saw cut.

Open up the groove with a half-round file. Shape it with a flat file.

Use sandpaper to do the final shaping and smoothing.

Tapered spirals are made by starting with a tapered block in place of the round one. The layout is similar except that in the initial spacing the divisions should become smaller as the diameter of the taper decreases. Otherwise the procedure is the same.

With work mounted in lathe, cut to spiral depth with handsaw. A block of wood clamped to saw blade will control cut depth.

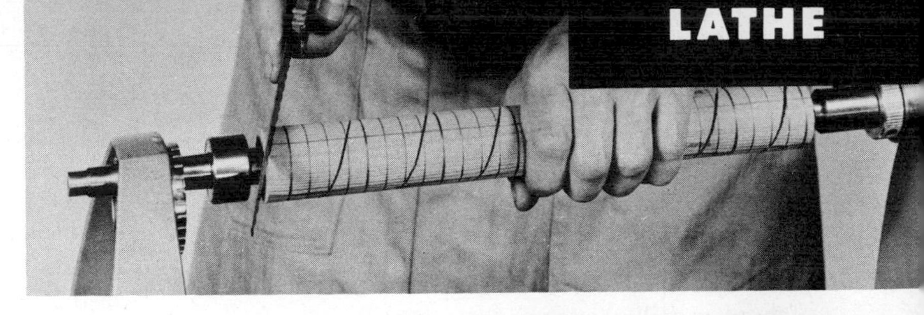

File to full depth of saw cut with a round file to start the actual forming of the spiral.

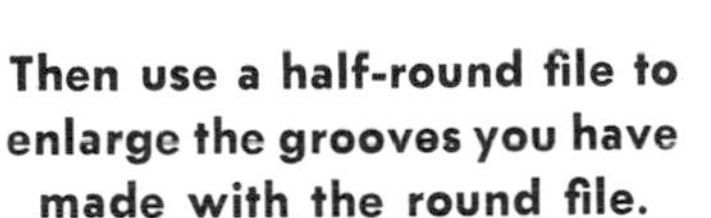
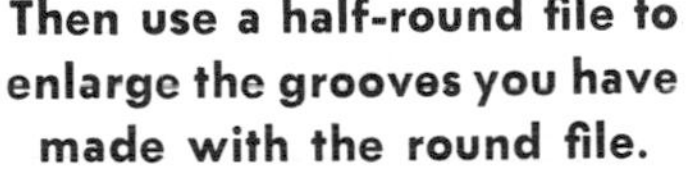

Then use a half-round file to enlarge the grooves you have made with the round file.

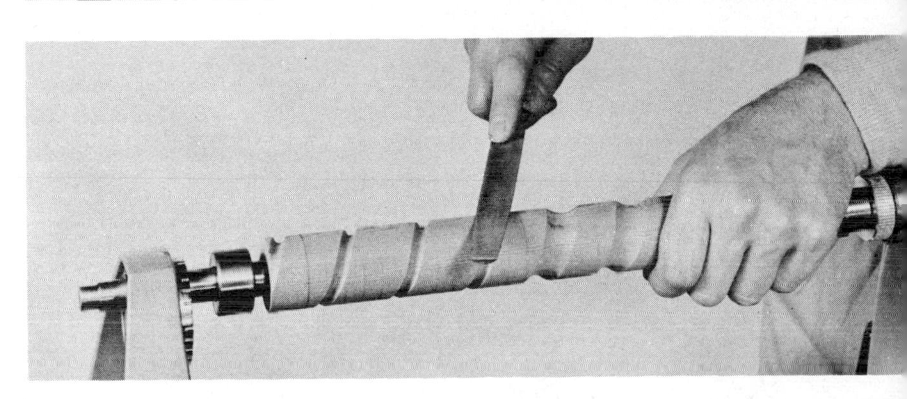

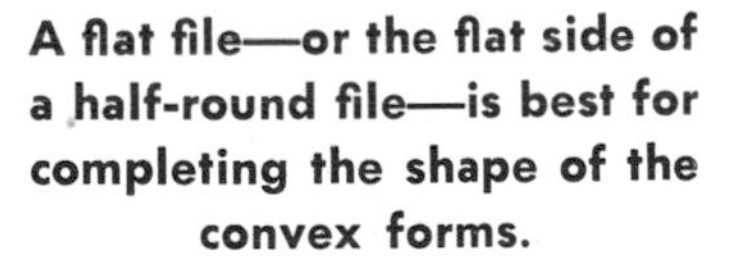

A flat file—or the flat side of a half-round file—is best for completing the shape of the convex forms.

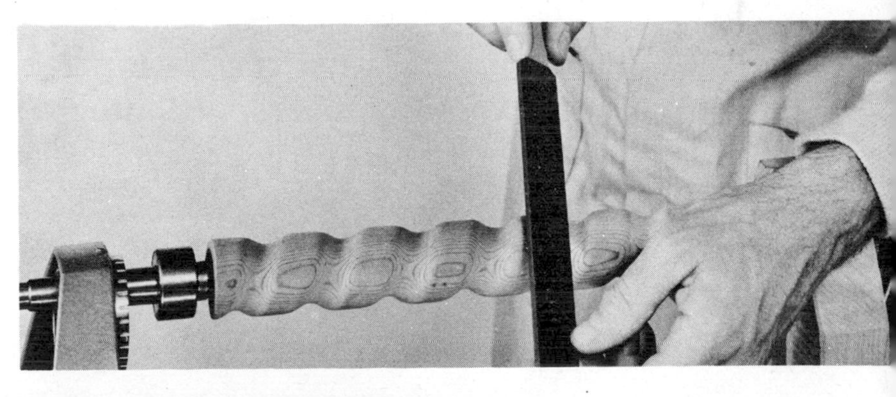

Use abrasive paper or cloth to do the final smoothing. Work from coarse down through progressively finer grits.

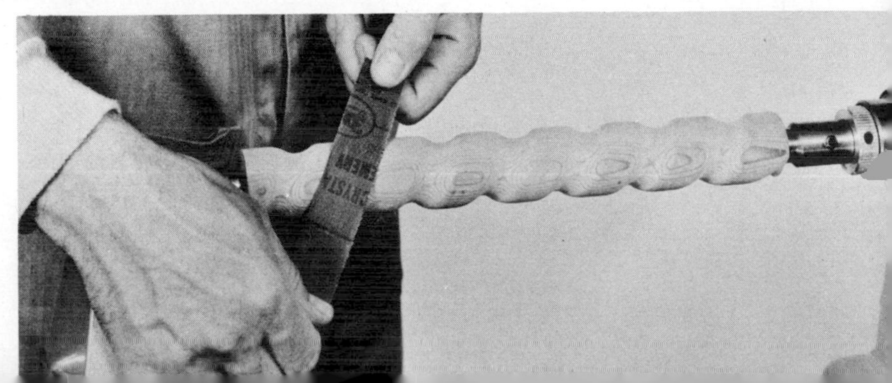

Using Wooden Chucks

When it's not possible to hold turning work between centers or to mount it on a faceplate or screw center, wooden chucks are needed. In drawing A below, the wooden chuck is drilled at one end to fit on the spindle and is secured with a setscrew that seats on the tapered flat. The opposite end of the chuck is drilled to take the tenon part of the work.

At B is a chuck held on a screw center; it is used to hold work with a center hole—napkin rings for example. The chuck has a tenon that fits the center hole of the work. The fit should be just tight enough to hold but not so tight that it must be forced.

Another type of chuck using the same principle is shown at C. Since this one is fitted with variable jaws, the tenon on the work doesn't have to be a precise fit in the hole. The work is positioned in the chuck; then the metal ring is drawn up on the taper, causing the jaw of the chuck to grip the work.

Use wooden chucks for work you can't mount between centers or on faceplate or screw center.

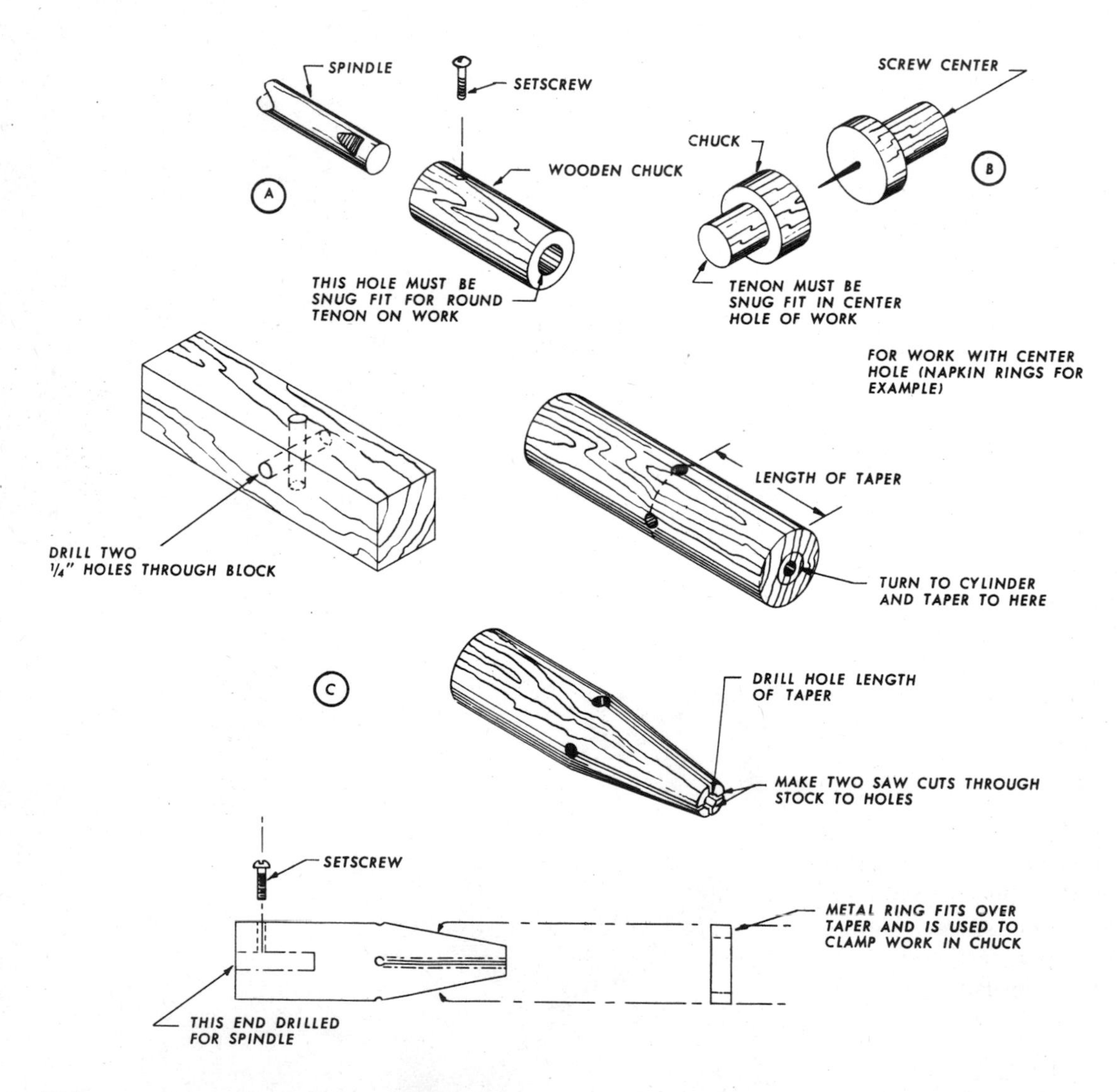
SPINDLE
SETSCREW
WOODEN CHUCK
A
THIS HOLE MUST BE SNUG FIT FOR ROUND TENON ON WORK
SCREW CENTER
CHUCK
B
TENON MUST BE SNUG FIT IN CENTER HOLE OF WORK
FOR WORK WITH CENTER HOLE (NAPKIN RINGS FOR EXAMPLE)
DRILL TWO 1/4" HOLES THROUGH BLOCK
LENGTH OF TAPER
TURN TO CYLINDER AND TAPER TO HERE
C
DRILL HOLE LENGTH OF TAPER
MAKE TWO SAW CUTS THROUGH STOCK TO HOLES
SETSCREW
METAL RING FITS OVER TAPER AND IS USED TO CLAMP WORK IN CHUCK
THIS END DRILLED FOR SPINDLE

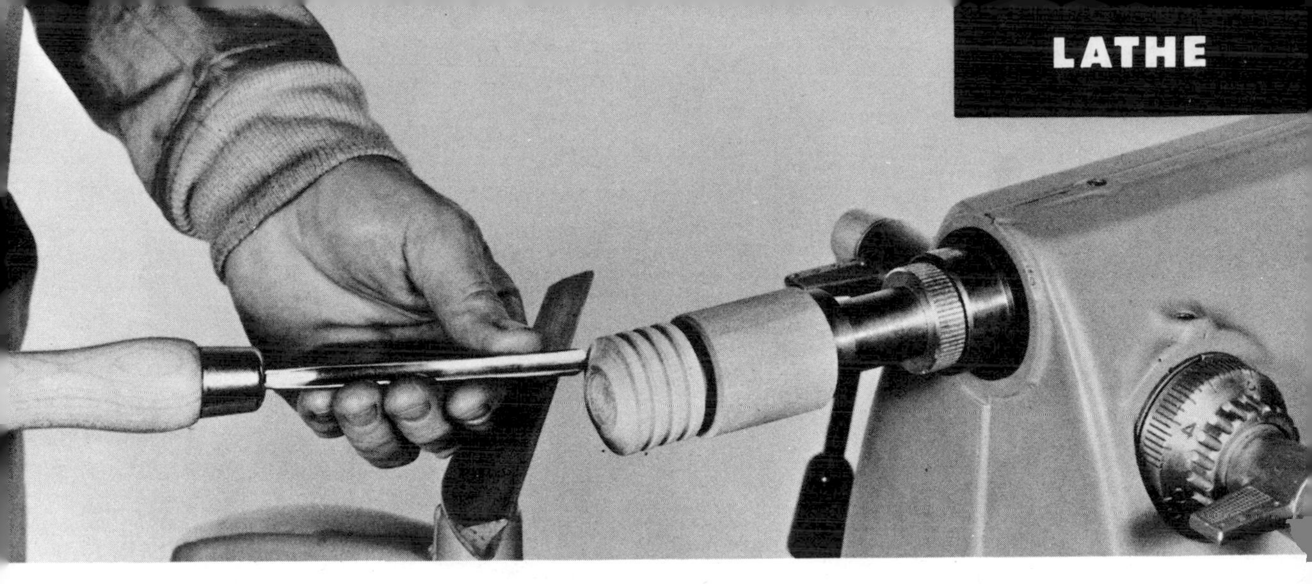

The tenon on the work must fit snugly in the hole if this type of wooden chuck is used.

A metal ring draws the split end of this chuck tightly over tenon of part being turned.

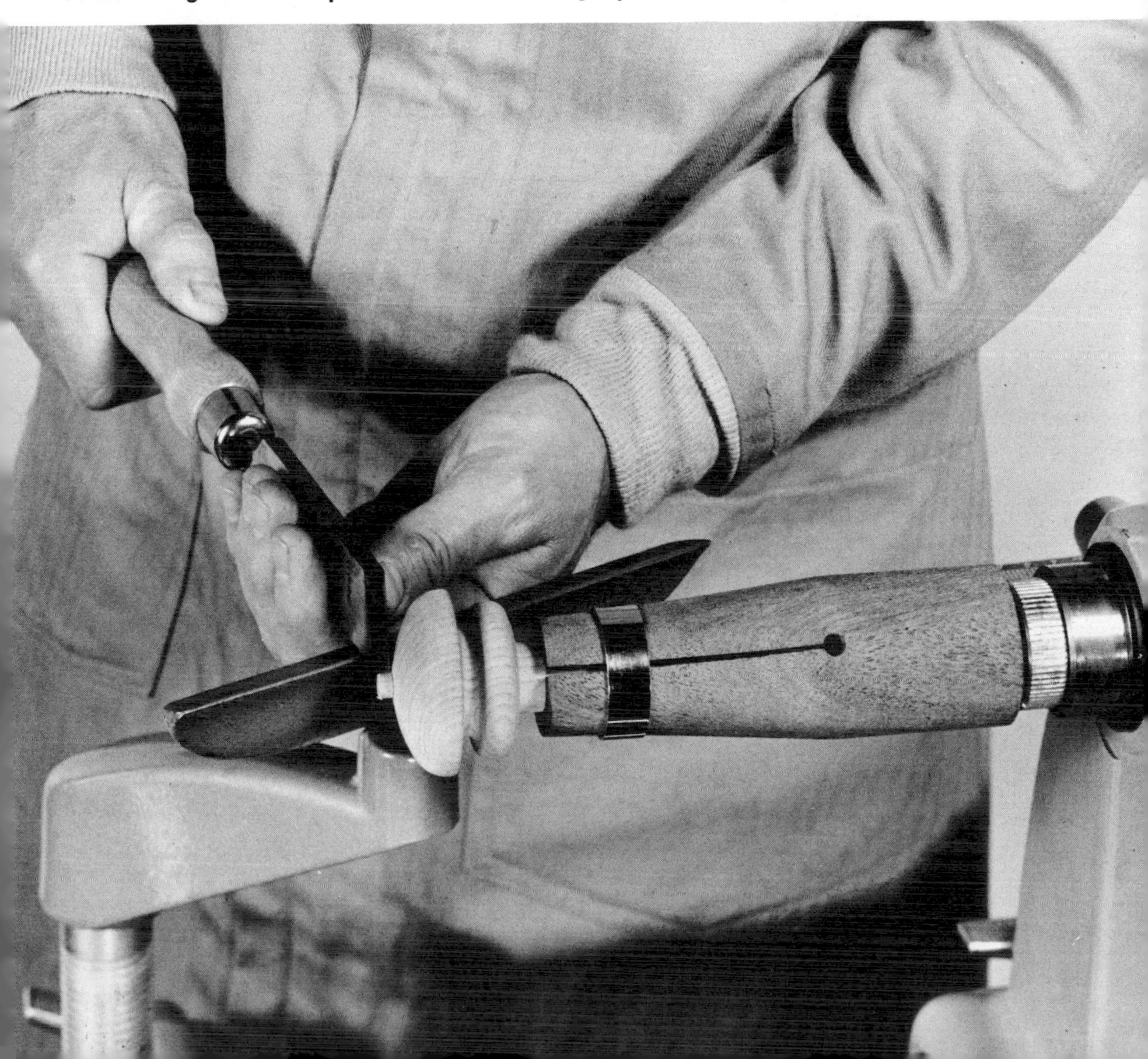

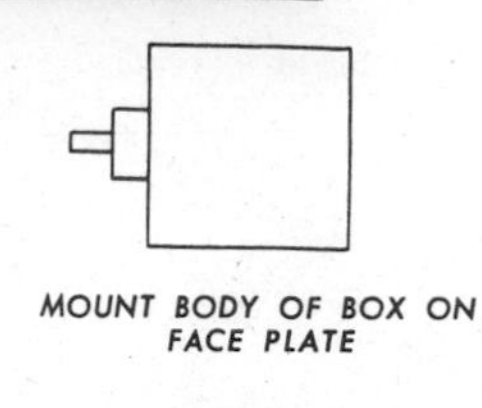
MOUNT BODY OF BOX ON FACE PLATE

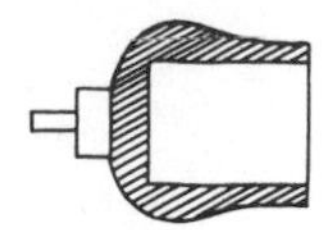
TURN BODY TO SHAPE INSIDE AND OUT

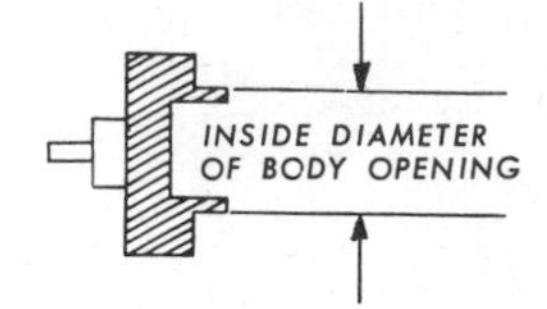

MOUNT COVER STOCK ON FACE PLATE AND TURN BOTTOM TO SHAPE

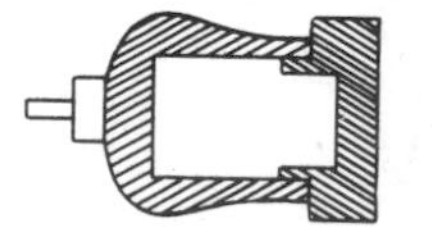
REMOUNT BODY OF BOX IN LATHE AND USE AS CHUCK FOR BOX COVER

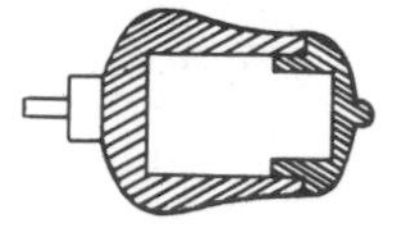
FINISH TURNING COVER TO SHAPE

WHEN COVER IS COMPLETE—REMOVE FROM BODY AND TOUCH UP INSIDE OF BOX SO COVER WILL NOT BE TOO TIGHT A FIT

Turn box with fitted cover this way, preferably using two faceplates.

How to Turn a Box with a Fitted Cover

Many home craftsmen earn spare-time income by turning cigarette boxes, powder boxes, humidors, and so on. It's a job that can be made a fast-moving production run.

Mount the body of the box on a faceplate and turn it to the shape desired (drawing above). Then mount the lid on a second faceplate and recess it to fit the body. Still mounted on the first faceplate, the body is replaced on the spindle and used as a chuck to finish turning the cover (photograph below).

The last step is to apply sandpaper to the lip of the body so the cover will not fit too tightly. If only one faceplate is used, be sure to mark the bottom of the work and the faceplate so the work can be remounted in its original position.

Use felt to hide the holes in the base.

Use the body of the box as a chuck when turning the outside profile of the cover.

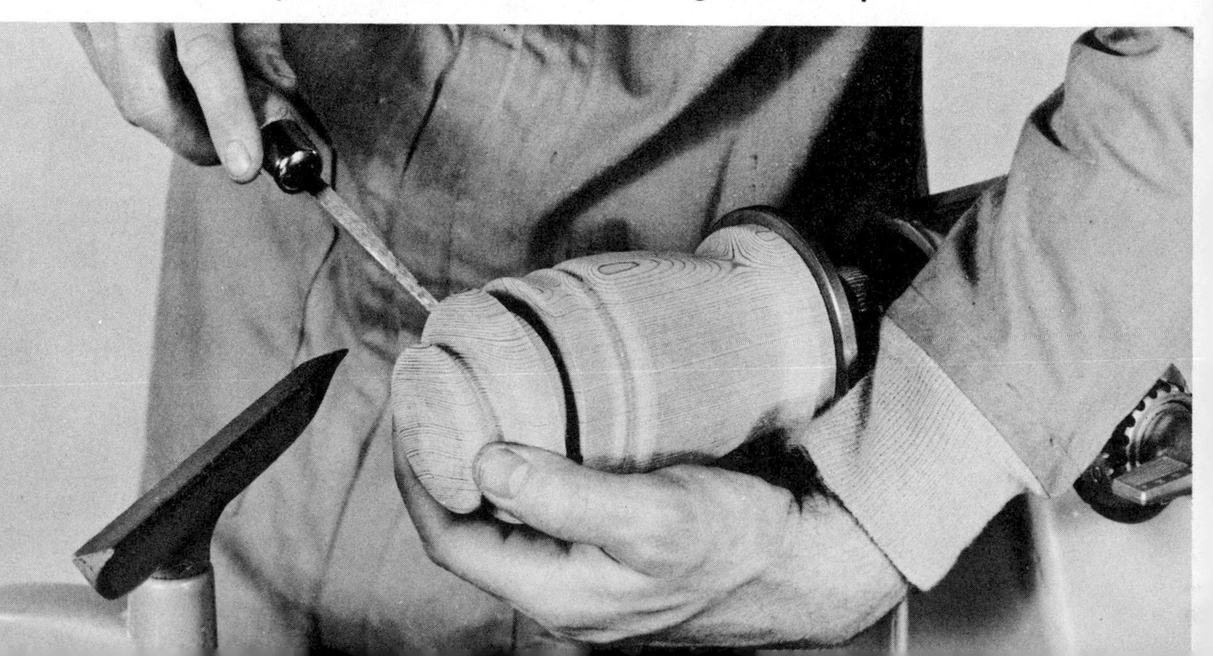

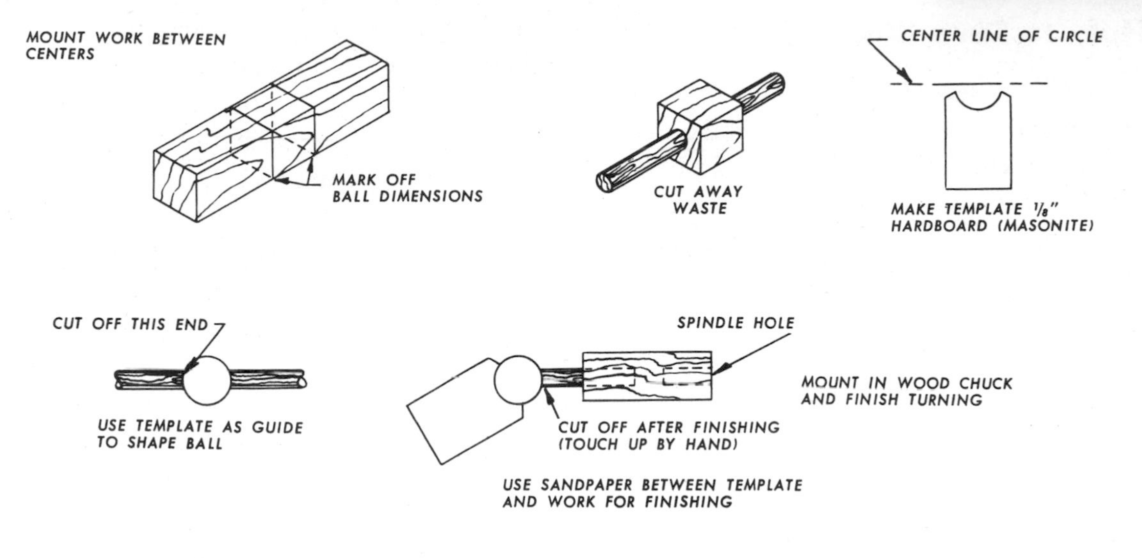
MOUNT WORK BETWEEN CENTERS
MARK OFF BALL DIMENSIONS
CUT AWAY WASTE
CENTER LINE OF CIRCLE
MAKE TEMPLATE 1/8" HARDBOARD (MASONITE)
CUT OFF THIS END
USE TEMPLATE AS GUIDE TO SHAPE BALL
SPINDLE HOLE
MOUNT IN WOOD CHUCK AND FINISH TURNING
CUT OFF AFTER FINISHING (TOUCH UP BY HAND)
USE SANDPAPER BETWEEN TEMPLATE AND WORK FOR FINISHING

This is the correct procedure to follow when turning a ball shape.

How to Turn Ball Shapes

A ball may be shaped on the lathe with the procedures outlined in the drawing above. A block is mounted between centers and turned to remove the waste material. A template of the ball is cut, as shown, to be used as a guide in rough-shaping the ball. One end of the project is then cut off and the work is mounted in a wooden chuck held on the spindle.

The shape of the ball is then completed, with the template being used—first as a guide, then actually as a forming tool by pressing sandpaper between it and the work as in the photograph below. The final step is to cut off the ball with the skew and touch up the end with sandpaper.

For final smoothing, use sandpaper and a template that fits the ball snugly.

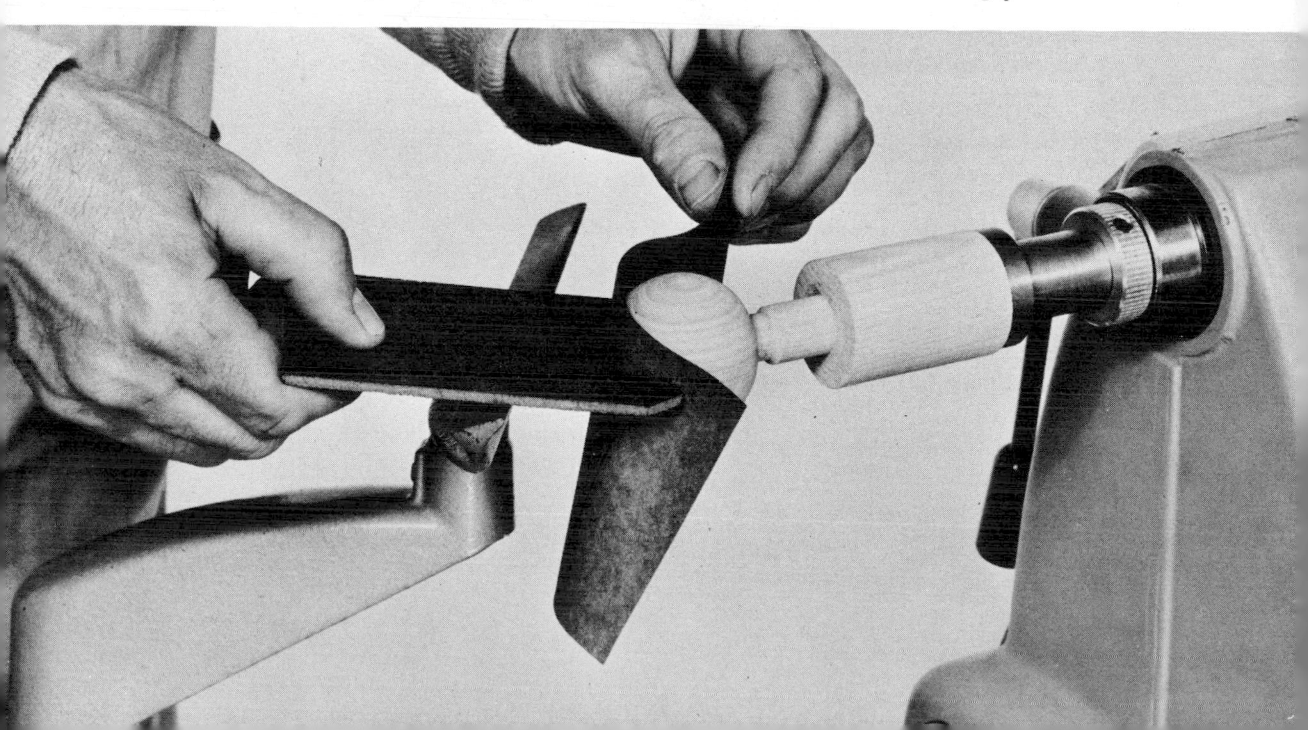

How to Turn Rings

There are several ways to form rings on the lathe, the choice depending on the shape of the work desired. In the drawing below, detail A shows a method of cutting a ring from solid stock mounted on a faceplate or screw center. Make the first cut with a parting tool on the edge of the turning. Make the cut a bit deeper than the thickness of the cross section of the ring. Make the second cut on the face of the stock. When the two cuts meet, the ring will fall off onto the shaft of the tool (photograph at upper left on opposite page) or remain revolving on the waste stock. The rim of the ring may be shaped before it is cut off, as in detail B below.

When the cross section of the ring is a true circle, a combination of faceplate and chuck turning is required (C). First mount the work on a faceplate or screw center and turn it to form half the face. Then make a chuck to hold the semiformed ring shape. Complete the ring by cutting out the center stock, then finishing the forming of the ring shape. Chuck work of this type requires an accurate dimension in the cavity that holds the work. If calculations are off and the work is a loose fit in the chuck, a piece of masking tape around the ring will make it fit snugly.

Rings are easily turned on the lathe if mounted on wooden chucks like those shown below.

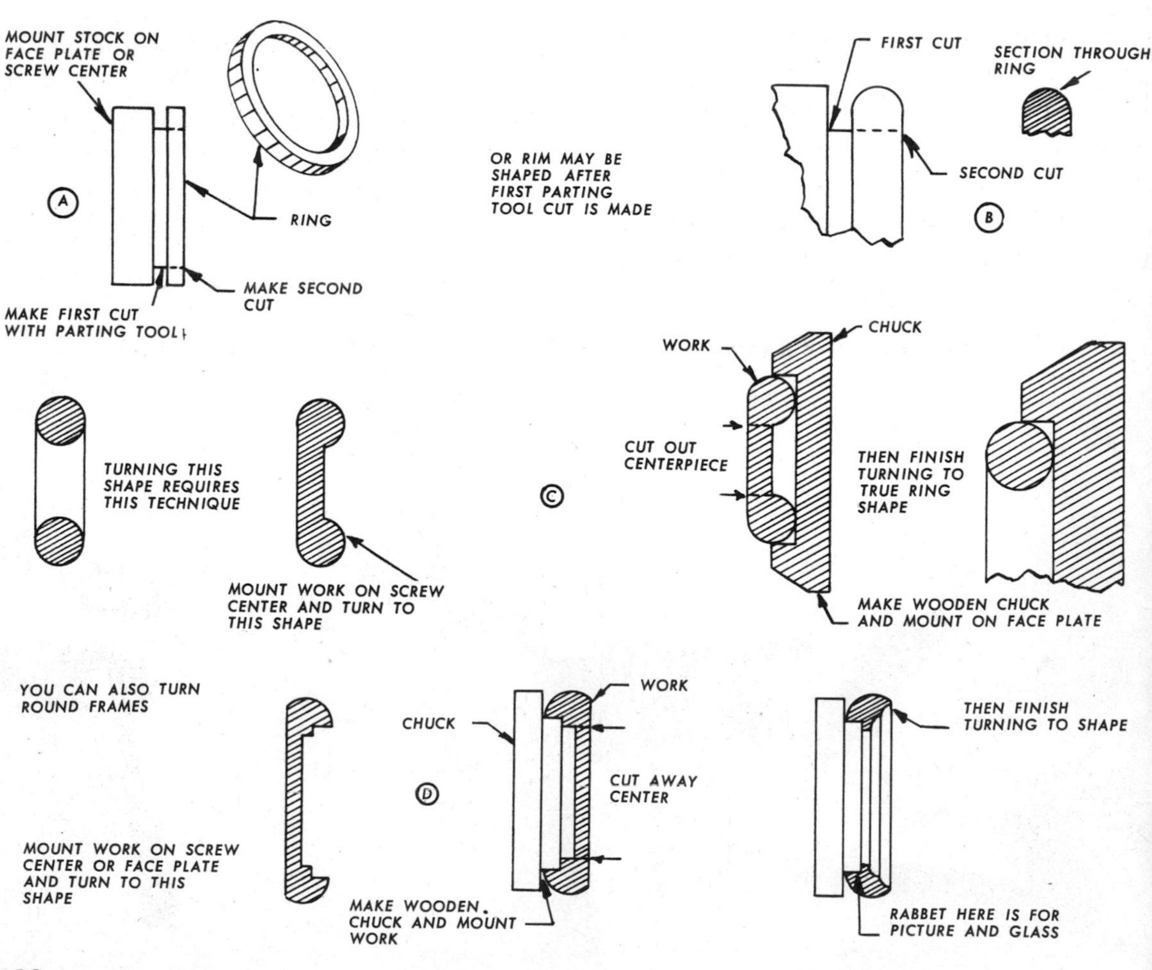
MOUNT STOCK ON FACE PLATE OR SCREW CENTER
A
RING
MAKE FIRST CUT WITH PARTING TOOL
MAKE SECOND CUT
OR RIM MAY BE SHAPED AFTER FIRST PARTING TOOL CUT IS MADE
FIRST CUT
SECTION THROUGH RING
SECOND CUT
B
TURNING THIS SHAPE REQUIRES THIS TECHNIQUE
MOUNT WORK ON SCREW CENTER AND TURN TO THIS SHAPE
C
WORK
CHUCK
CUT OUT CENTERPIECE
THEN FINISH TURNING TO TRUE RING SHAPE
MAKE WOODEN CHUCK AND MOUNT ON FACE PLATE
YOU CAN ALSO TURN ROUND FRAMES
MOUNT WORK ON SCREW CENTER OR FACE PLATE AND TURN TO THIS SHAPE
CHUCK
D
WORK
CUT AWAY CENTER
MAKE WOODEN CHUCK AND MOUNT WORK
THEN FINISH TURNING TO SHAPE
RABBET HERE IS FOR PICTURE AND GLASS

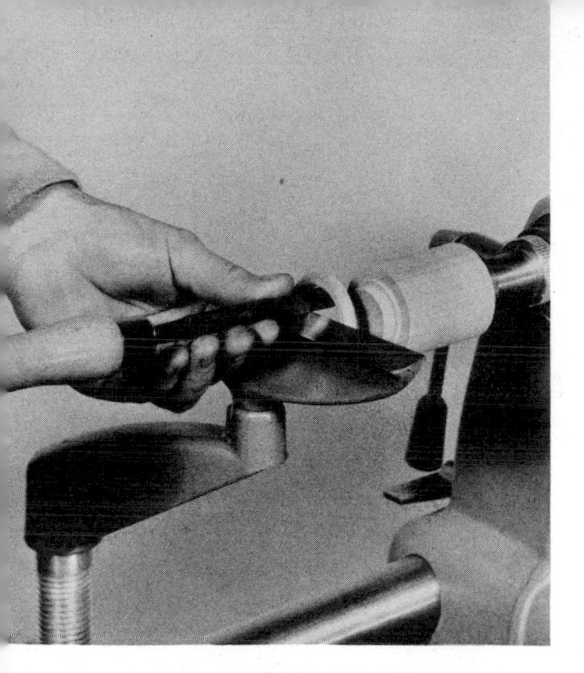

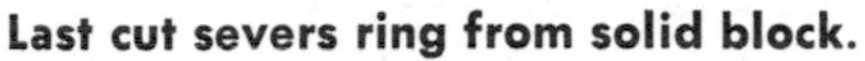

Last cut severs ring from solid block.

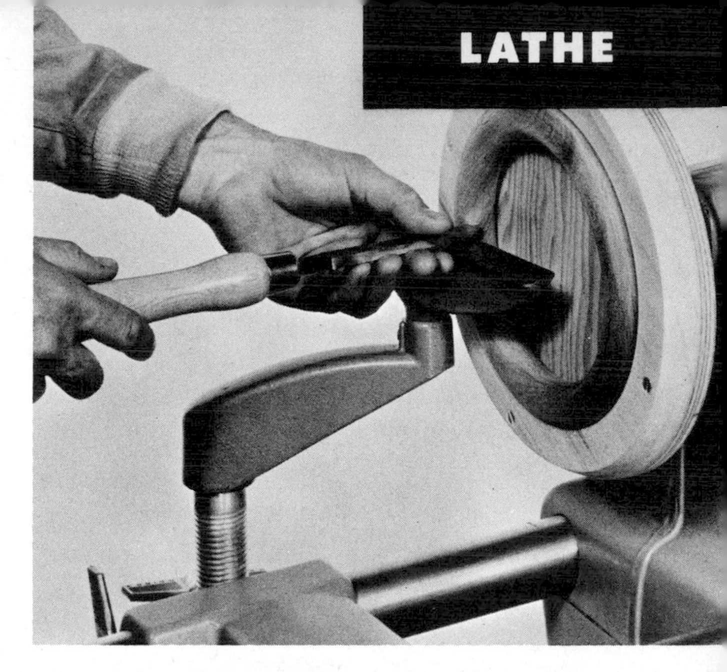

Mount ring of round cross section this way.

Projects such as round picture frames or one-piece circular moldings to edge a flat tray are handled this way:

The work is mounted on a faceplate and recessed as shown in the first detail of D on opposite page. A chuck is made to hold the work, as shown in the second detail. The final turning is accomplished with the work held on the wooden chuck (lower photograph). The original recess is the rabbet to hold the picture-frame glass and cardboard backing.

Use another type of wooden chuck for a shaped ring such as this circular picture frame.

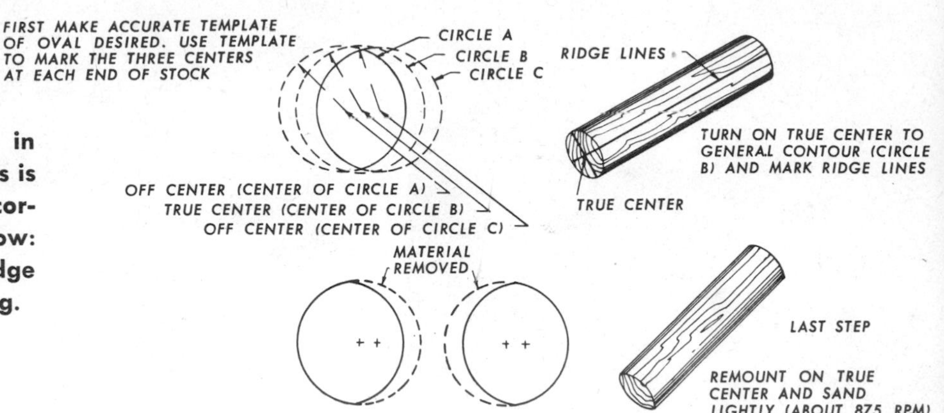
FIRST MAKE ACCURATE TEMPLATE OF OVAL DESIRED. USE TEMPLATE TO MARK THE THREE CENTERS AT EACH END OF STOCK
CIRCLE A
CIRCLE B
CIRCLE C
RIDGE LINES
TURN ON TRUE CENTER TO GENERAL CONTOUR (CIRCLE B) AND MARK RIDGE LINES
OFF CENTER (CENTER OF CIRCLE A)
TRUE CENTER (CENTER OF CIRCLE B)
OFF CENTER (CENTER OF CIRCLE C)
TRUE CENTER
MATERIAL REMOVED
LAST STEP
REMOUNT ON TRUE CENTER AND SAND LIGHTLY (ABOUT 875 RPM) TO REMOVE THE TWO EDGES
MOUNT ON ONE OFF CENTER AND TURN TO RIDGE LINE
MOUNT ON SECOND OFF CENTER AND TURN TO RIDGE LINE

Right: The trick in turning oval shapes is establishing the correct centers. Below: Sand to remove ridge line after shaping.

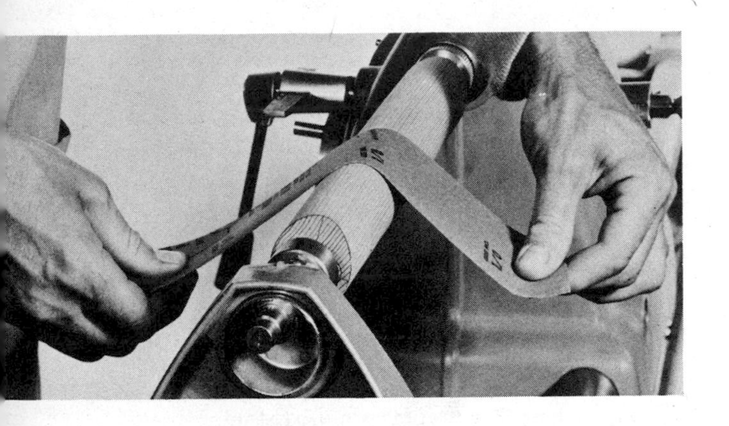

How to Turn Ovals

The most important part of turning a cylinder into an oval shape is the initial layout on the ends of the stock.

First make an accurate template for locating the true center and the two off-centers (drawing above). If the ridge line is located first it is easy to position the template at the ends of the stock and mark the centers with an awl.

Turn the work on true center until it is round. Re-mark the ridge line.

Mount the work on one of the off-centers. Turn it till cut nears ridge line. Now it's round on one side, oval on the other.

Mount the work on the remaining off-center; turn it down to the ridge line. Now the work is oval. Sand it as at left.

To make oval wooden blanks for mounting novelty jewelry, use a hollow-ground blade on the table saw to slice the oval.

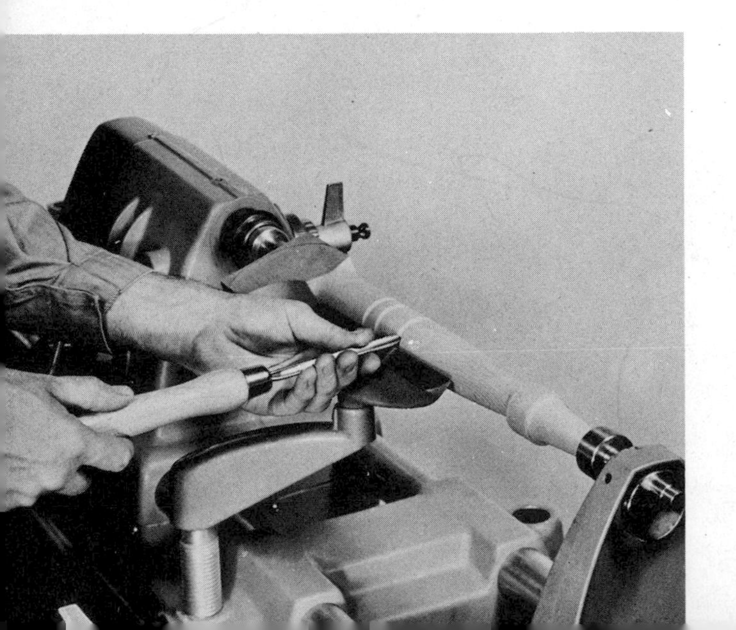

Special Leg Shapes

Combination legs, turned for part of their length but otherwise shaped with a jig saw or band saw, require the setup shown at the left. The end to be sawed is rough-shaped or left in the square until turning is completed. Because the work is unbalanced, operate at slower speeds than usual. Be careful to keep your hands clear of the unfinished end.

Offset Turning

It is possible to offset the cup center on the multi-purpose tool through use of the eccentric mount. This is calibrated in sixteenths of an inch and has a maximum offset of ½″. It may be turned to left or right, even though —see sketch at right—it may be calibrated in one direction only.

The direction in which the taper is formed is determined by the direction in which the eccentric mount is turned.

In combination with the controlled parallelism of the tool-rest, the eccentric mount makes it possible to turn tapers automatically.

A good system is to rough-turn the work to approximate taper and then, with a skew clamped to the tool-rest as shown in the photograph below, make the finishing cut by moving the carriage. Thus it is possible to duplicate tapered turnings of table and chair legs automatically or to make a single taper, perhaps for a table-lamp base.

After the eccentric mount is adjusted for the taper, it is necessary to raise the tailstock to bring the point on the cup center back to the same height as the point on the spur center. It should be fastened securely with the hand-grip lock.

Be sure the skew is clamped securely and situated for a light cut. Make the cut by advancing the carriage slowly. Several light cuts are better than one heavy one when much material must be removed. Smooth with sandpaper as you would any other turning.

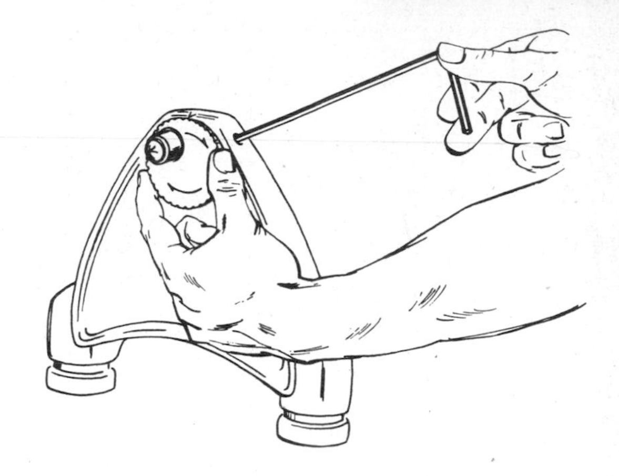

To turn tapers on multi-purpose tool, turn eccentric cup-center mount to left or right.

Accurate tapers may be shaped automatically, thanks to the combination of eccentric cup-center mount and a tool-rest that can be moved precisely along the work.

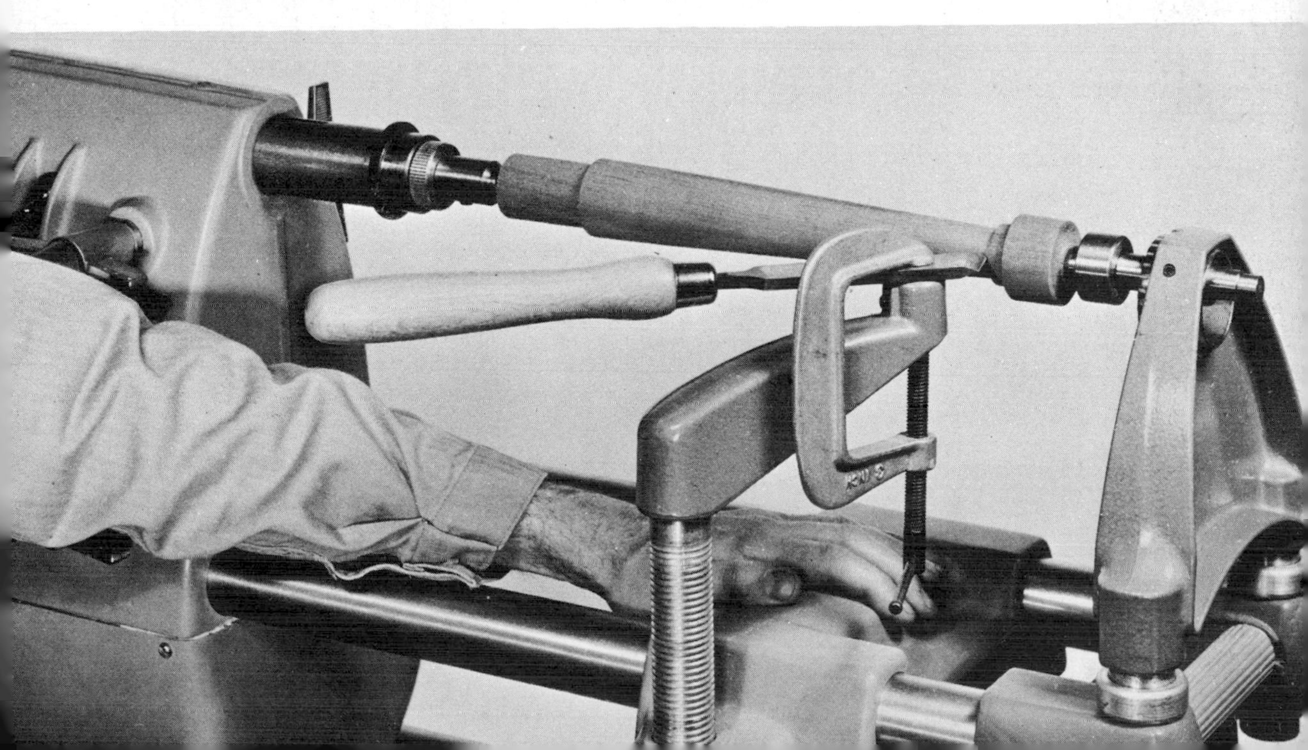

TROUBLE-SHOOTING CHART FOR THE LATHE

GENERAL

THE TROUBLE	POSSIBLE CAUSES	THE CURE	SEE PAGE
WORK BURNS AT CUP CENTER END	excessive friction	slack off slightly on quill extension	157
		use lubricant such as oil, tallow, or soap on cup center	157
		use live cup center	157
EXCESSIVE VIBRATION	excessive speed for large work	slow down to correct rpm	158
	work not on true center	re-establish centers if vibration is very bad—or—vibration will disappear as soon as work is turned to true round	174
WORK CHATTERS	excessive speed	slow down to correct rpm	158
TURNING TOOL HARD TO HOLD	dull tool	hone	160
	excessively deep cut and/or feeding too fast	slow feed and moderate bite is good shop practice and produces smoother work	159
	work loose between centers	extend quill	157
	work loose on faceplate	retighten or replace screws	—
	insufficient support for turning tool	maintain ideal tool rest position as much as possible	157
WORK STOPS TURNING AS TOOL IS APPLIED	spur center not seated correctly	on hardwoods be sure to cut diagonals for spur with saw	175
	spur works material away on soft wood	remove work from lathe, sand off damaged end and reseat spur	175

HARD TO REMOVE SCORED LINES LEFT BY SANDPAPER	jumping from very coarse paper to very fine	always work through progressively finer grits of paper until desired finish is achieved	—
	sandpaper held too long in one spot	keep paper moving when sanding	—
HARD TO GET GLASS-SMOOTH FINISH	'''nap'' on wood raises after final sanding	do final sanding by reversing work between centers—mount faceplate turnings on upper auxiliary spindle—use damp cloth on work before final sanding	—
SPINDLE TURNING "WHIPS"	work is long and thin	use back-up or steady rest	177
EXCESSIVE VIBRATION OR CHATTER ON FACEPLATE WORK	excessive speed	slow down to correct rpm	158
	stock not prepared before mounting	cut round on jig saw or band saw—remove corners with miter cuts before mounting	178
	faceplate not centered on stock	scribe circle slightly larger than faceplate diameter on work—then center faceplate in circle—vibration caused by slight misalignment will disappear as work is turned to true round	178
	mounting screws worked loose	check immediately at first sign of chatter—retighten screws—use heavier screws if necessary	—
WOOD SPLINTERS WHEN ROUGH-TURNING SQUARE TO ROUND	starting cut made at ends of stock	work from middle and out toward ends	164
	characteristic of roughing operation	minimize by removing as much waste material as possible beforehand by sawing	—
MOTOR LABORS WHEN SWITCH IS TURNED ON	usually caused by holding spindle turning too tightly	back off on quill just a little	157
SANDING BURNS WORK	excessive pressure	sanding heats work quickly—apply lightly	—
	excessive speed	change to slower rpm	158
WORK LOOSENS ON SCREW CENTER	possible on very soft wood	be sure screw is tight to begin with and do not cut too deep with turning tools	—
	incorrect application	mount work on screw center only when necessary—when possible, mount between centers or on faceplate	—

5 THE JIG SAW

How it works • blades • squaring the table spring hold-down • working position • patterns and layout cutting techniques • bevels • inlays • circles • saber sawing indexing chucks • metal • filing • plastics pad-sawing paper • two-tool setups • trouble shooting

THE JIG SAW converts the rotary motion of the spindle into an up-and-down movement. It does this by a crankshaft, like an automobile piston rod. This up-and-down motion is carried to a straight blade that cuts on the down stroke.

The main job of the jig saw is to cut curved and straight lines. These may be exterior cuts, started from the edge of the stock. Or they may be within the work—called piercing.

Because the jig saw can cut curves of very short radius, with an extremely fine kerf, it is especially adapted to intricate scrollwork and fretwork. Fine crafts such as inlay, intarsia, marquetry, and intricately pierced design work in metals are almost entirely dependent on the jig saw. In addition, a good jig saw is constructed with all the ruggedness of other woodworking machine tools, and fairly heavy stock can be cut. It's used to shape furniture legs, to do bevel cutting on straight or curved pieces, pad sawing, and fancy cutouts for ornamental overlays on cabinetwork.

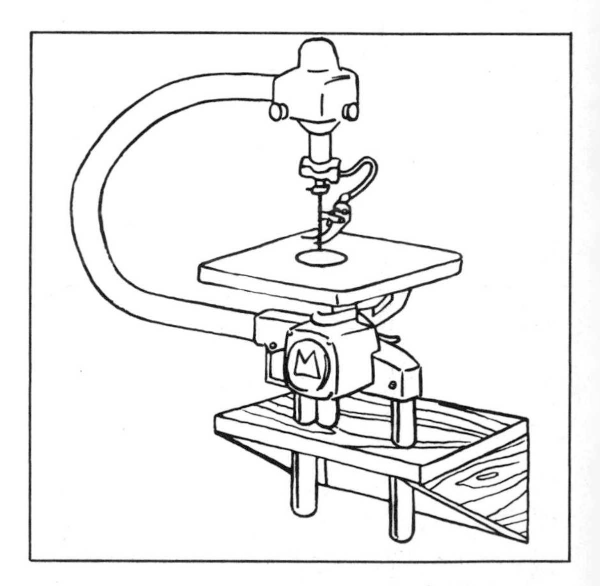

Jig saw is easily stored on a wall bracket.

The jig saw is the safest and easiest to use of all power tools. It's the logical tool for introducing a youngster to the fun of woodworking. Even a six-year-old can be taught

The modern jig saw is shown here on the Power Mount of the multi-purpose tool.

to operate the jig saw safely and efficiently.

Available as an accessory for the multi-purpose tool, the jig saw is easily mounted at the Power Mount end of the machine. The twin-tube mounting arrangement simplifies both attaching the jig saw for operation and storing it when not in use. Like other Power Mount accessories for the multi-purpose tool, the jig saw is easily and conveniently stored on a simple wall bracket like the one sketched on the page at the left. It can be taken down and mounted in a few seconds, since the

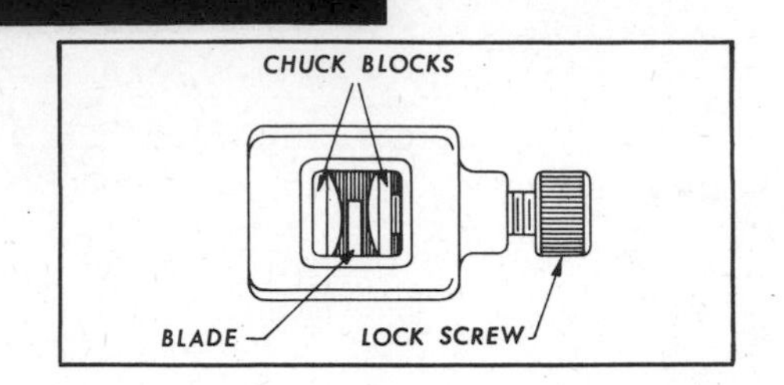

The top end of the blade locks securely between the blocks in the upper chuck.

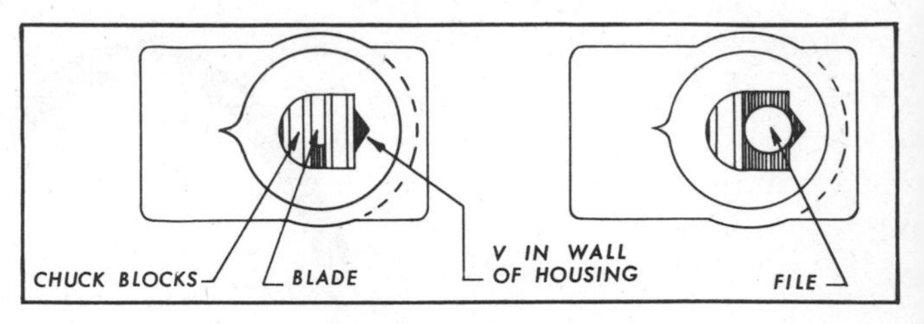

The bottom end of the blade locks between the blocks in the lower chuck; the V is provided to secure machine files and sanding-sticks.

special flexible coupling slips over a hub on the upper auxiliary spindle and transmits power from the ¾-horsepower motor in the headstock. This arrangement also makes it possible to use the headstock's variable-speed mechanism—a great advantage with a jig saw.

This jig saw has an 18″ throat (which means it can cut to the center of a 36″ panel) and it will cut through soft or hard wood 2″ thick. The tubular arm is easily removed or swung down out of the way; thus the jig saw may be used as a saber saw without limitations on size of work that can be cut—and with some increase in thickness of stock that can be handled. The saw table and extension table can both add support for cutting long stock or panels.

The top casting (at the end of the tubular arm) contains the upper chuck mechanism, and encases a pump which sends air through a plastic tube and out through the blade back-up tube to keep sawdust and chips from obscuring the cutting line; it also supports a hold-down assembly. The upper chuck (left, above) consists of the housing, two chuck blocks, and a tightening screw. The blade is held between the blocks and locked in place with the Allen setscrew.

The hold-down assembly includes the hold-down rod, which can be moved up or down to accommodate thickness of stock. It can be secured in any position with the hold-down lock-knob. The hold-down support at

Make correct adjustment of blade-guide, back-up tube, and hold-down spring.

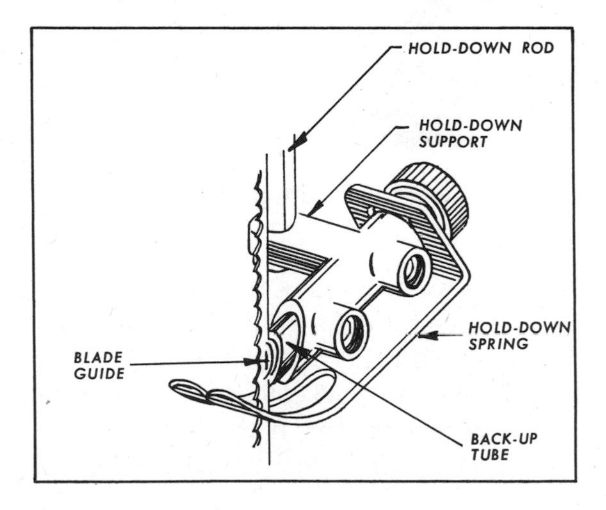

The blade is held rigid between upper and lower chucks.

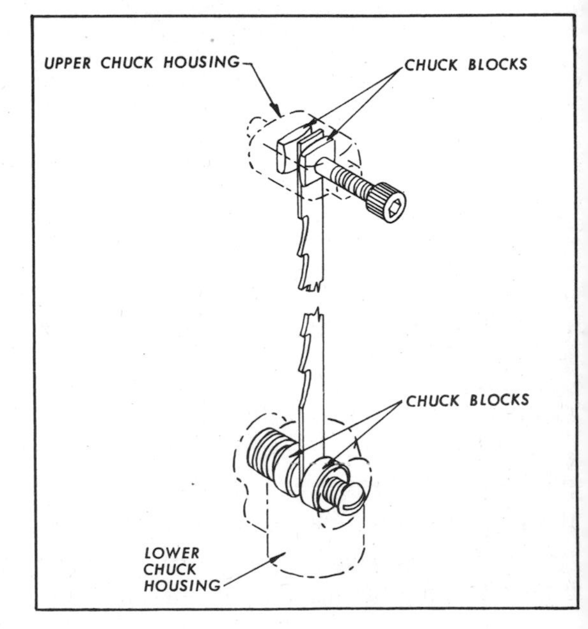

the bottom of the hold-down rod holds the blade guide, blade back-up tube, and hold-down spring—all of which are adjustable. The blade guide and back-up tube accommodate various blades, and the spring conforms with table tilt.

As shown in the drawing at left, the lower casting supports the crankshaft mechanism driving the lower chuck. The lower chuck consists of the housing—which has a V-cut in the right-hand inside wall—two chuck blocks, and a lock screw. The saw blade is held between the blocks and secured with the lock screw. The drawing at the lower right on the opposite page illustrates how the blade is held in place between the blocks of the upper and lower chucks. The V is used when filing or sanding; the shank of the tool is held securely in the V by the chuck blocks and the lock screw.

The drive mechanism is splash-lubricated. It is important, when first using the jig saw, to follow the manufacturer's instructions about the correct oil for filling the oil reservoir. The jig saw never should be operated without oil, and the oil should be changed about every 100 hours that it is used.

Jig-Saw Blades: How to Select and Insert Them

Jig-saw blades are usually identified by physical dimensions. The most common blade has blank ends and is about 5″ long. The chart shows and describes an assortment of blades that should be kept on hand to take care of most jig-saw jobs. This list does not include all available blades, but it is a good selection to begin with. Use it in choosing machine speeds—but also follow the general rules: the heavier the material, the heavier the blade and the slower the speed; the finer the cut required, the finer the blade and the faster the speed.

All blades can be classified in one of two

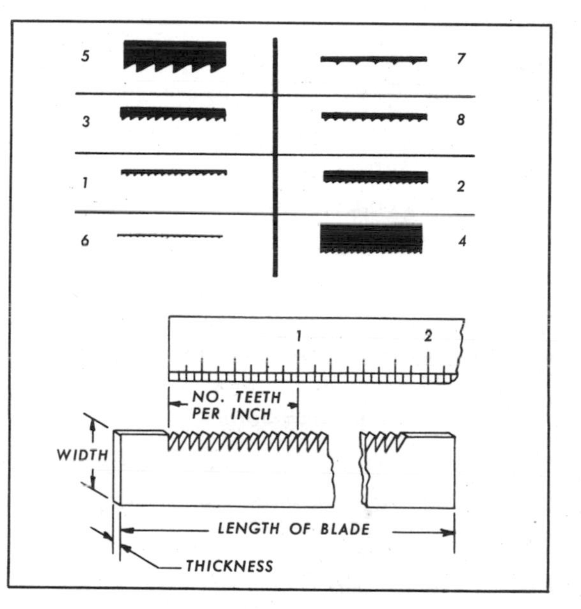

Chart at right and below gives appearance, characteristics, and uses of common blades.

BLADE	BLADE DIMENSION: THICKNESS INCHES	WIDTH INCHES	TEETH PER INCH	OPERATION: STOCK THICKNESS (Inches)	CUT RADIUS	KERF	BEST FOR	R.P.M. AND SPEED-DIAL LETTER
5	.028	.250	7	1/4 & up	large	coarse	soft & hard wood—pressed wood	745-A
3	.020	.110	15	1/8-1/2 in metal, 1/8 & up in other material	medium	medium	metal—wood—bone—felt—paper	1175-F
1	.010	.040	18	1/16-1/8	small	very fine	wood—bone—plastics	1600-I
6	.012	.023	20	up to 1/8	very small	fine	plastics—bone—fiber—comp. board	1050-E
7	.020	.070	7	up to 1/4	medium	medium	plastics—bone—hard rubber	1400-G
8	.010	.070	14	1/8-1/2	medium	very fine	wood—plastics—bone—hard rubber	1525-H
2	.020	.110	20	1/16-1/8	medium	medium	aluminum—copper—mild steel	940-C
4	.028	.250	20	3/32-1/2 (1/4 max. in steel)	large	coarse	aluminum—copper—mild steel	830-B

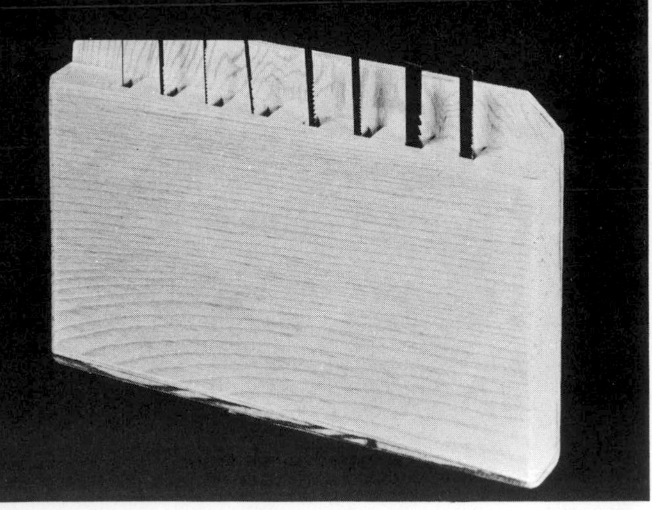

This easily made rack provides storage for a basic assortment of blades. Nail it to a wall or clamp it to the upper frame of the saw.

main divisions: "jeweler's blades," gripped by both the upper and the lower chucks; and "saber saws," gripped by the lower chuck only. The saber saws are usually larger, heavier, and coarser, some of the larger ones coming close to being small hacksaw blades.

An Allen setscrew in the lower housing securely locks the blade between the chuck blocks. (Table has been removed for photography.)

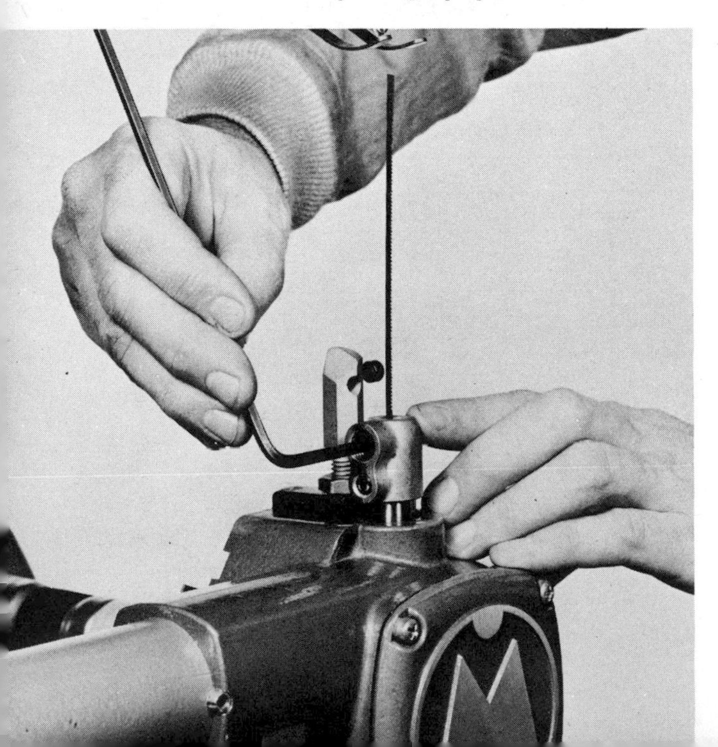

The heavy jeweler's blades may often be used as saber saws.

Saber saws are ordinarily used for heavy cutting, for curves that are not too severe, and for large panels being cut with the tubular arm of the jig saw removed.

To put a blade in the machine, place it between the blocks in the lower chuck and tighten the setscrew (lower left). Have the teeth of the blade pointing toward you, the points down toward the chuck. Secure the other end of the blade in the upper chuck. To simplify adjustments, set the blade so it butts against the housing at back of chuck.

The blade should be either perpendicular to the table or with its top end just slightly forward—so that when viewed from the side the blade makes slightly less than a 90° angle with the table.

The position of the blade may be checked by turning the flexible coupling by hand. If the blade rocks back and forth, it has been placed too far forward or too far back in upper or lower chuck. It should travel straight up and down or move a bit forward on the down stroke.

A further check can be made with a square; or a block of wood that is square to the table can be placed against the front or back of the blade. Any discrepancy will be apparent when the flexible coupling is turned by hand. After a few attempts at positioning the blade, you will find it easy to check by eye alone.

A tensioning device is provided to hold the blade rigid and straight. After the blade has been secured in the upper chuck, adjust the tension by pushing the spring cylinder up. The further up you push, the greater the tension. More tension is needed on fine blades than on heavier ones, but **excessive** tension on fine blades will cause them to snap. Experimenting with various tensions on different blades and materials will familiarize you with the feel of the tensioning device;

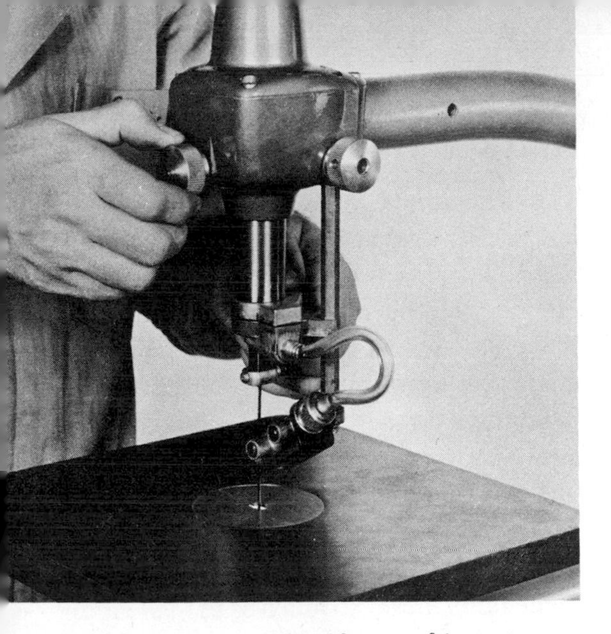

Provide correct tension by pushing up on spring cylinder and then tightening lock-knob.

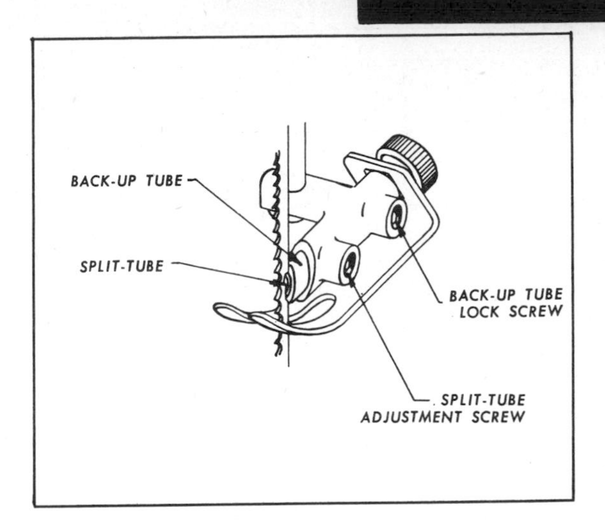

Back-up tube should just touch back of blade. Never over-tighten the split-tube blade guide.

soon you will be able to judge correct tension fairly accurately. With the tension set, the spring cylinder is secured in its position by tightening the spring-tensioning knob, as show above.

Having established the tension, tighten the rod lock-knob while the upper guide assembly is resting on the table. Loosen the two blade-guide lock screws and adjust the split-tube so its sides extend only to the bottom of the teeth. Allow clearance between the sides of the split-tube and the blade. Tightening the split-tube so much that it pinches can break blades. Adjust the back-up tube until it merely touches the back of the blade (above). The split-tube should cover the entire width of very fine blades.

The lower blade back-up is a hard fiber rod; adjust this rod until it bears lightly against the back of the blade. If you desire a slot in this back-up rod, merely reverse the blade and feed the rod into it. This fiber back-up provides blade support for saber sawing.

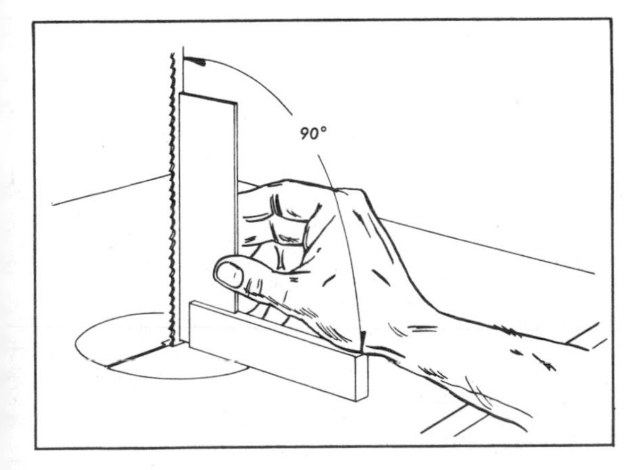

Angle between blade and table should be exactly 90° when tilt indicator is on "0". Check this setting periodically to insure square cuts.

Squaring the Table

The jig saw will produce straight cuts only if the table is 90° to the blade. To find out if it is, place a square on the table and against the side of the blade—not against teeth or back.

If the table is not correctly aligned, adjust the setscrew found behind the tilt indicator. One end of this screw rests against the lower assembly housing. Loosen the table-tilt knob and turn the setscrew until the square shows the blade and table properly aligned, as sketched at left. Line up "0" on the adjustable tilt-indicator with "0" on the trunnion, so that all future settings will be correct.

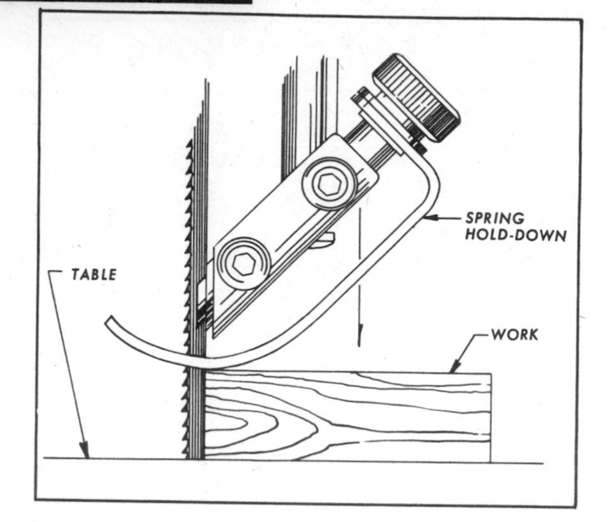

Hold-down-spring pressure on the stock should be just enough to keep the blade from lifting the work on the up stroke.

With the blade guide and the hold-down spring correctly adjusted, the jig saw will cut easily and smoothly. There will be no need of excessive feed pressure on the work.

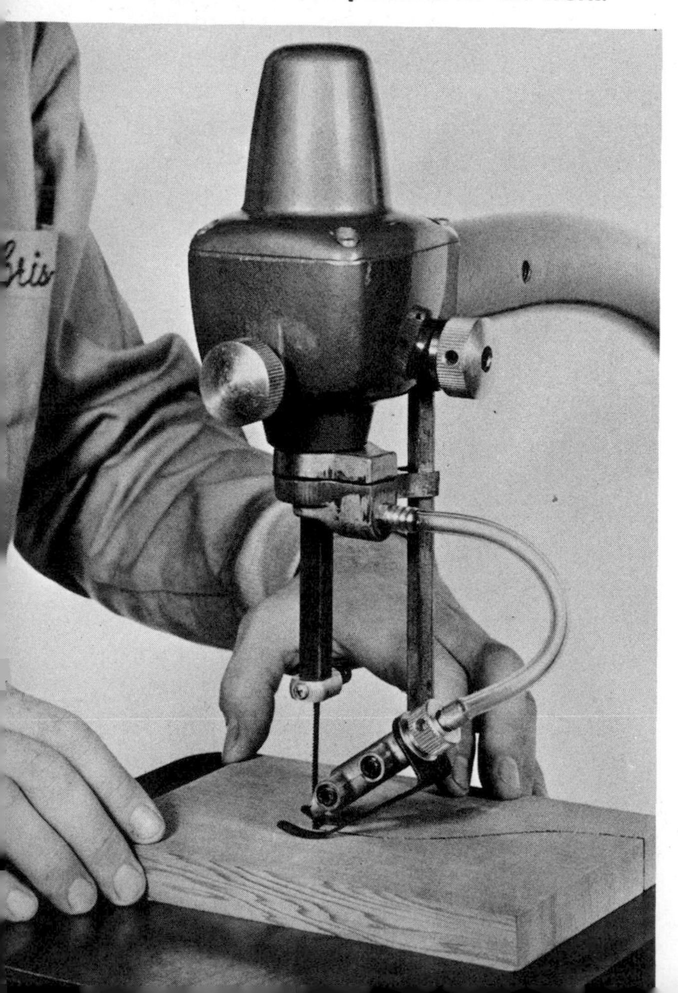

Adjusting the Spring Hold-Down

Before you begin to saw, adjust the spring hold-down so that it will press lightly on the stock. This keeps the work from being lifted off the table on the up stroke of the blade. Place the stock at the rear of the blade. Lower the guide assembly until the spring hold-down rests on the stock (see picture at upper left). Push down on the guide assembly with one hand, and tighten the rod lock-knob with the other.

Use only enough pressure to hold the work to the table, never so much as to make it difficult to move the stock. Excessive pressure on the spring hold-down may also cause it to mar the surface of the stock.

The knurled nut at the rear of the upper guide assembly secures the spring hold-down; this must be loosened when the spring requires adjustment to match table tilt during bevel cutting.

Many operators prefer working without the hold-down—having developed a method of feeding the work which includes a hold-down action with the hands. Beginners, however, should start out by using the hold-down. Blades, guides, and hold-down set up for the proper functioning of each part are shown in the photograph at the lower left.

Your Working Position

Take a natural, comfortable stance in front of the table; most jig-saw jobs take long enough for a strained position to tire you and affect the quality of your work.

Usually the left hand is used as a guide to keep the blade on the cutting line, while the right hand feeds the stock, but there is no standard routine.

Many times both hands are used in a combination guiding-and-feeding action. Often it is necessary to change position while

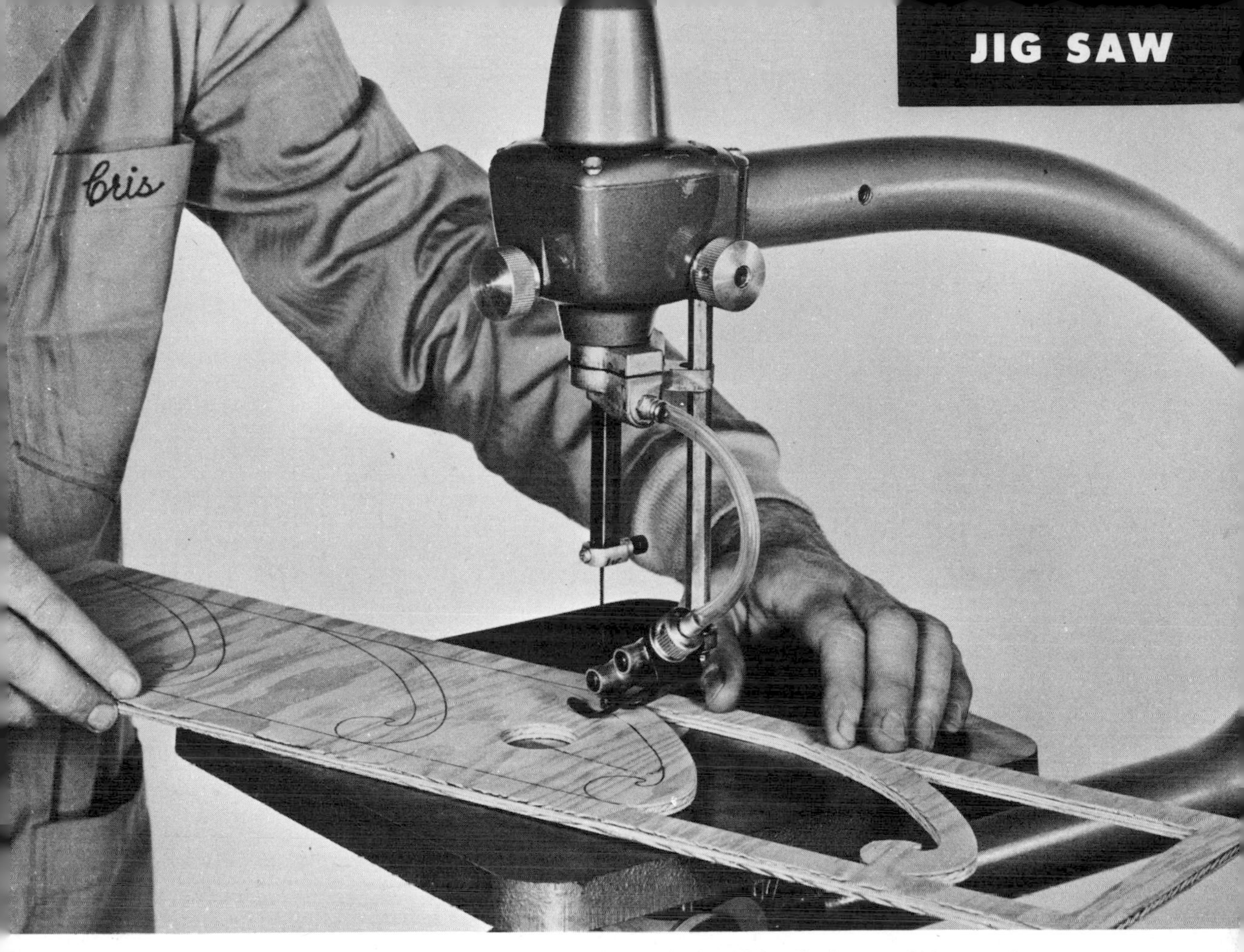

Usually the left hand acts as a guide while the right hand feeds the stock forward.

cutting, from directly in front of the blade to the left- or right-hand side of it.

Never crowd the blade in an effort to speed up the job. Maintain an even, steady feed, concentrating more on guiding the cut than on hastening the cutting. Forcing a blade around a corner too small for it will break it or make it run off the line. Most jig-saw blades will twist when forced, and will run off on a tangent.

Feed pressure should always be forward, never from the side.

If the width of the blade is kept tangent to curved lines, the cutting action will be true and the line will be easy to follow. If the blade runs off it means you're not feeding the work at the correct angle.

With a heavy blade, a good jig saw will easily cut through material as thick as 2″.

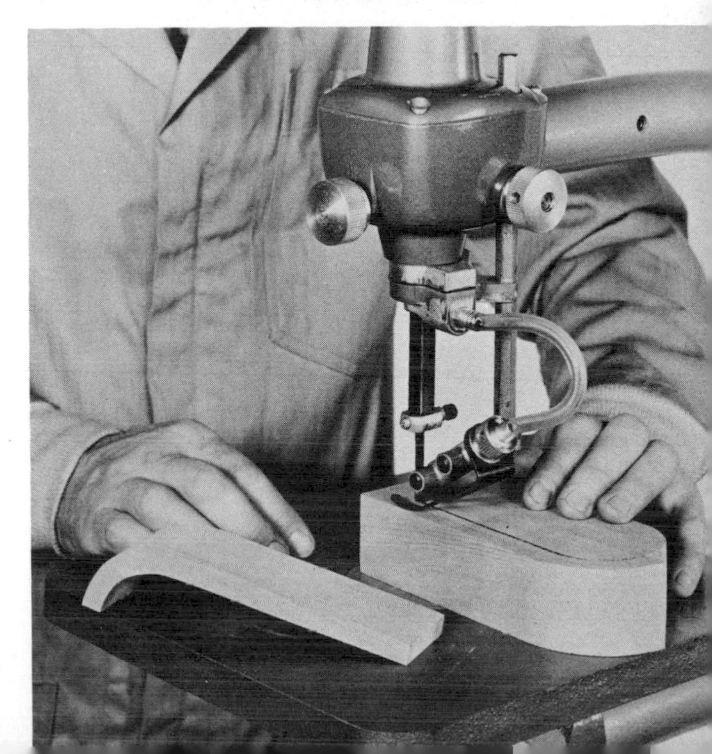

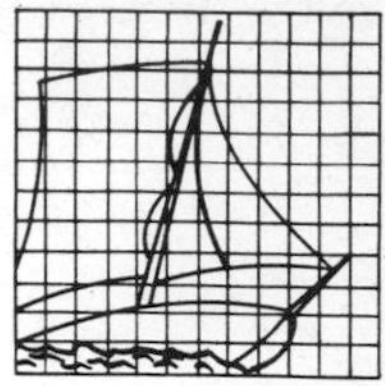

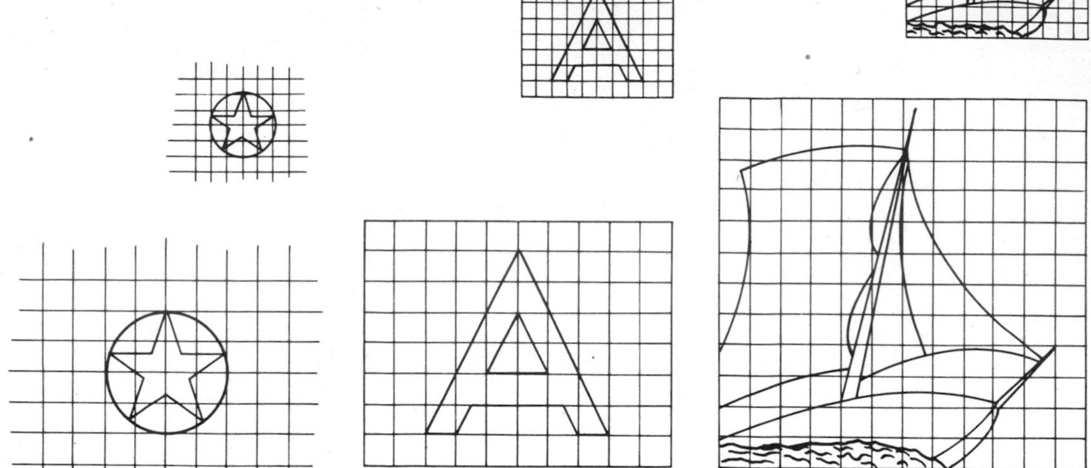

The enlarging-by-squares method is often useful when drawing jig-saw patterns.

Preplanning of cuts will eliminate waste material and considerably speed up the job.

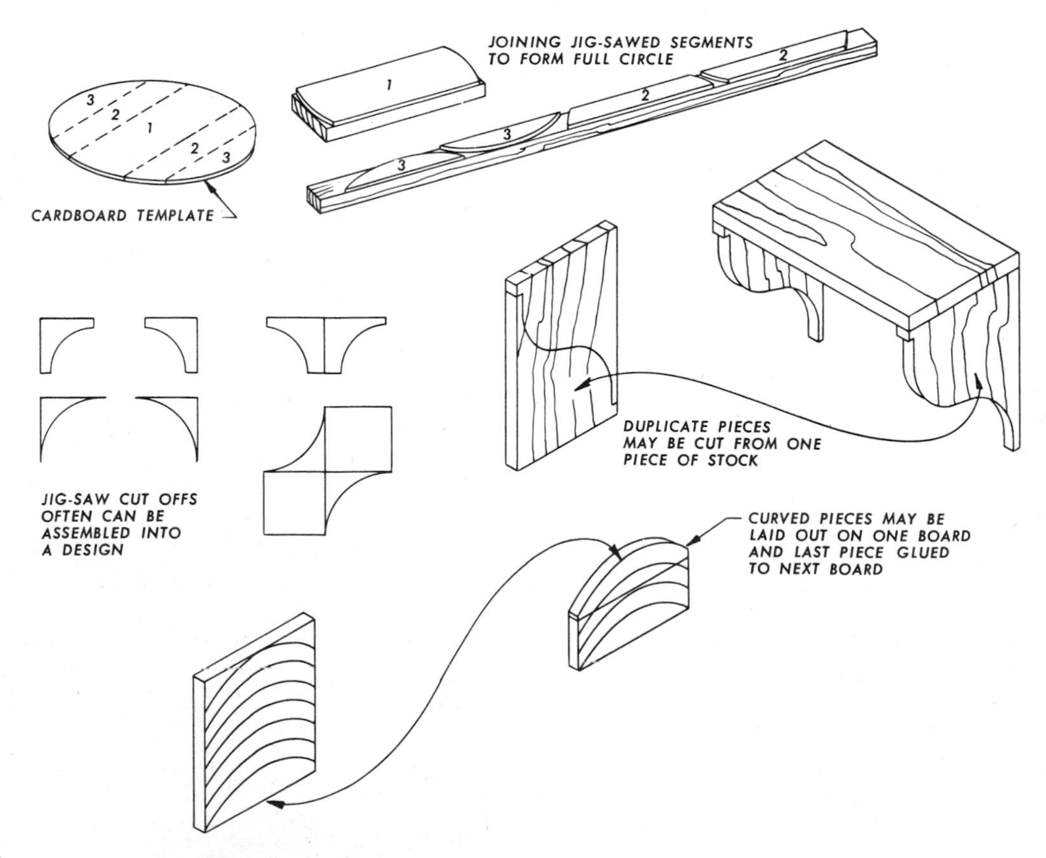
JOINING JIG-SAWED SEGMENTS TO FORM FULL CIRCLE
CARDBOARD TEMPLATE
DUPLICATE PIECES MAY BE CUT FROM ONE PIECE OF STOCK
JIG-SAW CUT OFFS OFTEN CAN BE ASSEMBLED INTO A DESIGN
CURVED PIECES MAY BE LAID OUT ON ONE BOARD AND LAST PIECE GLUED TO NEXT BOARD

A French curve (draftsman's tool) is useful for laying out any kind of scrollwork design.

Patterns and Layout

When the pattern is an original design, it can be drawn in full size—on the stock itself or on paper to be rubber-cemented to the work. Since this means destroying the pattern, it is often better to use carbon paper to transfer the original design to the work.

In production work the first piece cut is often used as a pattern to mark the others.

The most common method of drawing a pattern from a small illustration is the enlarging-by-squares system shown on the left-hand page. Most plans using this method provide a small-size drawing with the squares marked on it. Enlarging the drawing is done by reproducing the squares in a larger size. The points where the lines of the illustration cross the lines of the squares are then marked on the larger squares and these points connected.

This method is also useful when it is necessary to enlarge or transfer an illustration from a magazine or a book. The original picture is covered with tissue paper marked off in squares or with regular graph paper. Then a blank sheet is marked off with larger squares and the drawing is duplicated.

Some standard methods of work layout are sketched at the bottom of the opposite page. These eliminate excessive waste and make it possible, through joining, to form large items from scrap. When many parts are cut from a single panel it's wise to make all the patterns first, then lay them out on the panel for the least amount of waste.

A French curve (the draftsman's tool shown above) can be used to create original designs for scrollwork.

Another method is to cement a suitable illustration directly to a wood blank and cut it out on the jig saw, as illustrated below. This is an excellent way to make wall plaques and puzzles.

The same idea is used to make standing figures from photographs. Glue the photograph to a backing material, which can be plywood or Masonite. Then jig saw it and fit it into a base block that has been grooved on the table saw to take the cutout.

Pictures can often be cemented directly to the wood and cut out, as shown here.

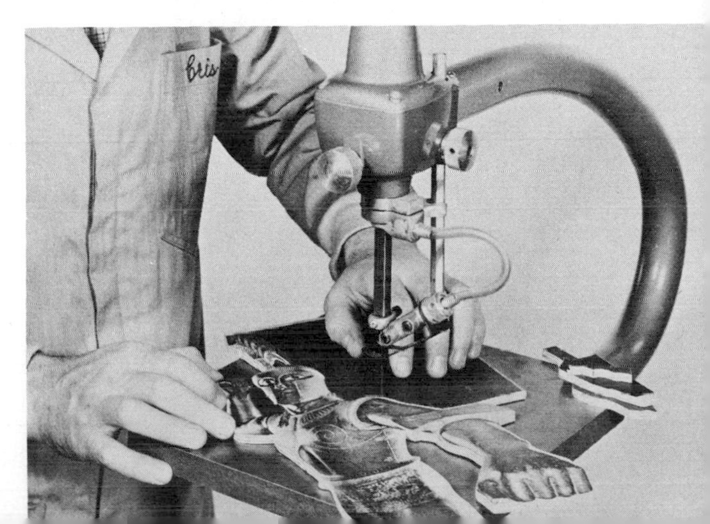

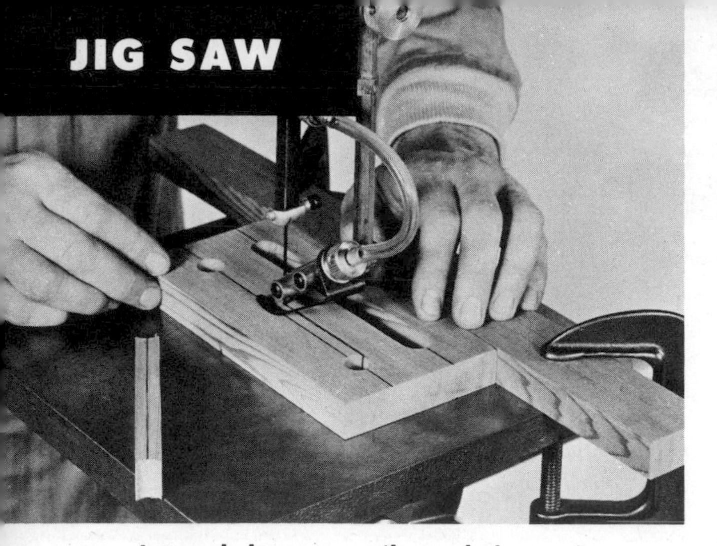

Internal slots are easily made by cutting away the material between two holes of proper diameter drilled on a common center line.

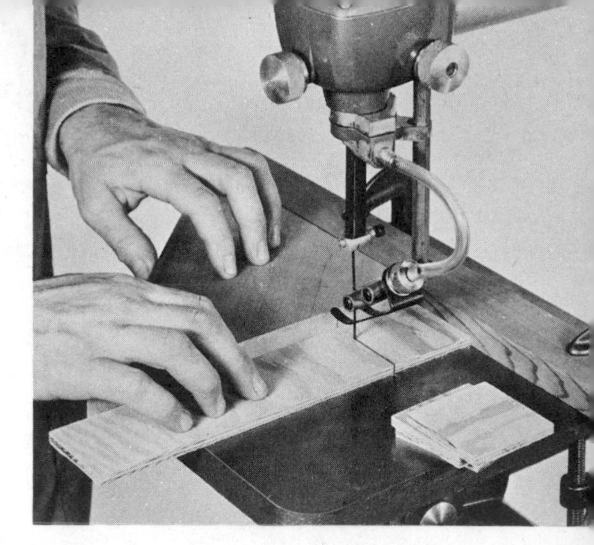

Unlike the table saw, the jig saw can use a fence when cutting off duplicate pieces. The back-up block is used like a miter gauge.

Cutting Techniques

The improvised fence above is a good guide for sawing internal slots. When the slot has round ends, drill at each end of a common center line holes of a diameter equal to the width of the slot. Insert the jig-saw blade through one of the holes and adjust the fence to guide the cut. With one side cut, readjust the fence to make the second cut.

Unlike the table saw, the jig saw can easily take the use of an improvised fence as a stop for duplicate cutoffs as shown above. The up-and-down motion of the jig-saw blade will not cause kickback or binding.

The jig saw does not cut as fast as the table saw. Move the work slowly against the blade.

Piercing—which produces an internal design without cutting in from the edge of the work—is shown in the two photographs be-

For each internal cutout required, drill a blade-insertion hole in a waste area of the project.

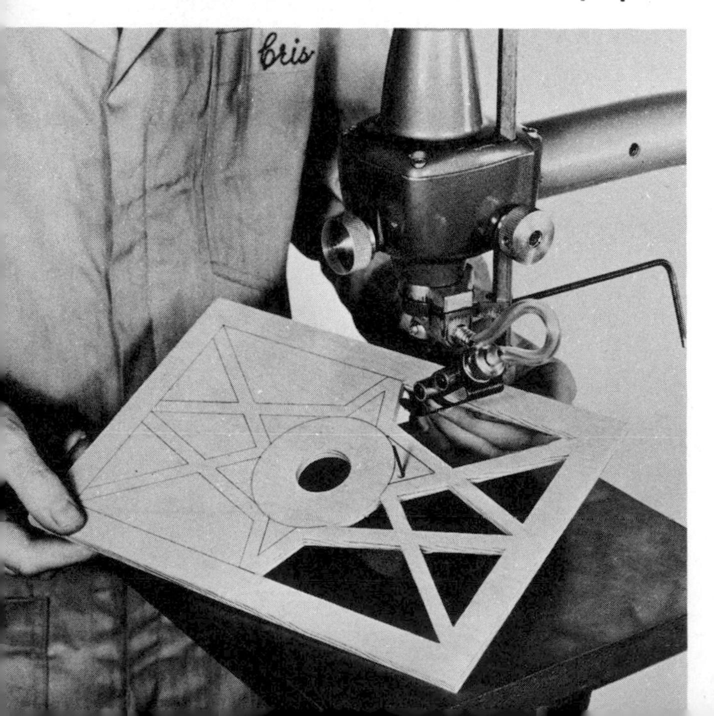

Insert the blade through the hole and lock it in the upper chuck. Then make the cut.

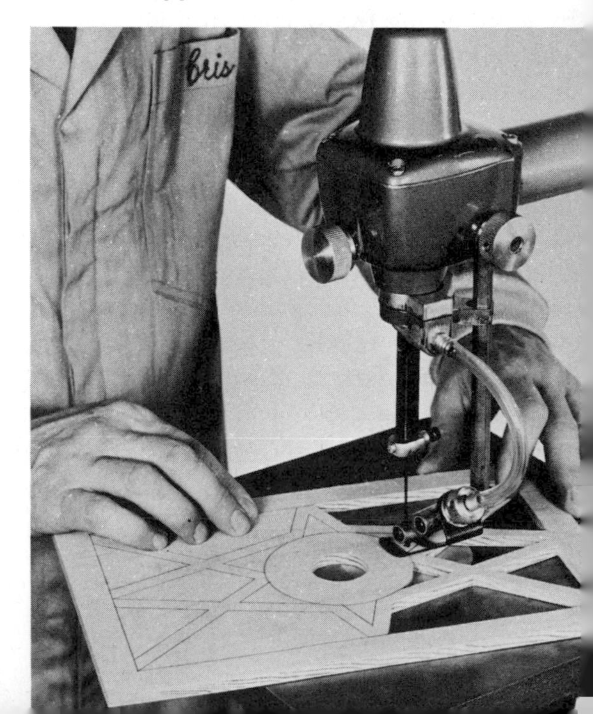

low. It is made possible by blade-insertion holes drilled in each area of the stock to be cut out. Loosen the blade from the upper chuck, insert it through the hole, and replace it in the upper chuck. Adjust the blade guide and hold-down, and proceed with the cutting.

Make your blade-insertion holes close to a corner if you wish to salvage the waste stock.

The techniques involved in turning round or square corners are shown below.

Approach the corner from the blade-insertion hole, as shown in the first detail.

Then back the work out, either to the hole or far enough away from the corner so that a second approach can be made, as shown in the second detail.

Follow these techniques to turn corners.

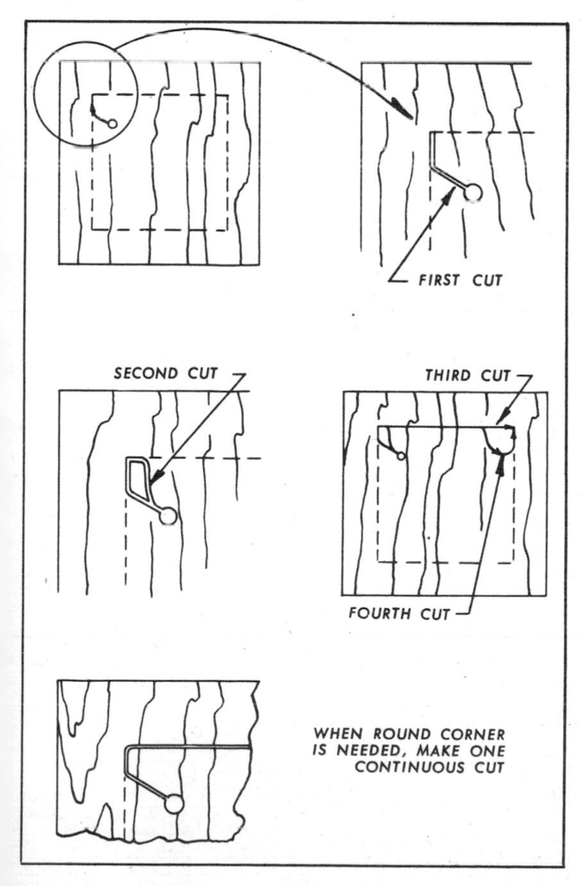

This cleans out the first corner.

Make the third cut as shown, starting from the cut corner and working on the line to the second corner.

Then back the work away and make another approach as shown in the fourth detail. Continue this until the job is complete.

The size of the blade determines how far you have to back out and how big a turn you may have to make to get set for the second approach to each corner. The finer the blade you're able to use, the less room you'll need to make the maneuver.

When the corner is not square, make the cut in one continuous pass. Select a blade that can cut the radius needed.

Cutting out a disc is a much simpler matter. Merely insert the blade through the hole and make one approach to bring the blade to the line. Continue around until the pass is complete. This is shown in the drawing below.

When round corners are called for, it is often possible to make the blade-insertion holes part of the design, as sketched at the bottom of this page.

Use a drill equal to the radius of the

Right: A blade-insertion hole, drilled to the radius desired, may form the round corner.

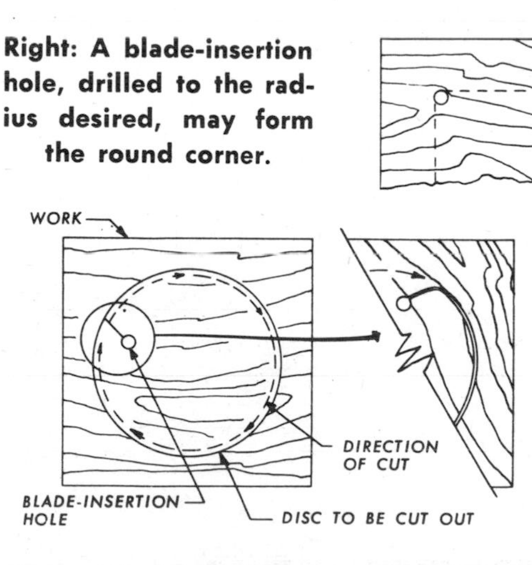

Above: A blade-insertion hole is required whenever an internal disc is to be removed.

Study the cut to be made, plan it in advance, and you'll save time in the end.

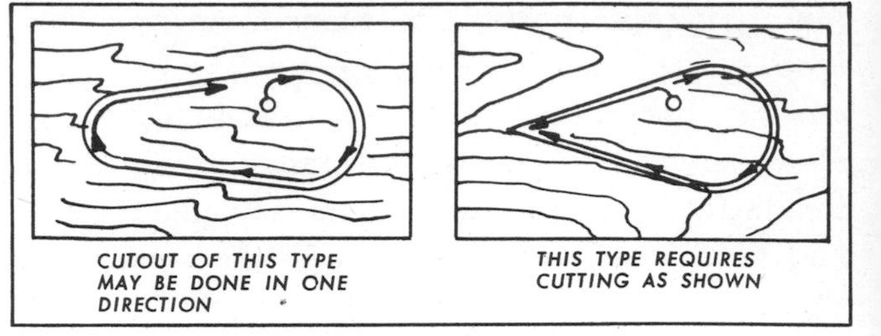

turn; position it accurately, so that the drilled hole actually forms the corner.

CUTOUT OF THIS TYPE MAY BE DONE IN ONE DIRECTION
THIS TYPE REQUIRES CUTTING AS SHOWN

One hole is sufficient for blade-insertion, but you can drill holes at all the corners and thus simplify the cutting.

You'll probably get neater and more accurate corners that way too.

Two other cutting techniques are sketched above. In the first, the cut is the same as for a circle. The approach is made to the line and the cut is carried around in one continuous pass.

In the second, the first cut is made from the blade-insertion hole to the corner. The work is backed out and the form finished by cutting in the opposite direction around the semicircle and down to the point.

It could also be done by drilling the blade-insertion hole close to the point, cleaning out the corner as you would for a square turn, then completing the rest in one pass.

The photograph below illustrates a method of cutting dowel to length, an operation that cannot be done conveniently on the table saw. An improvised fence is used as a stop, and a block is used to advance the dowel and keep it square to the blade. Have the spring hold-down just tight enough to keep the dowel from bobbing up and down with the blade.

To cut dowel to length, use back-up block to hold it square, improvised fence as stop.

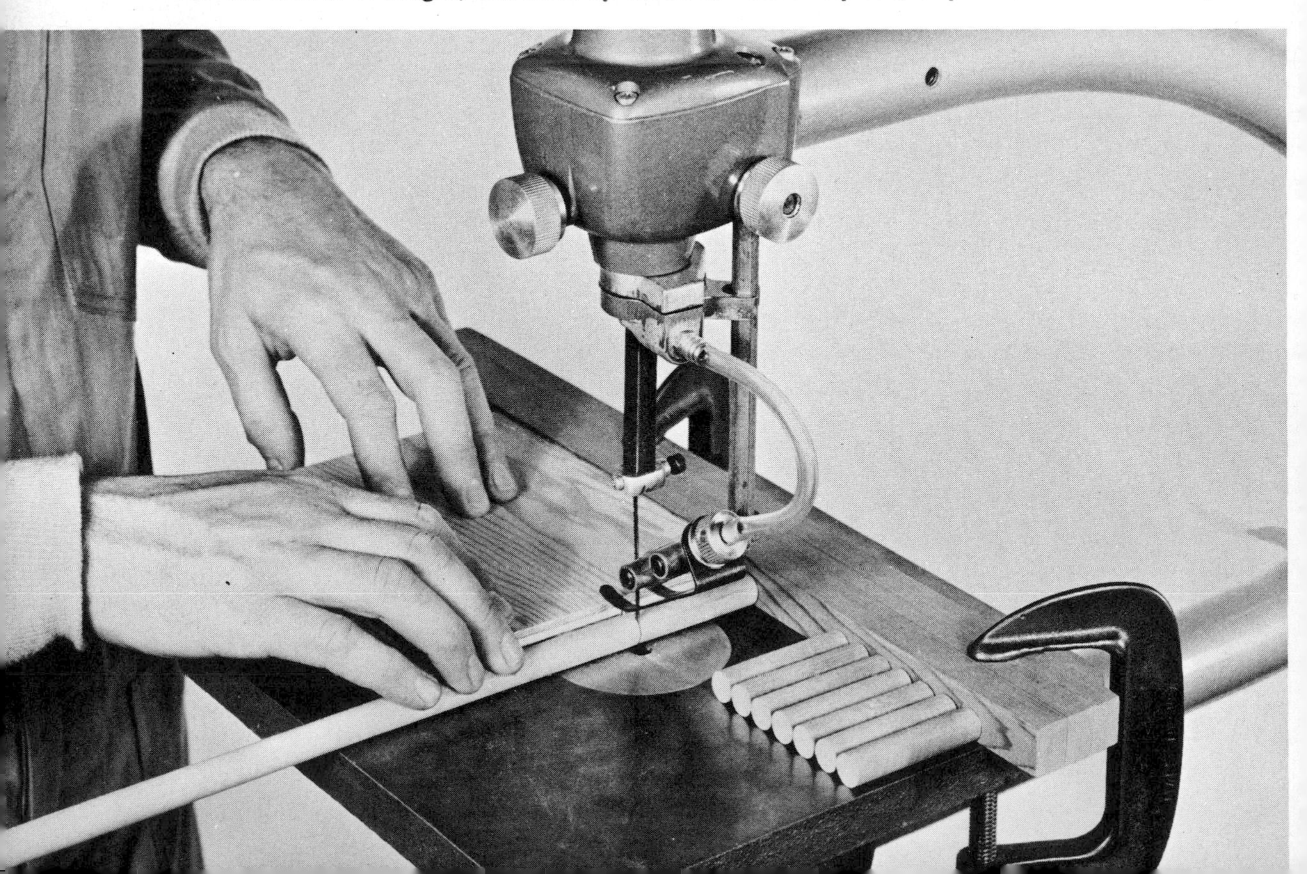

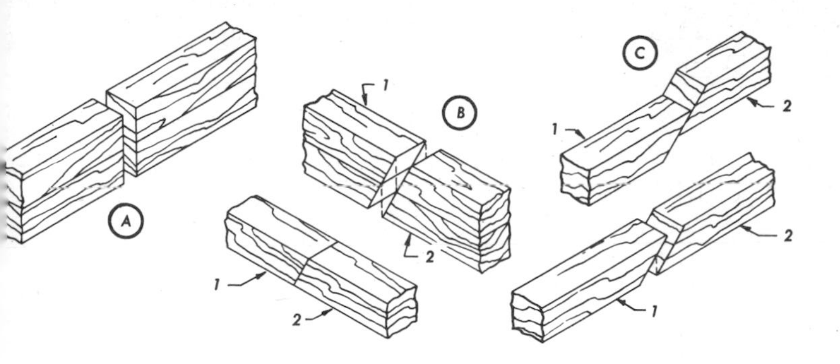

Bevel cuts are used so that any internal piece will jam tight when pushed through the piece from which it has been cut.

Cutting Bevels

On many types of inlay work, and on heavy stock, bevel cuts are used so that any internal piece will jam tight when pushed through the piece it has been cut from. The bevel may range from 1° to 10° and is adjusted by setting the table to the angle desired (below).

Cut precisely on the line, as you would for any job, but **keep the work always on the same side of the blade.** It cannot be swung completely, since this would change the direction of the bevel; then the pieces wouldn't fit.

The drawing above shows how bevel-cut parts fit together. At A is shown a kerf with the table in a normal, horizontal position. In inlay work, this kerf (very slight when the proper blade is used) is sealed with a filler, which also provides a defining border around each of the pieces.

When bevel-cutting, tilt table from 1° to 10°. Always keep work on the same side of blade.

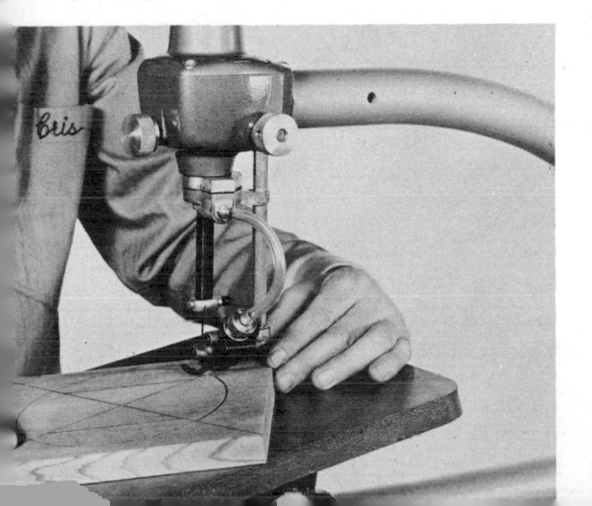

For a closed kerf line, the table is set for a bevel that produces the results seen at B. When part 2 is jammed into part 1, the two pieces form a perfect closed joint.

On heavier stock, bevel-cut pieces can be joined with the cutout piece raised above the surface of the piece it was cut from (C). An application of this technique is shown in the two photographs below. This is a good method of making raised bases, or hollow projects. The method may also be used to build up

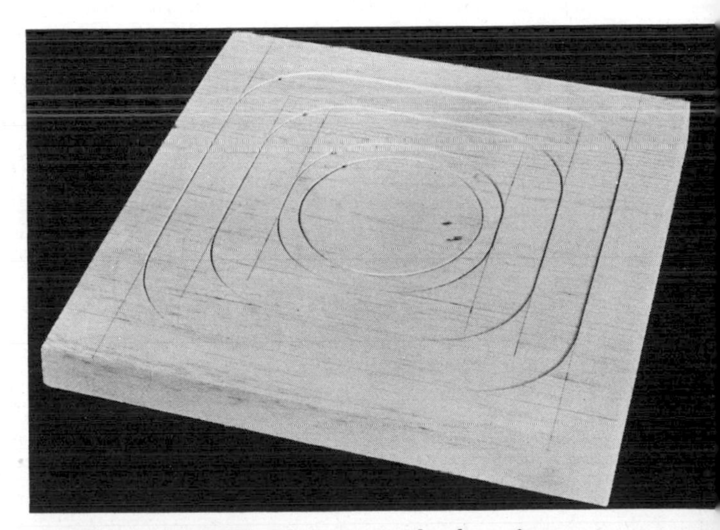

Bevel-cut a board (above). Push the pieces through to close the kerf for the result below.

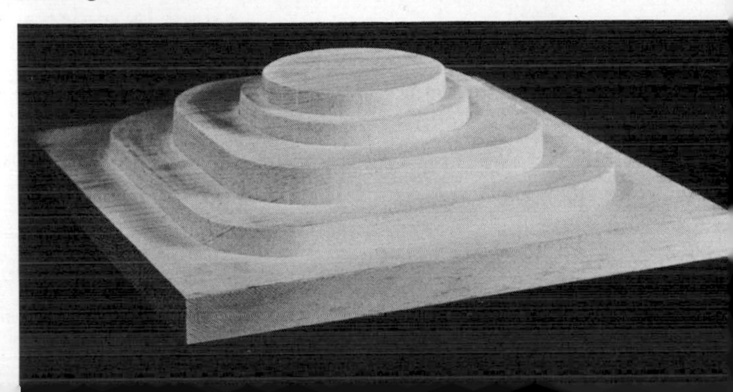

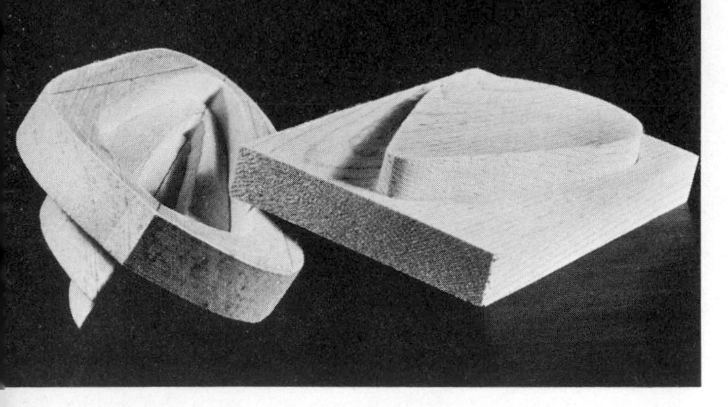

Bevel-cutting semi-shapes model-boat hulls.

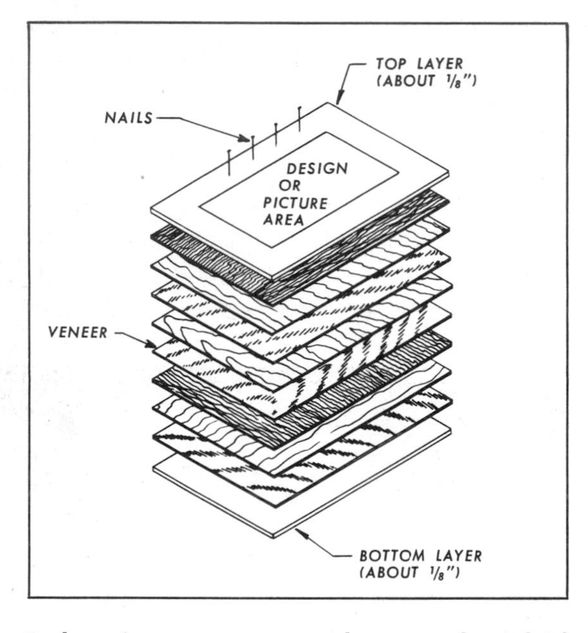

Pad-sawing veneers provides parts for inlaid pictures. Any piece cut from one veneer will fit the corresponding cavity in another.

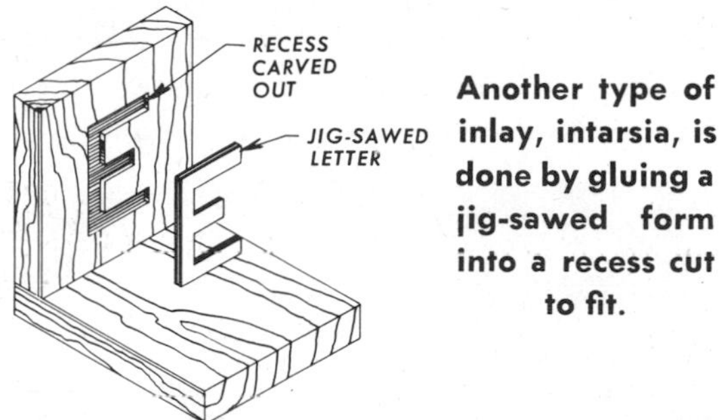

Another type of inlay, intarsia, is done by gluing a jig-sawed form into a recess cut to fit.

stock to be mounted and shaped in the lathe.

Model-boat builders will find the technique of value in forming boat hulls.

The layout of the pieces is made on the surface of the board, which is then bevel-cut in the manner explained.

When the pieces are extended, the boat hull takes the shape seen at the left, ready for final finishing.

Inlay Work

Inlay design work or pictures are made by using the pad method of sawing sketched at the left.

The veneers selected are fastened together between top and bottom boards with nails driven through waste areas. The picture or design is on the top board. Since all the veneers are cut at the same time, any piece cut out of one will fit the corresponding hole in another. The veneers should be selected for contrasting colors and grains.

As the cutting proceeds, each piece is placed on a flat board in the same position it occupied in the pad. This will eliminate having to search for and fit each individual piece.

When the cutting is finished, the pieces are joined together by placing them on a sheet of gummed paper. The assembled picture is glued, paper side up, on a backing board. Weights are used to keep the veneers flat on the surface to which they are being glued.

When the glue is dry, the paper is dampened with water and rubbed off. Then the exposed picture is sanded and finished as desired, usually with a smooth clear coating, so that the beauty of the veneers will not be hidden.

Inlays are also made by jig sawing a form from a piece of stock, and gluing it into place in a recess carved or routed out for it. This is shown in the sketch at the left.

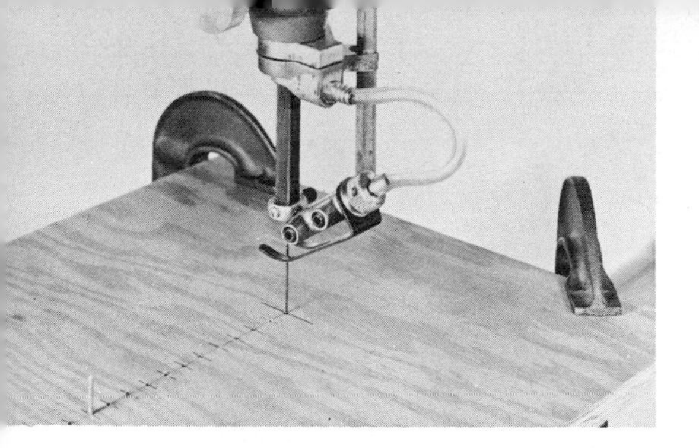

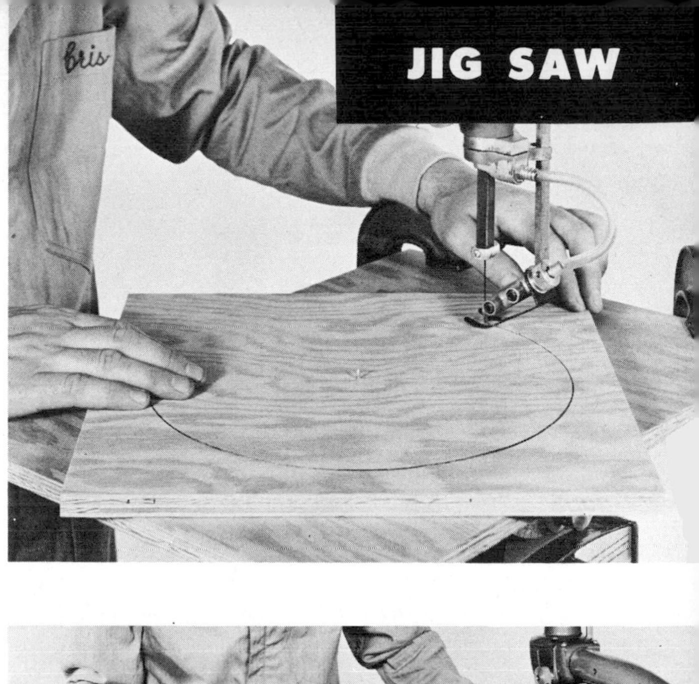

Cutting Circles

An accurate circle can be cut by using an auxiliary table clamped to the regular one. A nail acts as a pivot-pin. A series of holes ¼″ apart allows for adjustment of circle size. Drill a hole for the blade. Make the cut by revolving the work against the blade.

At right and below is shown an unusual and effective way to cut large circles for such things as wheels and the tops of even big picnic-size tables. Set the rip fence on the saw table with the lathe cup-center in the hole normally used for the mortising hold-down. Measure the radius as shown at right when setting table and fence. Make the cut as pictured below, with the lathe center providing the pivot on which the work revolves.

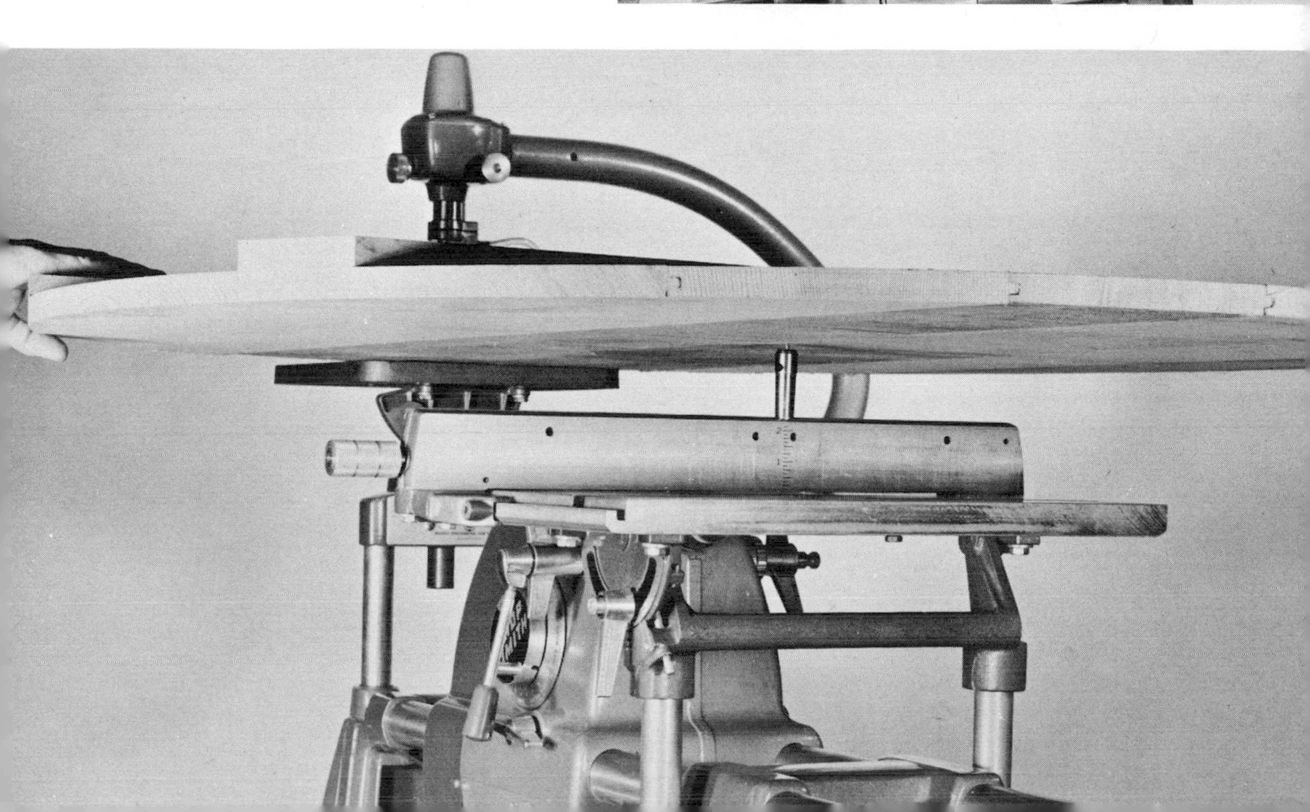

Saber-Sawing

The fiber rod used as an under-the-table guide and as a back-up for regular jig-saw blades is the only support for the blade when the jig saw is used as a saber saw.

The saber saw can do piercing work on heavy stock by the use of blade-insertion holes as shown in the photograph below. The hold-down and the hold-down spring can be used when the thickness of the stock permits (opposite page).

When jig-sawing a large panel, remove the

In saber-sawing the blade is locked in the lower chuck only, as shown in the closeup photograph at the left. Be sure to adjust the back-up rod correctly, since it provides the only support the jig-saw blade has when the machine is being used for saber-sawing.

Saber-sawing makes blade-insertion holes particularly quick and convenient to use. When the material that you are cutting is not too thick, it is possible to use the blade-guide.

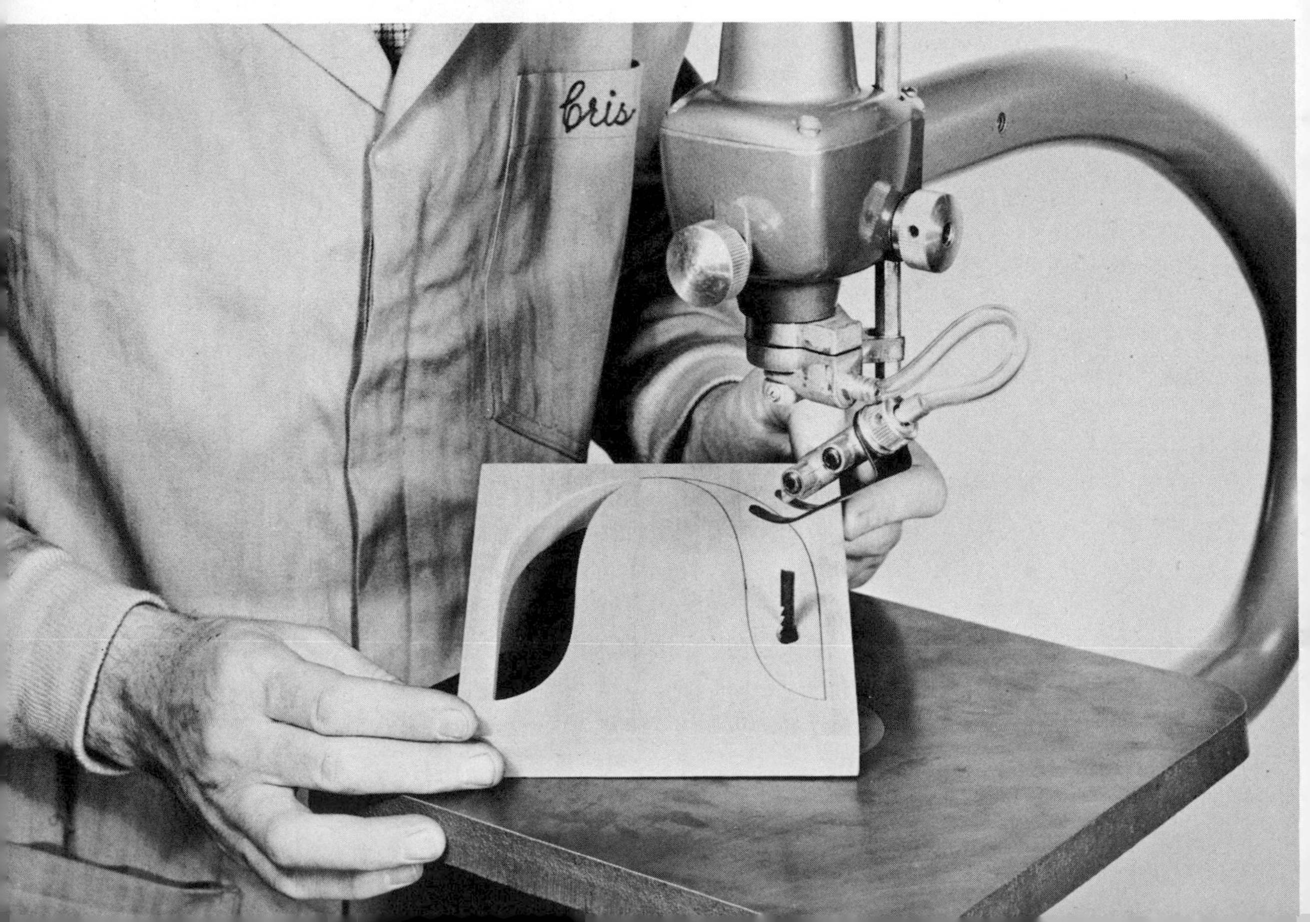

tubular arm by loosening the tube-arm lock screw and taking the arm out of the lower housing. Since the blade will be held in the lower chuck only, it is necessary that a heavier-than-average blade be used.

The heaviest jig-saw blades shown on page 207 are correct for saber-sawing. Many operators use pieces of broken hack-saw blades.

Properly adjust the lower blade back-up, as it provides the only means of vertical support. After a little practice you will discover the advantages of saber-sawing and will use this method many times in the future.

Don't force the work. Let the blade do the cutting, taking the bite it was designed for. Merely guide the stock and feed it forward.

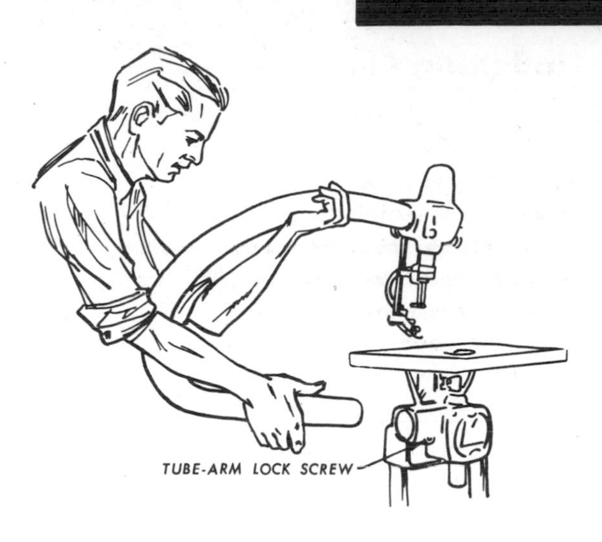

To lower or remove the tube arm, loosen the lock screw and remove the arm (or swing it down) from the lower housing.

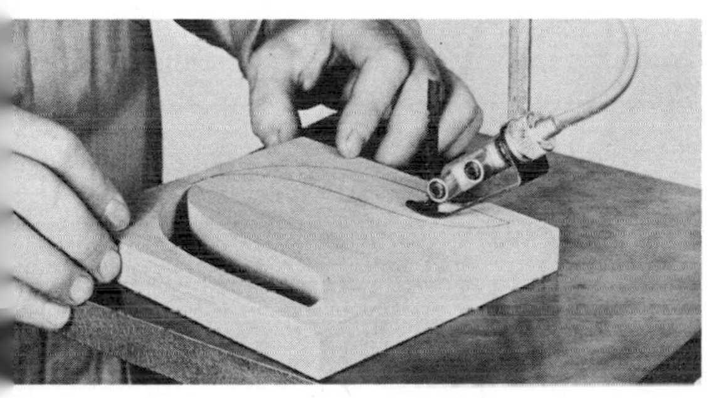

When stock thickness permits, the back-up tube and spring hold-down may be used in saber-sawing, as in photograph at left.

When the arm of the jig saw is removed and a saber saw is used, the size of work that can be handled is unlimited.

Indexing Chucks

In its normal position the jig saw will cut to the center of a 36″ panel. When, with a very wide panel, the tube arm gets in the way, you can turn the chucks 90°, as shown here, and make the cut from another direction. This is known as indexing the chuck.

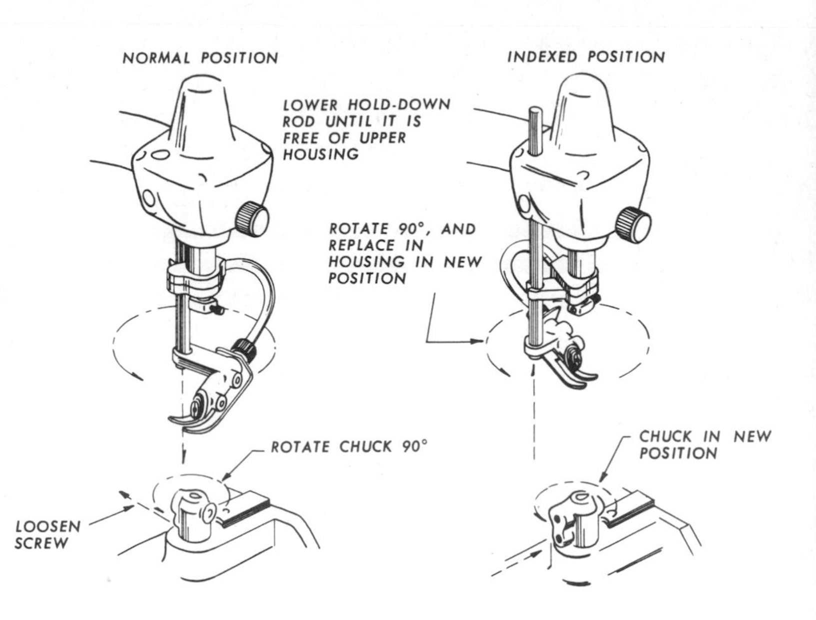
NORMAL POSITION
INDEXED POSITION
LOWER HOLD-DOWN ROD UNTIL IT IS FREE OF UPPER HOUSING
ROTATE 90°, AND REPLACE IN HOUSING IN NEW POSITION
ROTATE CHUCK 90°
CHUCK IN NEW POSITION
LOOSEN SCREW

Cutting Metal

Metal-cutting on the jig saw is similar to cutting wood except that special metal-cutting blades are used. They are made in both jeweler's and saber-saw styles. Lubricate them with beeswax to help when turning tight corners and to reduce breakage.

Burrs may accumulate as the blade cuts, catching in the cut and hindering the progress of the work. The action of the blade may bend very thin material, whether wood, plastic, or metal. To avoid bending, use the special auxiliary table, shown in the photographs below and on opposite page, that was made for the pivot-guide when cutting circles. It gives maximum support to the work, directly under the area being cut.

An auxiliary table (this one is also used for pivot-cutting) is one device for providing maximum support around the blade when cutting metal . . .

Instead of the auxiliary table, a special insert of wood, Masonite, or other thin material can be used when cutting metal, as shown at right.

Another way to avoid bending or breaking thin stock is to sandwich the work between layers of heavier material, such as ⅛″ (or ¼″) plywood. Sheet metal may be shellacked to a wooden base. The special table, however, is superior, and it provides a device that can be used over and over again.

Still another suitable method permitting repeated use is to make a special insert, like the one shown in the photograph at the right, to replace the regular insert.

You can make the special insert of wood, metal, or hardboard (Masonite). Drill and countersink the holes, as in the regular insert. And be sure that the insert is fitted flush with the table surface.

. . . The auxiliary table is needed to prevent the blade from bending the material and producing a jagged edge, especially on thin sheet metal.

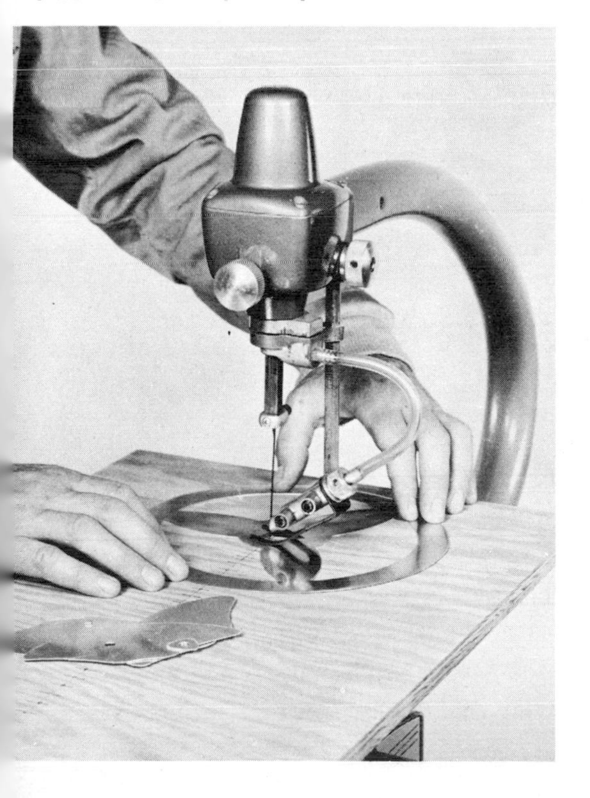

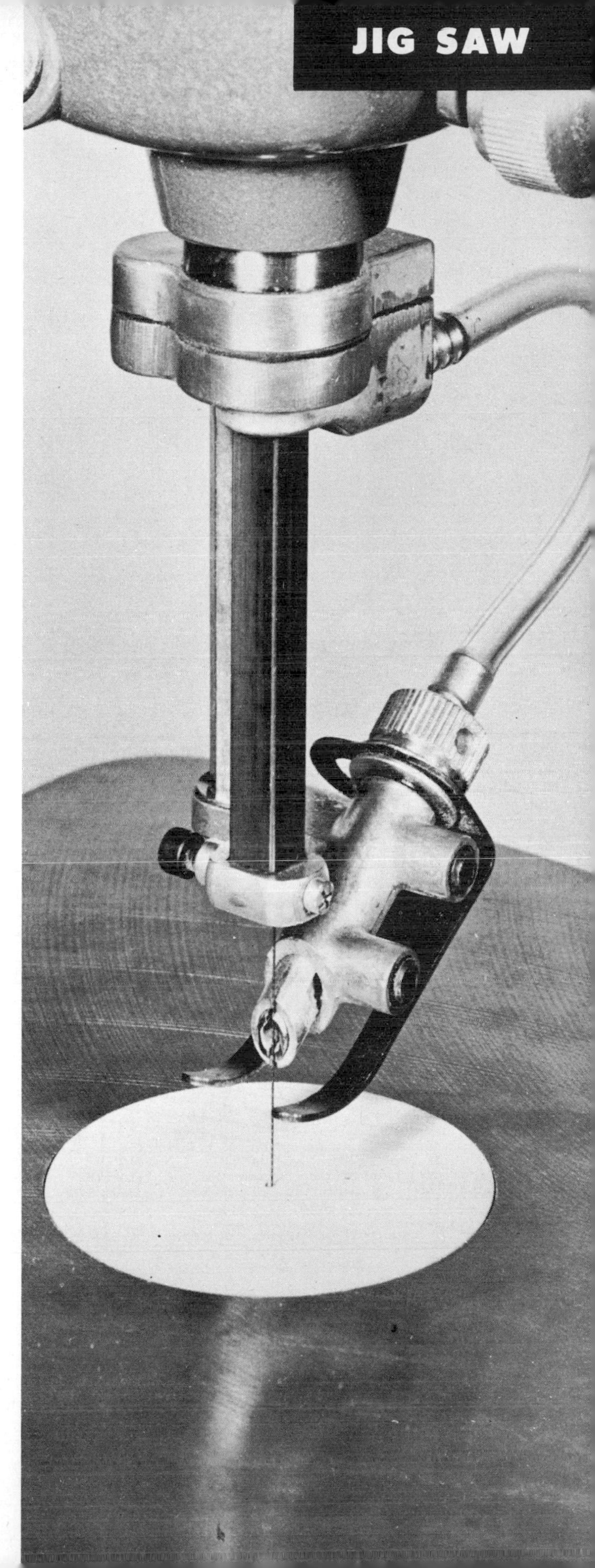

Protective paper covering should be left on the plastic sheet until cutting is finished.

Cutting Plastics

When cutting plastics, remember that the feed must be slower than when cutting wood. Although woodcutting blades may be used, a skiptooth type of blade will do a better job. The spaces between the teeth help clear away the chips; this avoids heating the work, which would cause the chips to weld and perhaps bind the blade. Cutting plastics is shown above.

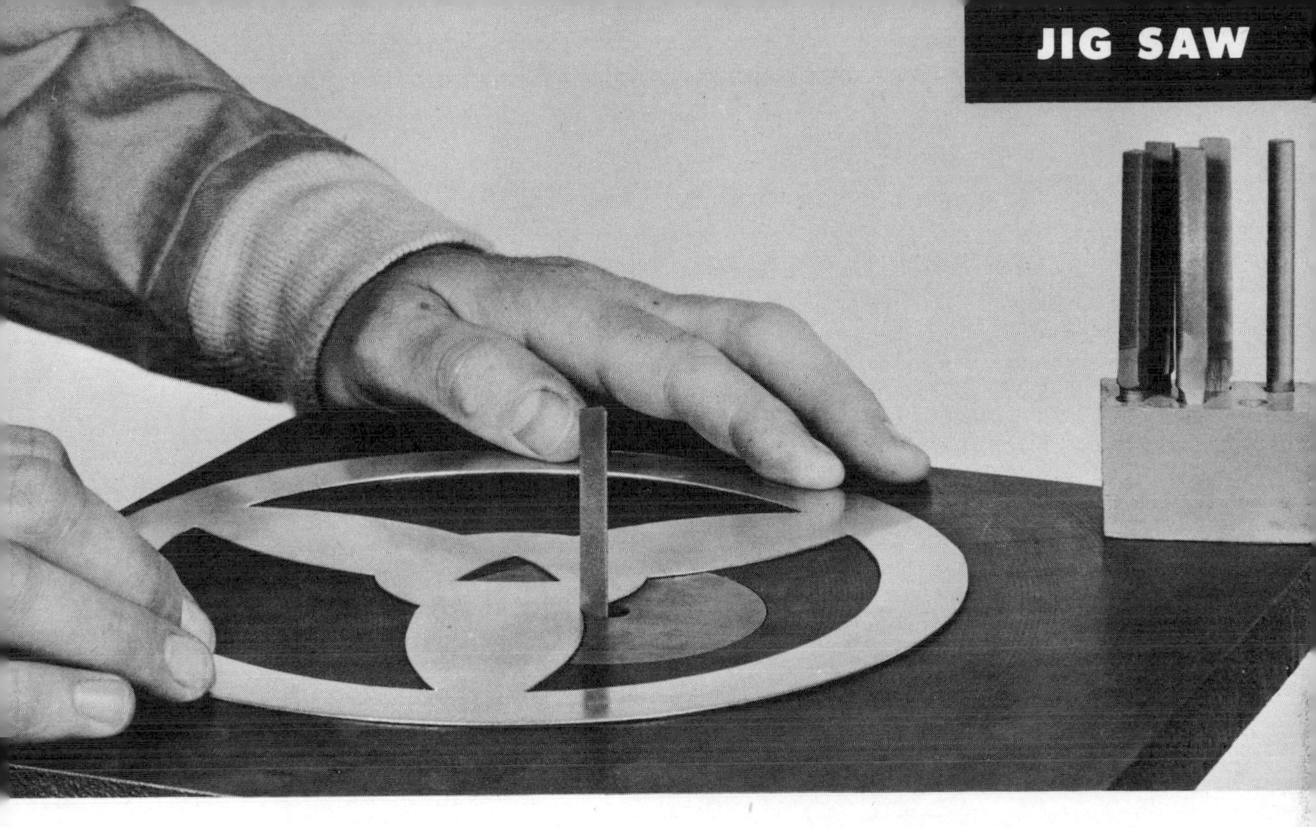

Filing with the Jig Saw

Filing is done at very slow speeds with special machine files gripped in the V of the lower chuck-housing wall. These files are available in a variety of shapes; the proper selection will enable you to smooth edges on the interior and exterior sides of almost any cutout.

Don't jam the work against the file or it may be lifted from the table. Feed the work gently against the file and move it slowly, bringing the file to bear against the whole edge of the piece being smoothed. If you remove the blade guide you can use the spring hold-down to keep the work flat on the table.

Special sanding attachments for use on wood are also available. These usually have one flat and one semicircular side. They almost always require a special insert to fit the shape of the sanding attachment and to provide support close to the work area. Sanding-sticks of this type may be made by fitting a wooden block on a ¼″ bolt, to be gripped in the lower chuck like a file. The sandpaper is cemented to the wooden block.

Machine files are available in a variety of shapes. They will enable you to smooth interior or exterior edges on almost any cutout. They are used as shown above, gripped in the V of the lower chuck-housing wall as in the photograph below.

Paper cut by sawing between plywood layers (above) will have unfrayed edges (below).

Pad-Sawing Paper

Sawing paper cutouts becomes a simple procedure when the sheets are sandwiched between two pieces of plywood.

The paper should be large enough so that the nails holding the pad together can go through it outside the pattern. Of course, if the edges of the sheets are to be bent back or otherwise hidden, then the holes do not matter.

Paper that has been cut in this manner will havc thc rcmarkably smooth edges you see in the picture at the left.

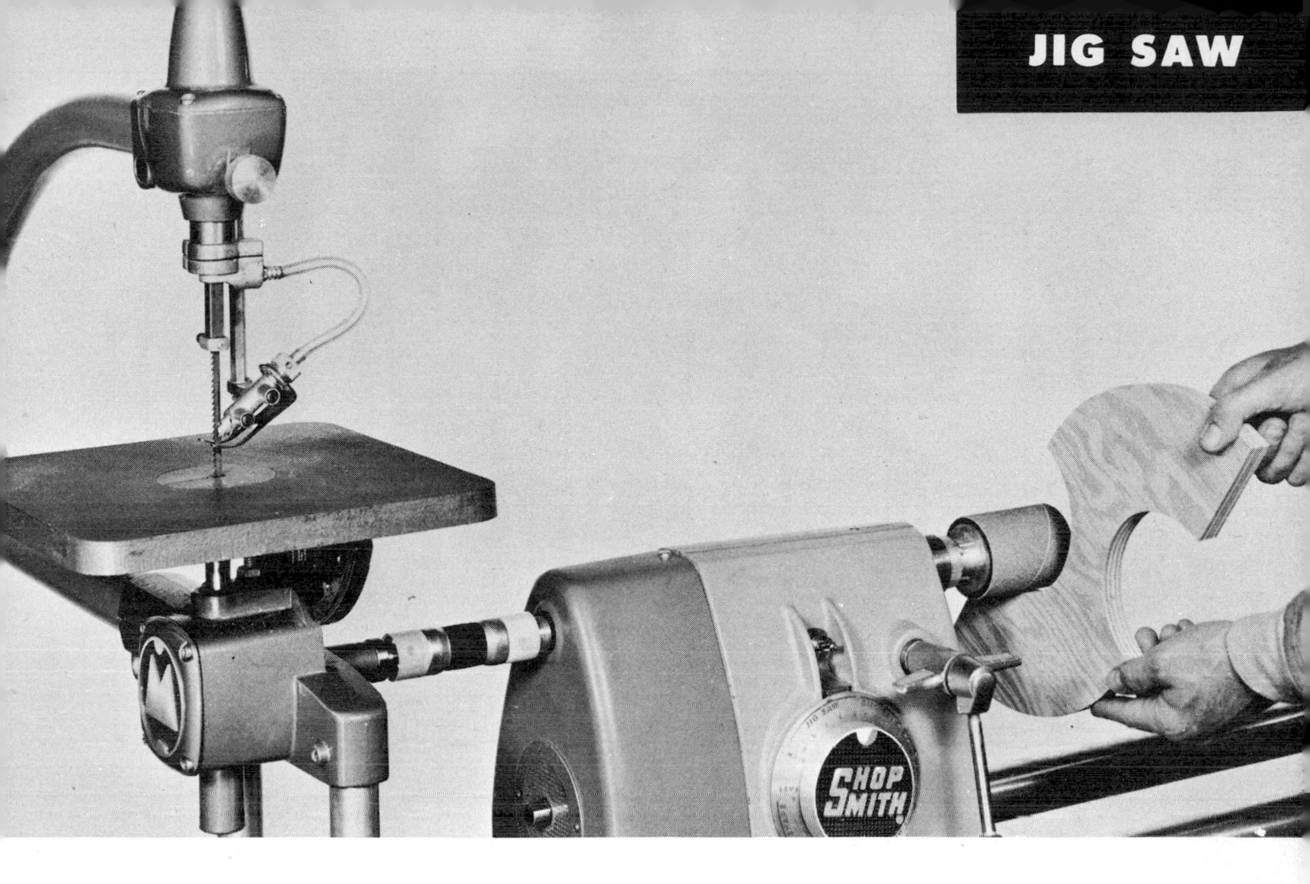

Two-Tool Setups

With the Power Mount on the multi-purpose tool, you can operate complementary tools at the same time. This is a great advantage with the jig saw, since you can mount on the main spindle either a drum sander (for smoothing inside curves, as above) or a disc sander.

The disc is highly effective on outside curves, as shown below, where the saw table is being used to hold the work square. Rough-cut discs can be quickly brought to perfect circles through use of the disc sander, either freehand or with a pivot jig. You can also mount on the main spindle such items as wire brushes, polishing pads, and buffing wheels, to polish metals or plastics cut on the jig saw.

TROUBLE-SHOOTING CHART FOR THE JIG SAW

GENERAL

THE TROUBLE	POSSIBLE CAUSES	THE CURE	SEE PAGE
BLADE BREAKS	incorrect procedure	use correct blade for operation, material, and material thickness	207
	wrong speed	consult speed chart for correct rpm	207
	incorrect blade tension	adjust tension for blade and operation	208, 209
	excessive feed pressure	let blade cut as much as it can—do not force work	211
	blade twists	avoid cutting radii too small for blade width	211
BOWED EDGE ON STOCK	incorrect tension	apply more tension	208
	fine blade used on heavy stock	use correct blade for material and material thickness	207
BLADE WALKS OFF LINE	misalignment	be sure blade guide and back-up are correctly adjusted	206
	blade guide not in line with chucks	loosen nut on bottom of hold-down rod and align blade guide with chucks	—
	forcing cut	feed slowly—accuracy is more important than speed	211
	blade tension inadequate	adjust tension for blade and operation	208
BLADE CUTTING TOO SLOW	blade teeth too fine for work	check chart for correct blade for material and material thickness	207
	blade worn	replace	—
	spring hold-down too tight	apply just enough pressure to do job	210
	incorrect speed (usually too slow)	change to higher speed	207

GENERAL	CUT HAS SLIGHT BEVEL	misalignment	check table for squareness to blade	209
	WORK LIFTS FROM TABLE	insufficient pressure on spring hold-down	check spring hold-down and adjust pressure	210
	EXCESSIVE VIBRATION	excessive speed	slow down to correct rpm	207
	SAWDUST DOES NOT CLEAR FROM CUTTING LINE	air tube clogged	remove and clear	see instructional materials supplied with tool by manufacturer
		air tube kinked	replace	
		mechanism inoperative	check manufacturer's maintenance instructions	
CUTTING METAL	CUT EDGES BEND	insufficient support around cutting area	use special insert or one of special methods described in text	223
	TEETH BREAK OR QUICKLY WEAR	wrong blade	check chart for correct blade	207
	EXCESSIVELY ROUGH EDGES	blade too coarse	check chart for correct blade	207
CUTTING PLASTICS	KERF CLOSES AND BINDS BLADE	incorrect procedure	check chart for correct blade and speed	207
CUTTING BEVELS	CUTS DO NOT MATCH	table tilt at fault	limit to maximum of 10 degrees	217
SABER-SAWING	HARD TO FOLLOW LINE	wrong blade being used	use heaviest blade available	220
		forcing cut	feed slowly—guide carefully	221
		no blade support	be sure to adjust lower blade back-up as support when saber-sawing	220
FILING, SANDING	FILE OR SANDPAPER QUICKLY CLOGS	wrong speed (usually too fast)	slow down to correct rpm	225

THE BAND SAW

Mounting blades • adjusting the guides • speeds adjusting the table • blades • blade storage • cutting techniques thinning-out • resawing • extra-long stock • compound cutting multiple-part cutting • pad sawing • pattern sawing parallel curves • cutting dowel • trouble shooting

THE BAND SAW is used mostly for sawing curved or irregular lines, but it's important for straight-line cutting too. In depth-of-cut capacity it is unequalled by any other woodworking machine. The ease and speed with which it cuts through 6″ timber is amazing.

In the home workshop it will do things that can't be done on other equipment. It does resawing (making thin boards out of thick ones), compound cutting (required, for example, when forming the cabriole leg), reducing stock thickness in confined areas (for spindle turning), pad-sawing (cutting many duplicate pieces simultaneously) . . .

Because you can use a blade only ⅛″ wide, many band-saw operations are similar to those on a jig saw; but each of these tools is an important home-workshop accessory. For example, the jig saw is the only machine that will make internal cutouts conveniently; the band saw is the only machine that will cut through very heavy material.

The band saw is a vertical machine with two large, rubber-rimmed wheels that rotate a flexible steel band with saw teeth cut into one of its edges. There are three kinds of band saws:

1. The **resaw** is used in factories and lumber yards for cutting heavy stock into thin planks;
2. the **mill** is a heavy-duty machine for cutting logs into planks; and
3. the **band-scroll saw,** the kind most useful for home-workshop needs, is used for sawing curved and irregular lines, straight-line sawing, and for resawing.

Band-saw capacities are measured in wheel diameter (slightly greater than the distance from the blade to the throat) and in the distance from the table to the blade-guides in their elevated position (this controls the thickness of the stock that can be cut).

The band saw leads all woodworking machines in depth-of-cut capacity and in cutting speed.

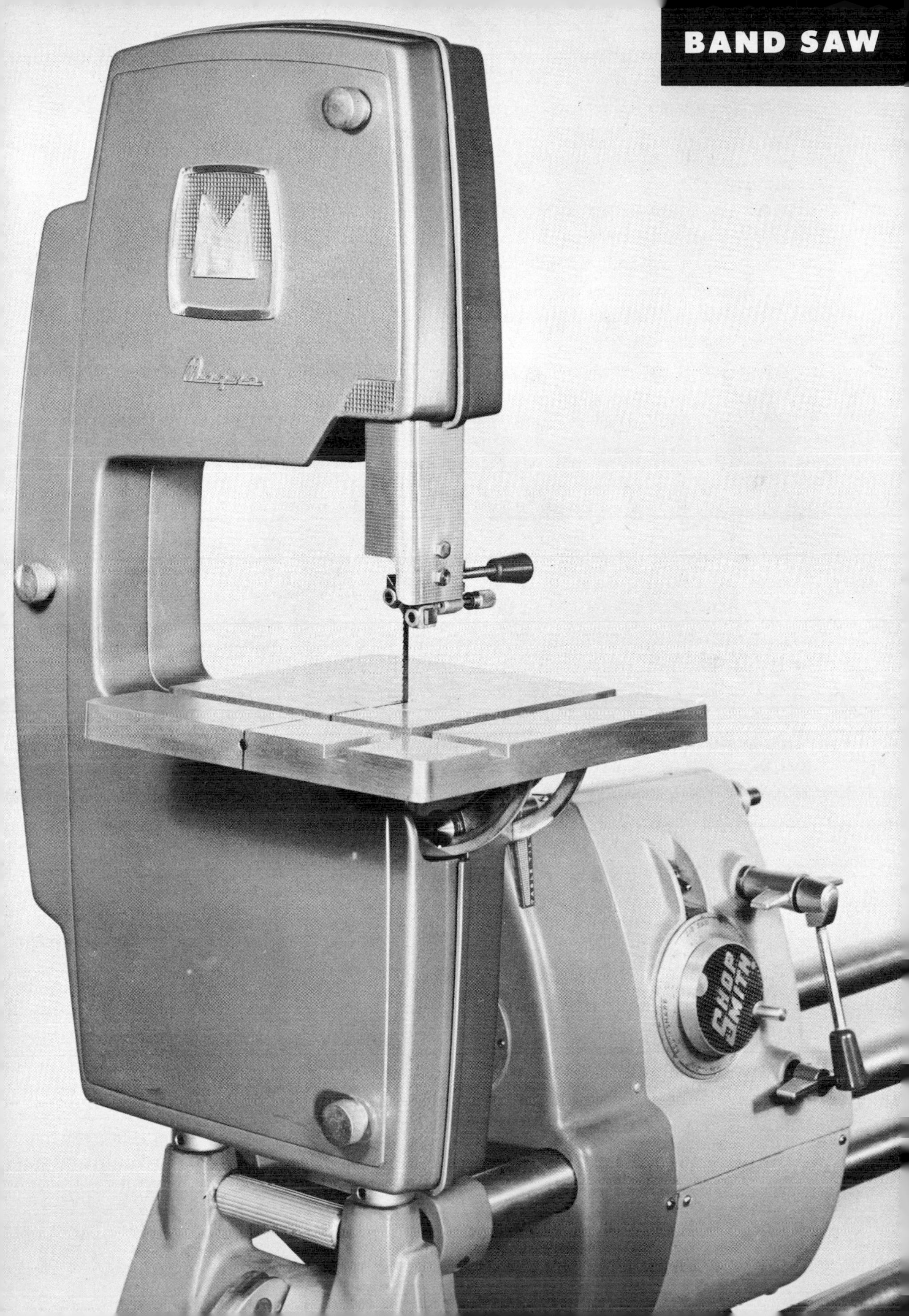

On the machine available as an accessory for the multi-purpose tool, the throat depth is 10½″ and the maximum vertical cutting clearance is 6″.

This band saw mounts at the Power Mount end of the machine, like any other major accessory, and is driven by a flexible coupling that connects to the upper auxiliary spindle on the headstock. This uses the ¾-horsepower motor and the variable-speed mechanism.

When not in use, this band saw can be conveniently stored on a simple wall bracket like the one sketched at the right. The saw mounts in seconds when needed.

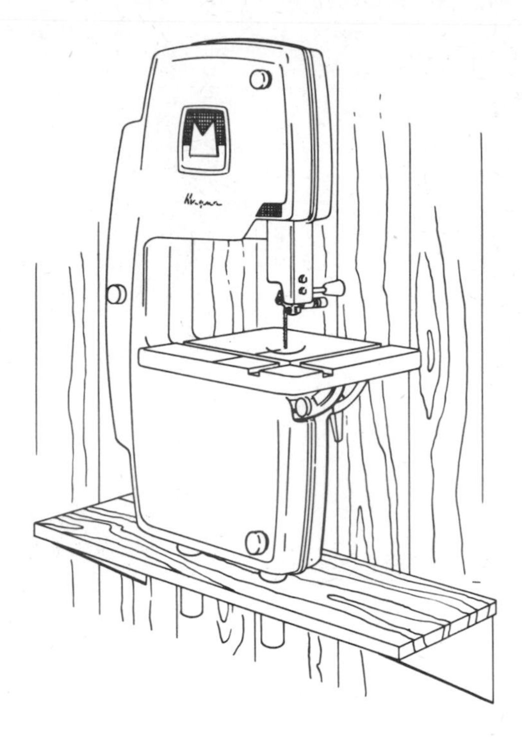

Band-saw accessory stores on a wall bracket.

Mounting Band-Saw Blades

Follow these four steps when replacing a blade:

1. Remove the Allen screw in the front edge of the table (it keeps the halves of the table aligned).

2. Remove the cover from the machine.

3. Use an Allen wrench to loosen the blade-tension screw (pictured below); this will lower the upper wheel, shortening the distance between wheels and permitting removal of the blade.

Be sure tension is correct for blade being used.

4. When changing from a wide to a narrow blade, move the guide blocks all the way back **before** mounting the new blade. After the blade is mounted, adjust the blocks to it.

To mount the new blade, hold it with the teeth facing you and with the points of the teeth slanting down toward the table. Slip it through the table slot, and position it on the wheels. Then use the Allen wrench on the tension screw until the gauge reads correctly for the width of blade being used. Replace the cover and Allen screw.

Most band saws require an adjustment that controls the angle of the upper wheel to provide correct blade tracking. The design of this machine eliminates this step. The blade will automatically track correctly, regardless of width.

In addition, this unique design eliminates the need to adjust the back-up rollers. Incidentally, the top back-up roller **does not** touch the back of the blade when it is running free. Its purpose is to support the blade **during** the cut.

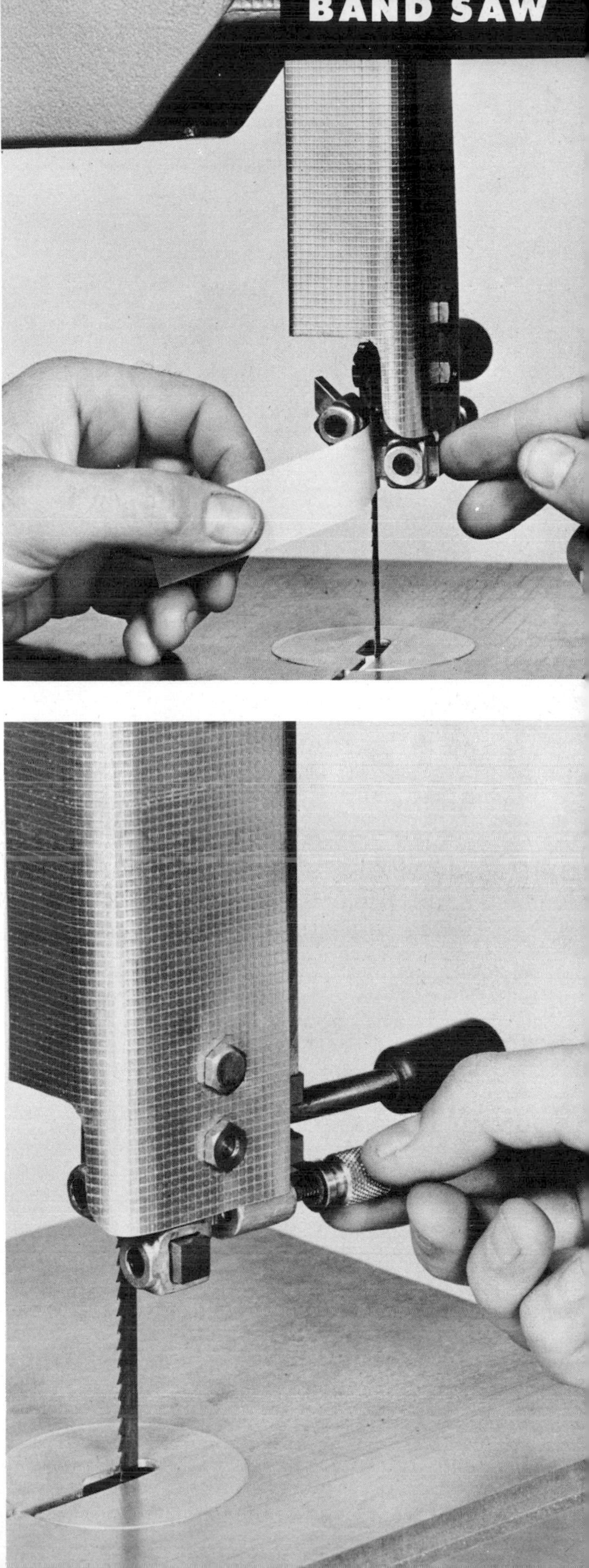

Use a piece of paper like this when making blade-guide adjustments. The guides should not rub against the blade when it's running free.

Adjusting the Guides

Adjust the upper and lower blade guides to the blade being used. They should never be forced against the blade; it is good practice to use a piece of tissue paper or cellophane between the guide and the blade, as shown at right, to assure the correct setting.

The forward position of the guides should be just **to** the depth of the gullet on the blade. This adjustment is controlled by the ridged knob shown at lower right. Turn this knob counter-clockwise (looking at front of knob) to move the guides forward. Turning it the opposite direction will move them back.

One clue to incorrect adjustment of the blade guides is called lead.

Normally, if a piece of wood is pushed against the blade, the kerf will be straight, and parallel to the side of the table. If the blade runs off, making it necessary for the operator to adjust the angle of feed to compensate for the lead, check the upper and lower guide blocks. If the guides are correctly adjusted, it is reasonable to assume that the lead has another cause—incorrect set of the saw teeth.

When lead is excessive, and is caused by the latter condition, it can be remedied only by removing the saw-blade and re-sharpening and re-setting the teeth.

When lead is not excessive, it may be remedied by lightly honing the **lead side** of the blade. Back up the blade with a block of scrap wood and apply a honing stone **very**

The forward position of the guides must be adjusted to the width of the blade. They should be set just to gullet depth.

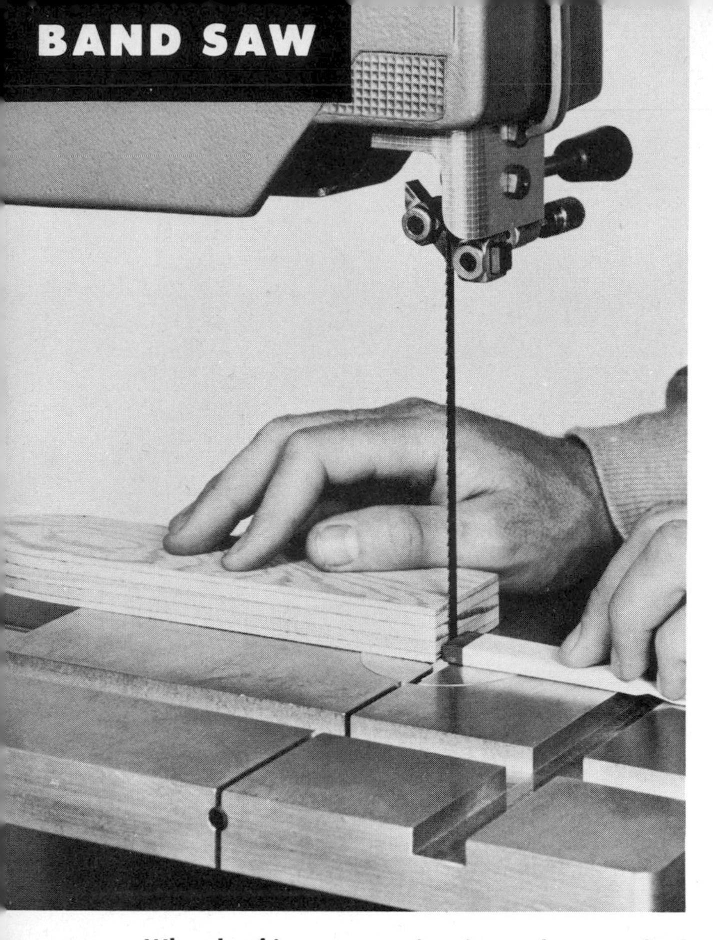

When lead is not excessive, it may be remedied by lightly honing the lead side of the blade. Be sure to use a fine stone. Back up the blade during honing with a block of scrap wood.

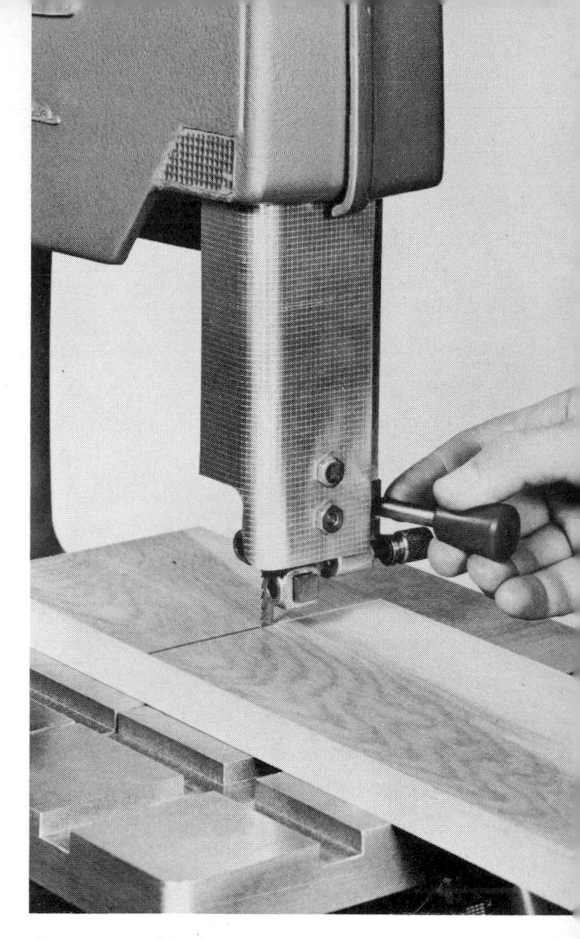

The upper blade guides should be ¼″ to ½″ above the surface of the stock you are cutting.

lightly to the other side as the blade turns. This is shown in the photograph above.

Always lock the upper guides so they are about ¼″ above the surface of the stock being cut.

For your protection, the length of blade above the upper guides is covered by a shield which is part of the upper guide assembly. This assembly is moved up or down and locked in place at the required height by adjustment of one handle. To unlock it, turn the handle toward the front of the machine; and, with your hand still on the handle, raise or lower the guide to the correct position. Then lock it again by turning the handle toward the back of the machine.

You can see this being done in the photograph at the upper right.

Band-Saw Speeds

The band saw will function most efficiently at a speed of from 2,000 fpm (feet per minute) to 2,500 fpm. On the multi-purpose tool this range is to be had with a Speed Dial setting of from SLOW to D. The band saw should not be run above these speeds.

The greater power needed for cutting very thick stock or resawing can be obtained by using a slower speed.

When the band saw is mounted on its own stand, use a pulley speed of about 875 rpm.

On some cuts—especially cross-grain—the blade will set up a chatter that produces an unusually rough cut. A change of speed will minimize this and may entirely eliminate it. If a variable speed is available, try slowing down the blade, or speeding it up, should you notice excessive blade-vibration.

Adjusting the Table

To check the table for squareness to the blade, follow the steps in the picture sequence on this page. With the tilt indicator set at "0", the angle between table and blade must be exactly 90°.

A leveling screw is provided so the table may be automatically returned to the correct "0" setting after any operation involving a table tilt. Once it has been adjusted as shown here, horizontal cuts will be exact and the table can be tilted to any required angle by taking the reading directly from the indicator scale. If a further check is ever necessary, it may be made by cutting a piece of wood with the table horizontal, then checking the cut with a square.

A rarely required table tilt, 5° to the left, is available by removing the leveling screw. After any operation requiring this tilt, be sure to re-position the leveling screw at the "0" table setting, as described.

Like the jig saw, the band saw is one of the safest machines in the shop. But a few simple precautions should be observed.

Before turning on the power, check all adjustments by hand-turning the wheels (use hands on the flexible coupling or pulleys).

Keep your hands away from the cutting path of the blade.

When backing out of a cut, do not force the work. Fast cutting, incidentally, will pack sawdust into the kerf, especially when narrow blades with a small amount of set are used. This makes it extremely difficult to back out the work. So cut slowly in such situations.

Adjust the upper guide for the thickness of stock being cut. Always maintain about 1/4" clearance between guide and stock.

Let the blade reach full speed before you begin cutting.

Never force the work. Never try to turn a radius smaller than the blade being used was designed to cut.

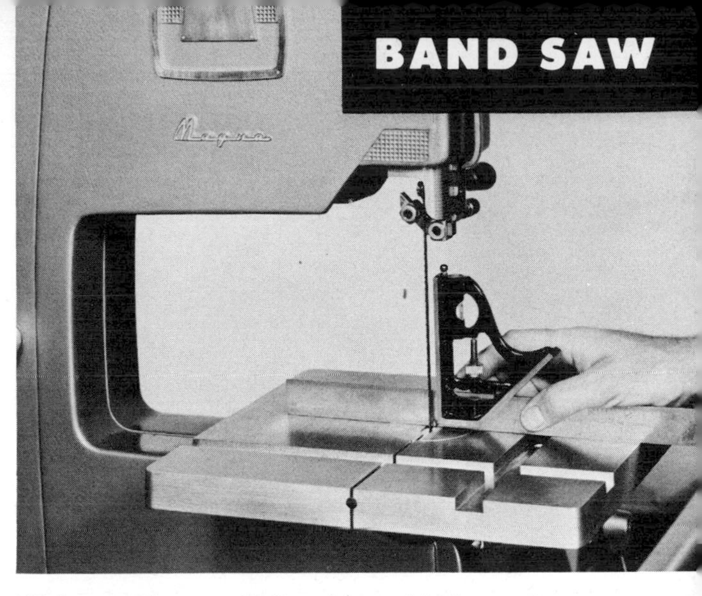

With trunnion at "0", table-to-blade angle (above) should be 90°. Adjust the table . . .

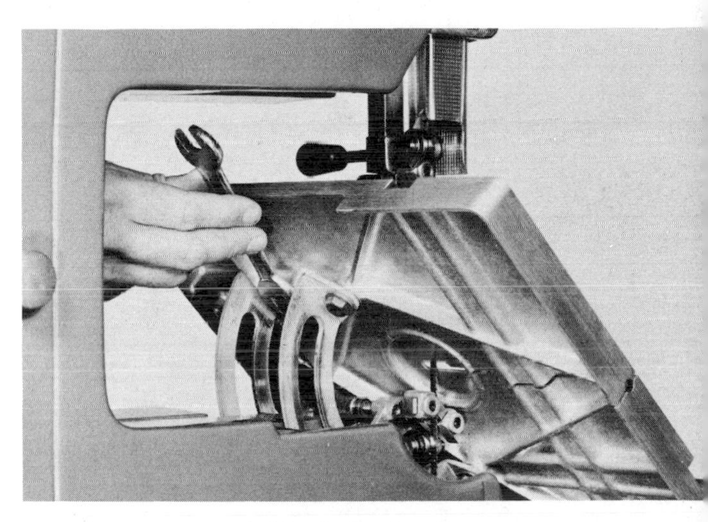

. . . if necessary, and lock the leveling screw (above). Then if "0" on trunnion doesn't line up with the center mark on scale, loosen the screws (below) and adjust the plate.

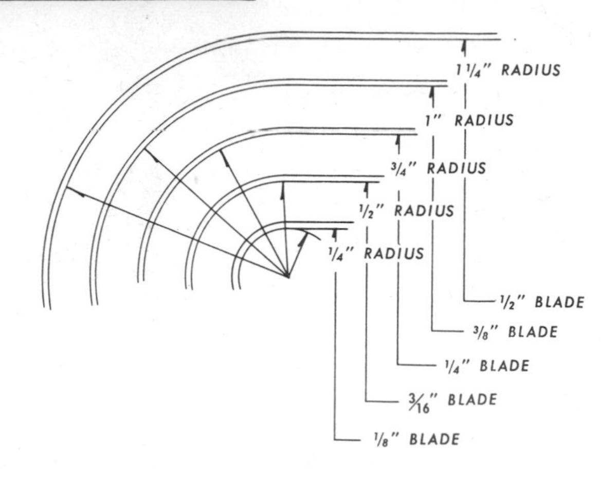

The radius of turn that band-saw blades of different widths can cut is indicated in this chart. It should be regarded as approximate only, since type of blade and degree of set will vary these figures somewhat.

Take this starting position when "folding" a blade. Point teeth on blade away from your body. Place your hands as shown.

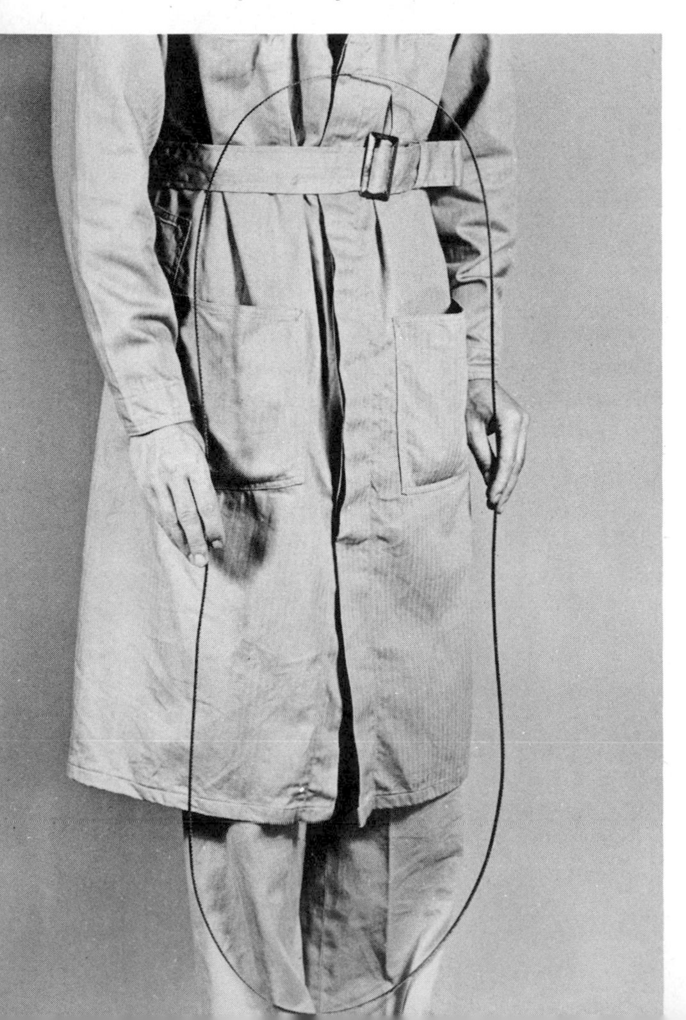

Band-Saw Blades

Band-saw blades for the home workshop usually fall into the narrow-blade category, ranging from 1/8" to 1/2" wide.

Two types are most popular with home craftsmen: one is the standard blade; the other, a skip-tooth blade that earns its name because of the distance between teeth.

A newcomer, resembling the skip-tooth in appearance, is known as a Roll-Chip blade. This is an all-purpose blade, excellent for woodcutting, which also does a good job on plastics, and on metals like aluminum, including the Do-It-Yourself variety. When cutting plastics or metal, use the lower end of the speed-range.

Thin blades with light tooth-set will give the smoothest cuts but require care to prevent blade breakage and binding. Heavier blades with more tooth-set are faster-cutting

Use your thumbs to fold the upper half of the blade down toward the floor while your fingers turn the teeth outward.

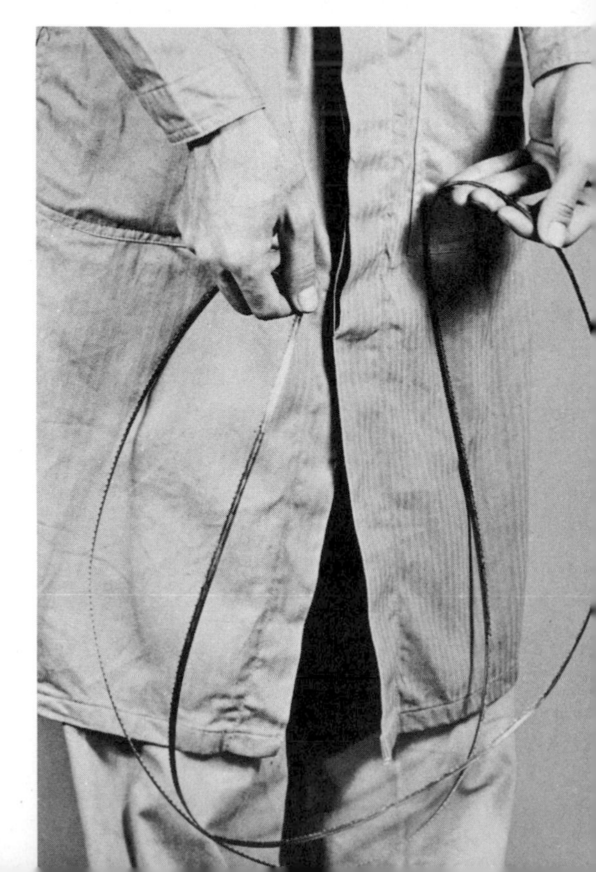

and provide freedom from binding, but do not cut as smoothly. The skip-tooth and Roll-Chip blades are generally all-purpose and do not have a great amount of set; these are probably best for average use in the home workshop.

One important thing that will help prolong the life of the blades is attention to the radius that the width of blade being used will turn. Minimum turning radii for blades ranging from ⅛″ to ½″ wide are given at the left. Remember, however, that blade thickness and the amount of set in the teeth will have some effect on the smallest arc it will cut. The thinner the blade and the shallower the set, the greater the tendency it will have to bind when turning sharp corners. Of course a blade with more set will be more maneuverable, because the set on the teeth provides a wider kerf.

Storing Band-Saw Blades

It is advisable to "fold" extra blades and hang them on pegs.

Using the procedure illustrated in the four photographs below, you can fold blades easily, without harm either to them or to you.

After the blade is folded, tie it with a piece of string or soft wire and place it on a peg or nail.

If it is to be stored for a long time, give it a coating of light oil.

Since the blades are flexible they have considerable spring in them, especially when being unfolded. So be careful when releasing them, particularly with wide blades. Hold them well away from your body.

Be careful, too, when folding or unfolding them, to avoid bending them at any point.

Let the upper loop fall into the lower one. Bringing your hands together, trade the loop in your left hand for the loop in your right hand.

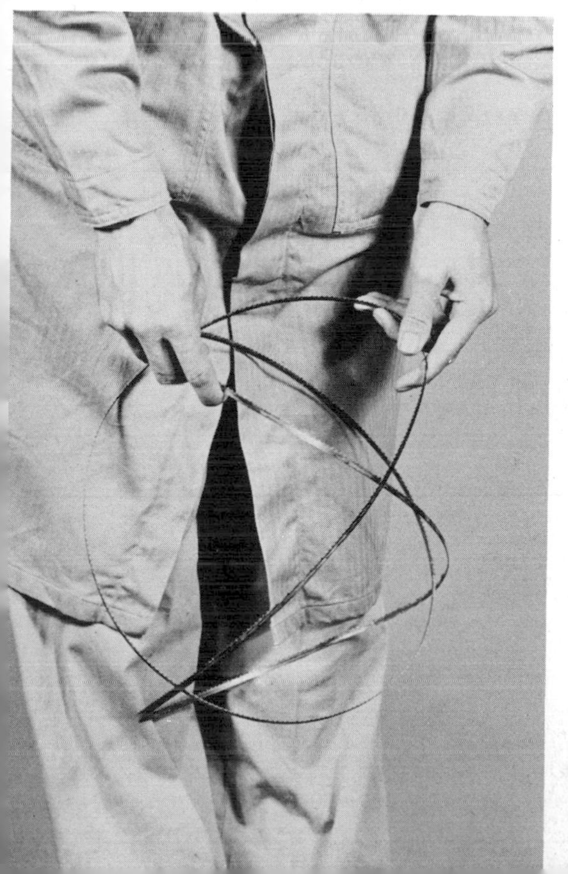

Bring the coiled blade against your body, where it will fall into three uniform loops. Be careful to avoid bending the blade during this procedure.

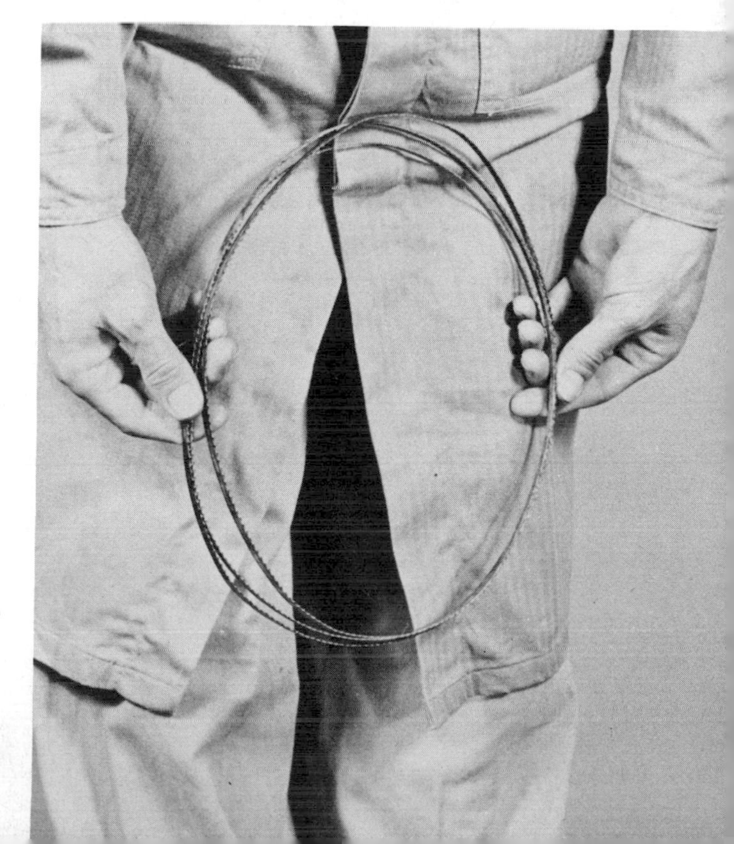

Cutting with the Band Saw

When you're cutting with the band saw, the left hand is usually used as a guide to keep the blade on the cutting line while the right hand feeds the work.

On many jobs the operator will find it more convenient to stand slightly to the left of the blade; but since most band-saw jobs involve turning the work along curved lines, this is not an invariable rule.

The most important thing is to keep hands away from the blade and to keep the blade cutting on the line. A little experimental work with scrap wood will give you the feel of cutting and will enable you to position yourself comfortably while you work.

Form the habit of visualizing the cut before you begin it. Some jobs can't be completed because the stock hits the throat of the machine at some phase of the operation, as has happened to the fellow in the photograph below. The cut could have been made in one pass, simply by starting it at the opposite end of the line—as in the photograph on the opposite page.

Remember that backtracking is more easily accomplished on short cuts. For this reason, when it is impossible to make the cut in one continuous pass, make the shorter cuts first, as diagrammed at the right. The jobs shown are typical band-saw operations, requiring backtracking one or more times. Follow the numbers which indicate which of the cuts should be made first.

Visualize the cut before you begin—and avoid throat interference such as is shown below.

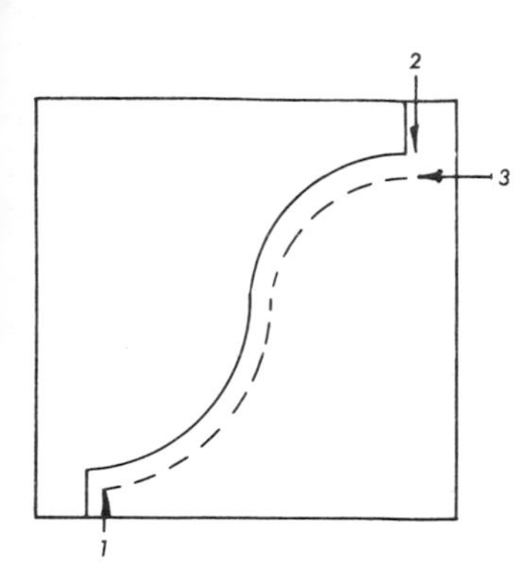

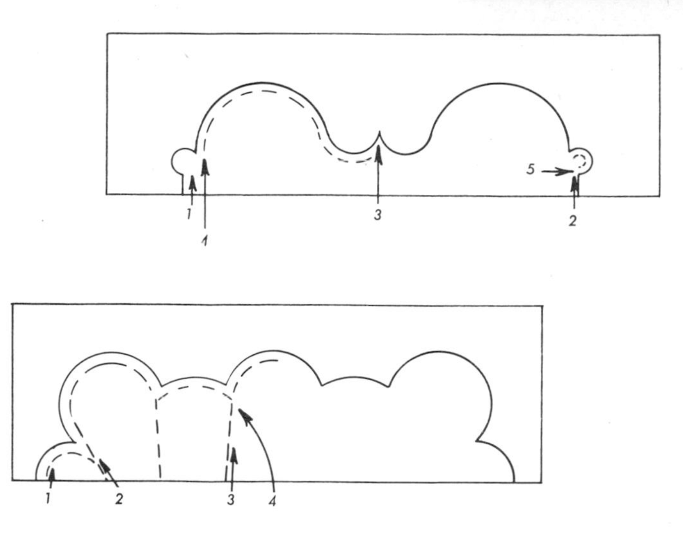

Many cuts require backtracking. When laying out the design, plan to make the shorter cuts first.

Here the same cut tried unsuccessfully on the opposite page is made easily in a single pass.

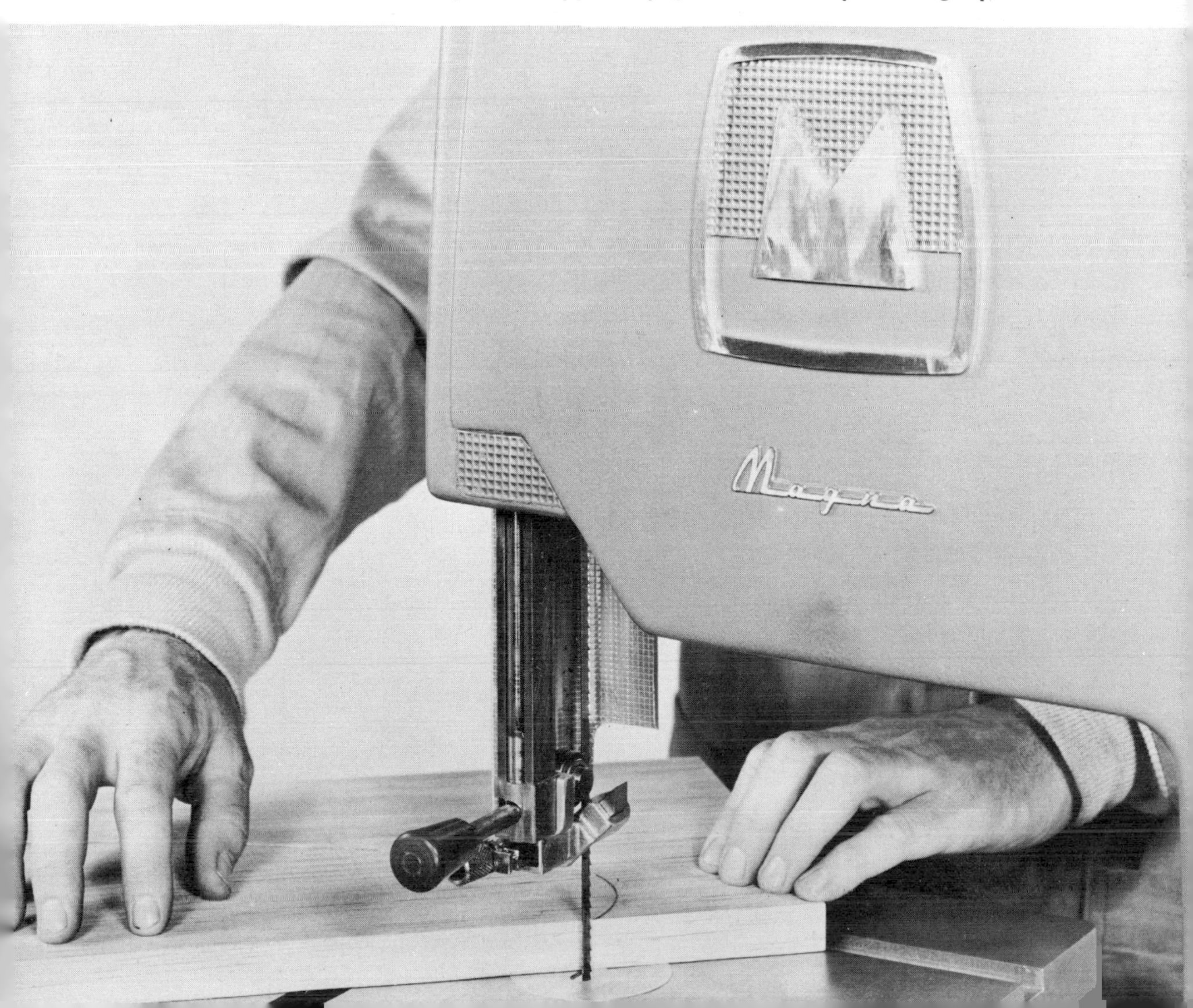

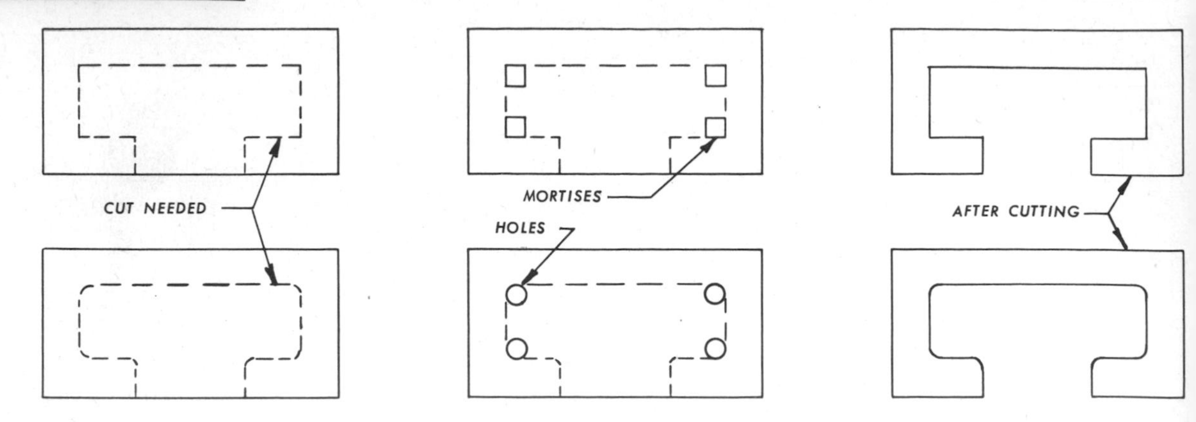

Relief openings, square or round, are frequently used to facilitate internal cutouts. They may often be used as part of the cut outline, as is shown here with two different shapes.

Corner cuts and turning holes (above) can be used to save time and material. Square corners can be cut with mortising chisels, following the instructions in the chapter on the drill press. Holes can be used when the blade will not turn the radius required, or when some other reason makes a corner hole especially applicable. In either case, be sure the layout for square cuts or for holes is accurate enough to fall in line with the design.

The radial and tangent cuts sketched at lower left make it possible to cut a curve smaller than the blade can normally turn. In A the radial cuts are made first. This permits the waste stock to fall away from the work, thus providing more room for the blade to turn.

Radial and tangential cuts help get a blade around an arc it normally could not turn.

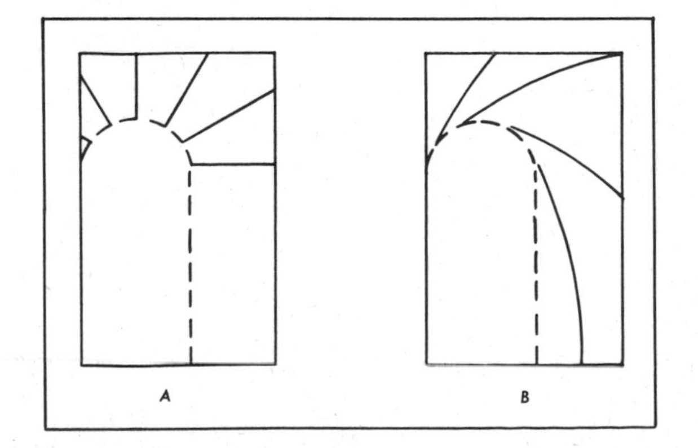

In B the cut progresses until the blade starts to bind; then it is run off at a tangent to the curve. The procedure is repeated until the cut is complete.

By wise planning of layout it's often possible to join cut pieces to form the required shape

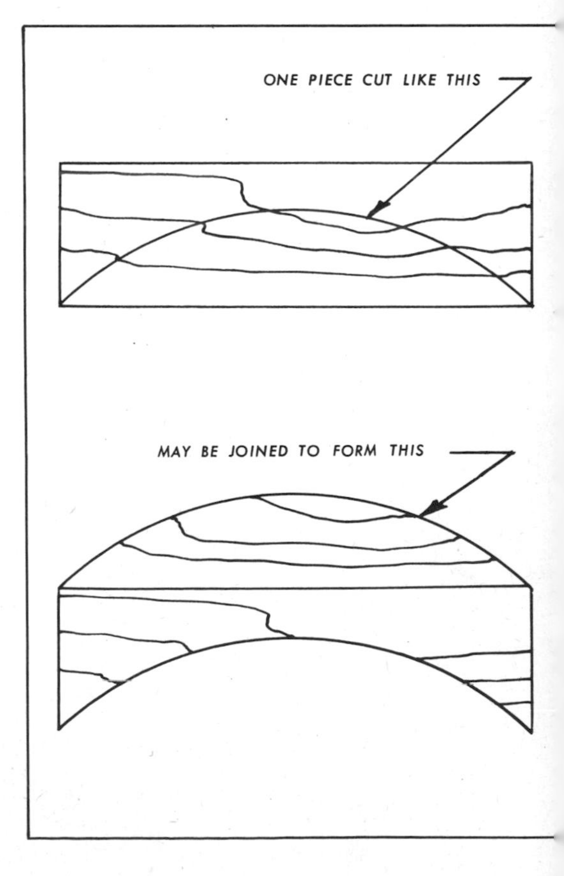

Most of the methods shown in connection with jig-sawing on page 212 can be used on the band saw to eliminate excessive layout and to save materials. A specific application, typical of these methods, is the forming of curved rails as shown at lower right on the opposite page. A piece of stock is cut as shown in the first detail. The two pieces are then glued together to form the arch.

The two-way slot in the table of this band saw is supplied so a miter gauge can be used for ripping as well as for crosscutting. Since it can be locked in the table it is easily positioned to maintain the width of the cut as the work is moved forward against the blade.

The slots in the miter-gauge head permit the attachment of extensions that may be cut to a size exactly suitable for the operation. A long, low extension is good for ripping; a shorter but higher one supplies the right kind of support for resawing.

You'll find you can feed with both hands while you stand slightly to the left of the blade; or you can use one hand over the fence to hold the work while the other hand feeds it forward.

Miter gauge, available as band-saw accessory, can be used for ripping as well as crosscutting.

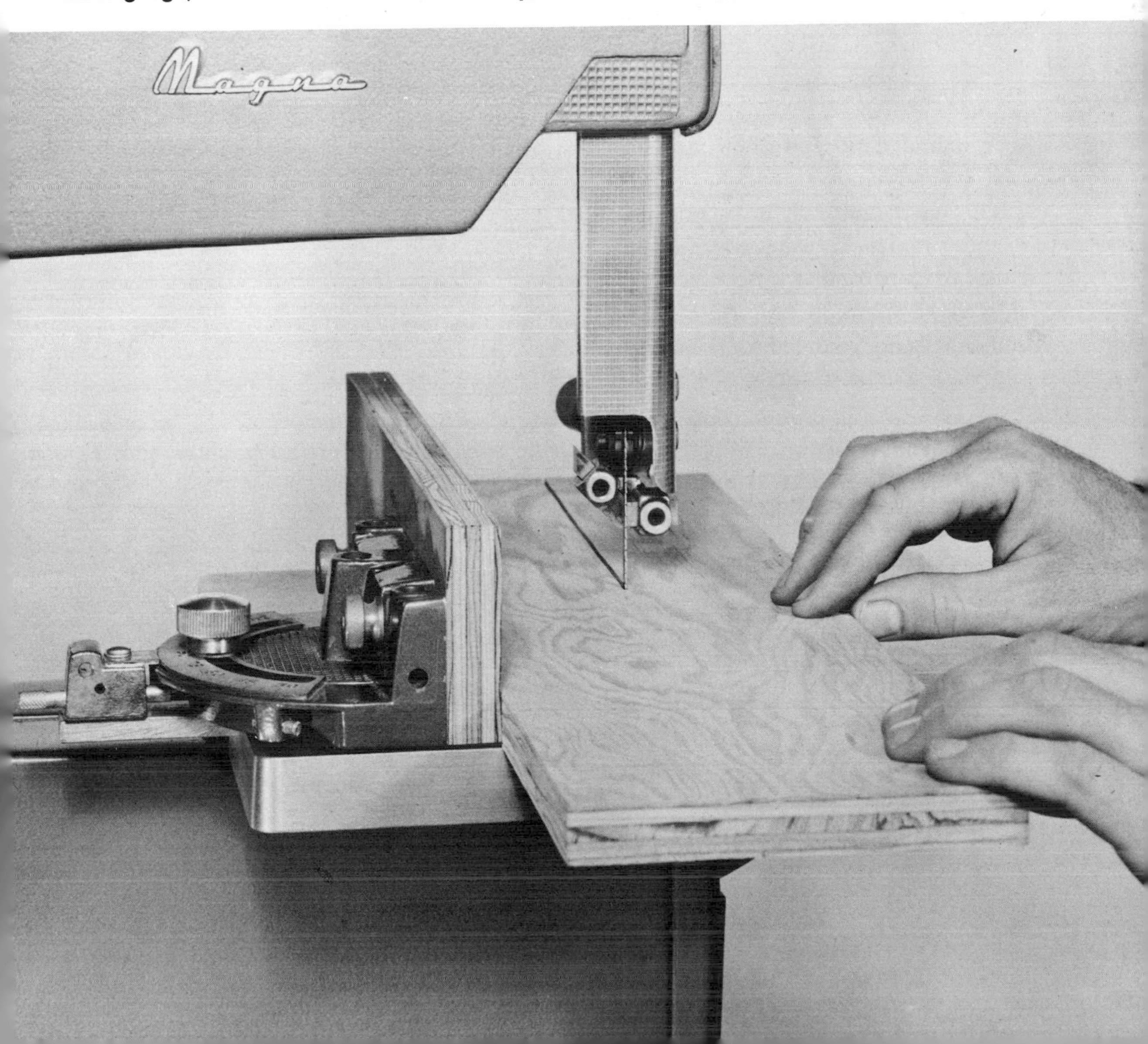

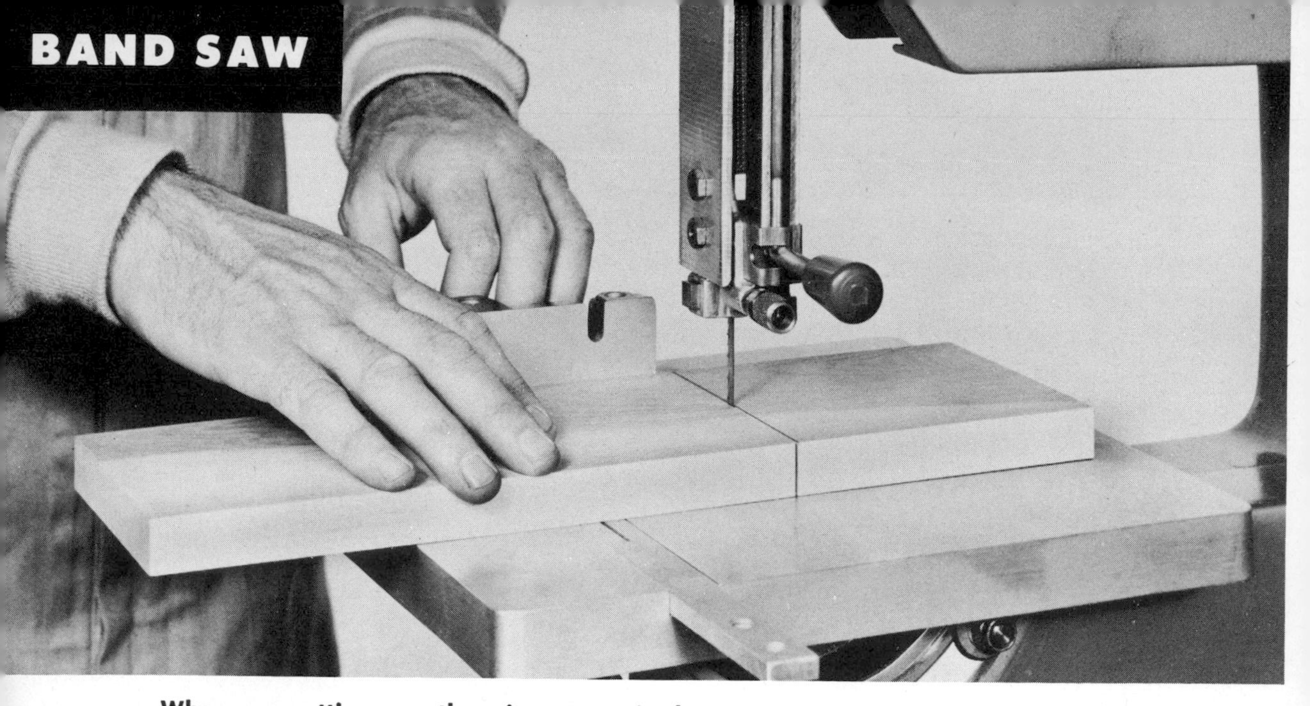

When crosscutting, use the miter gauge in the same way as you would use it on the table saw.

The same miter gauge is used when crosscutting stock (above). When duplicate pieces are required, a block of wood clamped to the table will serve as a stop to gauge length.

The band saw does an excellent job of cutting through very heavy stock. One instance of its particular capability in this type of work is shown below. Here a 6″-by-6″ timber is being rounded for a lathe turning job. Since a large section of the blade is hidden in the stock, it is unwise to force this work beyond the cutting capacity of the blade. Feed the work slowly; let the blade do the cutting.

An outsanding contribution to shop work is the band saw's ability to cut through very heavy material. Smoothness of cut on operations like this will not be consistent; roughest areas will be where blade quarters the grain.

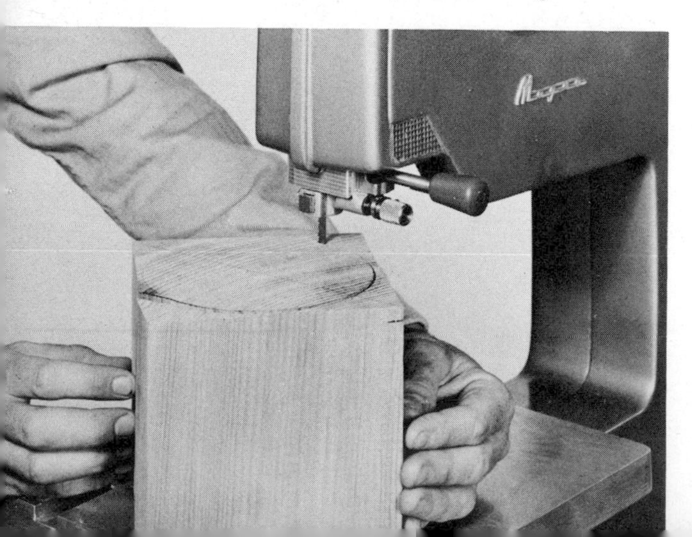

When a fence is used in beveling operations it should be positioned on the outside of the table so that both fence and work are below the blade, as shown at the top of the opposite page. That way you don't have to hold the work against the fence while making the cut.

With the table tilted 45°, as it is here, diagonal cuts for lathe-mounting can be made on the ends of turning squares. This is also a good way to cut triangular glue-blocks. No block is needed between work and fence, since a slight undercut on the bottom of the fence will provide sufficient blade clearance, even at this extreme angle.

When cutting circular blocks for mounting on a lathe faceplate, remember that making the cut with the table tilted (photograph at right) will remove much of the material you would ordinarily have to cut away with lathe chisels. This is an especially good technique for tapered projects or bowls. Angle of table tilt is determined by the design of the project.

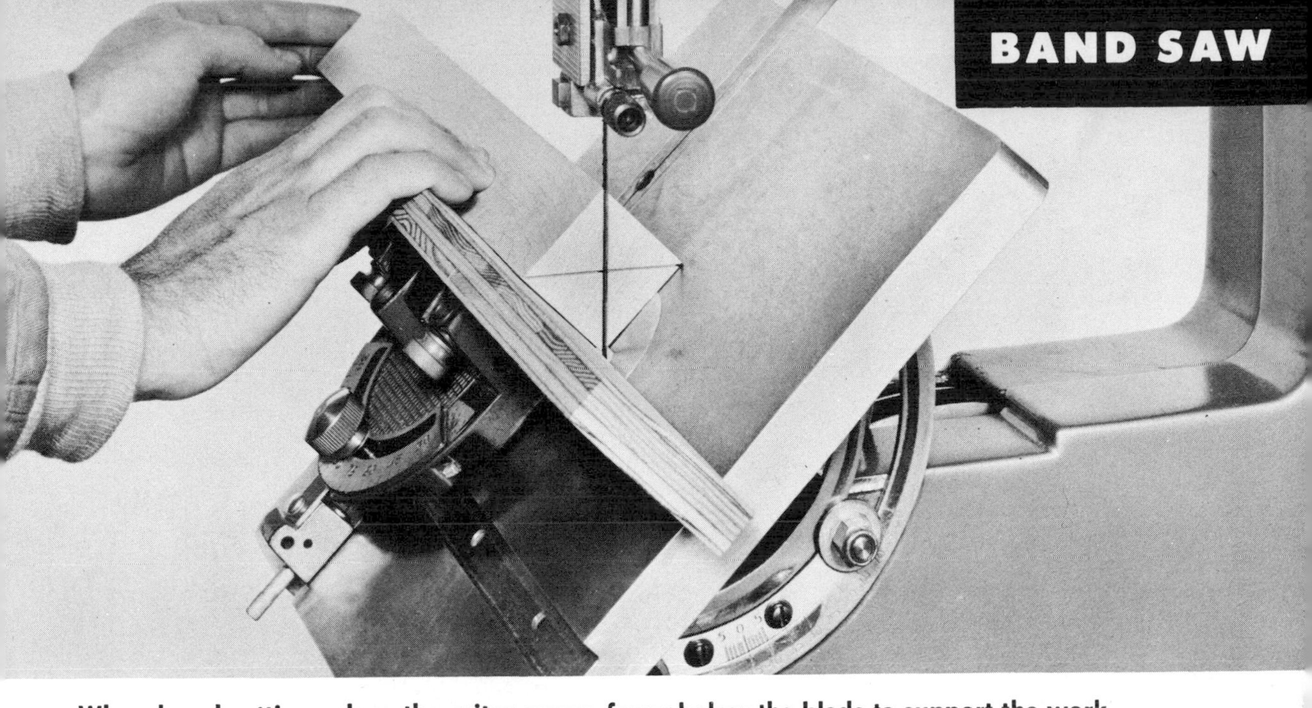

When bevel-cutting, place the miter-gauge fence below the blade to support the work.

Circular cuts with the table tilted produce coneshaped blocks. When lathe work is prepared this way it greatly reduces the amount of material that must be removed with lathe chisels.

Thinning out stock for bending is speedily done on the band saw, as described below.

Thinning Out

The band saw does a good job of reducing sections of stock to be used for bent facings on round corners.

Mark out the section to be thinned on one edge of the stock. It should be about 1″ longer than the corner to be turned. Make the two end cuts first. Then, starting from any point between them, make an oblique approach to the straight line and carry it forward until it meets the end cut. Turn the work end for end to put it on the opposite side of the blade, and complete the cut.

Use high extension on fence when resawing.

Resawing

Resawing is a band-saw operation that makes thin boards out of thick ones.

It is always best to use the widest blade available, although a good job of resawing can be accomplished with a ¼″ blade.

The miter-gauge fence is used as it would be in a normal ripping operation, but preferably with an extra-high extension of the sort shown in the photograph at the left.

Spring sticks, like those shown in Chapter 1, may be clamped to the table to hold the work against the fence.

Saw kerfs serve the double purpose of

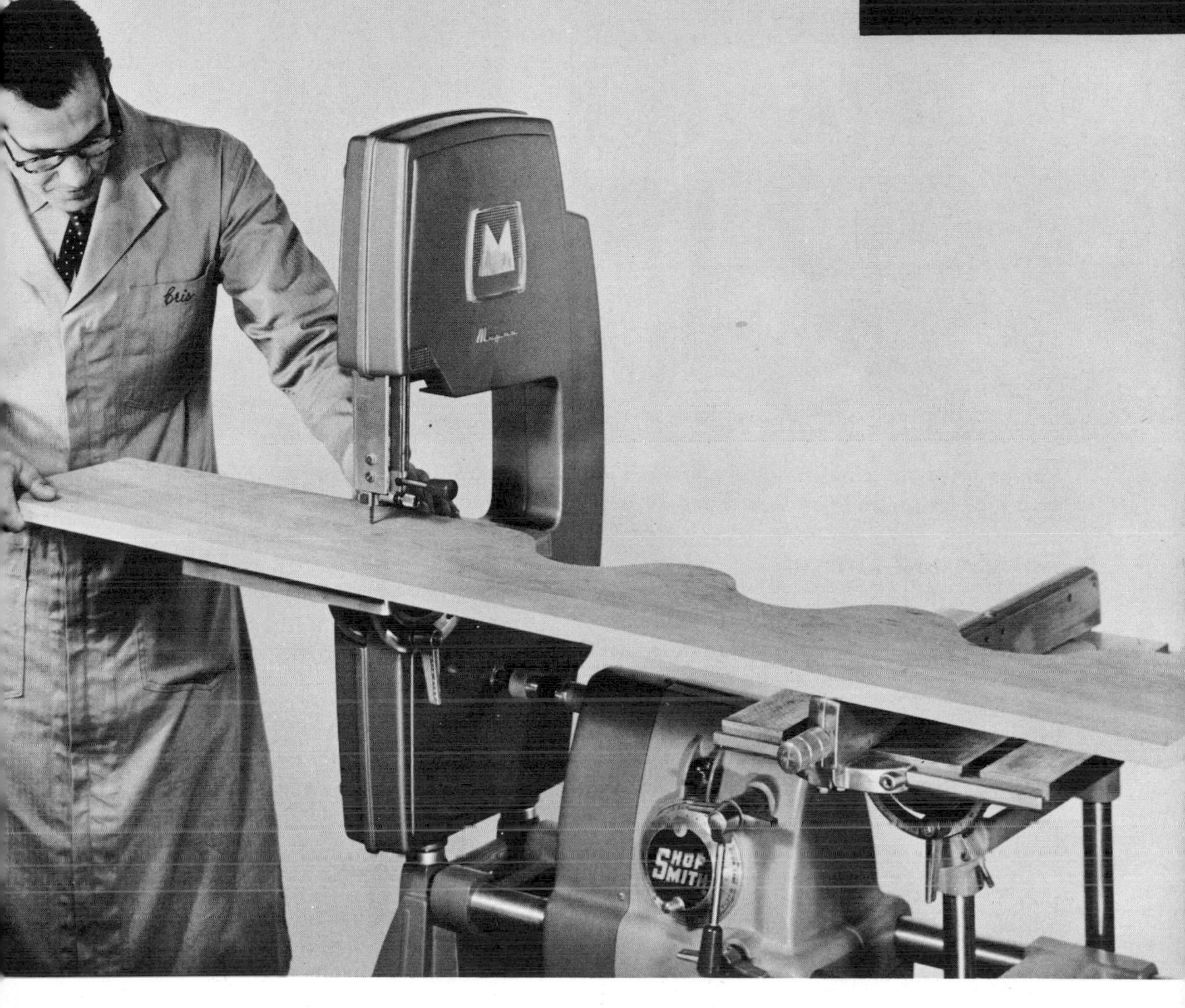

guiding the band-saw blade and reducing the amount of stock to cut. These kerfs (below) are made on the table saw before the resawing is done.

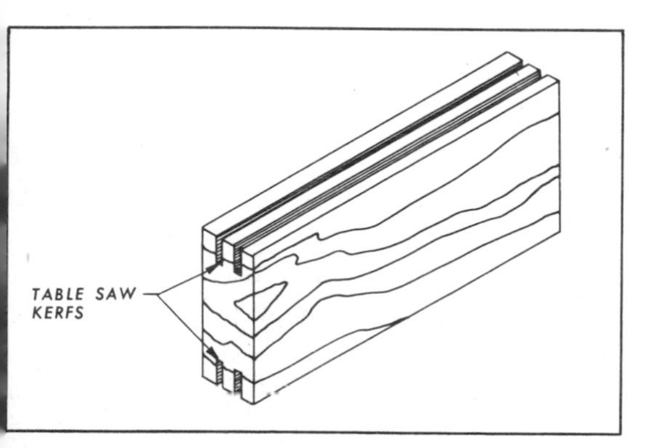

Support for extra-long stock may be provided by mounting the rip fence on the saw table.

Band-Sawing Extra-Long Stock

On the multi-purpose tool, the regular saw table or the extension table—or both—may be used to provide additional support when band sawing extra-long stock.

The saw table is placed as shown above. The rip fence is locked on, in order to match the height of the band-saw table.

When the stock being cut is excessively long, the extension table should be mounted at the tailstock end of the machine to provide even more support.

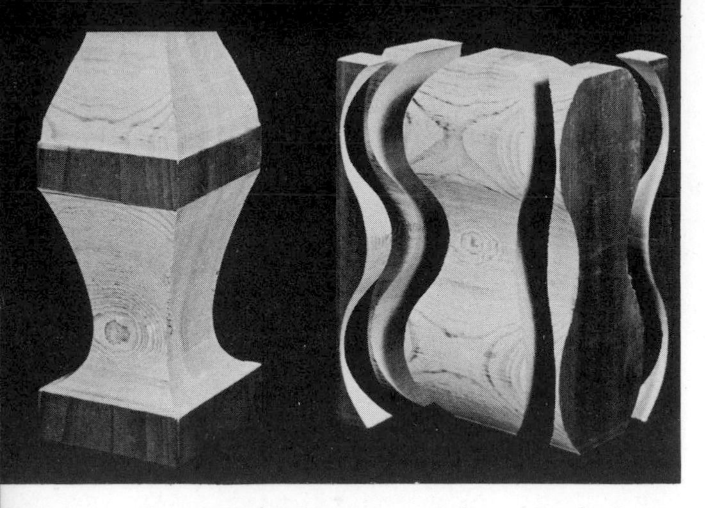

Compound cutting may produce a finished part, or it may be preliminary step to lathe turning.

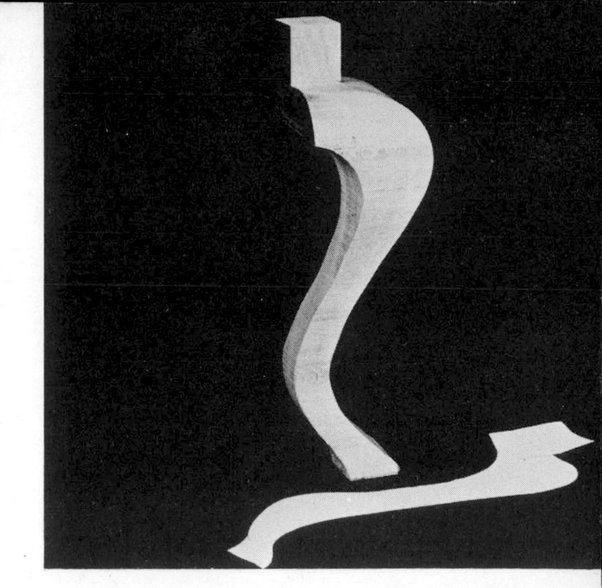

Cabriole leg is an example of a standard part produced by compound cutting on band saw.

Compound Cutting

Forms that require cutting on two or more sides are classified as compound cuts. A pattern is made first and used to mark two adjacent sides. After the work is cut on one side, the waste pieces are tacked right back on. Then the adjacent side is cut. When the waste pieces are once more removed, the stock is exposed, cut to the shape needed (photograph above).

This is another good way to prepare stock for lathe turning. The shape in the drawing at lower left, for example, when mounted in the lathe and turned, becomes a perfect ball shape when the two extending tenons are trimmed off; left on, the tenons may be used to attach the ball to another part.

The shapes shown at upper left, if mounted in the lathe and turned, would make good post tops or rail ends. (These shapes could be used as they are, of course, after being smoothed down and finished.) In lathe work, this technique not only removes most of the waste stock from a desired form, but also serves as a guide when using lathe chisels.

The cabriole leg, above, is another form that requires compound sawing. A template is first cut out of thin cardboard (or sheet metal) and two adjacent sides of the stock are marked. First be sure the stock is perfectly square. The nails used to attach the cut-off waste pieces should be placed so that they will not be in the line of cut nor mar the finished leg. Post blocking (Chapter 4) is a good method of building up stock for cuts of this kind.

Mark for compound cuts on two adjacent sides.

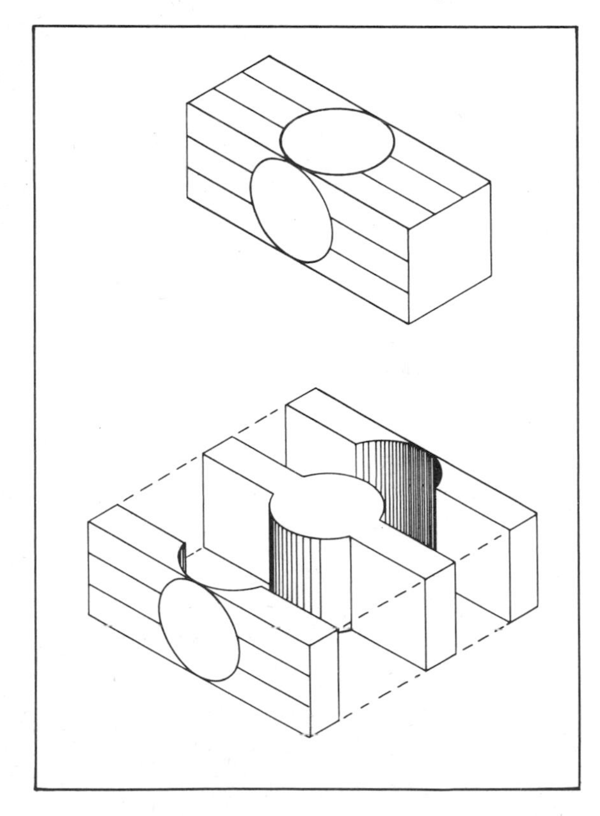

Cutting Multiple Parts

Because the band saw easily cuts through heavy stock, it is possible to pre-shape a thick board, then resaw it into thin pieces, all of them duplicates of the original design.

The shape of the piece needed is drawn on one face of the stock, as sketched at the right. Then it is cut out on the band saw. The shaped piece is then resawed, using the miter-gauge fence as a guide. After the fence is adjusted to maintain thickness of cut, the work is run through as many times as possible—or till enough pieces are cut—as pictured below.

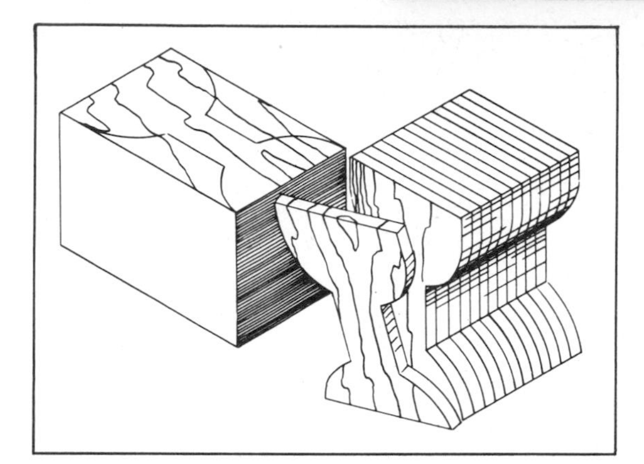

Duplicate pieces can be produced by pre-shaping a heavy block (above) and then resawing it into the number of pieces needed (below).

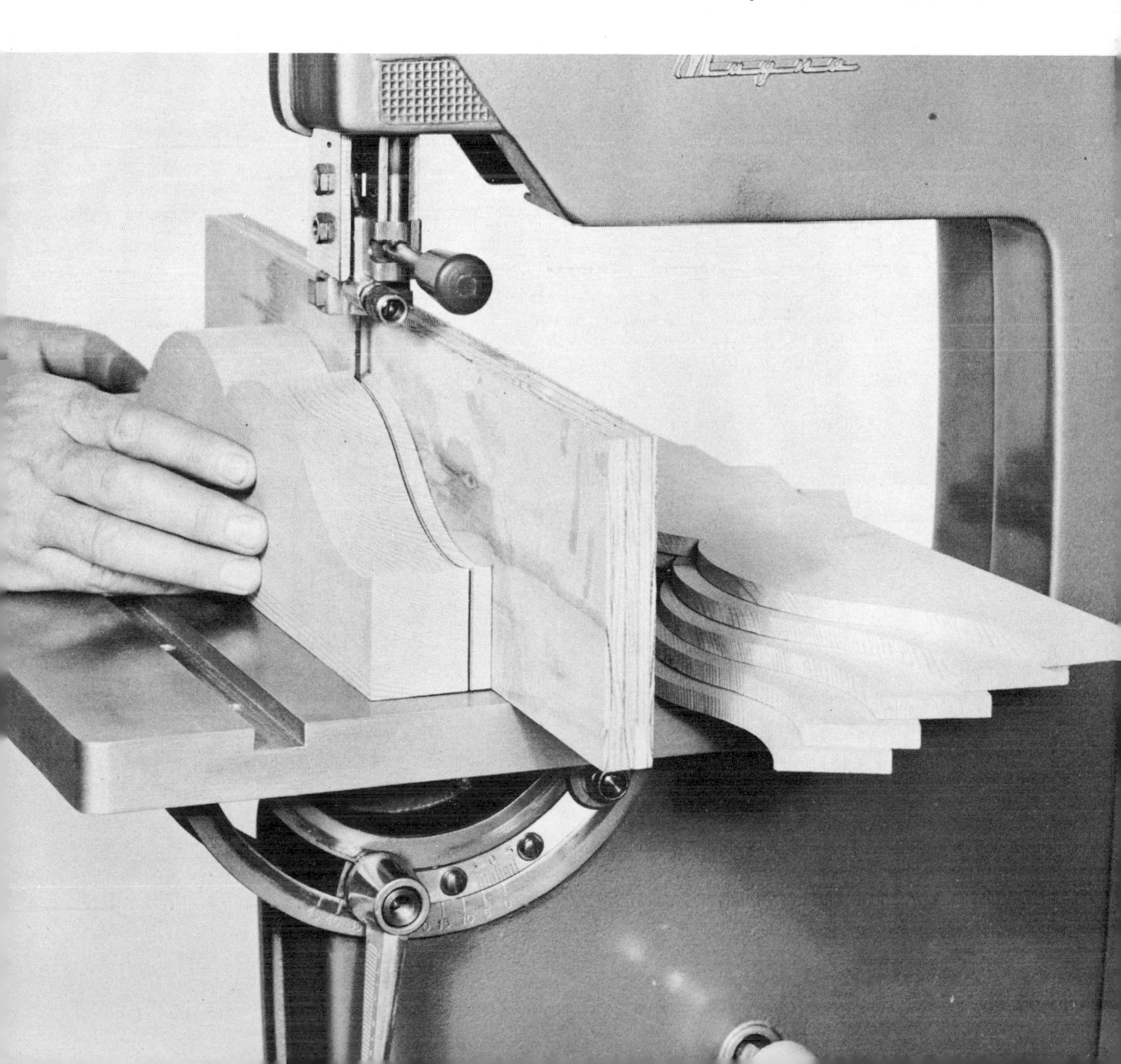

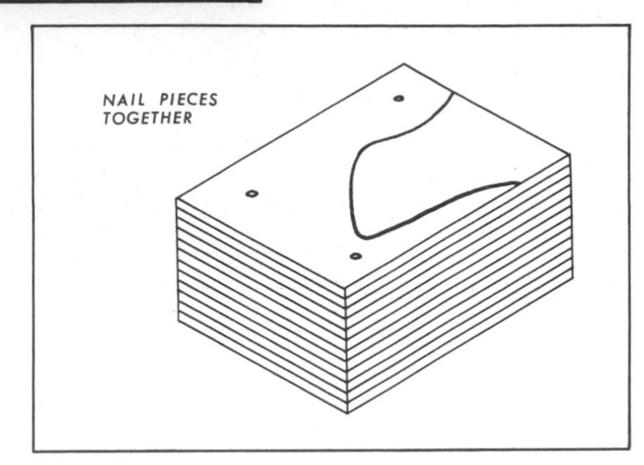

Pad-sawing may also be used to produce duplicate pieces. Individual parts are stacked, and held together with nails driven through waste areas, as sketched at the left. The top layer is marked off in the shape wanted.

The stacked parts are cut (middle picture) as if the pad were a solid block.

The parts are then separated into individual pieces, all of them exactly alike.

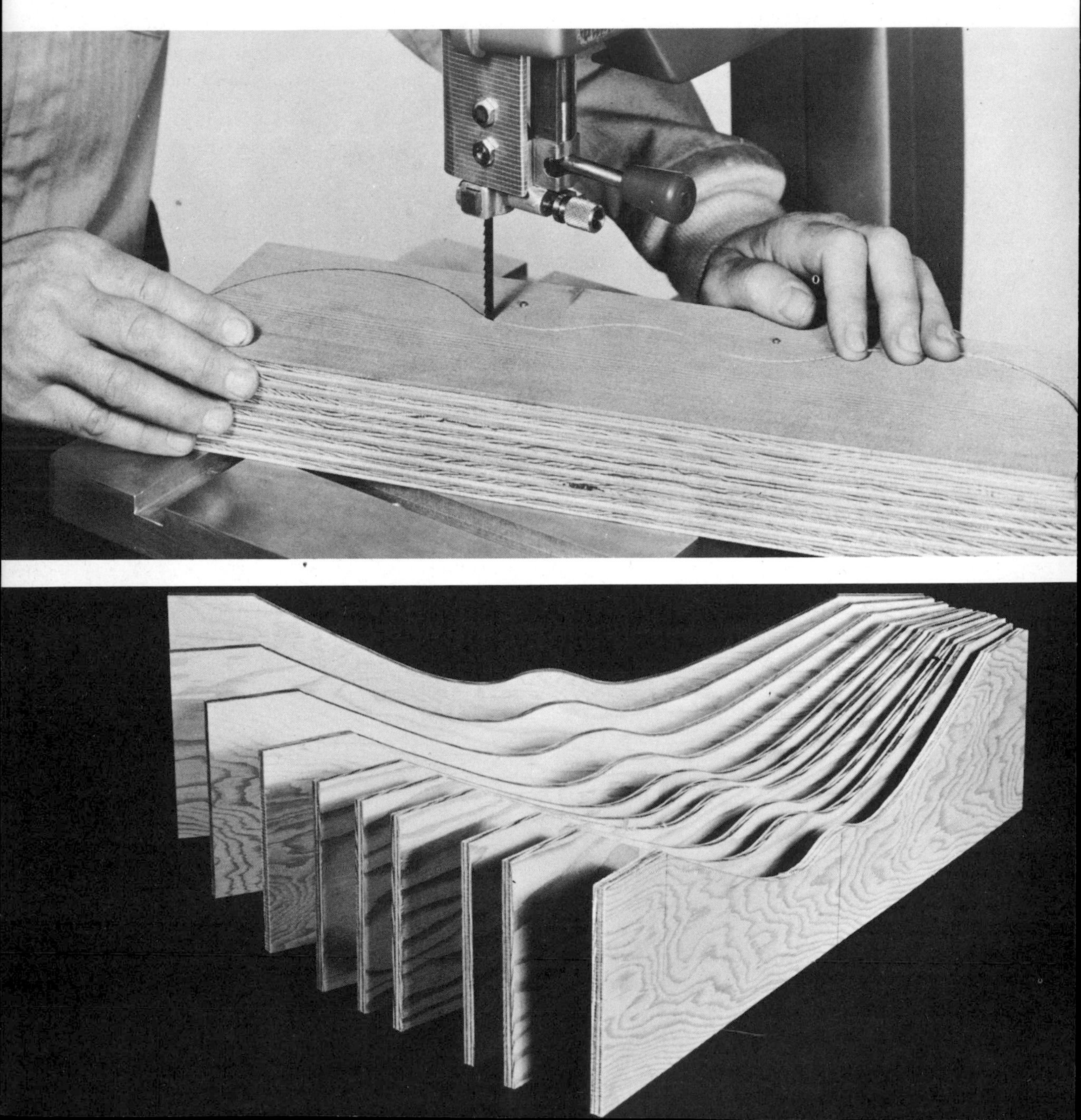

Pad-Sawing

The simplest form of pad-sawing consists of cutting layers of material held together by nails driven through waste areas.

How this is done is shown in detail on the left-hand page.

Other methods use end boards to hold the stack together, wedges driven into kerfs cut in the thickness of the pad, or box jigs.

The latter are boxes cut to the shape needed, with an opening into which the layers of the material are placed. The cutting is then done by following the shape of the box.

For production work it is wise to investigate these various procedures. But for home-workshop jobs, nailing in waste areas is efficient enough.

Pattern-Sawing

Pattern-sawing is a method of setting up the band saw so that a pattern in the shape of the parts needed can be used as a guide to cut duplicates. This eliminates the need for layout on each piece and assures exact duplication.

The drawings below show the setup. The guide block, which is undercut at one end to permit the passage of material being cut, is notched to allow for blade width and thickness. It is clamped to the table as shown.

Work is held under the pattern by projecting pins (short brads that protrude from the pattern just enough to catch the work).

Cutting is done by running the pattern against the guide block. Since the saw blade is in the same position as the edge of the guide block, the work is automatically cut to the shape of the pattern.

The setup shown here is often used for accurate cutting of duplicate odd-shaped pieces. The work must first be rough-cut to a convenient form that is small enough for easy handling on the band saw.

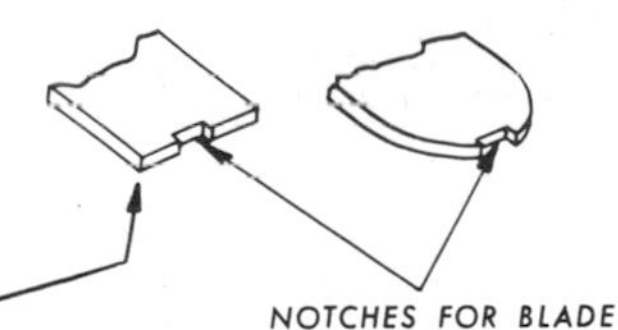

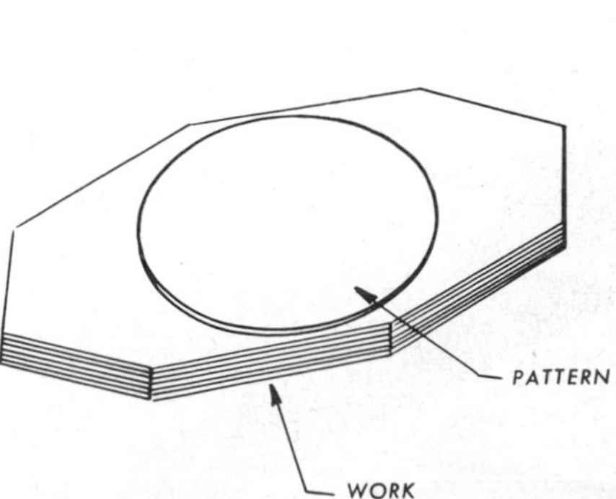

Cutting Parallel Curves

Some duplicate curved pieces can be cut with the miter-gauge fence as a guide. The first cut is made by following a penciled line. The fence is set to gauge the width of the cut, and the remaining pieces are cut as shown in the photograph below. The important rules are to keep the work tangent to the fence at all times and to feed slowly.

A fence can't be used for work involving reverse curves. For jobs of this kind, the setup shown in the drawings and photograph on the opposite page is required. A guide block with one pointed end is clamped to the table with its point directly opposite the blade. The distance between block and blade controls the width of the cut. It is essential to keep turning the work so that contact between the side of the work and the end of the guide block is maintained all the time.

It is almost impossible to make the cut oversize, but if the work moves away from the guide the cut will be narrower than it should be. You can avoid this by careful handling and easy feeding.

The shape and width of some duplicate curves can be automatically controlled with this simple setup. Keep the work tangent to the fence—touching it at all times—and feed it slowly.

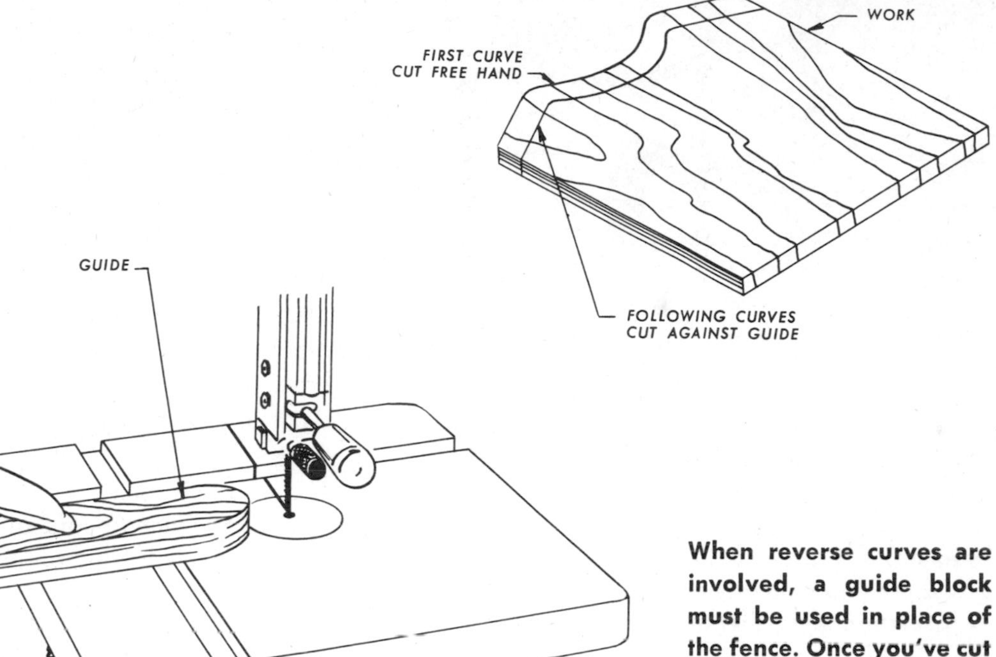

When reverse curves are involved, a guide block must be used in place of the fence. Once you've cut the first curve freehand, you can make the duplicates quickly and automatically.

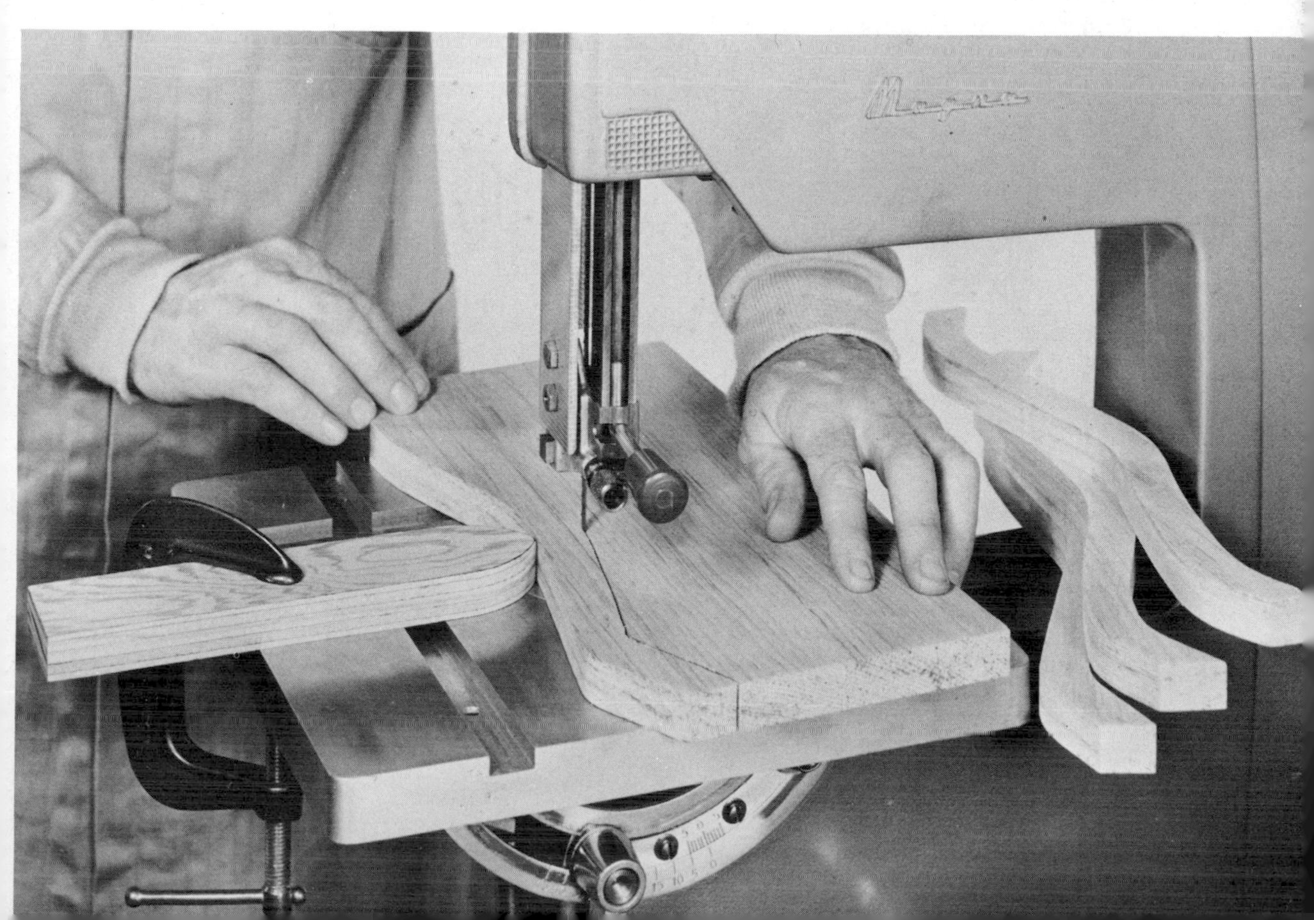

A stop block, clamped to the table, can be used to gauge length of duplicate pieces. The band saw is probably the safest machine to use when cutting short lengths of doweling.

Spirals can be cut in dowels or other wooden cylinders by using the technique shown here. Turn the dowel slowly. Use the miter gauge to control the depth of the cut. The table tilt determines the pitch of the spiral.

Cutting Dowel

The stop method used on the jig saw for cutting many duplicate pieces of doweling will work on the band saw, too. A stop block clamped to the table gauges the length of cut pieces. The miter gauge, used to feed the work forward as shown at the left, assures squareness.

Spiral grooves can be cut in dowels with the setup shown below. They give a dowel superior holding qualities in a glue joint.

Spirals may be decorative, too, either in dowels or in pieces that have been turned on the lathe.

Tilt the table from 10° to 20° and lock the miter gauge in place to control depth of cut. The saw blade will automatically turn the dowel as the cut is made, but controlling the turning by hand will better maintain uniform depth.

This same setup can be used to mark the spiral layout for lathe work. It can also be used for cutting to the depth of groove needed, the job done with a handsaw on page 193.

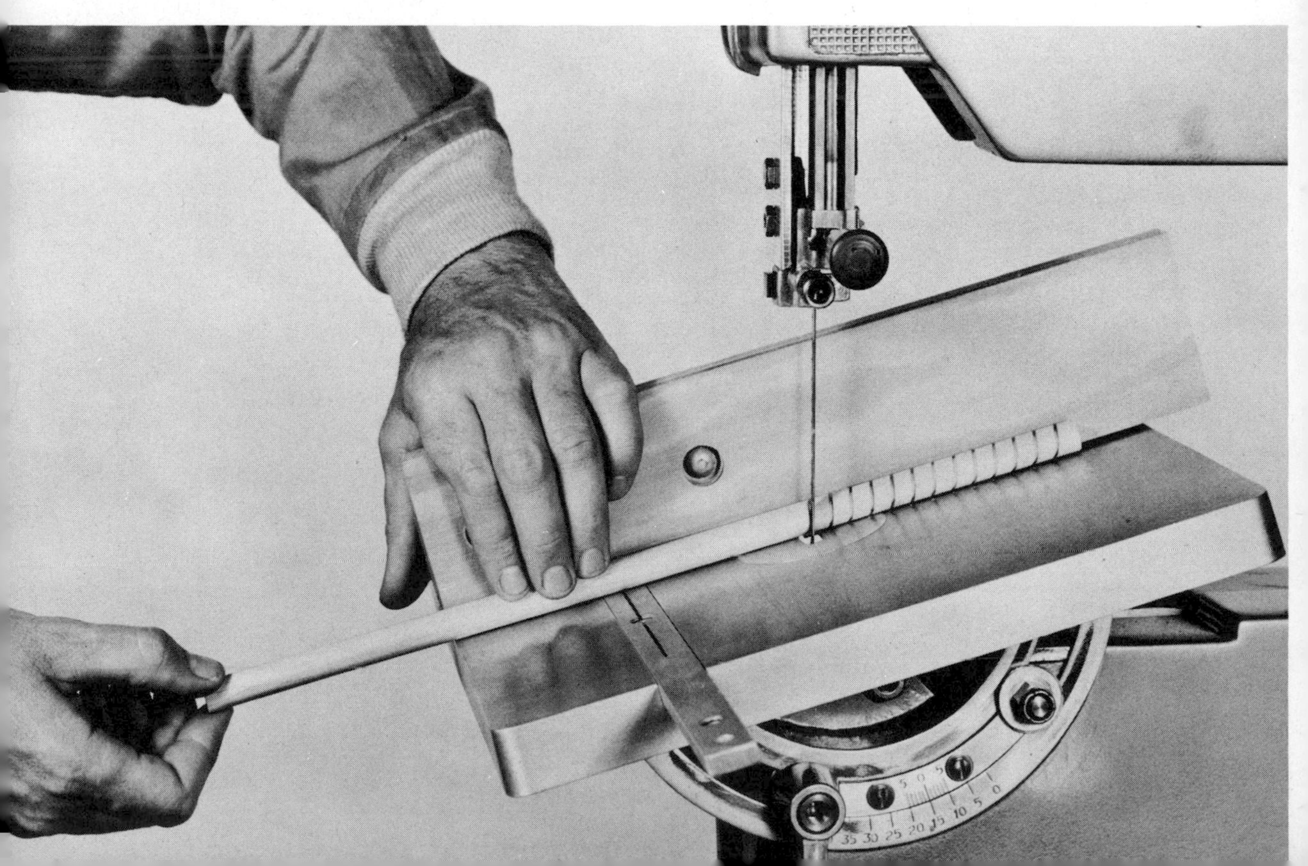

TROUBLE-SHOOTING CHART FOR THE BAND SAW

	THE TROUBLE	POSSIBLE CAUSES	THE CURE	SEE PAGE
RESAWING	BOWED CUT	blade too small	use largest blade available	244
		insufficient tension	adjust tension to blade being used	232
GENERAL	BLADE MOVES AWAY FROM CUTTING LINE	excessive lead	hone lead side	234
		blade guides incorrectly adjusted	adjust guides to blade being used	233
		failure to guide work correctly	use left hand to guide work; right hand to feed forward	238
		wood is very knotty or has very uneven grain structure	no cure; very slow feed and careful handling will minimize	—
	CUT IS NOT SQUARE	misalignment	adjust table square to blade; reset auto-stop	235
	BLADE BINDS IN CUT	turning too sharply	don't cut radii too small for blade being used	236
	KERF JAMS, SO YOU CAN'T BACKTRACK	sawdust has piled up in kerf behind blade	cut slowly, especially with fine blades	235
	BLADE BREAKS	excessive feed pressure	never force blade beyond its cutting capacity	—
		turning too sharply	don't cut radii too small for blade being used	236
		blade dull and worn	sharpen; replace if necessary	—
	ROUGH CUT	characteristic of blade being used	change to smoother-cutting blade	236
	BLADE MAKES SCRAPING NOISE WHEN RUNNING FREE	guides rubbing against blade	guides should not touch; use paper between blade and guides	233
	BLADE KNOCKS WHEN CUTTING OR RUNNING FREE	blade bent or twisted in one place	remove from machine and straighten; replace if necessary	—
	QUALITY OF CUT INCONSISTENT			
	STOCK HITS MACHINE THROAT	work layout results in interference	visualize and plan cut procedure before starting	238

7 ABRASIVE MACHINES

Abrasives • the disc sander
sanding to exact length • sanding to width
circular work • duplicating round corners • miters and bevels
chamfering • sanding curves to width • pattern sanding
pointing dowel • sanding metals • the drum sander • surface sanding
sanding to width • fitting legs to round columns • sanding rabbets
jointing an edge • pattern sanding • belt-sander adjustments • speeds
end sanding • miter cuts • cross-bevel cuts • surface sanding
edge sanding • curves • special devices • trouble shooting

SANDING OPERATIONS, except for a few that also bring the piece down to the right size, are done to get a project ready for finishing. And whether this finish is stain, lacquer, paint, or varnish, a workmanlike job will depend on the quality of the sanding.

Good sanding used to be hard to do. When done by hand with inferior abrasives, it depended on a vast amount of patience. Modern equipment and abrasives have made a great change in this, so that it is usually quite easy to bring even the roughest surface to smoothness.

On old or new work, it is common practice to start with a coarse paper and work down through several grits to a very fine one. But often, because the surface is in fair condition to begin with, it isn't necessary to go through the entire cycle. One pass with a fine paper may do the job. Here, as in many other woodworking operations, experience will be your best guide.

Abrasives

There are three points to consider in choosing the abrasive for the job.

One is the difference between open and closed coatings. On a closed coat the abrasive grains are closely spaced, presenting a complete work surface. An open coat has spaces between the grains so that sanded particles do not fill or clog the surface of the paper. This is useful when doing a lot of rough sanding or when removing old finish.

The second consideration is the proper abrasive for the material being worked. A great improvement over the crushed sea shells once used as an abrasive material are the five minerals used in today's coated abrasives. Emery is the only one of these five not shown in the chart on the next page; it is used almost exclusively for polishing metals.

Flint is widely available in paint and hardware stores—because it is the cheapest abrasive coating obtainable. Most woodworkers use it occasionally but depend on harder, sharper, longer-lasting garnet for general use. It costs more than flint, but—because it is more durable—its cost per unit of work is usually less.

Aluminum oxide, a manufactured abrasive, is good for both wood and metal. It is tougher than garnet. The wedge-shaped crystals provide an excellent cutting action. It holds up under considerable power sanding.

Silicon carbide is the hardest of all abrading materials. In addition to the uses given in the chart, it is good for sanding undercoats and in-between coats, producing exceptionally fine finishes on wood and metals.

The third factor is selecting the correct grit. The varied classifications in use can be broken down into understandable terms, such as coarse, medium, and fine. Many manufacturers and suppliers, having become aware of confusion on the part of home users, are labeling their packages with names instead of numbers. Charted on the next page are the various number classifications broken down into five categories to make it easier to select the proper grit.

The Disc Sander

Because of the basic versatility of the machine, the disc sander on the multi-purpose tool (below) is among the most efficient of its type. The disc itself is large—12″ in diam-

A locking miter gauge and a fence can be used to advantage on many disc-sander operations.

ABRASIVE	USE	GRIT			REMARKS
		ROUGH	MEDIUM	FINE	
aluminum oxide	hardwood aluminum copper steel ivory plastic	2½-1½ 40 40-50 24-30 60-80 50-80	1/2-1/0 60-80 80-100 60-80 100-120 120-180	2/0-3/0 100 100-120 100 120-280 240	Manufactured, brown color, bauxite base, more costly than garnet but usually cheaper to use per unit of work
garnet	hardwood softwood composition board plastic horn	2½-1½ 1½-1 1½-1 50-80 1½	1/2-1/0 1/0 1/2 120-180 1/2-1/0	2/0-3/0 2/0 1/0 240 2/0-3/0	Natural mineral, red color, harder and sharper than flint
silicon carbide	glass cast iron	50-60 24-30	100-120 60-80	12-320 100	Manufactured, harder but more brittle than aluminum oxide, very fast cutting
flint	removing paint, old finishes	3-1½	1/2-1/0		Natural hard form of quartz, low cost, use on jobs that clog the paper quickly

Use the chart above for selecting an abrasive. Garnet and aluminum oxide are best for general use in the home workshop.

TYPE	VERY FINE	FINE	MEDIUM	COARSE	VERY COARSE
flint	4/0	2/0-3/0	1/0-½	1-2	2½-3½
garnet	6/0-10/0	3/0-5/0	1/0-2/0	1/2-1½	2-3
aluminum oxide and silicon carbide	220-360	120-180	80-100	40-60	24-36

Above chart groups abrasives into five classes, indicating the grit numbers that fall in each.

8/0 = 280	3/0 = 120	1½ = 40
7/0 = 240	2/0 = 100	2 = 36
6/0 = 220	0 = 80	2½ = 30
5/0 = 180	½ = 60	3 = 24
4/0 = 150	1 = 50	

Listed at the left are the number equivalents of the various grit sizes.

eter—and mounts on the spindle in the usual manner.

You'll usually find it most convenient to put the headstock and table at the right end of the tubes so that you can stand facing the disc as with any conventional disc sander. But the work itself should be the determining factor. For example, if you're sanding the ends of a 10′ board, you'll want the headstock at the left end of the ways so you can use the table extension for additional support.

A practical setup on the multi-purpose tool is illustrated below. Here, through the use of an extra sanding disc mounted on the upper auxiliary spindle, it is possible to have two kinds of abrasives, or two different abrasive grits, operating simultaneously. Such a setup is especially nice when sanding plastics, where working through progressively finer grits of paper is an absolute must if the necessary scratch-free, glass-smooth surface is to be achieved.

At most times, it is efficient to keep the top of the table at the horizontal center line of the disc, or about ½″ below it, to give maximum abrasive surface. Here, too, the operation and size of the work will have some bearing on the position of the table.

Maximum speed for the 12″ disc sander is about 1,800 rpm.

Abrasive-paper discs are available in various types and grits. An assortment of coarse, medium, and fine should be kept on hand at all times. It is also a good idea to have two or more discs available so that an assortment of grits can be kept ready-mounted.

Two types of adhesives for holding abrasive sheets to the disc are available: Distic, the familiar stick-shellac; and a new liquid cement, easier and more convenient to apply. Whichever is used, it is important to get the sandpaper sheet flat on the disc, free of little bumps which would result in imperfections on the abraded surface.

The Distic, which melts with heat, is held against the turning disc long enough to coat it. Never apply it to a cold disc. First place a piece of softwood firmly against the revolving disc and keep it in place about 30 seconds. The friction-generated heat is enough to melt the shellac. Keep the wood in

A dual mounting makes two grits, or two kinds of abrasives, available at the same time.

This liquid adhesive is easy to use. It is applied to both abrasive paper and disc.

place while you hold the Distic against the revolving disc (below), moving it from the edge to the center until a smooth, even coat has been applied. Then remove the Distic, push back the table, and press the abrasive sheet firmly into place. It is a good idea to place the disc abrasive side down on a flat surface for a few minutes before using it, preferably under weights.

The new cement—a viscous liquid—is applied directly from the can to both the sanding disc and the abrasive paper (above). Spread it smoothly, and cover both surfaces completely. Then apply the abrasive paper to the disc and place it abrasive side down on a flat surface. It's a good idea to stand on it, "walking" on the rim for a few seconds.

When using a contact bond cement, you'll be unable to shift the disc around once the contact has been made. Be certain that the paper is centered on the disc; then press it firmly into place. The disc is ready for immediate use.

To replace an abrasive sheet, just pull it from the disc, whether Distic or liquid adhesive has been used. In either case, a fresh sheet may be applied by renewing the adhesive coating; but it is good practice to clean the disc first. Stick shellac can be removed by dampening it with alcohol or some similar solvent, then rubbing it off with a cloth or very fine steel wool. The cement can be rubbed off cleanly with the fingers.

Distic should be applied to a warmed disc. It should evenly cover the entire surface.

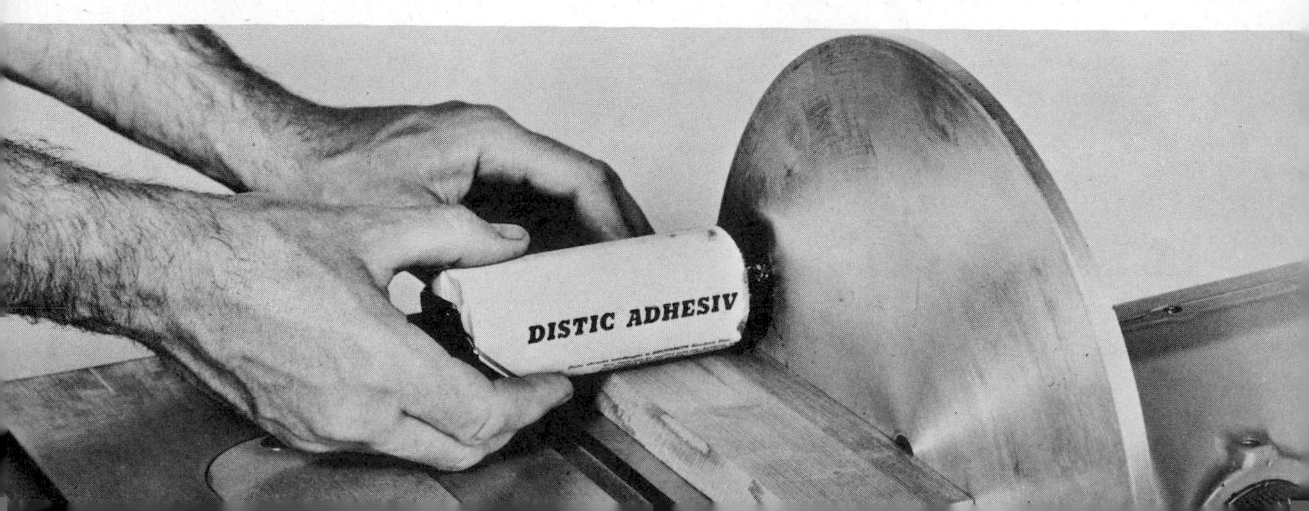

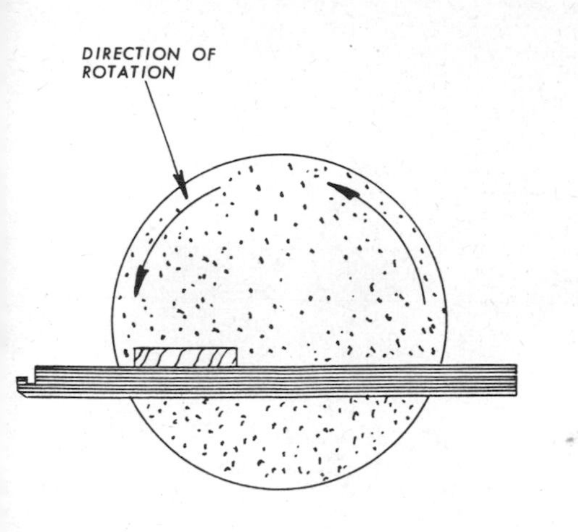

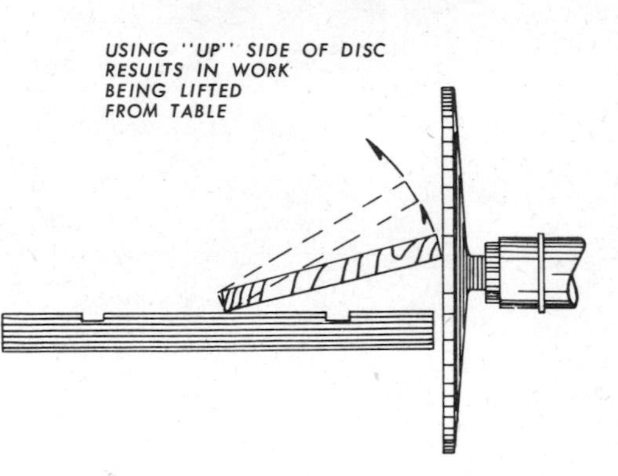

USING "UP" SIDE OF DISC
RESULTS IN WORK
BEING LIFTED
FROM TABLE

Diagrammed here is the reason for always using the "down" side of the disc.

Operating the Disc Sander

Sanding is always done on the "down" side of the disc's rotation, which means placing the work on the left side of the table (see diagram above). Exception: If you're using the disc on the upper auxiliary spindle of the multi-purpose tool, place the work on the right side of the extension table.

Work held on the "up" side would be lifted from the table.

Hold the work flat as you move it into the turning disc. If the edge is flat, move the work squarely in toward the disc; if it has curved edges, revolve it in a sweeping motion.

Feed should always be light and smooth, even when a good deal of material must be removed. It is better to touch the work to the disc three or four times than to force it against the abrasive all at once, especially when finishing edges longer than the radius of the disc.

The disc has a fast cutting action under excessive pressure and it also may create enough heat to burn the wood. Burn marks on the abraded surface indicate excessive pressure.

Although a disc will not cut to the inside corner of a right-angle cut, you can get close enough so that only a slight touch-up by hand is required to complete the job.

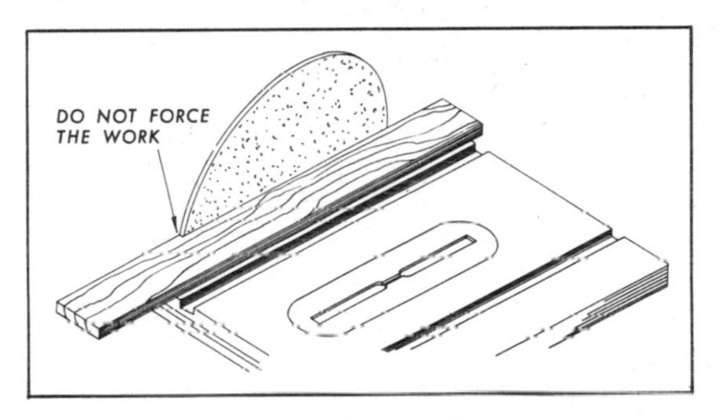

Avoid excessive pressure, especially when the work (as above) is longer than the disc diameter. Keep the work flat on the table as you move it into the disc. Outside curves, such as the one shown below, should be turned slowly.

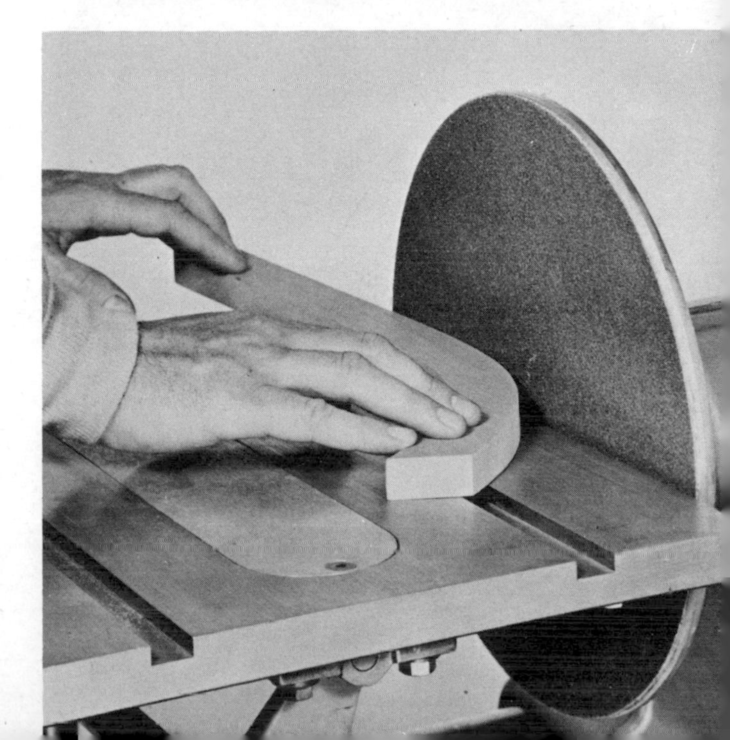

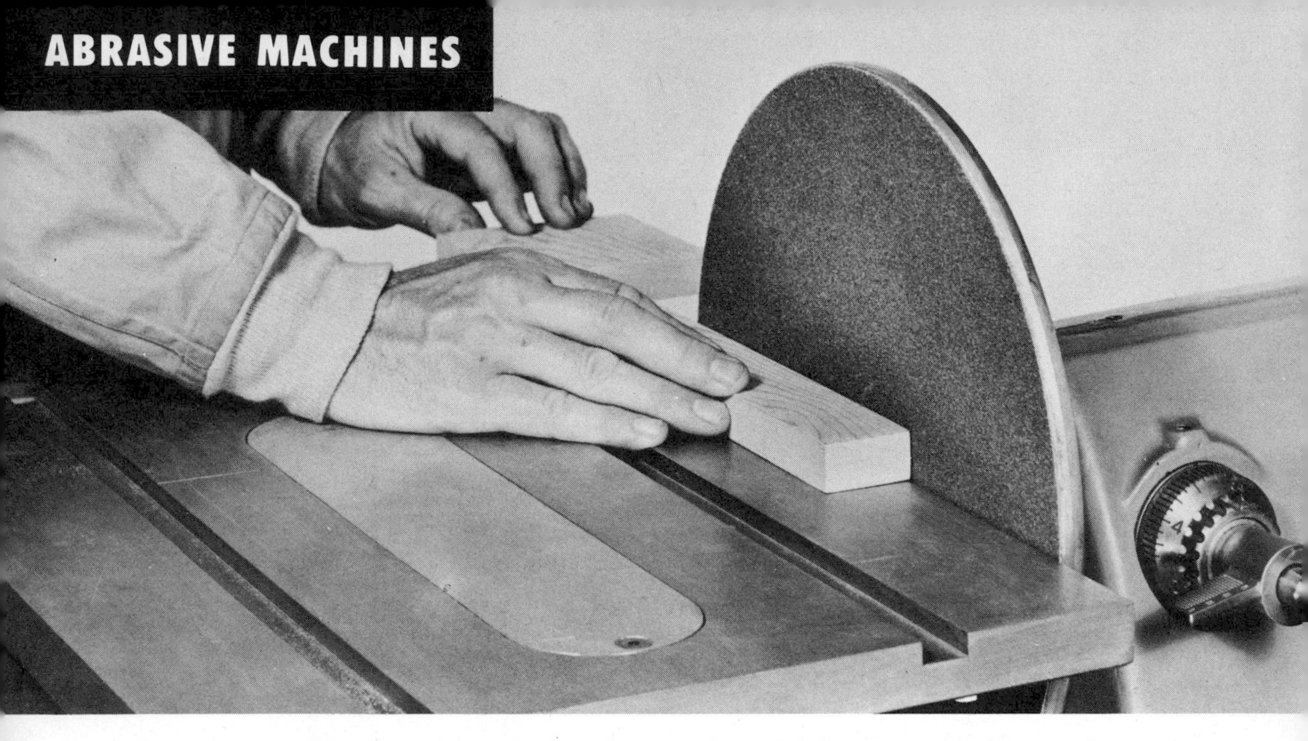

To sand inside corner, move work across face of disc; stop just before rim hits corner.

Make the first pass by starting at one end of the work (photograph above) and moving from the edge of the disc toward its center. Pressure, as always, should be light.

Hold the work flat on the table and move it slowly across the face of the disc. Smooth the second edge by moving the work forward into the face of the disc, as pictured below. Hold the work close enough so that the rim of the disc just misses touching the first edge. Do not force it, or the exposed metal rim of the disc will mar the work.

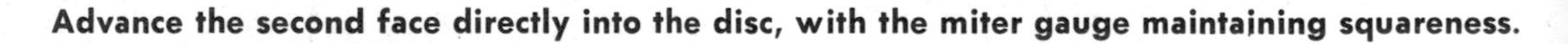

Advance the second face directly into the disc, with the miter gauge maintaining squareness.

This setup permits sanding any number of pieces to exactly the same length.

Sanding to Exact Length

Finishing to exact length as illustrated above is a graphic example of the advantages in having a forward feed available on the disc sander. The rip fence acts as a stop and the miter gauge keeps the work square to the disc.

Move the table forward so the end of the work is about ¼″ from the disc. Use one hand to keep the work flat on the table, the other to feed the disc forward. Once the setting is made, it is maintained by setting the depth-control dial. In this setup there's no danger of sanding some pieces shorter than others.

Sanding to Exact Width

Long, straight edges are sanded smooth and square in an operation that combines sanding, jointing, and finishing to exact width.

Use the fence offset screw to set up the fence so the distance from it to the disc on the "down" side is slightly less than the width of the piece. Feed the work slowly from the back toward the front, or switch, side of the machine. Keep contact with the fence throughout the pass.

There is no limit to the length of work that can be handled in this manner. And duplicate short pieces can be fed through, one after the other.

Offset fence to sand pieces to width, as shown below and at right. Contact should run from edge of disc almost to center. Besides working well with lumber, this is ideal with plywood.

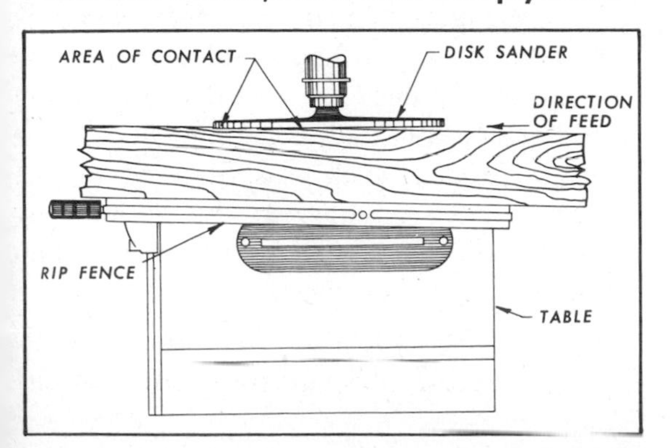

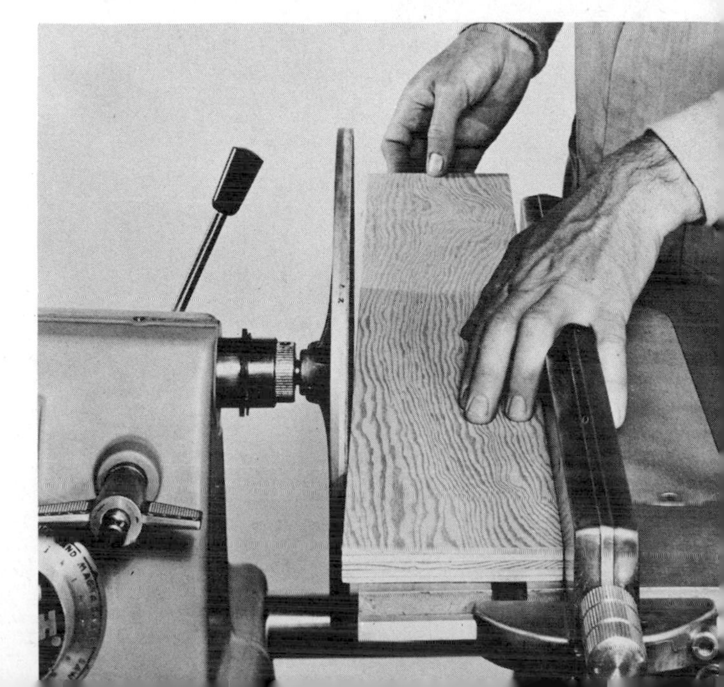

Pivot-sanding (photograph above) guarantees perfect circles. If the work lacks a center hole, use a brad as a pivot.

Pictured at upper right: The same technique may be used to round off the ends of straight pieces. This is especially useful when duplicating.

With the table tilted as shown below pivot-sanding can be used to bevel or chamfer the edges of circular pieces. The pivot gives enough support to make it safe and efficient to tilt the table toward the disc. For a double bevel, simply turn the work over.

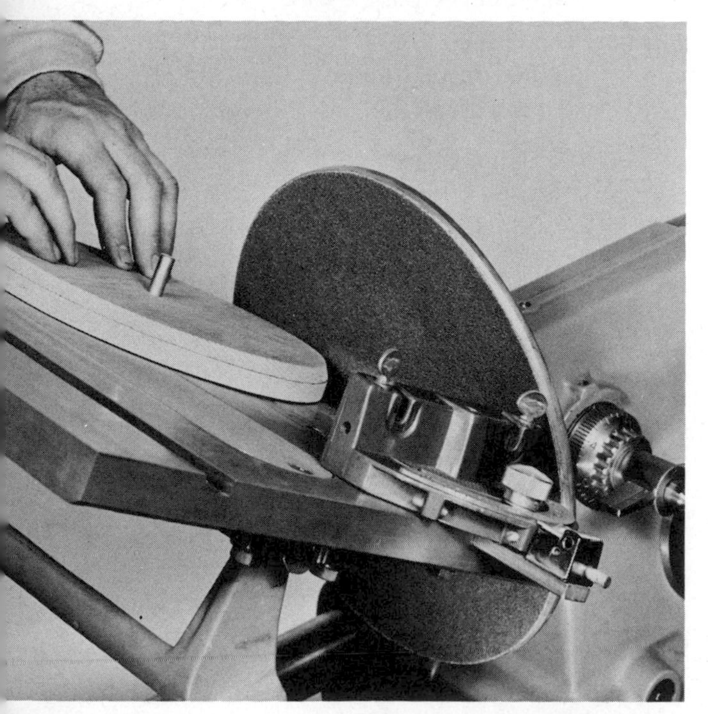

Sanding Circles

The best and most accurate way to sand circular pieces is with a pivot jig. This can be a pin set into the free end of the miter-gauge bar. After the work is sawed it is set on the sander and rotated slowly on the pivot.

If the work has a center hole, the pin in the miter-gauge bar can extend right through it. Otherwise substitute a shorter pin placed in a shallow hole drilled in the underside of the work. Or use a small brad, placed in a short piece of dowel, in the pin hole in the miter-gauge bar. Allow the brad to protrude just enough to engage the work.

When using the pivot jigs, situate the work about 1/8″ away from the disc and use the forward feed to adjust the bite of the abrasive. A strip of hardwood or metal bar stock can be substituted for the miter gauge.

This same arrangement is useful for rounding off the ends of a straight piece (above). The pivot hole is drilled in the center of the work, and the ends are rounded by making successive passes, adjusting the disc for a deeper bite after each pass. Short, duplicate pieces can be handled in this fashion by rounding off the ends of a single piece, then cutting it to size on the table saw.

The photograph at the left shows how, by tilting the table, you can bevel edges of circular pieces.

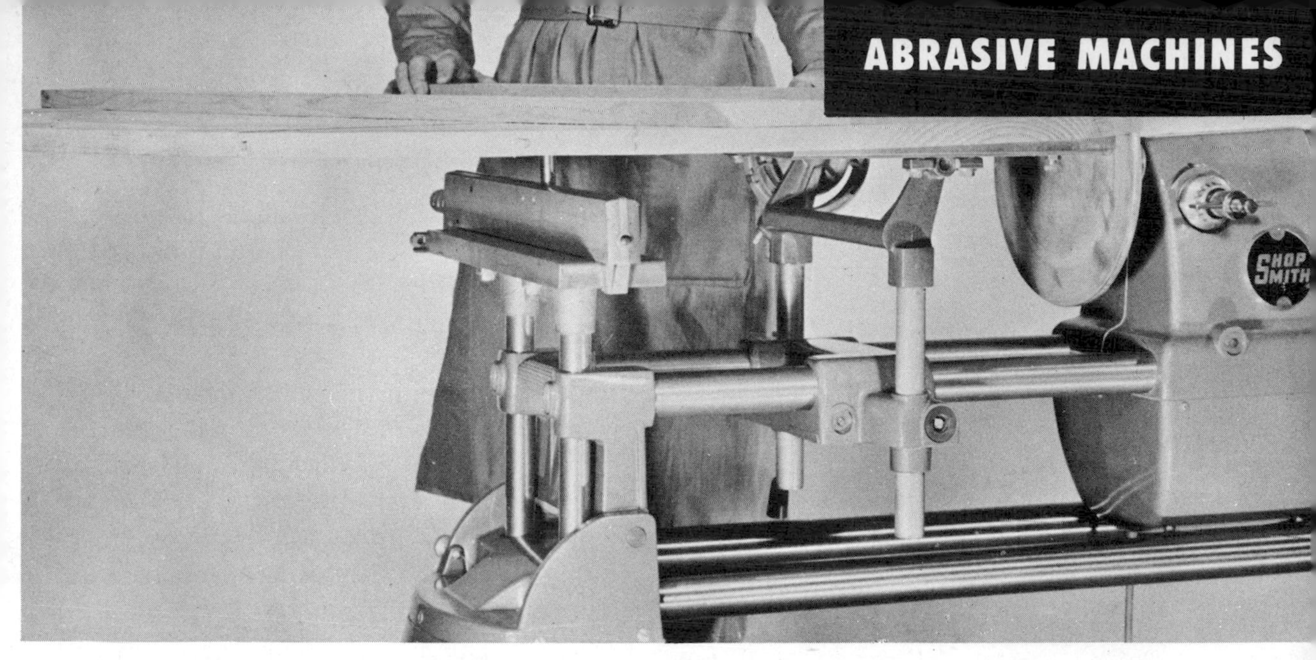

A pivot for sanding extra-large circles can be obtained by locking the rip fence on the extension table and mounting the lathe cup-center in the hole normally used for the mortising hold-down. Distance from pivot to disc should equal radius of work. Be sure the measurement is taken with the disc locked in extended position.

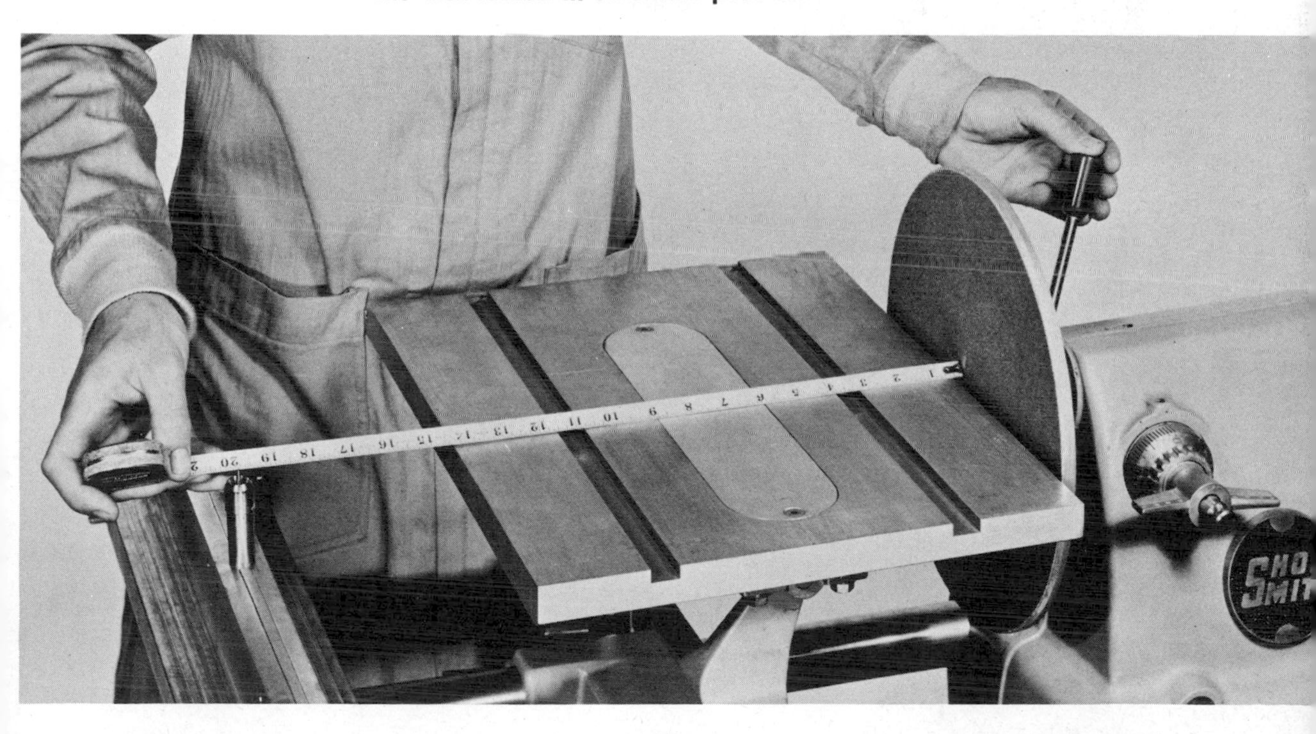

A pivot jig for handling large circular pieces is shown at the top of this page.

The rip fence is mounted on the extension table. The lathe cup-center is set in the rip-fence hole used for the hold-down, and the disc is situated to handle the work. When positioning the disc, extend it about ½″, lock it in position, and set the depth-control dial. Then set the dimension from disc to pivot (above). Unlock the quill, set the work in position, and bring the disc forward to engage the work.

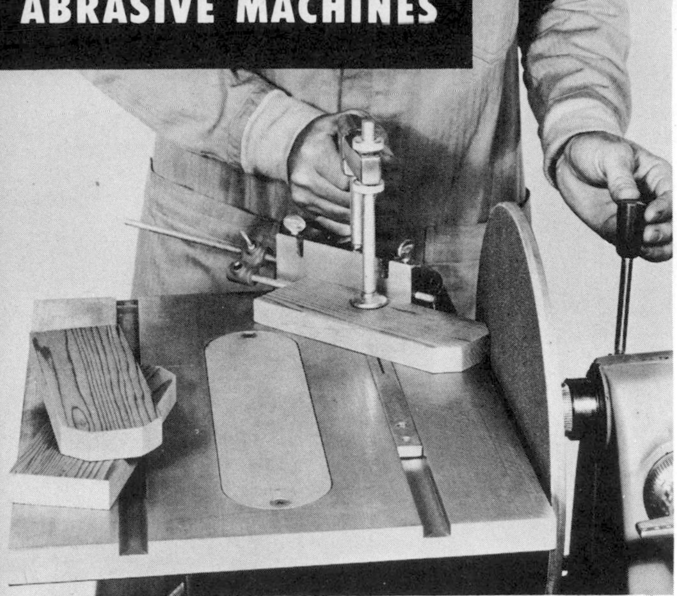

When making round corners on many duplicate pieces, it's wise first to sand off the corner (above), then remove the remaining material freehand (below). One sweep on each corner is often enough to do it.

Duplicating Round Corners

The best way to handle round corners, especially when duplicating, is to sand them to a 45° angle, as shown in the picture at the left. This creates a sanded edge tangent to the curve.

Use the miter gauge to maintain the angle, and the stop rods to position the work. Hold the work firmly on the table, and feed the disc forward to make the cut. (Notice the use of the Miter Gauge Safety Grip.)

Setting the depth-control dial will assure the same depth of cut on all corners.

When the corners have been sanded this way, finish the job freehand, as in the picture below, by placing the straight edge against the disc, then swinging the work first to the left and then to the right.

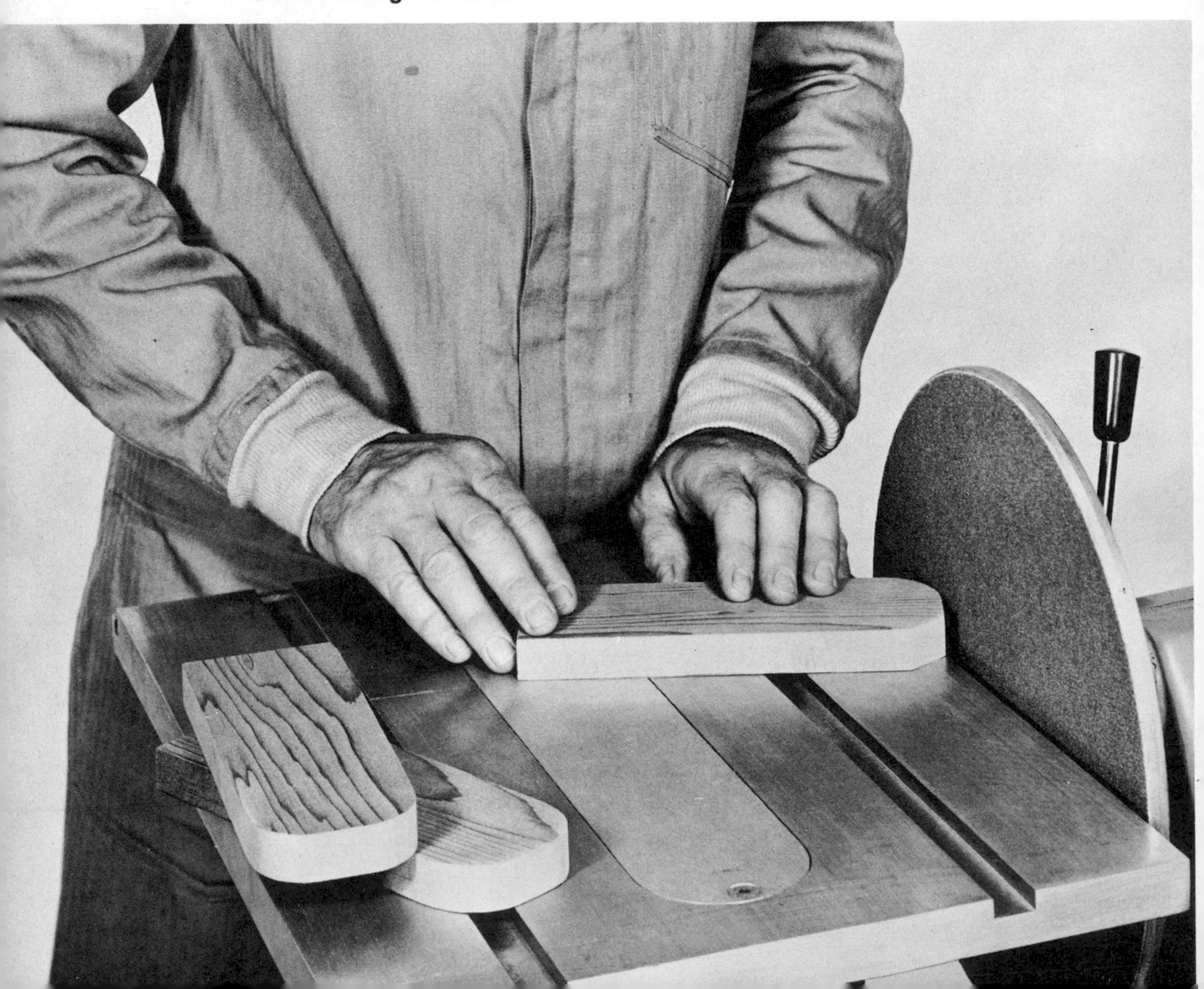

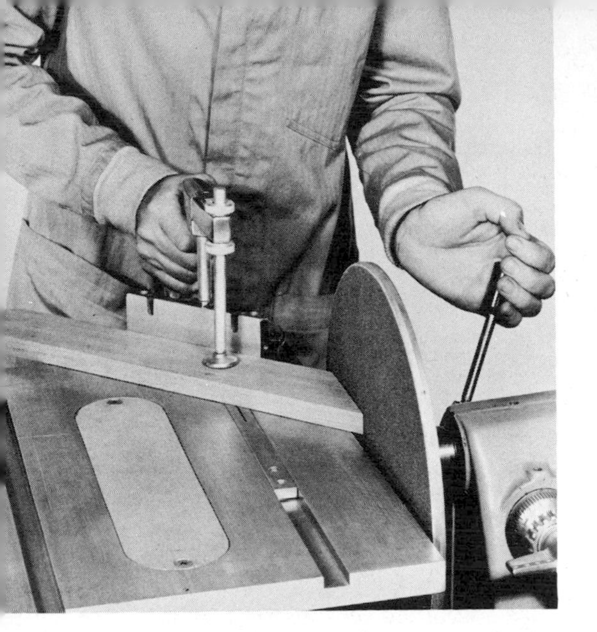

Use the miter gauge when sanding any miter. Feed either the work or the disc.

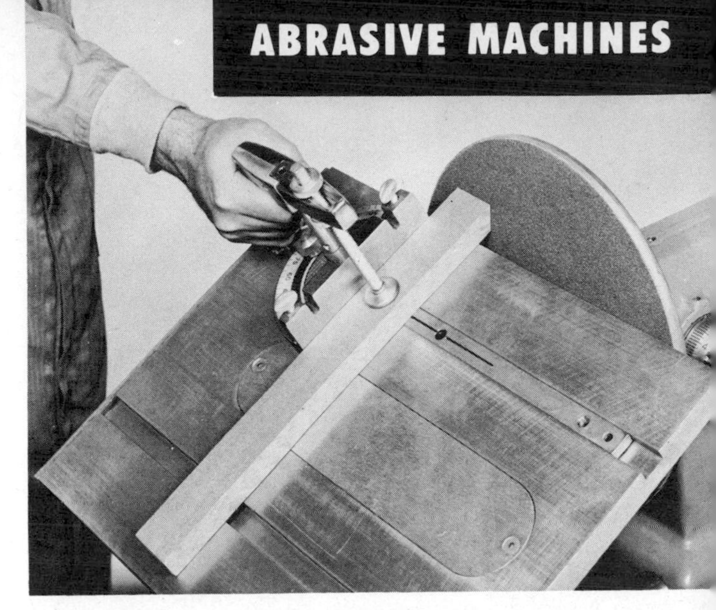

Sand bevels by tilting the table to the angle required. Use the miter gauge.

Miters and Bevels

When sanding miters, always use the miter gauge (as shown above) to position the work on the table. The sanding can be done either by moving the work against the disc, or by feeding the disc forward. When duplicating pieces, it is best to set the work by using the miter-gauge stop rods and feeding the disc forward, with the depth dial controlling depth of cut.

Bevels call for tilting the table to the angle needed. Use the sander at the end of the ways (picture above at right) and use the miter gauge to hold the work square. When sanding bevels, the angle needed will determine the amount of disc to be exposed. If the angle is extreme and the workpiece wide, put it against the miter gauge and make the cut by advancing the gauge, passing the edge of the work across the face of the disc. The edge of the table is beveled, so the distance from table-edge to disc is reduced to a minimum at any angle.

Sand compound miters as at left below, beveled edges as at right.

Sand compound miters with the same table tilt and miter-gauge setting used to make the cut.

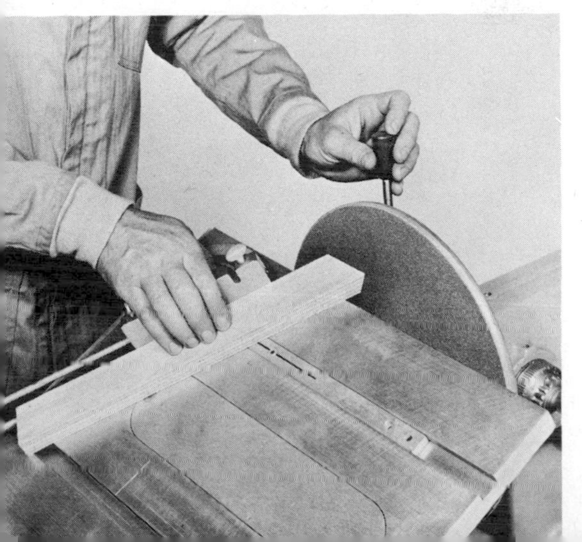

Use the offset-fence technique, but with the table tilted, to sand rip-bevel cuts.

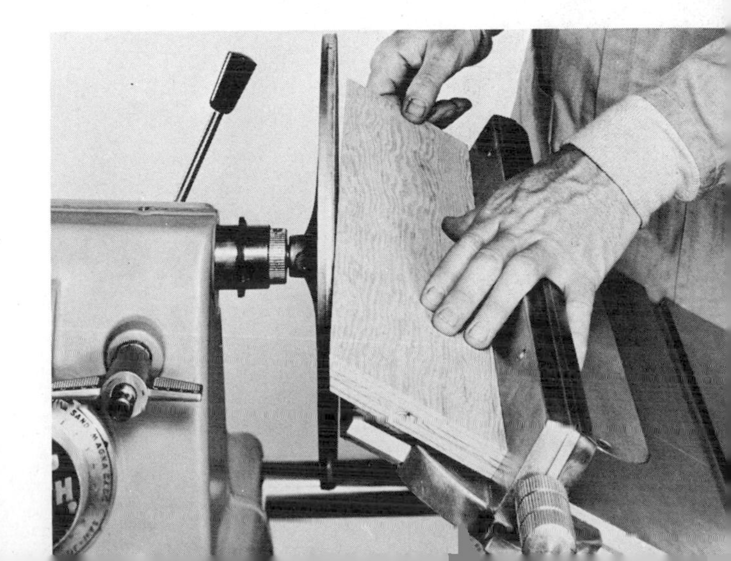

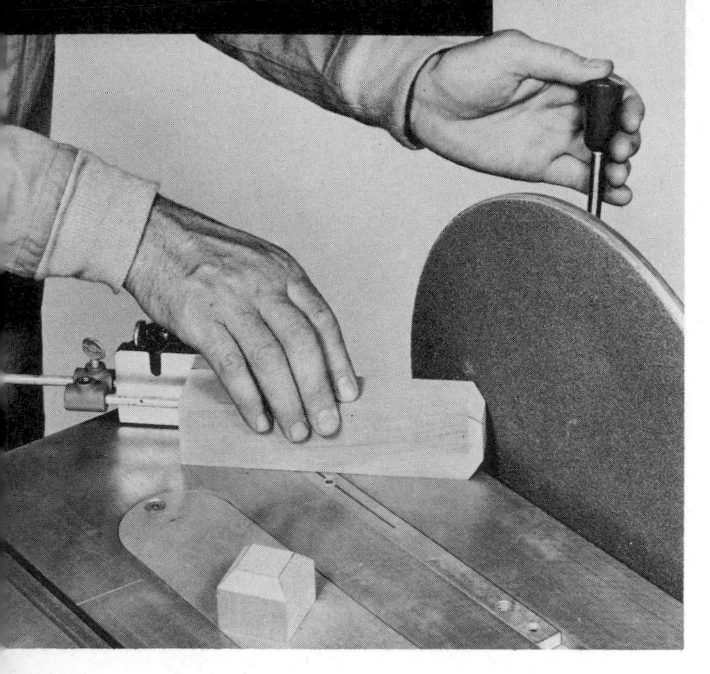

Use the miter gauge and stop rods, and feed the disc forward, to make perfect chamfers.

Chamfering

By using the fence and miter gauge to form a jig, any number of pieces may be sanded exactly alike. This is a useful method for such jobs as pointing fence pickets.

Sanding Curves to Width

Curved work that must be of uniform width throughout its length is handled as shown in the photograph below.

A guide stick, pointed at one end, is clamped to the table to gauge the width of the stock. The work is then passed between stick and disc.

The important thing, to insure uniform width, is to keep the curve of the work tangent to the disc at all times.

Work of this nature, after being cut to shape on the jig saw, should have its inside face smoothed on the drum sander (see page 268) so it will have a smooth edge to ride against the guide stick.

Pass curved work between a guide stick and the disc to assure uniformity of width. The inside face is first smoothed on a drum sander.

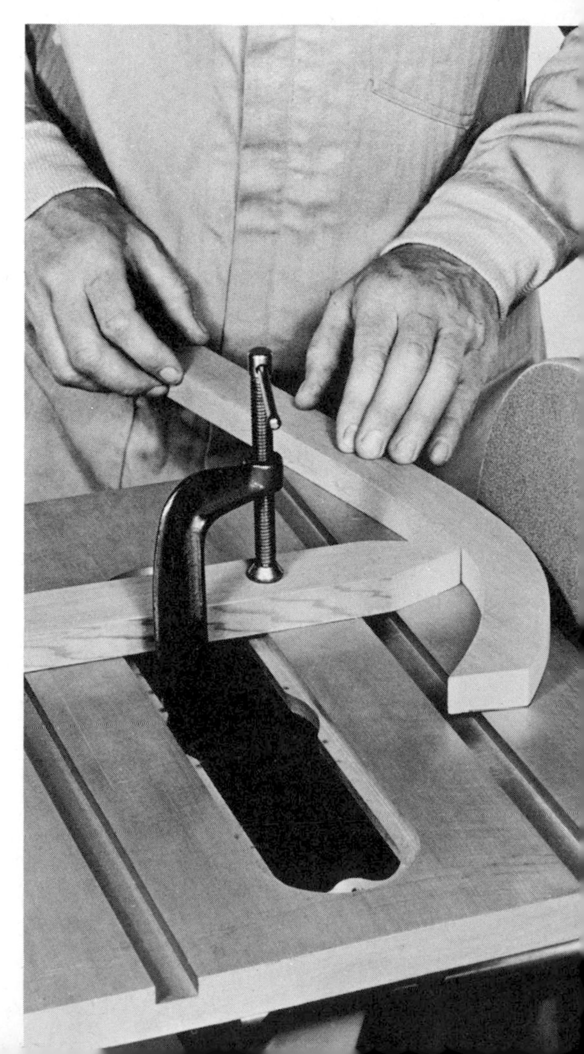

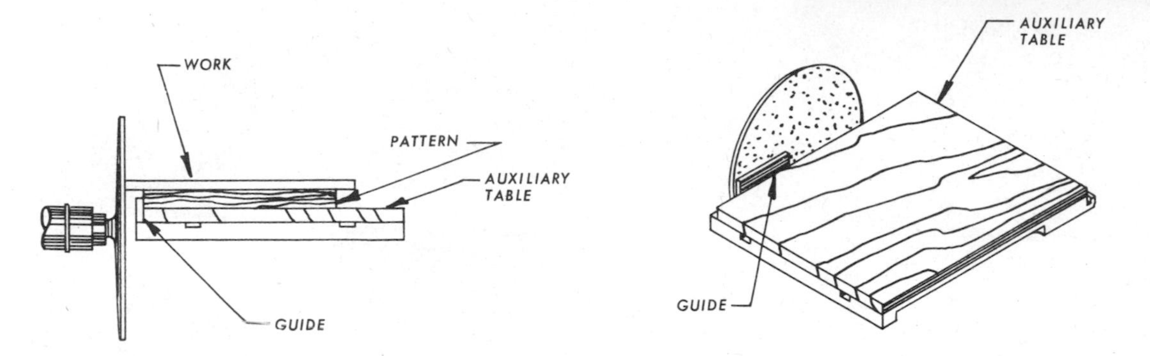

This setup for pattern sanding is useful when many identical pieces are needed.

Pattern Sanding

Pattern sanding uses a guide strip (above) against which the pattern rides. The work projects beyond it, against the disc. The metal guide strip should be screwed to a wooden table clamped to the regular one. Position the guide about ⅛″ away from the disc, and allow for this when shaping the pattern. Use projecting brad points to anchor the work to the pattern.

Pointing Dowel

Doweling to be pointed to a specific bevel is handled on the disc sander by using the miter gauge to maintain the angle. The dowel is held against the miter-gauge head and pushed forward until contact is made with the disc. Then it is rotated slowly. When duplicate pieces are needed, use the stop rods to hold the dowel, and advance the disc for the depth of cut. Then set the depth dial, lock the quill, and rotate the dowel. Repeat the procedure for the remaining pieces.

Sanding Metals

Except for the selection of the proper abrasive, sanding metal (below) does not differ much from sanding wood. The feed, on materials harder than wood, should be less, and the pass made more slowly. Place a protective cover over the tubular ways directly under the sanding disc. (See page 323 for construction details.)

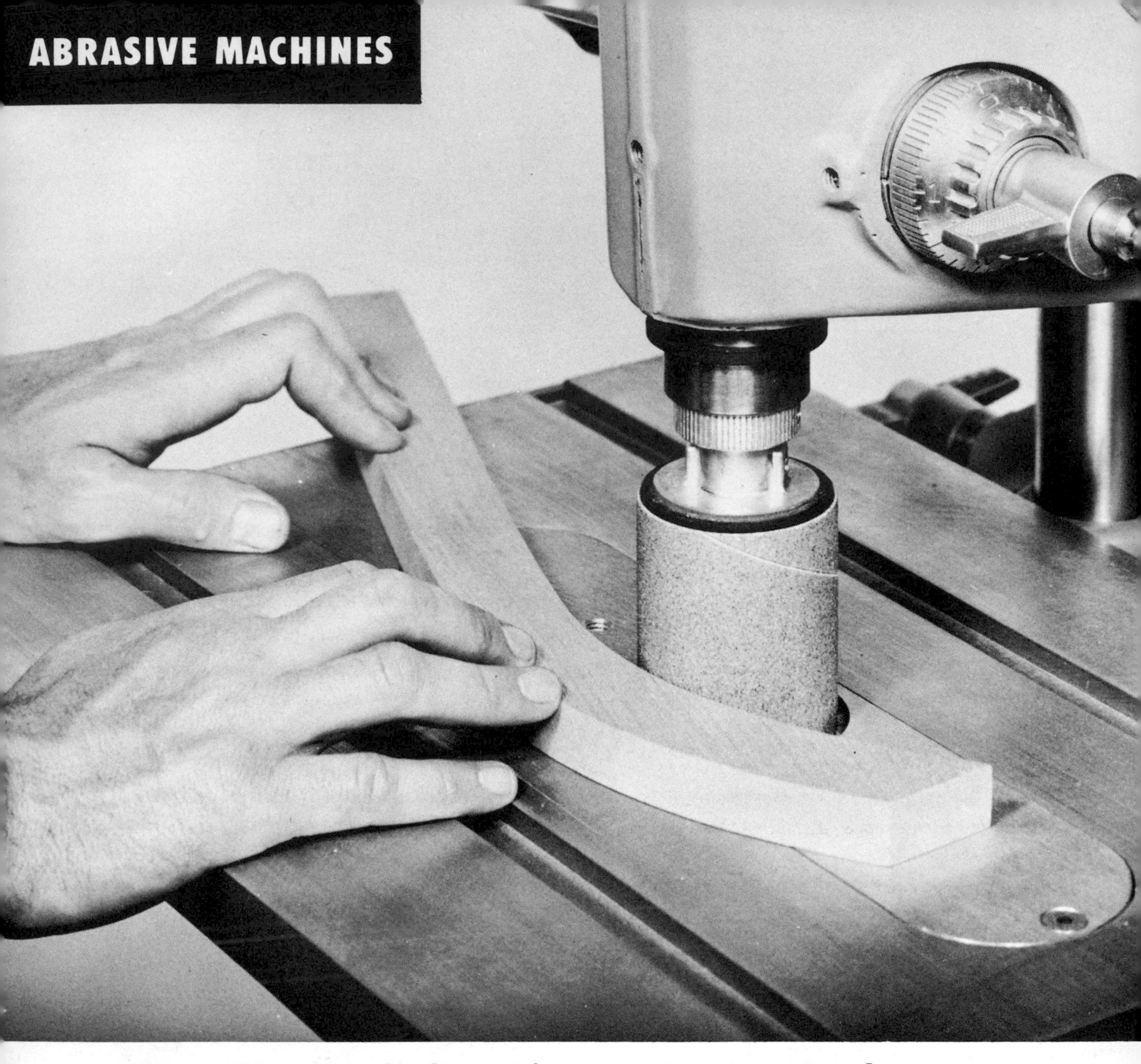

When possible, set up the drum sander as shown above to assure edges that are square to adjacent surfaces. The 3″ drum is shown below.

The Drum Sander

Drum sanders are special drums, made in various diameters, on which abrasive sleeves can be mounted. The most popular size, the 3″, has an inset nut at one end which, when tightened, expands the rubber drum to grip the sleeve. When the nut is loosened the sleeve can be removed for replacement.

Although they will function at faster speeds, drum sanders are usually run between 1,800 and 2,000 rpm.

The difficulty with excessive speeds, even though the cut produced is smoother, is that the friction created burns the wood unless

Smoothing the cabriole leg is typical of sanding operations best handled freehand on a drum.

the feed pressure is feather-light. It is also true that, because the heat created draws pitch from the wood, faster speeds produce more rapid filling and clogging of the abrasive. So the drum sander should be used at a reasonable speed and with light feed pressure.

Operating the Drum Sander

On the multi-purpose tool the drum sander can be used either in horizontal or vertical position and with or without the table.

Woodworking jobs such as sanding down the cabriole leg above are typical of the sanding operations best handled on a drum. Because of the elaborate contours of the leg it's impossible to rest the work on a surface. By working freehand you can move and turn the work to suit the contour. Keep a firm grip on it and move it along steadily; resting it in one place will produce an indentation.

When doing edge sanding that can be rested on a flat surface, it is best to use the machine in a vertical position. The special shaper insert shown in use on the opposite page can replace the regular insert to let the end of the drum be set below the table surface.

Thickness-sanding may be accomplished by passing the work between table and drum sander.

Surface Sanding

The drum sander, used as shown above, will do an efficient job of surfacing narrow boards.

Place the table under the drum and raise it until the work just touches the abrasive sleeve. Withdraw the work, turn on the motor, and feed the work **against the rotation** of the drum. This means standing behind the machine and feeding the work forward toward the switch side of the headstock.

Wider boards may be handled the same way by using the fence as a guide (shown below) and readjusting it for successive passes.

A type of drum sander you can make for yourself, to use on the multi-purpose tool in the lathe position, is illustrated on the next page. The large table surface provides excellent support for the workpiece. The drum should be made of a hardwood such as birch or maple, and turned down on the lathe so that it is of exact diameter throughout its length. It is best to mount the drum on a small-size faceplate, instead of the spur center. The regular cup-center can be used in the tailstock, but a live center is better.

When thickness-sanding wide boards, use the rip fence as a guide. Take a light cut.

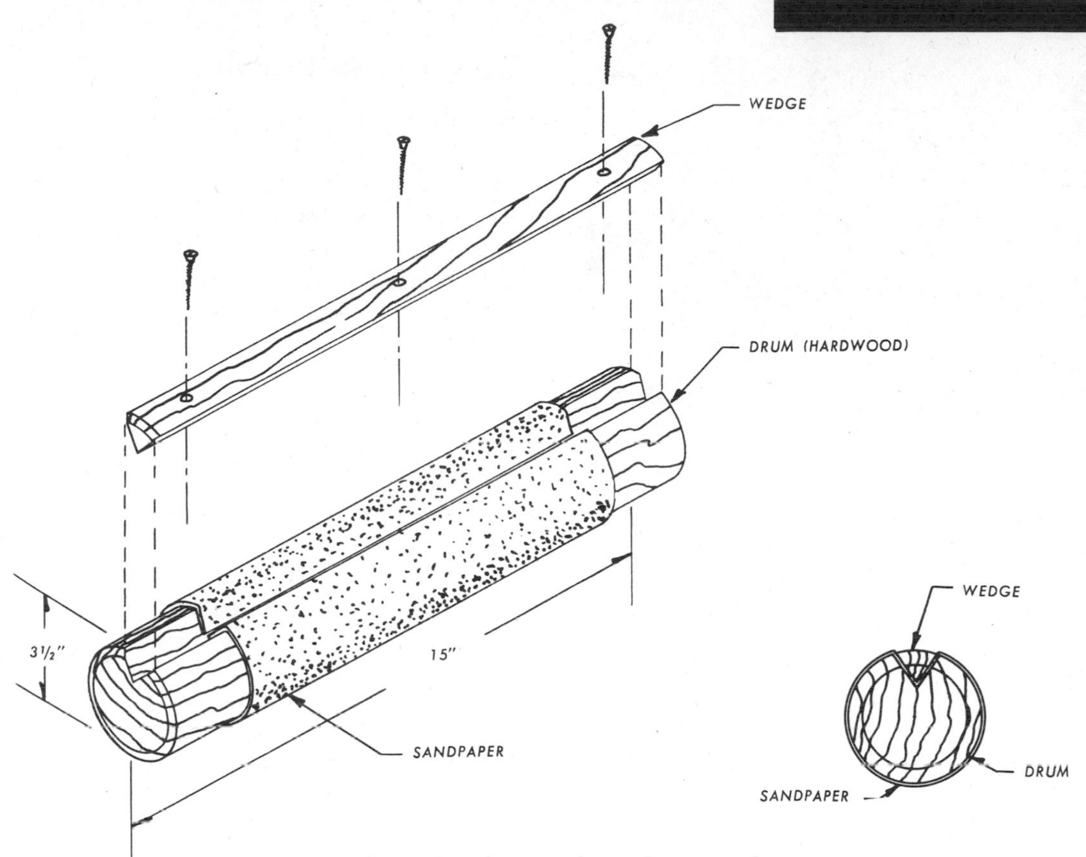

Use these details to make a drum sander.

A V-cut is made in the drum, as sketched above. The V-wedge holds the abrasive paper in place. If the wedge is a tight fit the abrasive sheet will pull tight about the drum. Be sure the wedge does not protrude above the surface of the drum.

Do not use excessive speeds, and do not attempt too deep a bite in one pass. This is important. You'll find that surfacing the wood in two or more passes will give better work.

Home-made drum sander mounted between lathe centers is used to surface-sand wide stock.

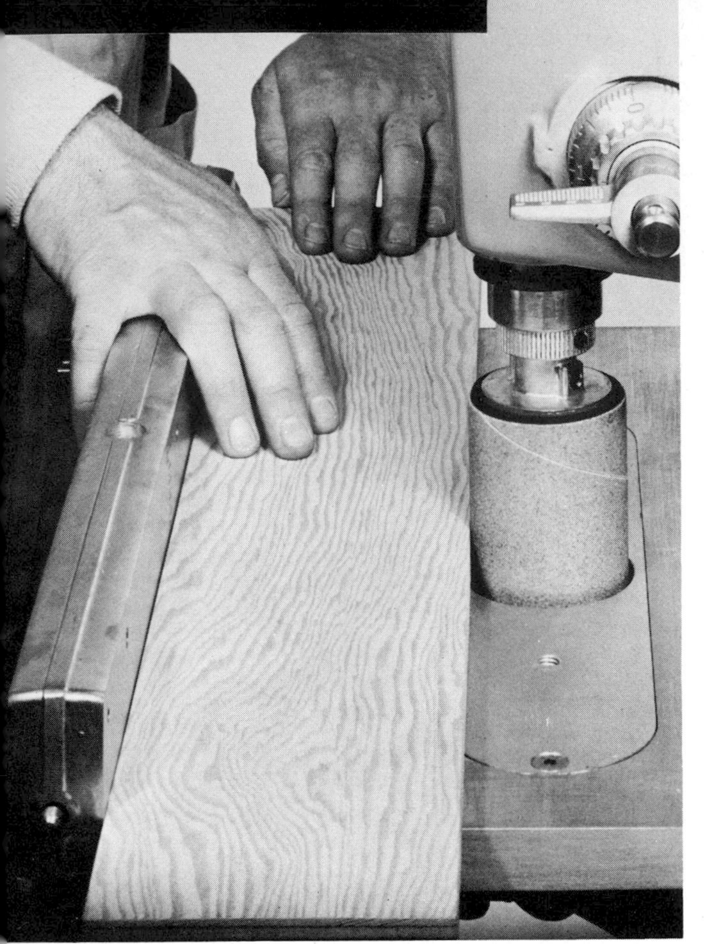

Sanding to Width

Straight pieces can be drum-sanded to width by using the machine in a vertical position. Pass the work between the rip fence and the drum, as shown in the photograph at the left. Heavy side pressure on the spindle is unnecessary. If it becomes excessive, it can even damage the machine.

Fitting Legs to Round Columns

A furniture leg to be fitted to a round column must have a radius formed on the face that mates with the column. This is done by using the machine as shown below. The table is set so the center line of the workpiece is on the center line of the drum. The fence is used to keep the work square. The work is fed forward against the drum to form the radius. Of course the diameter of the sanding drum must be at least approximately equal to the diameter of the round column to be fitted.

Jointing an Edge

When used with a shaper fence, available as an accessory for the multi-purpose tool, the drum sander can be used to joint edges. The amount of material to be removed is controlled by adjusting the infeed fence.

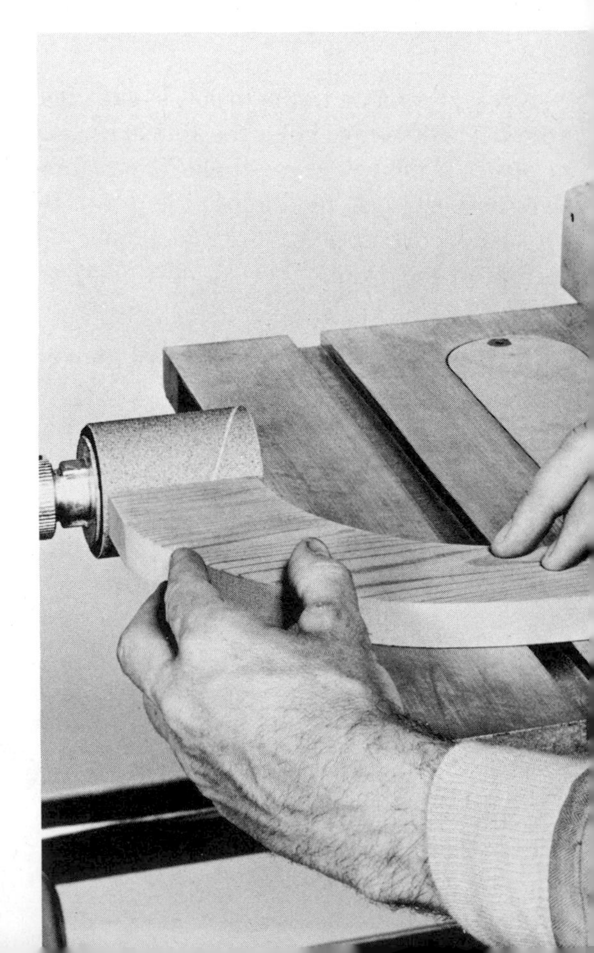

To smooth a rabbet cut, have the sleeve extend about 1/32" beyond the drum, like this.

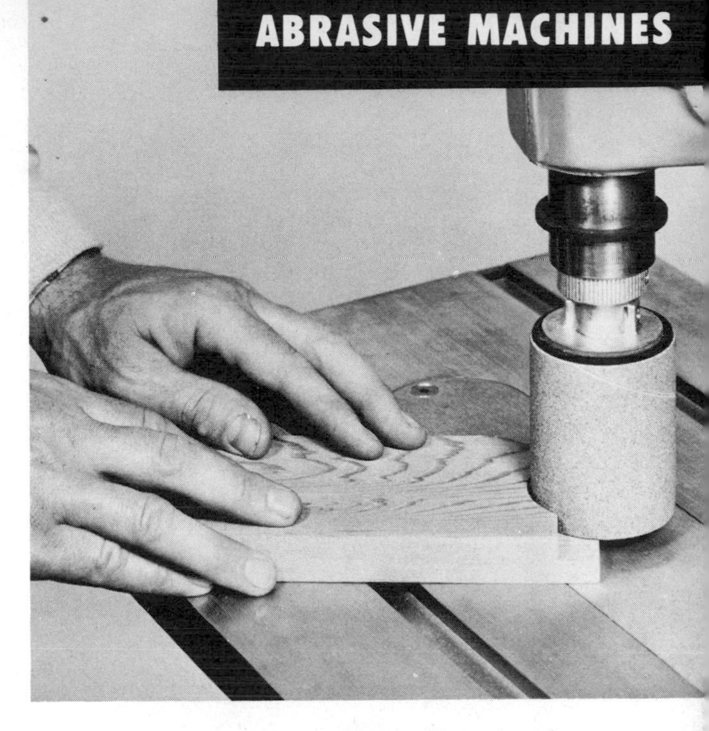

Some special cuts, like a rabbet with an inside curved face, are sanded as shown here.

Sanding Rabbets

The inside corners of rabbets and similar cuts are smoothed on the drum sander as shown above.

Place the table at the correct height, then bring it close to the drum.

Set the fence as a guide against which the work can ride.

Advance the drum to fit into the corner.

Then feed the work forward to make the pass.

Operations like this require that the sleeve be mounted so it projects about 1/32" beyond the bottom of the drum; thus the inside corner can be finished cleanly.

Such special types of cuts as a rabbet with an inside curved face are sanded in a similar manner (above). The machine is set in a vertical position, and the table is brought up to allow for the thickness of the work that will pass under the drum. After the rabbet has been cut in the conventional manner on the table saw, the curved edge is pencil-marked and the drum sander finishes the cut to the line.

Pattern-Sanding

Pattern-sanding on the drum sander uses a wooden or metal disc equal in diameter to the drum and fastened directly under it. This is a guide against which the pattern rides.

Work is held to the pattern by the usual method of projecting brad points.

With the work in place, the pattern is held against the guide, and the contact maintained as the work is revolved.

The work should be jig sawed about 1/16" oversize by using the pattern to mark the work, then cutting just outside the line.

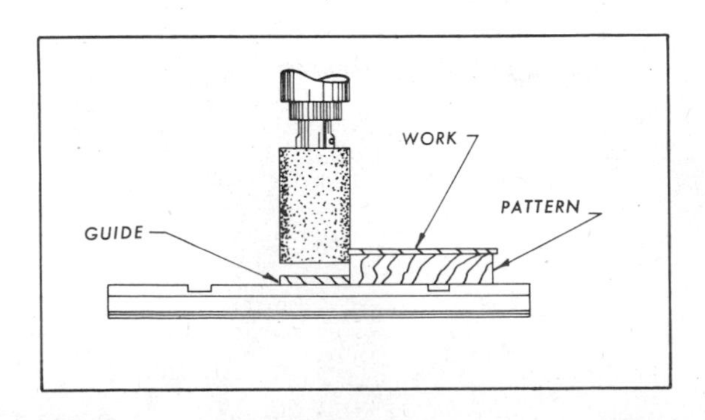

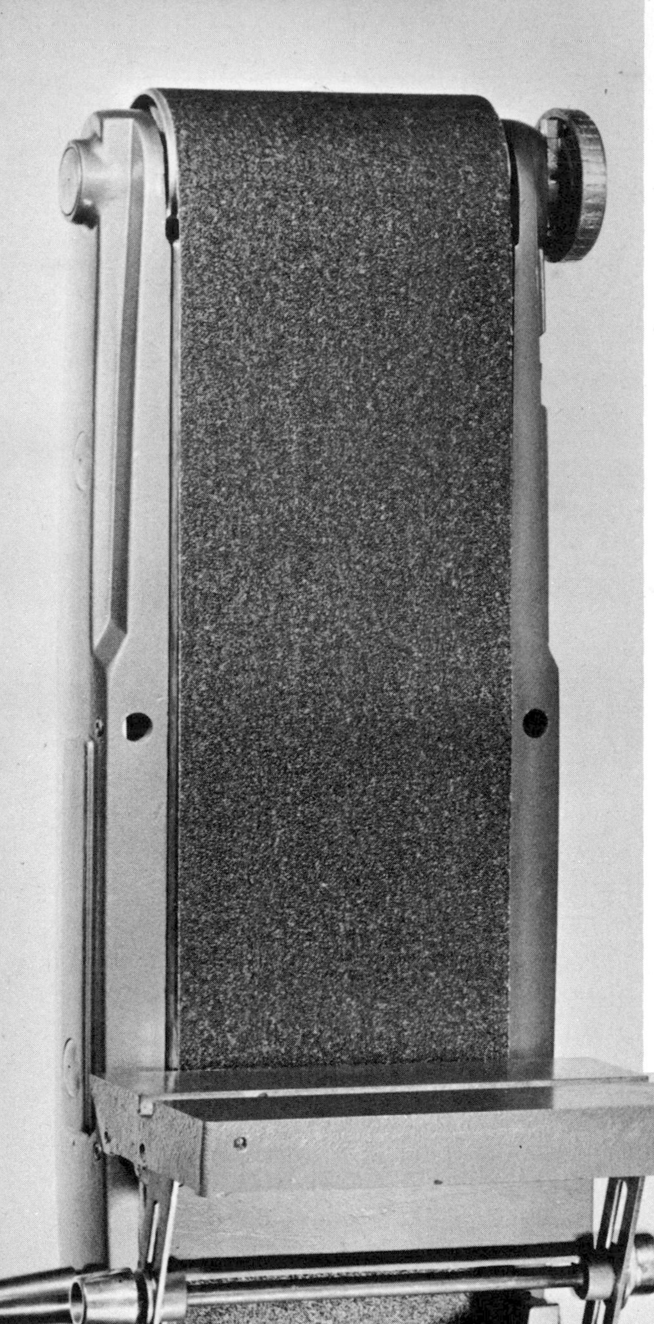

The Belt Sander

The belt sander uses an endless abrasive belt rotated by two drums. Since the abrasive moves in a straight line, the belt sander is particularly useful for sanding parallel to the wood grain.

Belt width does not limit width of stock that may be sanded, since repeated passes will permit smoothing boards that are wider than the belt itself. The 6″ by 48″ belt sander shown here is available as a Power Mount accessory for the multi-purpose tool.

Like all major accessories it may be stored on a wall bracket (opposite page) when not in use and is easily mounted for operation when needed. This permits using the variable-speed drive and the ¾ horsepower motor. Like other Power Mount accessories, it may be mounted on its own stand if desired. On the multi-purpose tool, it is possible to create setups which permit, for example, the operation of a disc sander and a belt sander at the same time.

Abrasive belts are available in various

The straight-line action of the abrasive on a belt sander makes this machine especially useful for sanding with the grain of the wood.

grits, usually classified as fine, medium, and coarse. An assortment of them should be readily accessible to handle any sanding job that might occur. The facts about abrasives at the beginning of this chapter apply to the belt sander as well as to the others.

Belts are easily changed; it's just a matter of releasing the tension on the idler drum (the drum not powered). This shortens the distance between drums, providing enough slack so the belt can be quickly slipped on or off.

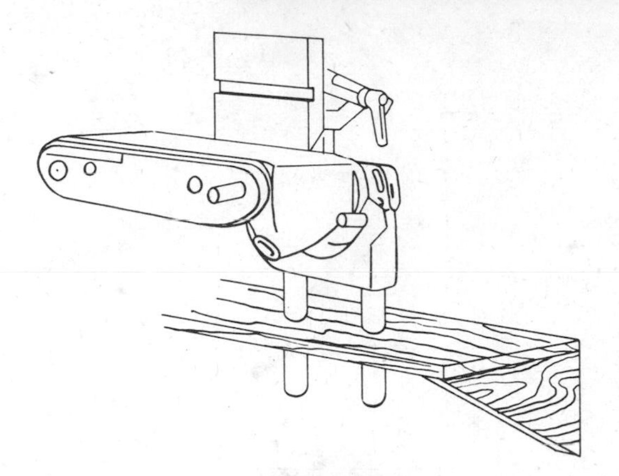

The belt sander may be conveniently stored on a simple wall bracket like this one.

Adjusting the Belt Sander

Of the two adjustments on the belt sander, one provides the correct belt tension, the other assures that the belt will remain centered on the drums. The latter is referred to as tracking. On some belt sanders the tension adjustment is a manual operation, but on the one shown here it is automatic, since the idler drum is spring-loaded and set to provide exactly the right tension for good performance. Loosening one adjustment knob is all that is necessary.

Turn this knob counter-clockwise until you hear an internal catch snap into place. This locks the idler drum in the lowered position, making it possible to replace the belt. When putting on the new belt, center it over the drums as closely as possible. Then grip

This setup for simultaneous operation of belt and disc sanders often proves most useful.

To change belts, release the tension on the idler drum; this shortens the distance between drums so belts are easily slipped on and off.

the adjustment knob so that the lever, inset in the perimeter of the handle, is depressed. This releases the internal catch, and the adjustment knob will automatically turn clockwise and provide the right tension. This automatic tensioning device is designed to compensate for slight inconsistencies in belt lengths. Make all belt changes with the Speed Dial set at the lowest speed.

Once the belt is in place, the machine may be turned on and the belt checked for tracking. If the belt shifts to either side of the drums, adjust the tracking nut (located just under the tension knob) slightly to left or right until the belt is exactly centered. (See photograph at lower left.) Be sure to adjust the tracking nut while the belt is running.

Belt-Sander Speeds

The sander will operate most efficiently if the belt moves at 915 to 1830 sfpm (surface feet per minute). This may be obtained on the multi-purpose tool in the range between E and L on the Speed Dial. This encompasses almost the entire range of both disc and drum sanders.

If the belt sander is powered by V-belt, the speed range should be from 1150 to 2300 rpm. The lower speeds will provide greater power. So when sanding a large area—especially when surface sanding—always set the Speed Dial at the lower end of the speed range.

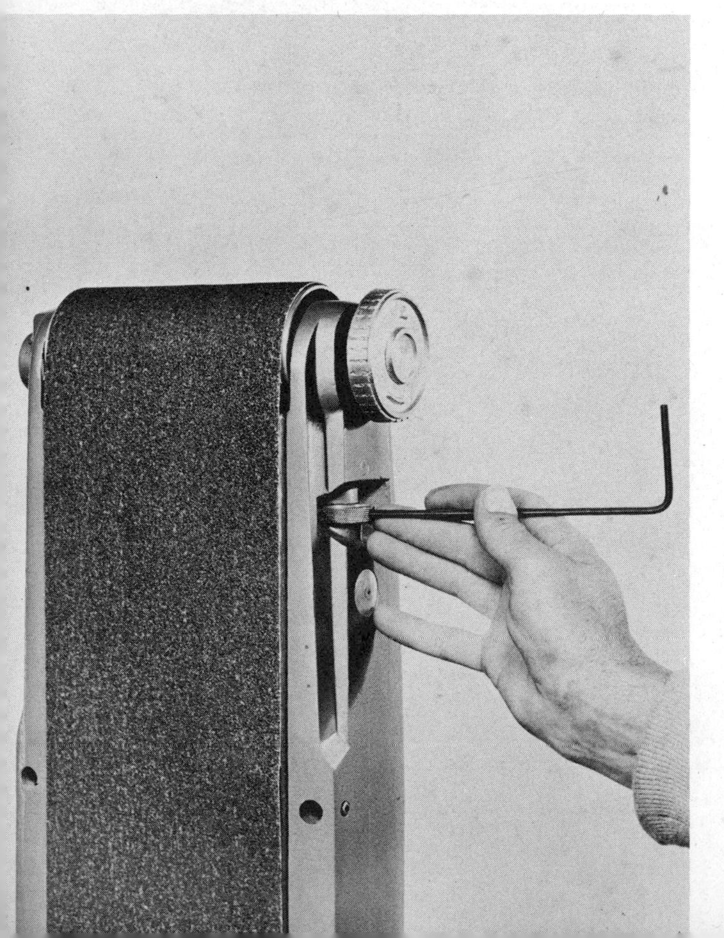

If the belt is not centered on the drums, adjust the tracking nut slightly to left or right. Do this with the machine running.

End, Miter, and Cross-Bevel Sanding

End sanding is simply a matter of placing the work on the table, then moving it forward against the belt, as in photograph at right. Use a miter gauge if possible.

Avoid heavy pressure against the belt. Remember that an abrasive is a cutting tool and so should be permitted to take the bite it was designed for. Excessive pressure may stall the belt, clog the abrasive, burn the wood, perhaps tear the belt.

Make miter and cross-bevel cuts as shown in the two photographs below.

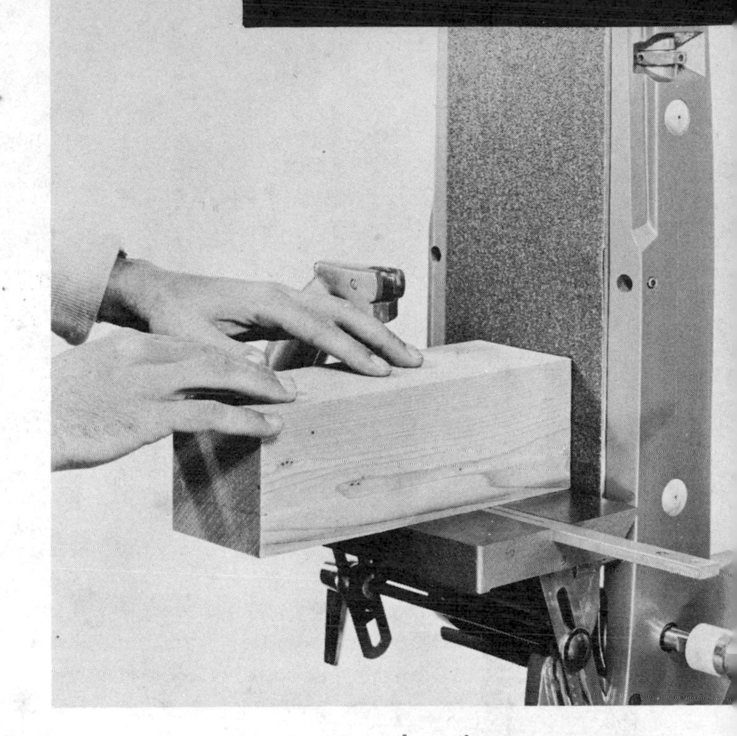

To assure squareness, use the miter gauge whenever possible when end-sanding.

Use the miter gauge to maintain the original saw angle when sanding miter cuts. Hold the stock firmly against the head of the miter gauge, and feed it slowly. On wide boards it's all right to move the work across the face of the belt.

On cross-bevel cuts, tilt the table to the angle required and use the miter gauge to hold the stock square. If possible, tilt the table to form an open angle with the belt. Using a closed angle—especially with thin stock—might result in jamming the work between belt and table.

On small projects, such as this file box, it is possible to sand all surfaces after the parts have been completely assembled. Note the use of the table as a stop.

Surface Sanding

Surfacing is best done with the belt sander in the horizontal position shown below.

Lowering the machine is just a matter of loosening one nut, bringing the sander down to its new position, and then retightening the nut. The table, in its original position, acts as a stop for the work.

Because of the straight-line action of the abrasive, sanding with the grain is one of the best features of the machine.

On such small projects as the file box at the left, it is possible to assemble the parts, then sand all surfaces. After sanding, the top of the box is cut off on the table saw or band saw to create a lid that matches perfectly with the body of the box. The table is used as a stop, and as a support for the work. Re-

For convenience on most surfacing operations, use the belt-sander in a horizontal position.

member, the drag on the belt increases with the size of the area being sanded; so apply even less pressure on this kind of operation.

To provide a guide and support when sanding long stock, the table is designed so it may be locked parallel to the belt, as shown at the right. You can use the table for support as you are moving the stock over the abrasive surface. The best technique is to keep the work snug against the table as you move it against the direction of belt rotation (middle photograph at the right). Hold the left hand lightly on the surface and place the right hand against the end of the stock to supply forward feed. When one pass will not sand the entire width, merely turn the stock end for end and make a second pass.

It is also permissible to remove the table, entirely, and make the passes freehand. Almost always, the weight of the work will supply adequate pressure down on the belt. Use your hands merely to hold the work firm and to move it forward.

Keep the stock moving—always against the direction of belt rotation. Holding it still and then putting it in another place to sand an adjacent area will inevitably result in an imperfect surface.

When a hold-down can be clamped to the table, as shown at lower right, it is possible to create a setup that helps keep opposite surfaces parallel.

This is especially useful when many similar pieces—or a very long piece—must be sanded. You have merely to hold the work snug against the table and pass it slowly and steadily under the spring blades. They will do the job of keeping the stock down on the abrasive belt.

Do not place the springs so they exert a lot of pressure; adjust them so the stock will not be moved up by the belt. And, before turning on the power, be sure the blades will not snap down on the belt after the stock has passed beneath them.

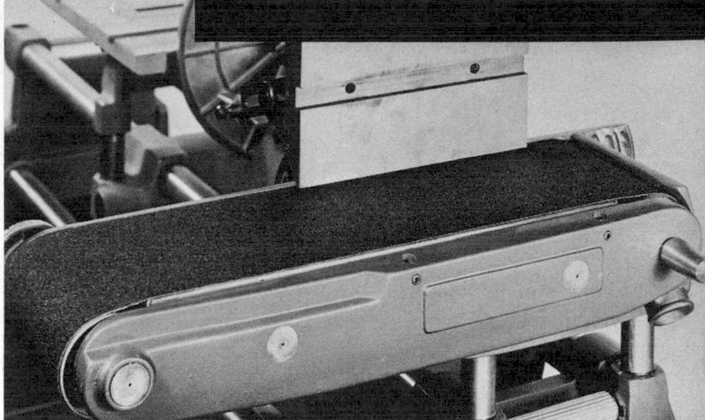

Table may be placed parallel to belt for sanding long pieces.

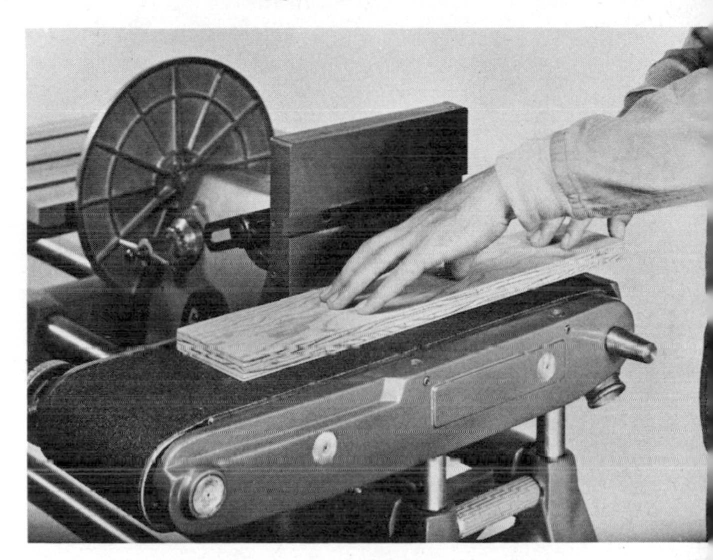

When surface sanding, move the work against the direction of belt rotation. Maintain contact with the table throughout the pass.

A hold-down, clamped to the table, will help keep opposite surfaces parallel. Before turning on power, make sure springs will not snap down on belt after work has passed through.

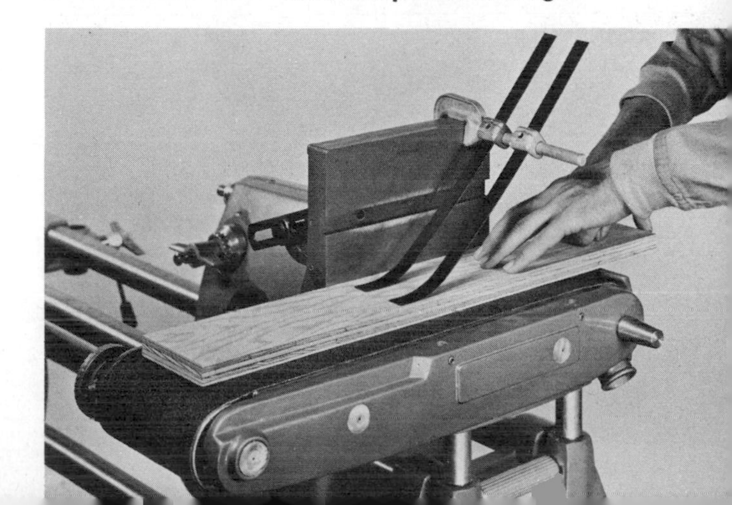

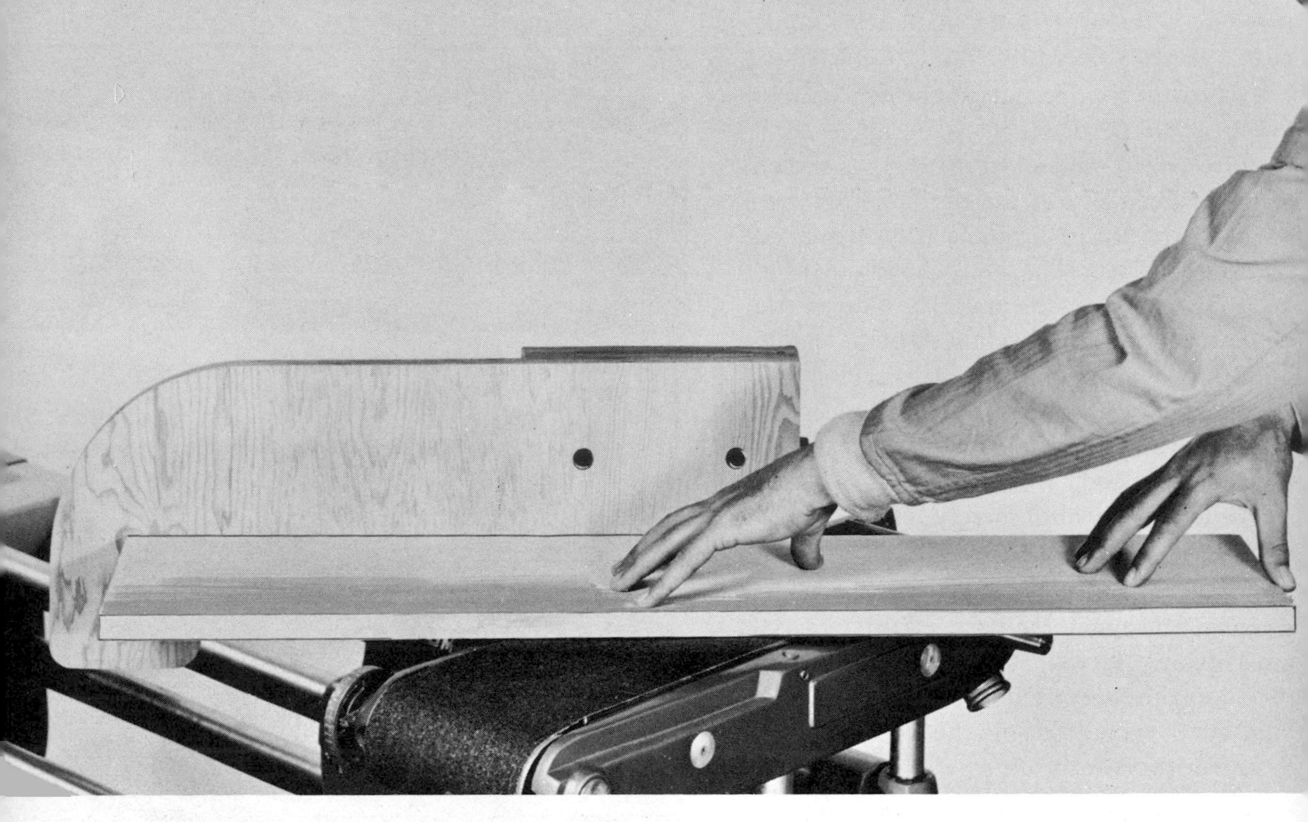

Extra-wide stock can be sanded by passing it diagonally across the belt. An extension bolted to the table will help support the work.

Try this setup when stock is very rough and much material must be removed.

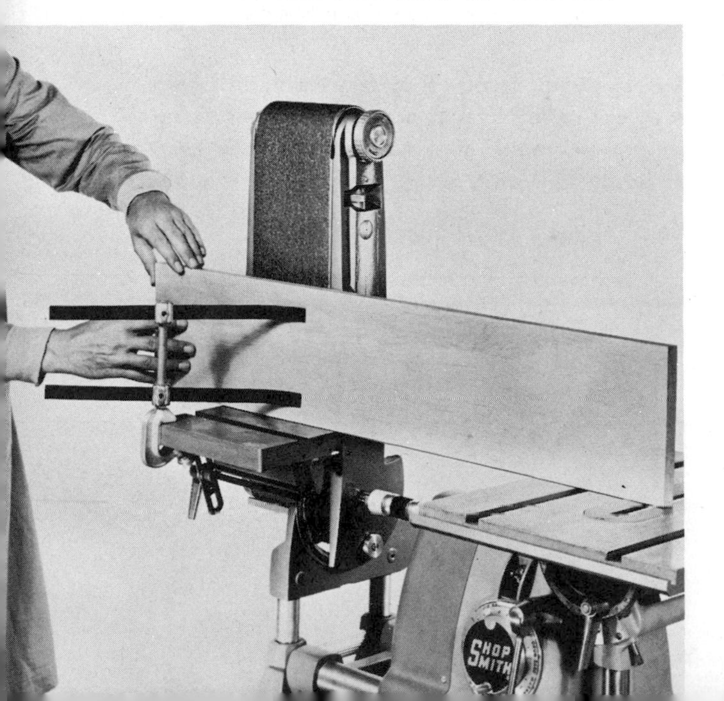

Although most belt sanding is done with the grain of the wood, you can do cross-grain sanding when the stock surface is very rough and it is necessary to remove much material. The table, with a wooden extension bolted to it, is locked on one rod only, so that it is angled to the abrasive surface. The work is then passed diagonally across the belt, as in the photograph above.

This, of course, will leave marks that must be removed before final finishing. It's a good method to use with coarse sandpaper on very rough stock. For the final sanding, use a fine belt, and move the work parallel to it.

Another method is shown at the left. Here the belt sander is locked in its vertical position, the saw table is raised and locked on a level with the belt-sander table. The Universal Hold-Down is used to hold the work against the abrasive belt. The stock is passed through on edge, as shown here.

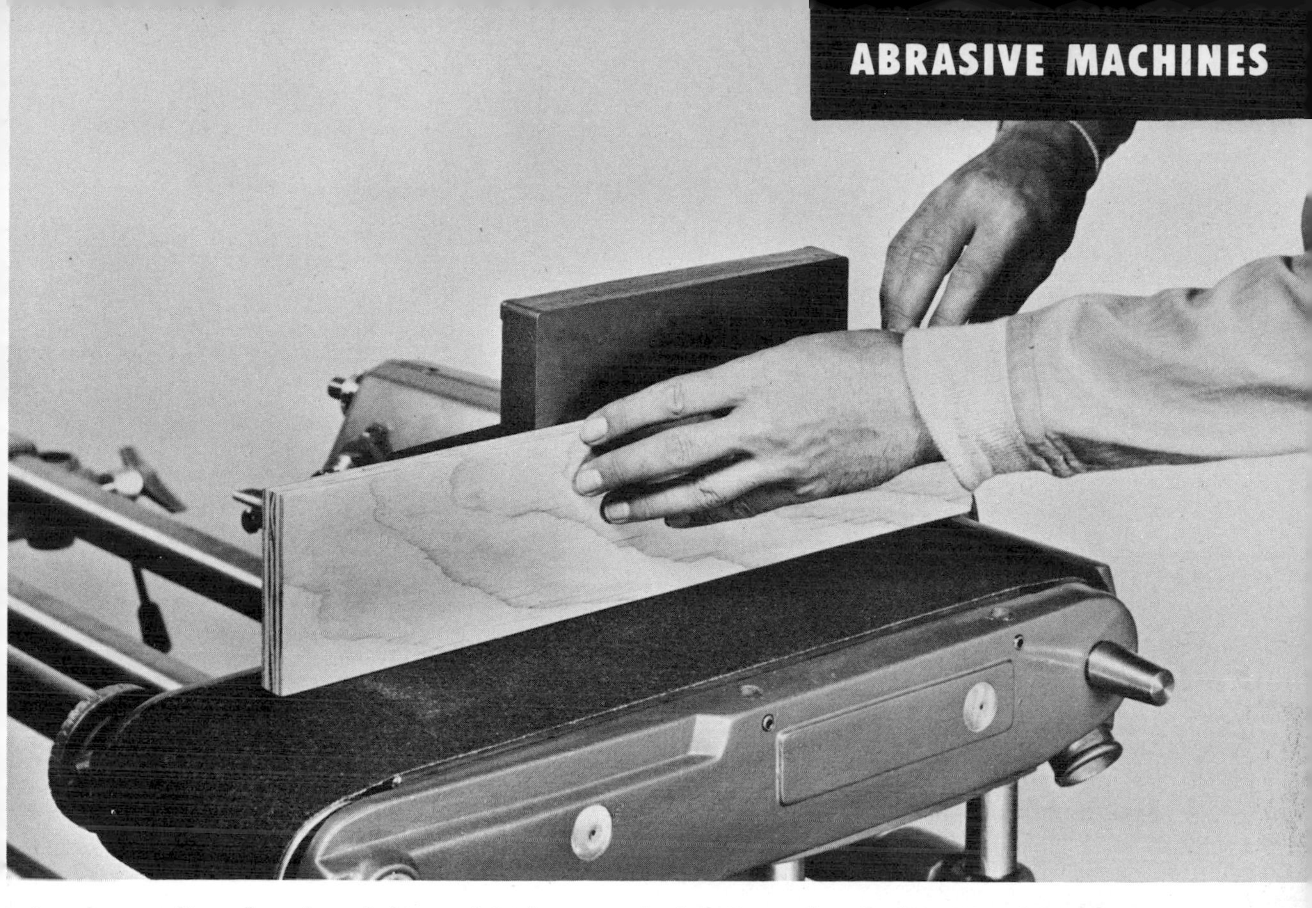

In edge sanding, the edge of the stock is down on the belt, its surface flush against the table.

Edge Sanding

Edges of short or long pieces of stock are sanded with the machine in horizontal position, with the table locked parallel to the belt. The pass is made as it would be in surface sanding, except that it's the edge of the stock that's down on the belt and the surface of the stock that's against the table. You see this in the photograph above.

Because of the two table holes, it is possible to attach a long board for use as an auxiliary fence that will provide additional support when sanding edges of excessively long stock.

Sanding across end-grain is accomplished in a similar manner when the stock is very wide. When stock width permits it, however, place its surface against the table, then lower it slowly until contact with the belt is made, as in the picture at the right.

When sanding across end-grain, hold the stock flush against the table and slide it down to make contact with the belt.

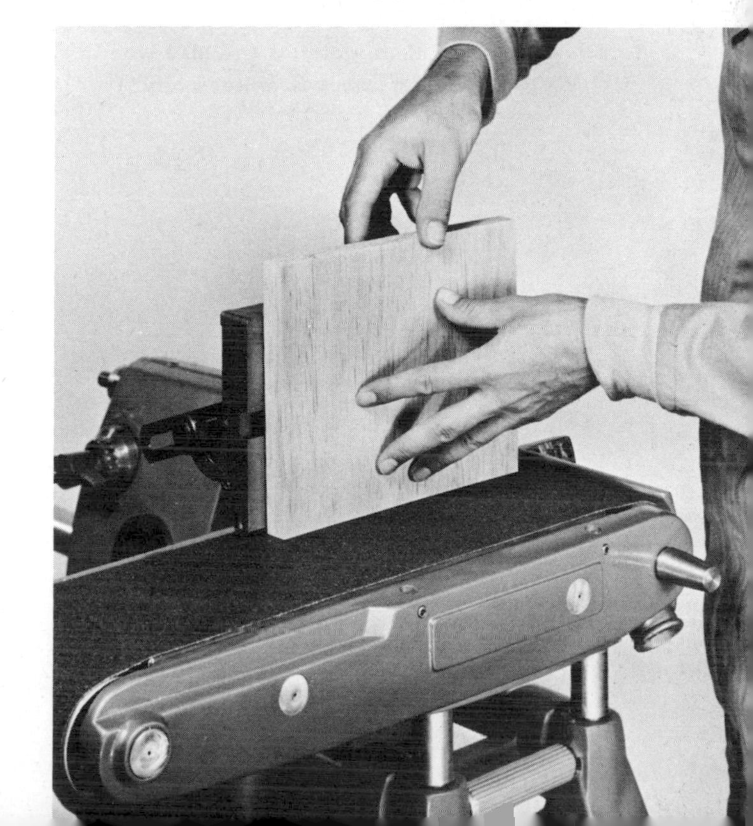

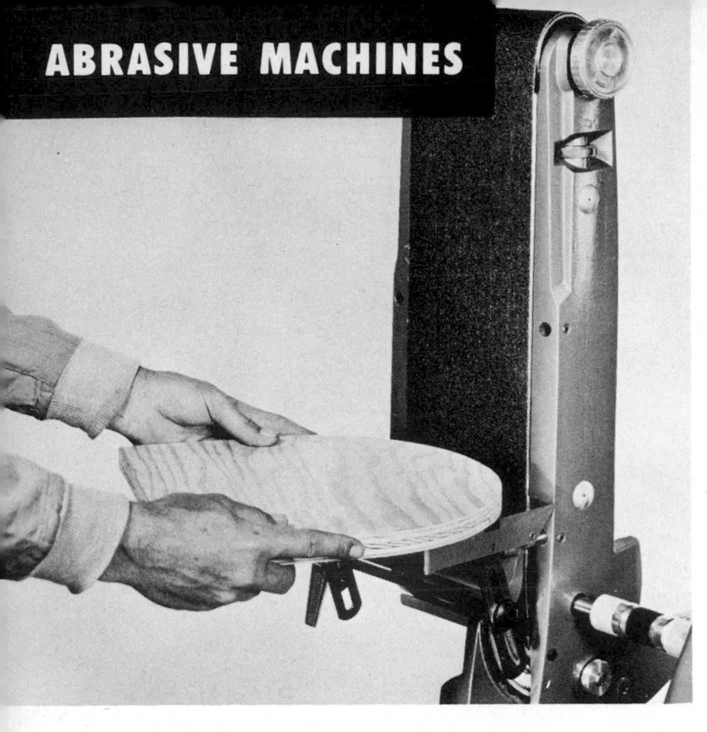

Outside curves are handled just as they would be on a disc sander. Hold the edge lightly against the abrasive surface and turn it slowly.

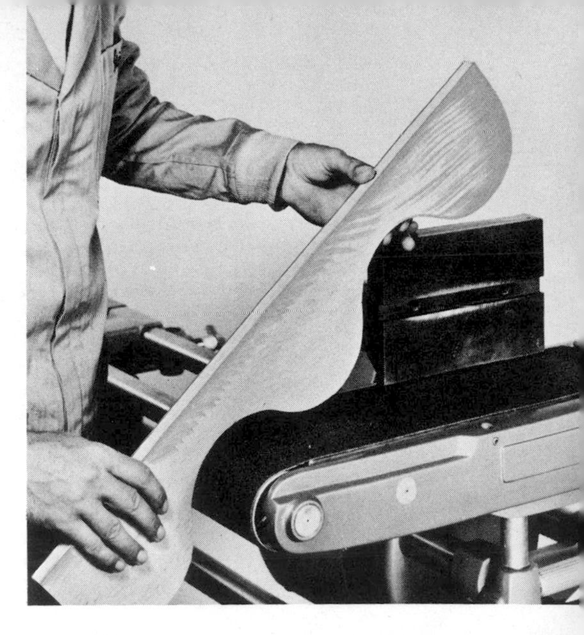

Use idler drum to smooth inside curves, with belt sander either vertical or horizontal.

Sanding Curves

Since the rear of the sander does not have a back-up plate, the slack area of the belt can be used to sand round ends, knobs, and similar shapes. To avoid shifting the belt off center, use its center. Keep pressure light to avoid removing too much material and also wearing one part of the belt excessively.

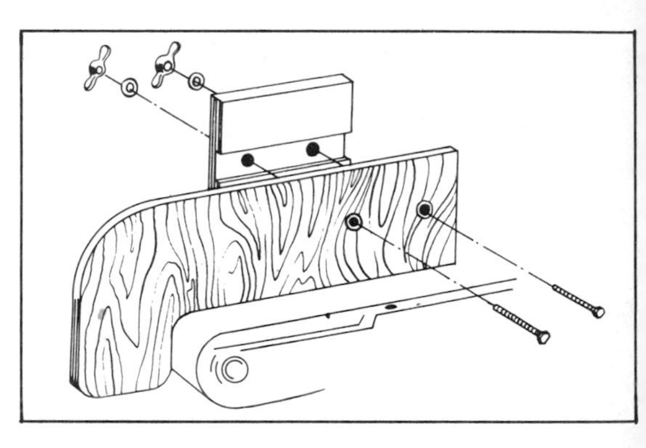

An L-shaped board is easily bolted to the table to provide an auxiliary fence for drum sanding. The auxiliary fence will assure that the sanded edge is square to adjacent surfaces.

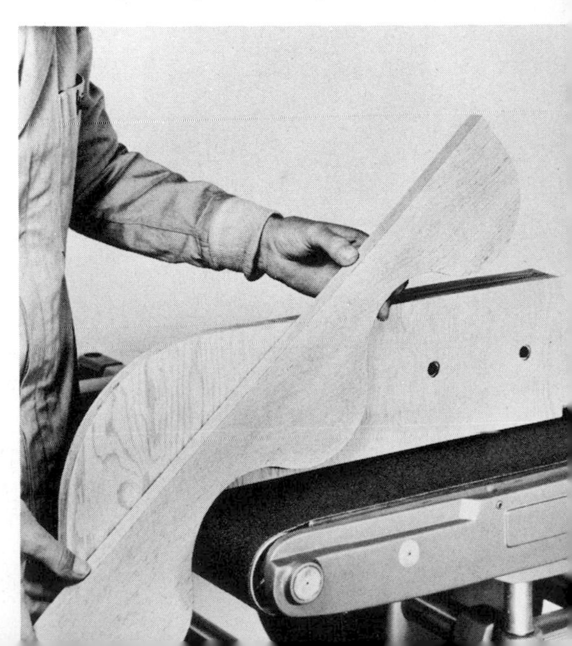

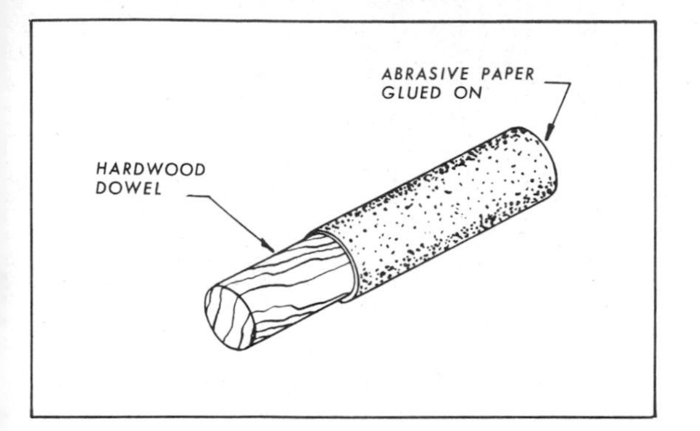

Spindle sanders are easily made by gluing abrasive paper around a length of suitable dowel.

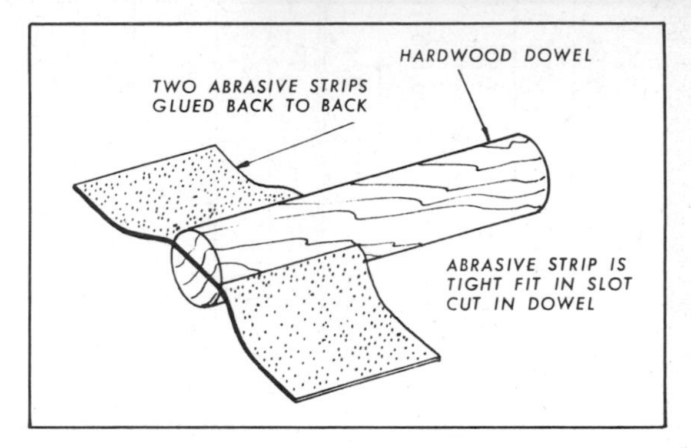

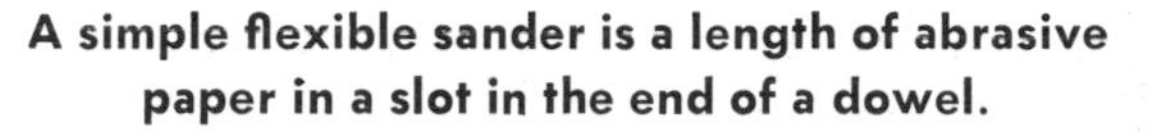

A simple flexible sander is a length of abrasive paper in a slot in the end of a dowel.

Special Sanding Devices

Typical of the many handy sanding devices you can make for yourself are spindle sanders in various sizes. Disc cement will hold the abrasive paper to the hardwood doweling, or a small kerf can be cut in one end of it and the sandpaper held with a wedge. Small sanders of this type can be used in the jig saw, lathe, drill press, or flexible shaft. They are especially useful when sanding the inside edges of jig-sawed cutouts.

A simple type of flexible sander is shown at upper right. Here again doweling is used, but these abrasive strips are held in a slim slot cut in the end of the dowel. This sander is good for drill-press and lathe work, and does a fine job of sanding inside cutouts or compound curves.

There are some jobs that can be made simple by letting the sanding operation do the shaping. Typical of these is the useful item for model boat makers sketched below. This will taper dowels for masts of ships.

With the machine vertical and the dowel held in the three-jawed chuck, set the table parallel to the ways to be used as a guide-surface for the jig. Set the jig against the table, and then—with the dowel turning—push it up slowly.

The dowel will conform to the taper set by the jig. Size and taper of the jig will, of course, depend on the size of the mast.

Sometimes a special jig is required for an unusual sanding application. This one will automatically taper doweling for use as masts on ship models or some similar project.

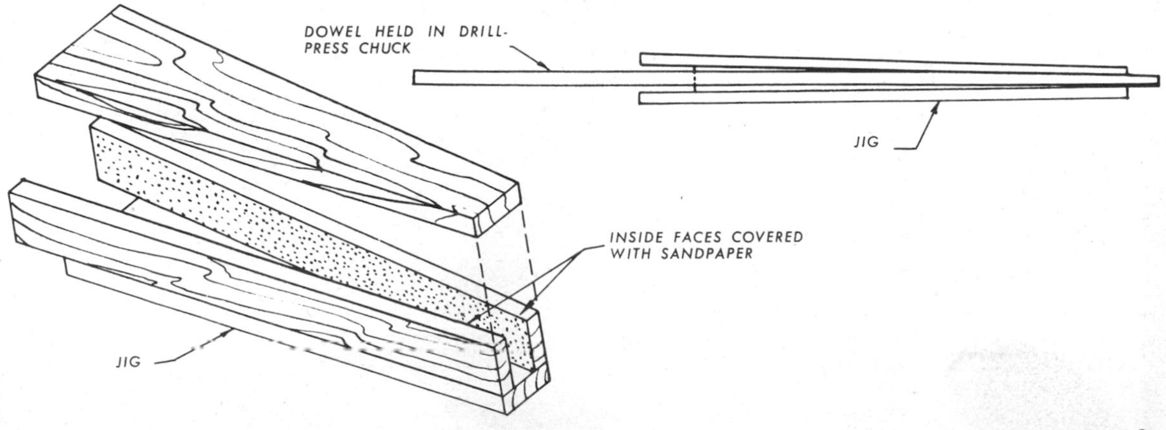

TROUBLE-SHOOTING CHART FOR ABRASIVE MACHINES

	THE TROUBLE	POSSIBLE CAUSES	THE CURE	SEE PAGE
APPLYING ADHESIVE	DISTIC DOESN'T SPREAD ON DISC OR IS LUMPY AND UNEVEN	cold disc	warm disc (as explained in text) before applying adhesive	258
		dirty disc	clean disc with solvent before applying new Distic	258
	INADEQUATE BOND (LIQUID ADHESIVE)	paper placed too soon after adhesive application	allow adhesive to turn black before making bond	see label
		uneven application	apply full, even coat to both disc and abrasive paper	258
DISC SANDING	WORK BURNS	feed pressure too great	never force work into disc	259
		work held motionless	good idea to keep work moving	—
		excessive speed on hardwoods	slower speed and reasonable feed will eliminate	257
		wrong grit paper	use coarser grit for stock removal	256
	WORK LIFTS FROM TABLE	using wrong side of disc	always place work on "down" side of disc	259
	WORK JAMMED BETWEEN DISC AND TABLE	table too far from disc	keep table as close to disc as possible	259
	ABRASIVE GRAINS QUICKLY RUB FROM DISC	abrasive bond has lost original properties	do not store paper where it is extremely dry—or where temperature is extremely high	read instructions on package
	ABRASIVE PAPER MOVES OFF DISC	incorrect application	be sure to follow instructions when attaching paper	—
		incorrect storage	be sure to store discs, paper side down on flat surface	read instructions on package
	SANDED MITER NOT ACCURATE	misalignment	check out miter gauge	5
		work moved	hold work firmly—use Miter Gauge Safety Grip	265
	SANDED EDGE HAS SLIGHT BEVEL	misalignment	check out table	4
	INADEQUATE JOB ON METAL	wrong abrasive	use aluminum oxide or silicon carbide paper—not flint or garnet	256
	SANDING MARKS ON WORK	work held motionless	keep work moving	—
		paper too coarse for finish required	use very fine paper for final finish	256
		work sanded across grain	when surface sanding, use very fine paper—then finish by hand, working in grain direction	—

	DISC QUICKLY GLAZES	excessive speed	check speed setting	257
		sanding painted surface	use open-grain, flint paper	256
		wood is wet or gummy	no cure	—
	RAISED CIRCULAR AREA ON WORK	table low and work held against disc center	center of disc is "dead"—will only score unless work is moved across it	—
	WORK CHATTERS	inadequate support	provide maximum support for work as close to disc as possible	259
DRUM SANDING	ABRASIVES SLEEVE SLIPS OR MOVES OFF DRUM	loose sleeve	tighten nut to expand rubber drum	268
	SANDED EDGE NOT SQUARE	result of freehand sanding	hard to hold work square to drum—use table to provide alignment	268
		misalignment	check out table	4
	SLEEVE BURNS, CLOGS QUICKLY ON THICKNESS SANDING	biting too deep	adjust for slight abrasive action and make repeated passes	270
	INDENTATIONS IN WORK	work held motionless in one spot	keep drum or work moving	269
	SANDING DRUM DISTORTS	excessive bite or feed pressure	allow abrasive sleeve to cut freely—do not force	269
BELT SANDING	BELT MOVES TO EITHER SIDE OF DRUMS	belt not centered	adjust tracking nut	276
	BELT SLIPS, OR MOTOR STALLS	excessive feed pressure	hold work lightly against belt	277
		excessive speed	change speed setting	276
	INSIDE CURVE NOT SQUARE TO ADJACENT SURFACES	work held incorrectly	use extension fence	282
	WORK SCRATCHED OR OTHERWISE MARRED BY ABRASIVE	paper too coarse for final finish	change to finer abrasive	256
		sanding cross-grain will leave marks	finish by sanding with the grain	280
	WORK BURNS	feed pressure too great	never force work into belt	277
		excessive speed	change speed setting	276
	SANDED MITER NOT ACCURATE	misalignment	check angle of miter gauge to belt surface	6

8 THE SHAPER

How to use three-lip shaper cutters • drop-leaf joint shaping against the fence • shaping cross-grain stopped-edge shaping • slim moldings using the jointer head • shaping against collars special applications • trouble shooting

THE DIFFERENCE between a plain edge and a shaped one is often enough to lift an ordinary project to a professional plane.

The shaper provides an easy means of embellishing otherwise square, straight edges, but it also serves in the more functional capacities of forming edge and drawer joints, rabbeting, jointing, panel raising.

Shaping operations are not difficult to master and they are of tremendous value in producing quality projects and in increasing the variety of your output.

Efficient shaping can be done on the drill press, a basic and usually available machine, and shaping operations as they apply to it will be discussed. In fact, the operations as performed on the drill press rarely differ from the techniques used on a regular shaper.

The addition of a shaper fence, secured to the table with two U-shaped clamps and two cap screws, turns the multi-purpose tool into the efficient shaper on the left-hand page. Also available is a special shaper insert which, in addition to being used for freehand shaping of curved edges, should always be used with the shaper fence to provide maximum support for the work around the cutting tool.

The shaper fence can be used with the machine in either the vertical or horizontal position, whichever is more convenient for the job on hand. Both fence parts are adjustable endwise, so the opening for the cutters can be kept small for safety. The infeed fence is screw-adjusted for depth of cut.

There are three important things to remember when doing shaping operations: **speed; safety; sharp tools.**

The faster the speed (use speed between 4,000-5,000 rpm—between T and FAST on the Speed Dial) and the sharper the cutter, the smoother the cut. To work safely, follow these rules:

1. Work against the shaper fence whenever possible.
2. Try to have the cutting tool under the work at all times. (Some of the operations in this chapter show the cutting tool over the work to demonstrate the cut clearly. Many of them could be performed with the cutter under the work.)
3. Feed the work into and against the rotation of the cutting tool.
4. Keep your hands away from the cutting tool.
5. Keep the fingers of both hands hooked over the edges of the work to eliminate danger of slipping.
6. Never force the work; make passes with a slow, steady feed.
7. Use push sticks when necessary, and never let the hands pass above the cutter. On shaping operations there is always the danger that the wood may split under pressure and drop your hand into the blade.
8. Use the Universal Hold Down, especially on narrow work. Then your hands won't have to come too close to the cutting tool.
9. Follow each procedure as outlined.

It is not always possible to follow each and every rule. Some passes will require an exposed cutting tool. Be a little afraid of the machine, and work cautiously and slowly, especially when doing freehand shaping against collars. Working this way will not only keep your hands safe, but will also increase the quality of your output.

Addition of a shaper fence turns the drill press on the multi-purpose tool into an efficient shaper.

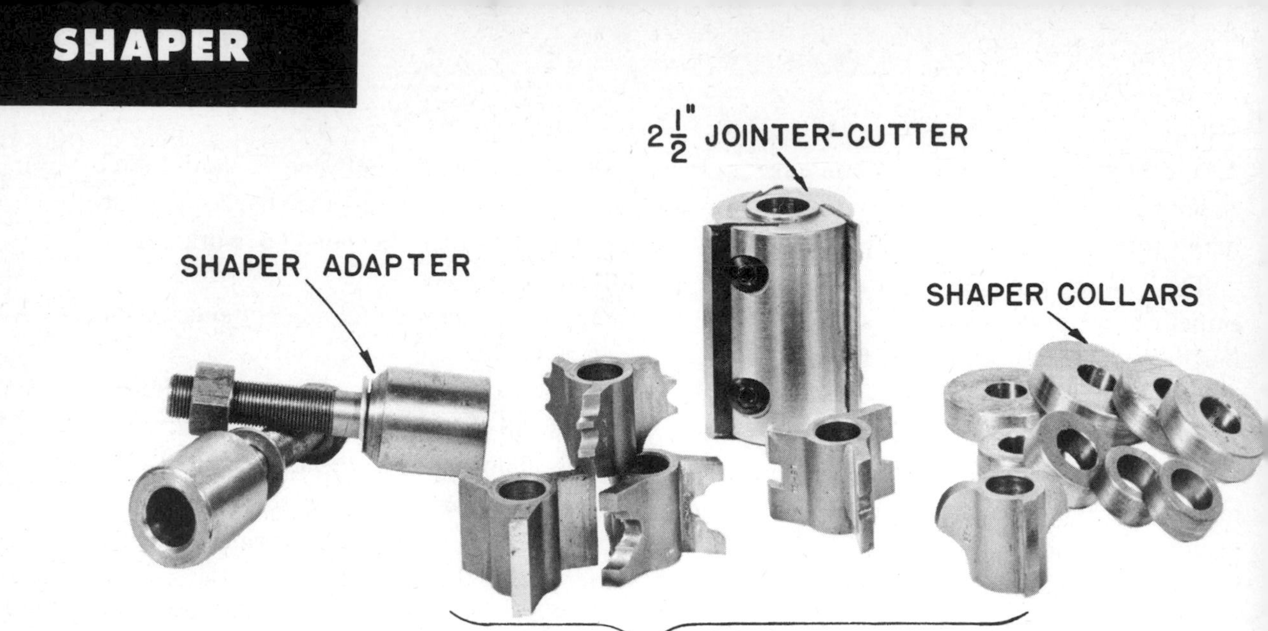

The three-lip shaper cutter is the safest and most practical shaper knife for the home workshop.

Listed here and illustrated in the chart below are some of the many shaper cutters available.

1. bead molding
2. crown molding
3. combination bead and quarter-round
4. ½″ and ¼″ quarter-round
5. groove cutter
6. tongue cutter
7. blank cutter (1″)
8. blank cutter (¼″)
9. bead and bevel
10. quarter-round and cove
11. glue joint—½″ and up
12. clover leaf
13. 3-bead and bevel
14. bead and cove
15. cabinet-door lip
16. drop-leaf joint cutters (set of 2)

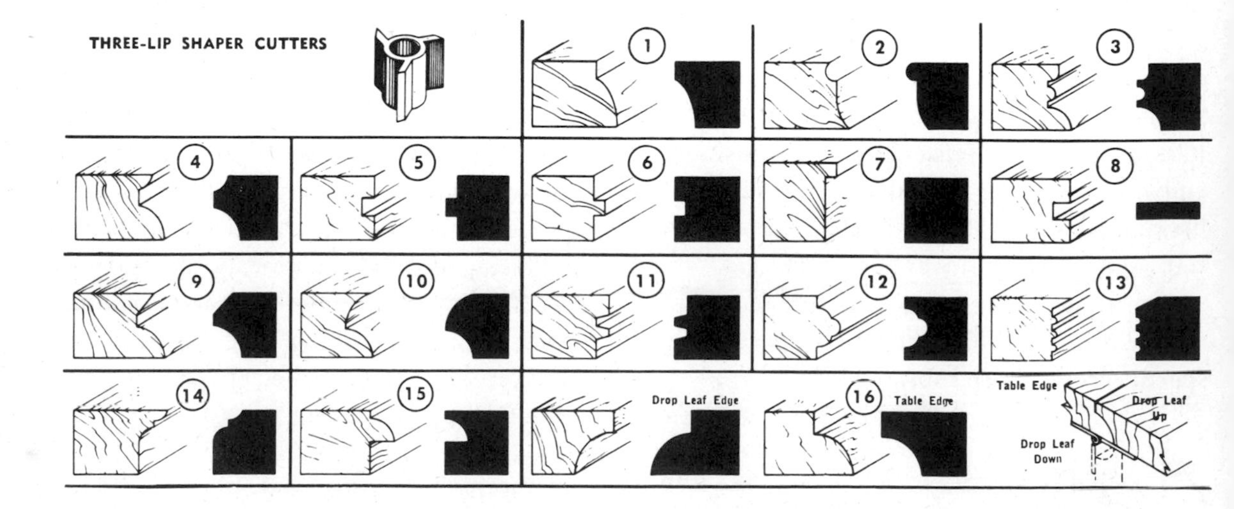

Three-Lip Shaper Cutters

Probably the safest and most practical type of shaper knife for home-workshop use is the three-lip shaper cutter shown in the drawings on the opposite page. It is available in various shapes to take care of almost every need.

Attempting to maintain a complete assortment of cutters can be expensive. A careful selection of from ten to twenty shapes, picked for value in the type of work you do, is adequate. With a basic assortment on hand, you can always add a new cutter as the need for it arises.

The shaper adapter is similar in construction to an arbor and is long enough to hold standard shaper cutters and collars. The adapter is secured to the spindle in the usual manner.

At the top of the opposite page you see a number of collars that mount on the shaper-adapter shaft for depth-of-cut control and for cutter spacing. The cutters and collars are secured to the adapter with a nut. Be sure the nut is tight before starting operation. Also shown is a jointer cutter head which can be used with the shaper fence to do many types of jointing operations.

When positioning for cutter height, make the major adjustment by raising or lowering the table. The final setting is made with the quill feed lever. On shaping operations, especially at high speeds and on hardwoods, quill extension should be held to a minimum.

It is not usually desirable to use the full shape of the cutter to form a molding. How most cutters are intended to be used partially is described and shown at the right.

A wide variety of shapes can be made by changing one or more of the following:

1. The depth of cut, which is adjusted by moving the table or the fence, or by using collars.
2. The height of the cutter in relation to the work, which is controlled by the table or the quill feed lever.

Many operators make the mistake of using the entire face of the cutter to form a molding, thinking that the full profile is the shape the cutter was intended for. This is true in some cases, but more often than not the cutter is to be used partially, with a single pass to make the cut—or a series of passes, with the cutter reset after each one.

For example, in the photograph above a combination cove and quarter-round cutter is rounding off the top edge of a piece of stock. Below, the same cutter, after being reset, is making a cove cut.

With some slight variations in the setting of the fence, the cutter, the table, or the collars, the same three-lip shaper cutter will shape an unlimited variety of forms.

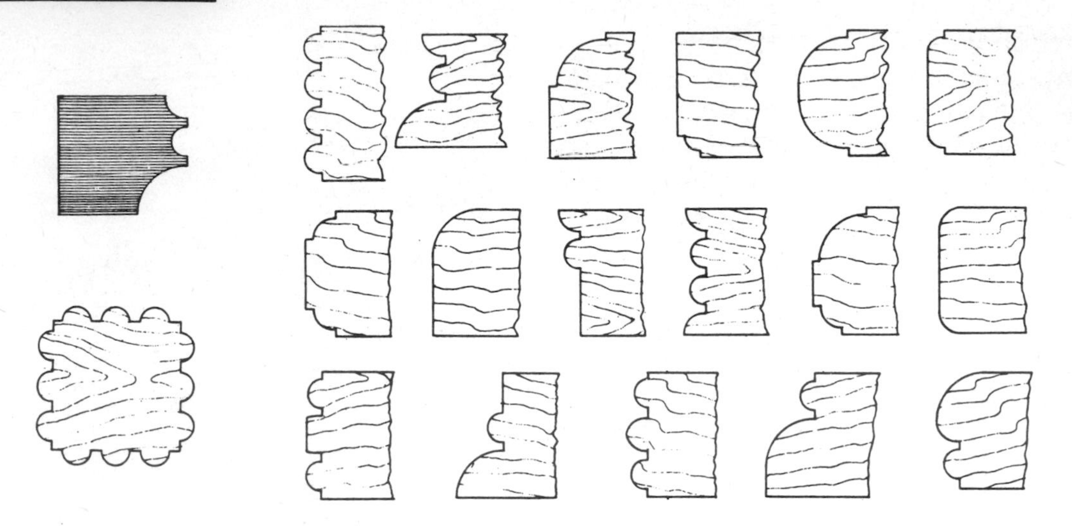

These shapes are typical of the variety of cuts obtainable with a single combination cutter. This one is a combination bead and quarter-round.

3. The position of the work when making the pass.

The pictures above and below show a few possibilities formed on a single cutter, in this case a combination cutter that can be used to shape a bead or two sizes of quarter-round. Some of the shapes were cut in a single pass, others required two or more passes, but the same cutter was used every time.

The important thing to remember is that not all cutters are intended to cut their full profile shape, even though they can be used that way. Most of them are combination cutters.

Collars come in various sizes and are used to control the depth of cut and also as spacers to position the cutter. As shown in the drawing above, they may be set over or under the cutter or between two cutters. They should be kept clean and should be carefully stored.

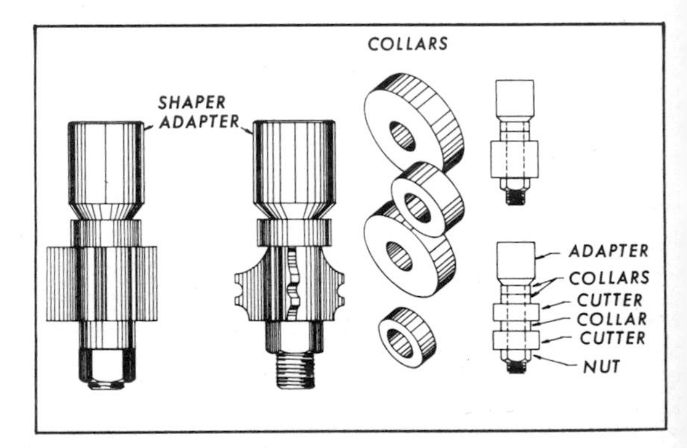

Collars may be used above, below, or between cutters to control the depth of the cut.

This cutter produces all these shapes, depending on its position, height, depth of cut.

How to Shape a Drop-Leaf Joint

This popular joint is used to extend the size of a table by means of drop leaves hinged to a fixed center section. Usually there are two leaves and one center section.

The drop-leaf joint, or rule joint, as it is sometimes called, is preferred over a simple butt joint because of its neater appearance.

With a set of special cutters, it is possible to shape the mating forms on both the table edge and the drop leaf.

The shoulder does not have to be as wide as it is on the cutter; this will be dictated by the thickness of the table top and controlled by the height of the cutter when making the pass.

The full radius, however, should be cut, since this determines the appearance of the joint when the leaf is up.

The shape of the joint is diagrammed below. How the table edge is shaped with one cutter is shown in the photograph at the upper right. Shaping the leaf edge with its mating cutter is shown at right below.

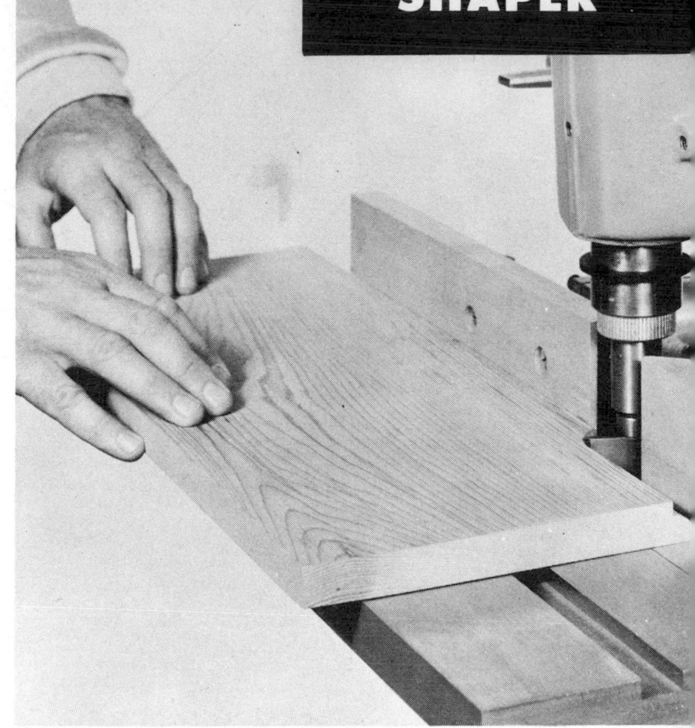

The table-edge shape is formed with one cutter; let the width of shoulder be determined by the thickness of the table top you're making.

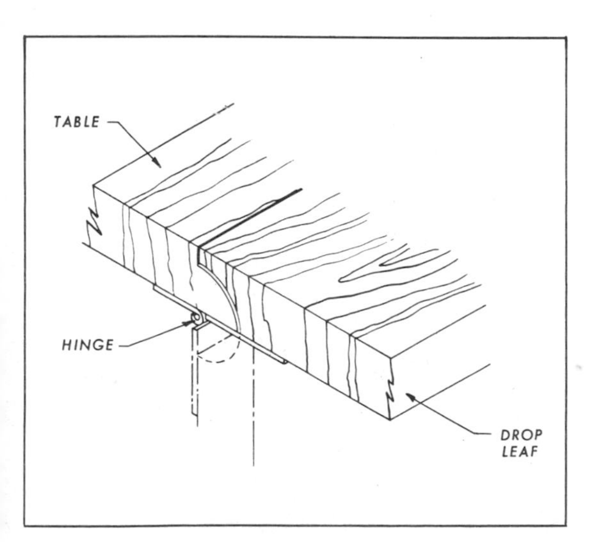

The popular drop-leaf joint is used to extend the size of a table by means of drop leaves hinged to a fixed center section.

The drop-leaf edge shape is formed with the mating cutter. Make test cuts on scrap wood before shaping the project itself.

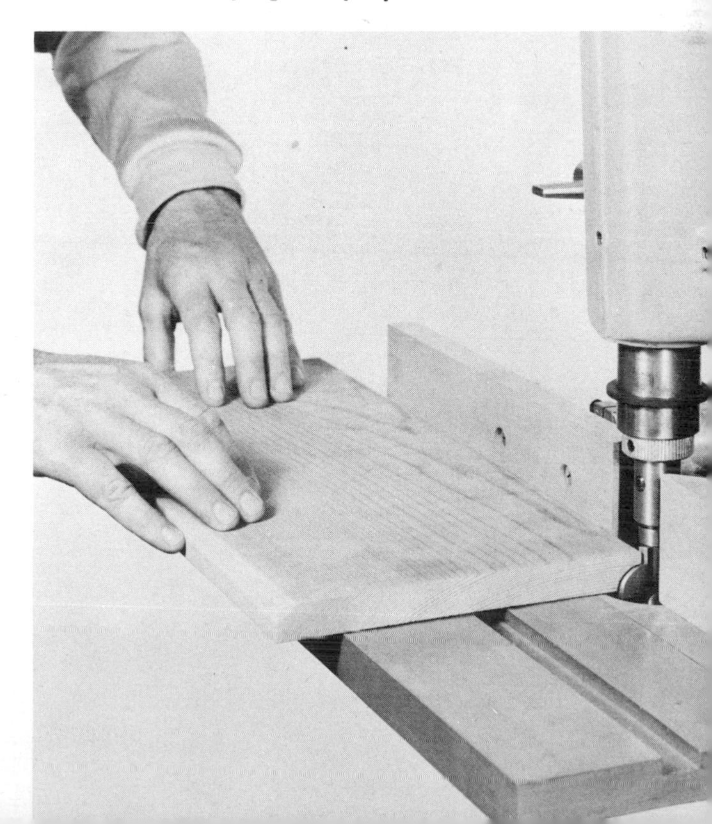

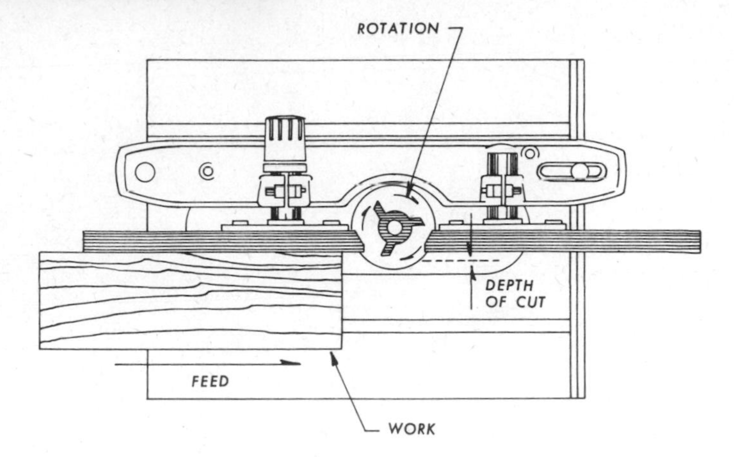

WITH FENCES IN LINE, CUT REMOVES PART OF WORK EDGE

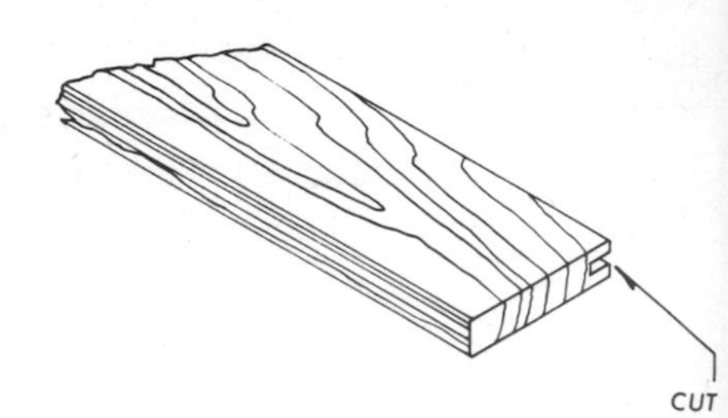

WRONG!

WHEN ENTIRE EDGE OF STOCK IS REMOVED, OUTFEED FENCE IS ADJUSTED TO PROVIDE SUPPORT AFTER WORK HAS PASSED CUTTER

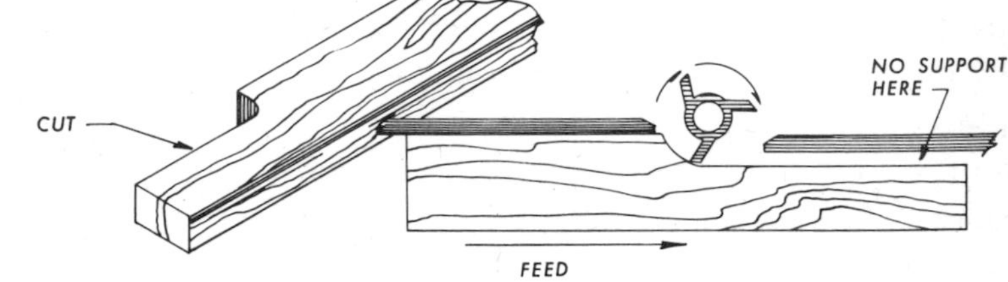

WORK SUPPORTED HERE AFTER CUT IS MADE

FENCE MOVED BACK

CUT

RIGHT!

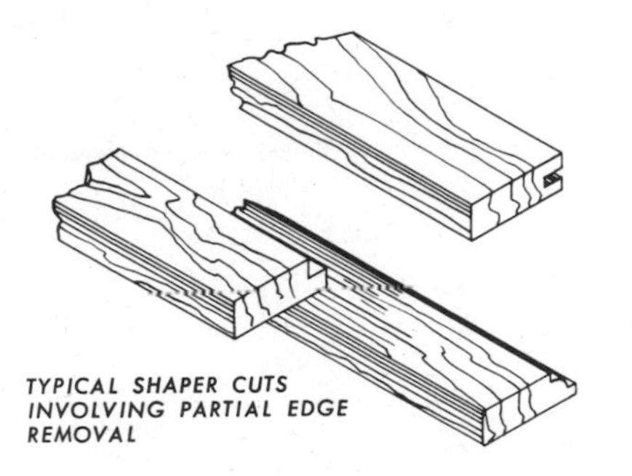

TYPICAL SHAPER CUTS INVOLVING PARTIAL EDGE REMOVAL

TYPICAL SHAPER CUTS INVOLVING ENTIRE EDGE REMOVAL

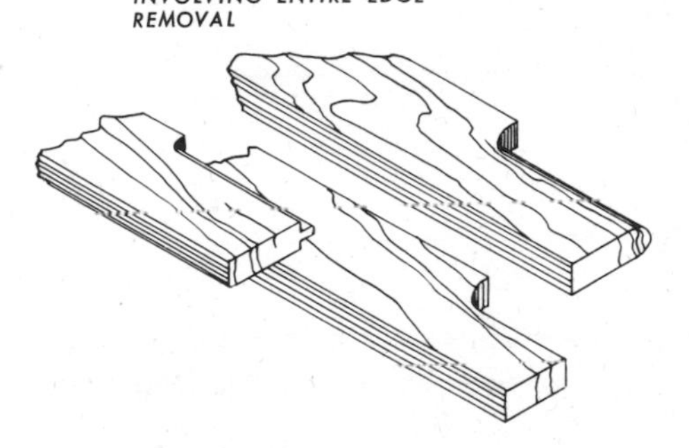

This is a good technique when width of stock permits. Mortising hold-down adds safety.

Shaper fence and horizontal position give a good setup for shaping edges on very wide stock.

Shaping Against the Fence

Shaping against a fence (shown in the drawings on opposite page) is the safest and most satisfactory method of operating. It should be practiced whenever the work permits.

Study of the drawing will reveal two important points:

1. When the cut being made does not require removal of wood from the entire edge of the workpiece, the front and rear shaper fences are kept in perfect alignment.

2. When the entire edge of the stock is removed, the front fence is adjusted for depth of cut. The work then receives full support from the fences, both before and after the cut.

After the cutter and fences have been set, the work is placed against the front fence and moved forward against the cutter.

Never force a shaping cut, and always try to keep the fingers hooked against the sides of the work for safety.

An excellent method of making straight shaping cuts on the multi-purpose tool is shown above. The rip fence has been set to the width of the work, and the mortising hold-down has been set to the thickness.

If the hands are used as shown, the operation is conducted with perfect safety and maximum accuracy. The last inch or two of stock can be pushed through with a slim push stick which will slide under the hold-down.

The shaper fence may also be used with the machine in its horizontal position shown above. This setup will prove more convenient for some types of work, but remember to keep the hands from working directly over the cutters.

Shown below is a cut involving partial shaping of the edge. Both fences are in line, and the stock has bearing surface—both before and after the cut.

Shaping against the fence: always adjust fences to provide support before and after the cut. Alignment of fences determines whether entire edge of stock is removed —or only part of it.

The two fences are placed on the same plane when only part of the edge is being removed.

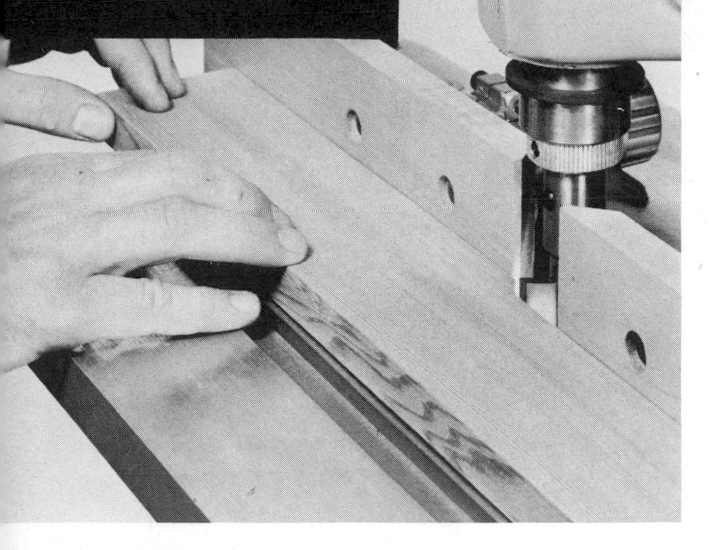

This is typical of operations requiring offset alignment of fence. Blank cutter is removing entire edge. Work is placed against front fence and advanced into cutter. The new face that's on edge of stock after the cut will then ride the rear fence, receiving firm support.

A typical operation requiring a fence adjustment is shown at the left. A blank blade (sometimes called a planer blade) is removing the entire edge of the stock. With the setting made so that the rear fence is tangent to the cutting circle of the blade, the front fence is set back for the depth of cut.

Some shapes are attained by making two or three passes on a standard cutter, repositioning the work and the cutter after the first pass to provide the additional cut that completes the form. The photograph below shows the first pass being made to start the form which is being completed with a second pass in the picture at the bottom of the next page.

Operations like this are best handled by first sketching the shape required on the edge of the stock, then selecting cutters that

This first of two passes with a combination cutter to produce bead-and-cove molding . . . .

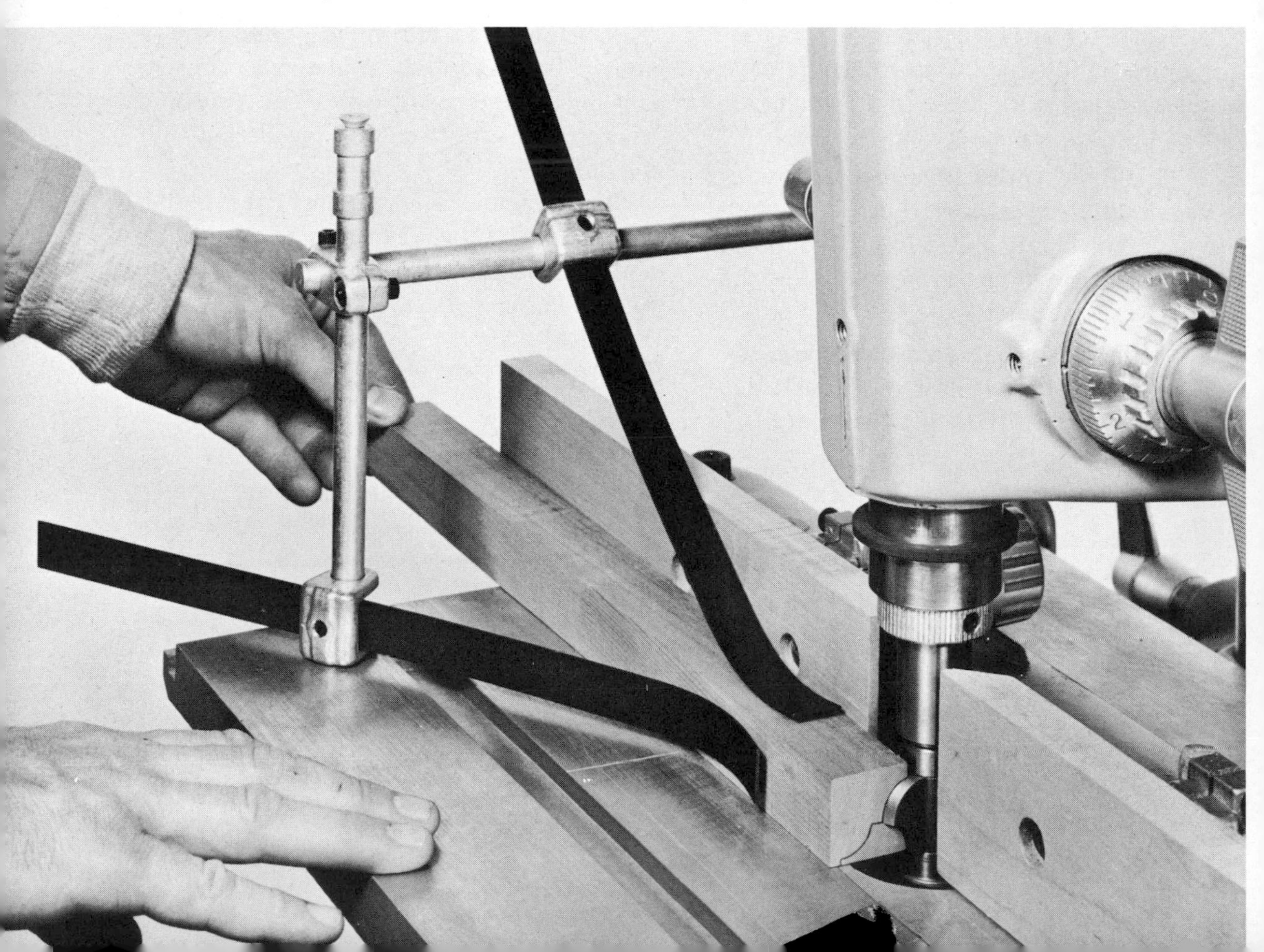

will fit the contours of the form. The shape shown required two passes on the same cutter. Other shapes may require more passes and with different cutters.

When it is necessary to work with slim pieces, use a spring stick, hold-downs, or the molding-jig setup shown on page 297.

The big difference between a regular shaper and a drill-press shaper is that the spindle on the latter is over the table. This will not interfere with most work, although surface cuts on unusually large pieces will occasionally be limited by contact with the quill or top of the adapter. Surface cuts—within limits of the setup—can be made with the shaper fence in the conventional manner, while end-surface cuts, such as for a drawer joint, can be made with the machine in a horizontal position.

A certain amount of surface-shaping is possible when the drill press is used as a shaper. The headstock position over the table limits width of work, however. Here reeds are being cut on the surface of a piece by successive passes with a combination cutter.

. . . is followed by this second pass to complete it. The Universal Hold Down makes the job safe.

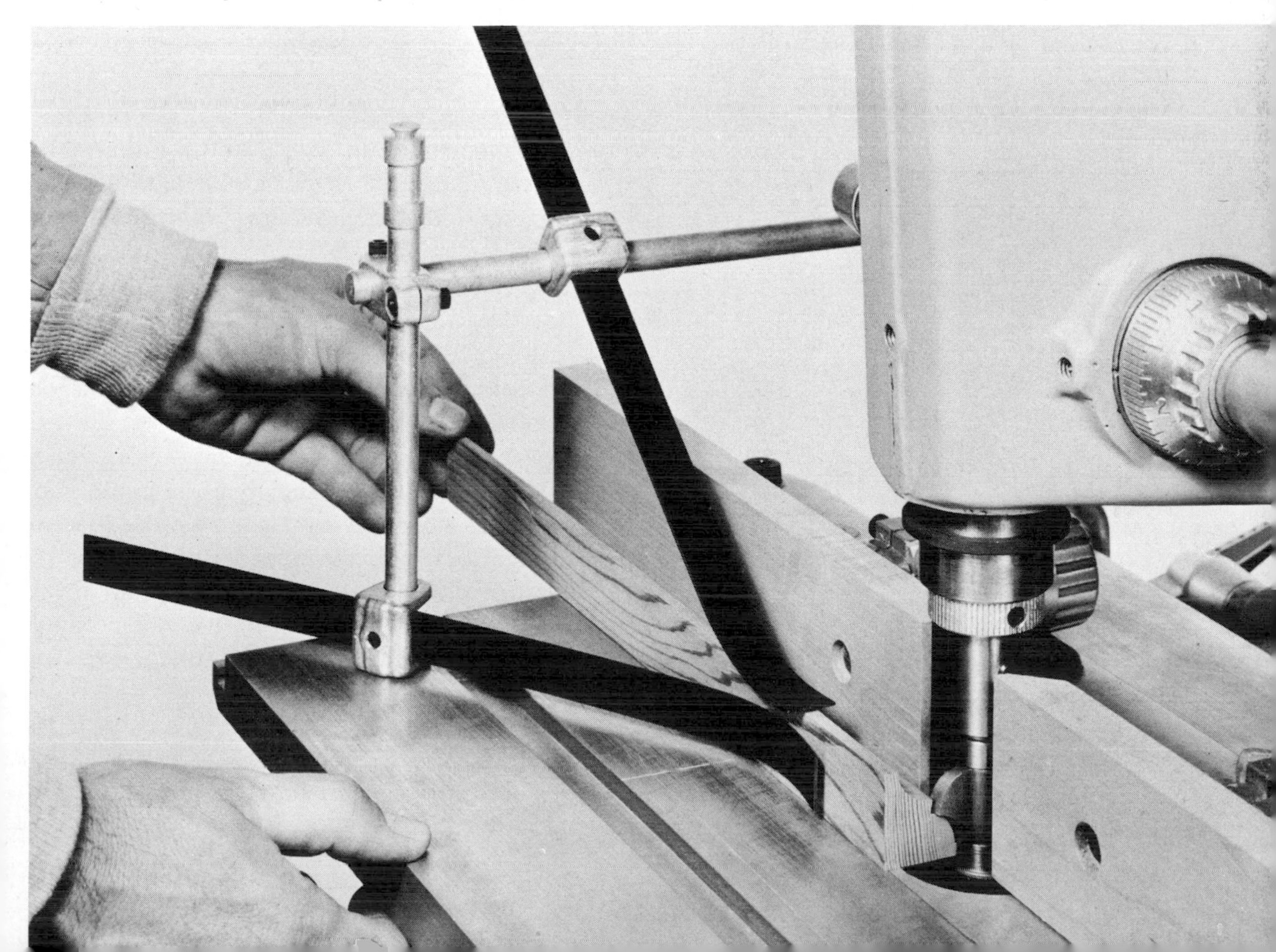

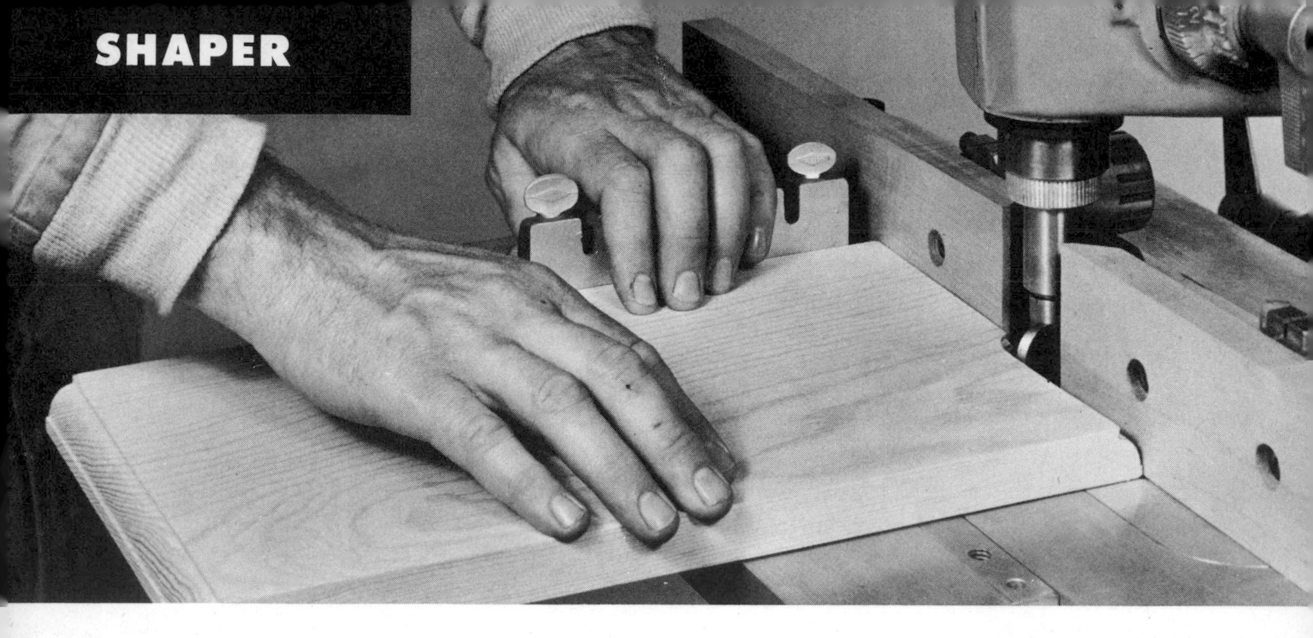

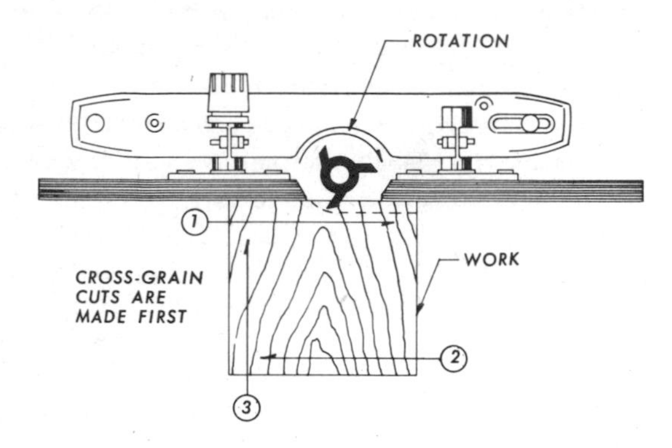

Above: Use the miter gauge when shaping cross-grain. Keep your hands away from the cutter.

Left: Always make cross-grain cuts first.

Below: A Miter Gauge Safety Grip helps.

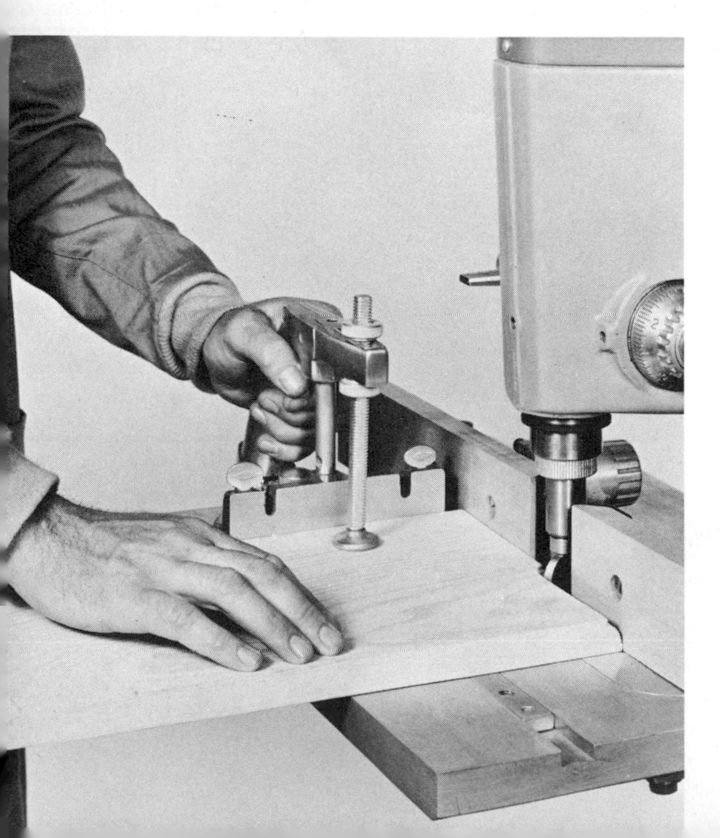

Shaping Cross-Grain

Whenever possible, shaping cuts should be made with the grain of the wood. However, when "returning" moldings, or when shaping pieces on four sides (table tops, door frames) the first cut is always across the grain, as diagrammed at the left. The cuts that follow are made so that the last cut is in the direction of the grain.

Shaping cross-grain is always harder. Use a slow feed and in making deep cuts take two or more bites, adjusting the cutter after each pass until the full depth of cut is obtained.

The best way to handle cross-grain cuts is to use the miter gauge as in the photograph above. Keep the right hand on the forward edge to secure the work firmly against the miter-gauge head. The left hand, with fingers hooked over the head of the miter gauge, keeps the work flat on the table and feeds it forward.

A Miter Gauge Safety Grip, used as at the left, is very useful on such work. The left hand is on the grip, the right hand as before.

Stopped-Edge Shaping

Stop blocks, which can be clamps, are used on the fence to limit the length of a cut, as shown at right. Place the end of the work against the forward stop and then move it slowly into the cutter until the edge of the work rides on the fence. Then make the pass, continuing until the front of the work hits the rear stop.

Slim Moldings

Don't feed thin strips freehand against the cutters. Handle them as shown in the middle photograph. The combination guide and hold-down consists of a piece of stock equal in thickness to the material being worked, and a second piece secured to the first. The bottom piece is placed so the cut strips pass between it and the shaper fence; the top piece extends over it and butts against the fence. This is a good setup for a quantity of similar pieces. If all you need is a single piece, shape the form on a board wide enough to handle safely. Then cut off the shaped edge on the table saw.

Using the Jointer Head

The cutter head at lower right is a useful accessory for light jointing operations. It is secured to the spindle with two set screws. When cutting, the rear fence is set tangent to the cutting circle of the cutter head. The front fence is adjusted for depth of cut, usually not more than ⅛″.

Make the pass slowly and keep the work firmly on the table. Whenever possible, keep your fingers hooked against the sides of the work, use the rip fence and mortising hold-down, and pass the work between the shaper fence and the rip fence.

Rabbeting operations are accomplished by setting the cutter head above the table.

Use stop blocks to limit the shaping cut.

This combination guide and hold-down can be used when shaping quantities of slim pieces.

The jointer head can be used in the horizontal position too, and on heavier stock this is usually more convenient.

This 2½″ cutter head is used with the shaper fence for edging and rabbeting operations.

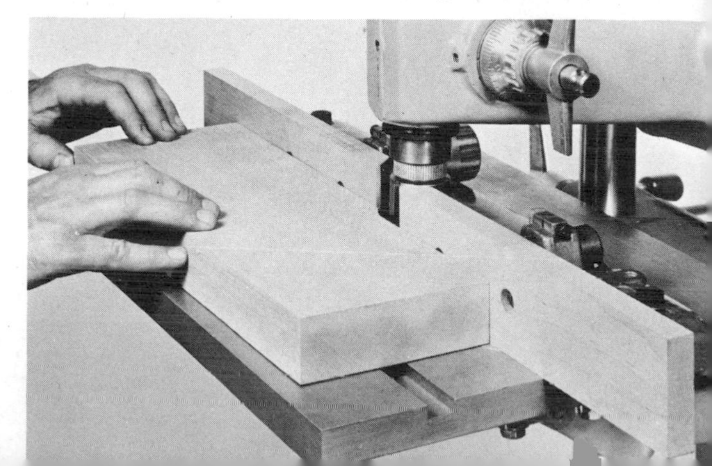

Freehand shaping of curved edges calls for a shaper insert with pins to start cut against.

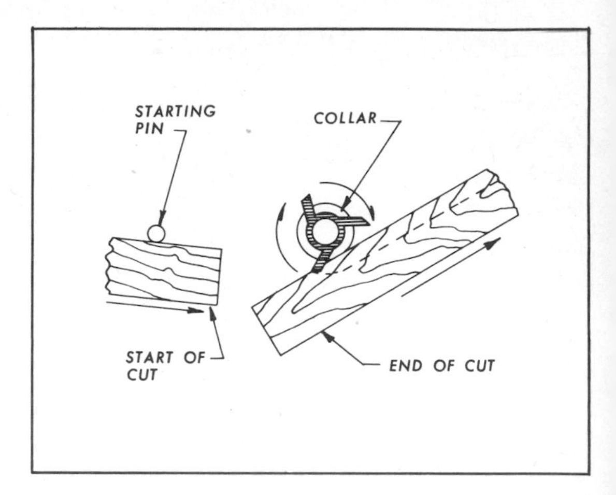

Fulcrum pin provides support so work engages cutter without danger of being kicked back.

Shaping Against Collars

Work that is circular or has irregular curves should not be handled against the shaper fence. Collars are used to control the depth of cut and to provide a surface against which a portion of the edge being shaped can ride.

The collars should be clean and true and free of gum, dirt, or dust. They should be inspected frequently and cleaned with a stiff brush and turpentine or some similar solvent. They may be used above or below the cutter or between two cutters, the last being convenient when it is necessary to shape both edges of a piece.

The cutters may function over or under the work. When they are used over the work the cut is easily seen. This makes it easier to control the operation, but if the work is not kept flat on the table the cutter will dig in and spoil the job. Also, an exposed cutter increases the danger.

Cutters used under the work are safest, and slight accidental lifting of the job as the cut progresses will do no harm. The cut cannot be seen, but careful passes will produce satisfactory results.

One danger point in working against collars is the initial contact of the work with the cutter. If moved into the cutter without support, the work will inevitably be kicked back into the operator's hands. To overcome this the shaper insert shown at upper left should be used in the table opening. It supplies support area adjacent to the cutter and is a means of securing starting pins or fulcrums to the table; these are needed when advancing the work to make the initial contact.

To begin the cut, use the starting pin to support the work so it may be advanced to engage the cutter without danger of being kicked back (above). With the work resting on the pin, advance it along an imaginary line through the side of the pin and the edge of the collar. After the cutter is engaged and the cut well started, the work may be swung free of the pin to ride against the collar only.

Inside cuts on circular work are handled as shown in the sketch at upper left on the next page. The table is lowered and the work placed under the spindle and against the starting pin. Then the table is raised to an approximate position and the final adjustment for height of cutter made with the quill. Hold the work firmly against the pin and move it slowly to engage the cutter. Revolve

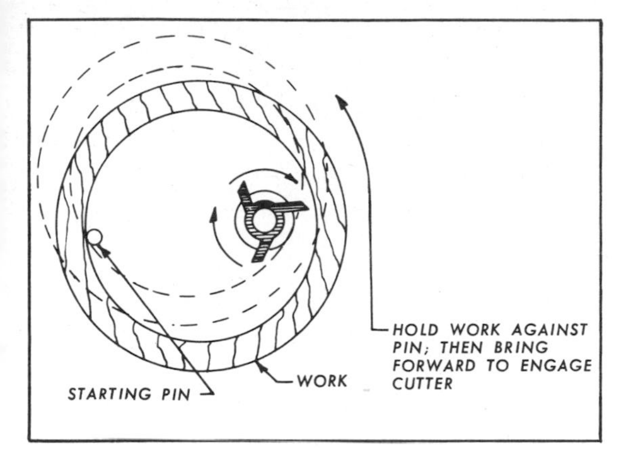

The inside edges of circular cutouts may be shaped freehand, as shown here.

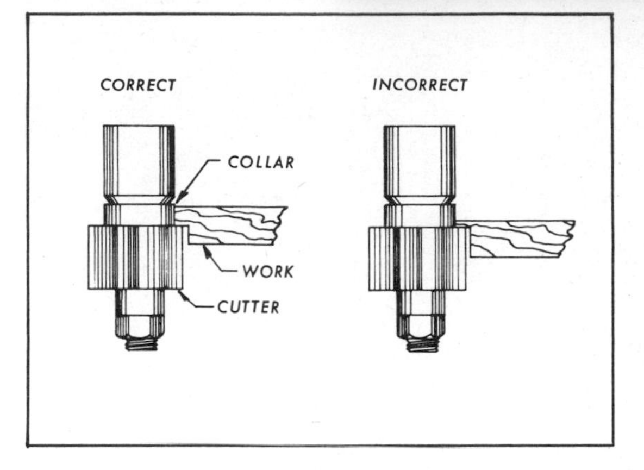

When shaping against collars, always check to be sure the work has enough bearing surface.

it around the cutter to complete the pass. On this type of work, the entire pass can be made with the work riding both the starting pin and the collars. Or (as with a straight or curved piece) the work can be removed from the starting pin after the cut is started.

It is difficult to obtain maximum protection on operations of this nature. Therefore always proceed with great caution, making the pass slowly and feeding steadily. Never use the hands directly in front of the cutter. Place them on the outside of the work, away from the cutting tool, so that if they do slip they will move harmlessly past the cutting tool.

There are two factors to remember when shaping against collars:

1. Make certain that the work will have enough surface bearing against the collars (above).

2. Never attempt to shape work that does not have enough body for the hands to hold onto, unless a special setup is made. As shown below, when single slim moldings are needed, shape the edge on a wider piece, cut to the curve required, and then cut off the shaped edge on the jig saw or table saw.

Shown on the next page are four types of operations that call for working against collars.

When a very narrow piece of molding is required, play safe by using the method sketched below.

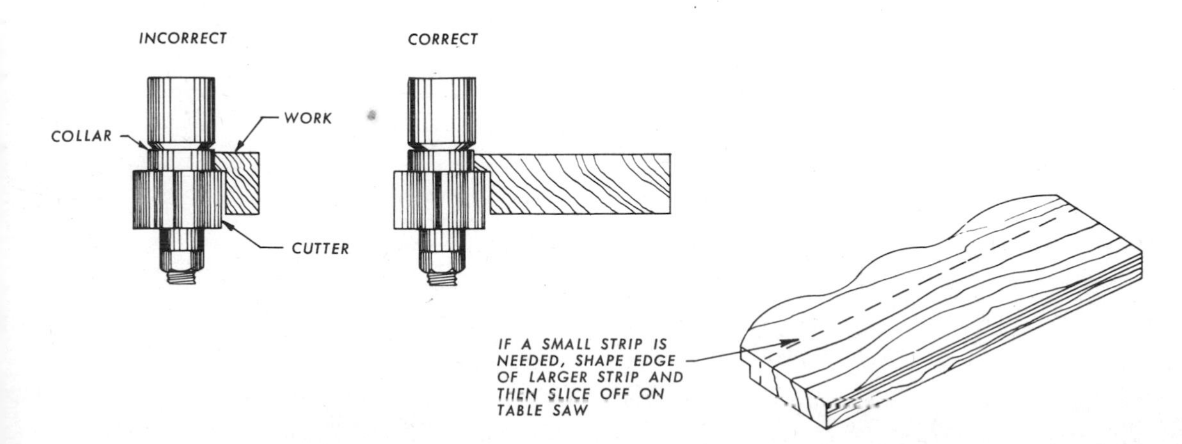

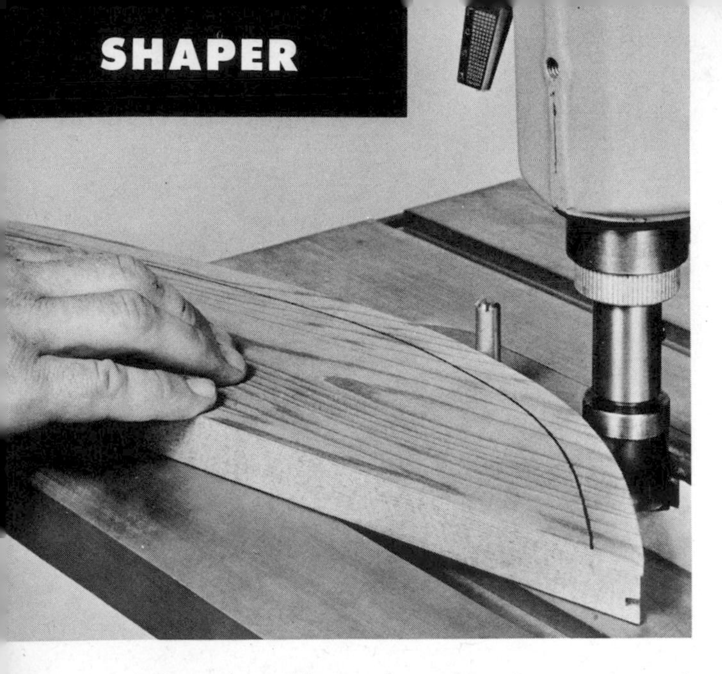

Curved moldings that must fit contours of furniture and cabinetwork are shaped after the curve has been cut on the jig saw (or band saw) and sanded square and smooth. The edge is shaped as shown, then cut off on the jig saw.

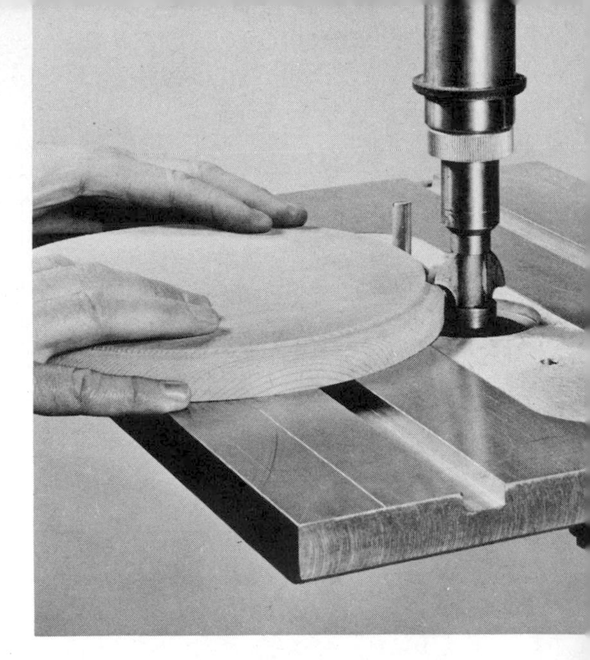

When shaping the edge of a circular piece, be sure to rest it solidly against the fulcrum pin first. Advance it slowly to engage the cutter. Then revolve it to complete the pass. To do this, rest the work on the pin as the cut progresses; or swing it clear of the pin after the cut is started and rest it against the collar only.

Work with irregular edges, such as fancy picture frames, wall plaques, and free-form table tops, is also shaped against collars. Start the cut, then swing the work clear of the starting pin to complete the pass. Work slowly and carefully, especially on corners. Keep the work bearing constantly against the collar, turning it to keep as much of it as possible between you and the cutting tool. Keep hands away from cutters.

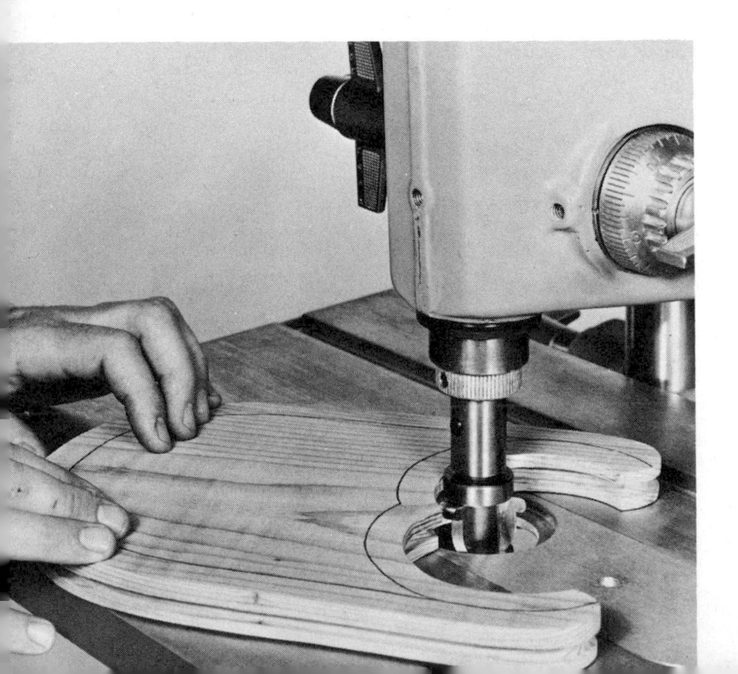

A rabbet for glass, often required inside a circular picture frame, can be formed as shown here. Place work in position, then extend the quill to depth of cut necessary. The height of the cutter determines the depth of the rabbet. The collar controls the width.

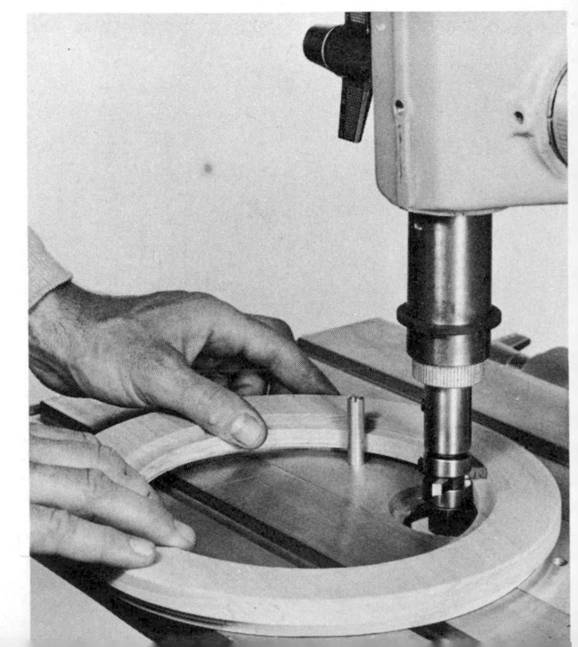

Special Applications

For production runs on specially shaped pieces, it is a good idea to create a setup that will increase safety and accuracy.

Jigs of the type sketched at the right are not needed except when the quantity of work is large.

All the jigs shown here are cut to shape on the jig saw and clamped to the regular table to serve as guides for the work. Quite often it is possible to use the scrap material from a cut piece as the guide. The scrap piece from a circular cutout, for example, would make a good guide for shaping the edge of a circle.

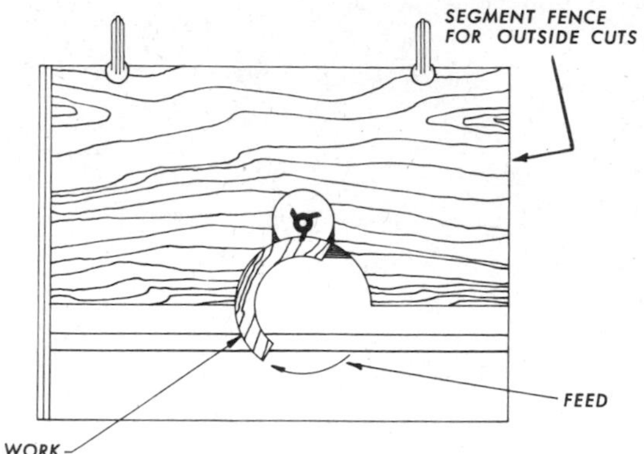

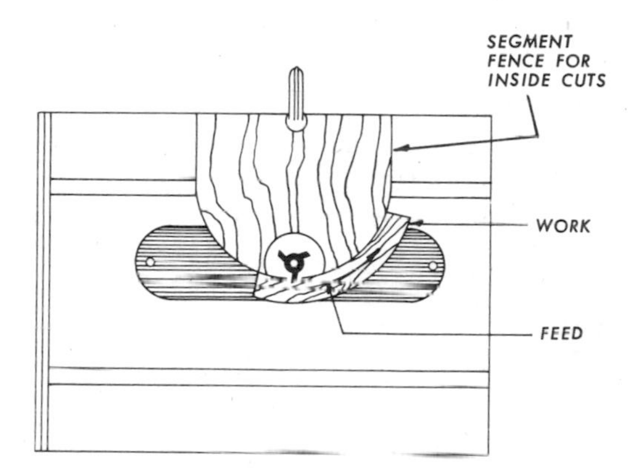

When shaping many duplicate pieces, it's good shop practice to create a special setup like the three sketched at the right.

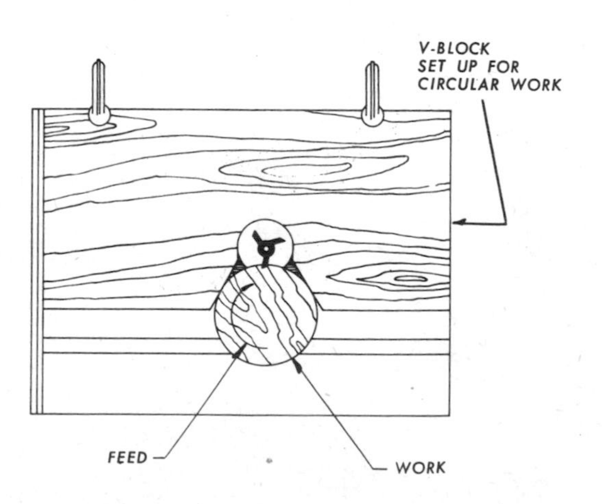

When it is possible to tilt the table, as it is with the multi-purpose tool, even bevel cuts can be made on a shaper. Use the arrangement shown below to form a tongue on a cross-bevel cut to engage a groove on a mating piece. Hold the work firmly against the miter gauge, and make the pass slowly.

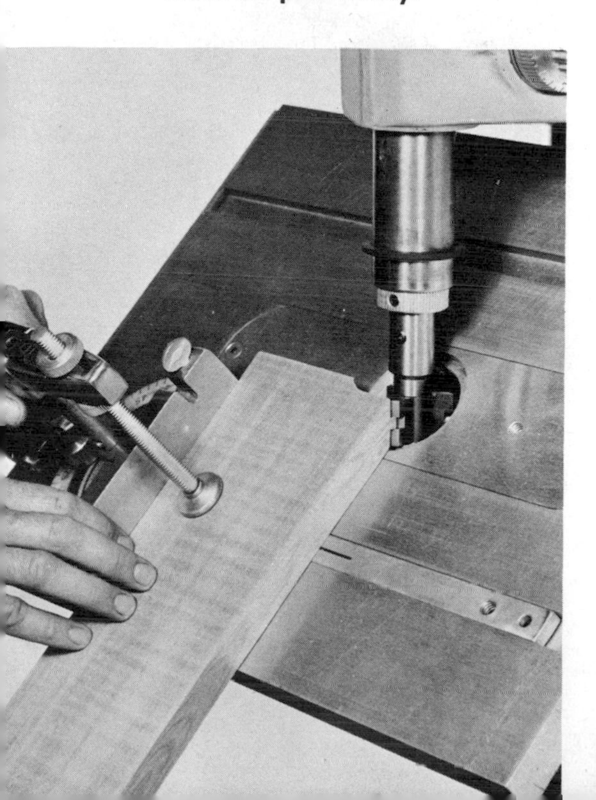

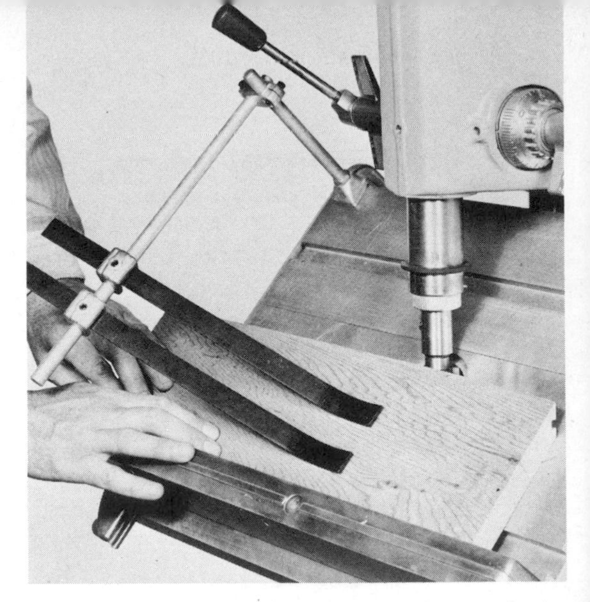

A tongue-and groove joint may be used in place of a spline for joining rip-bevel cuts. The tongue is formed as shown in the photograph above, and . . .

. . . the groove is formed like this with the mating cutter. Operations of this nature require very accurate settings. Trial cuts are recommended.

When it is necessary to surface-shape the end of a piece, as when forming a drawer joint, the machine can be used in a horizontal position. Advance the table as far forward as you can without touching the adapter. Set table height for depth of cut and the rip fence to position work for the pass. Hold the work firmly down on the table and against the miter gauge.

Make the pass slowly; if the cut is deep, complete it in two or more passes, adjusting the height of the table after making each pass.

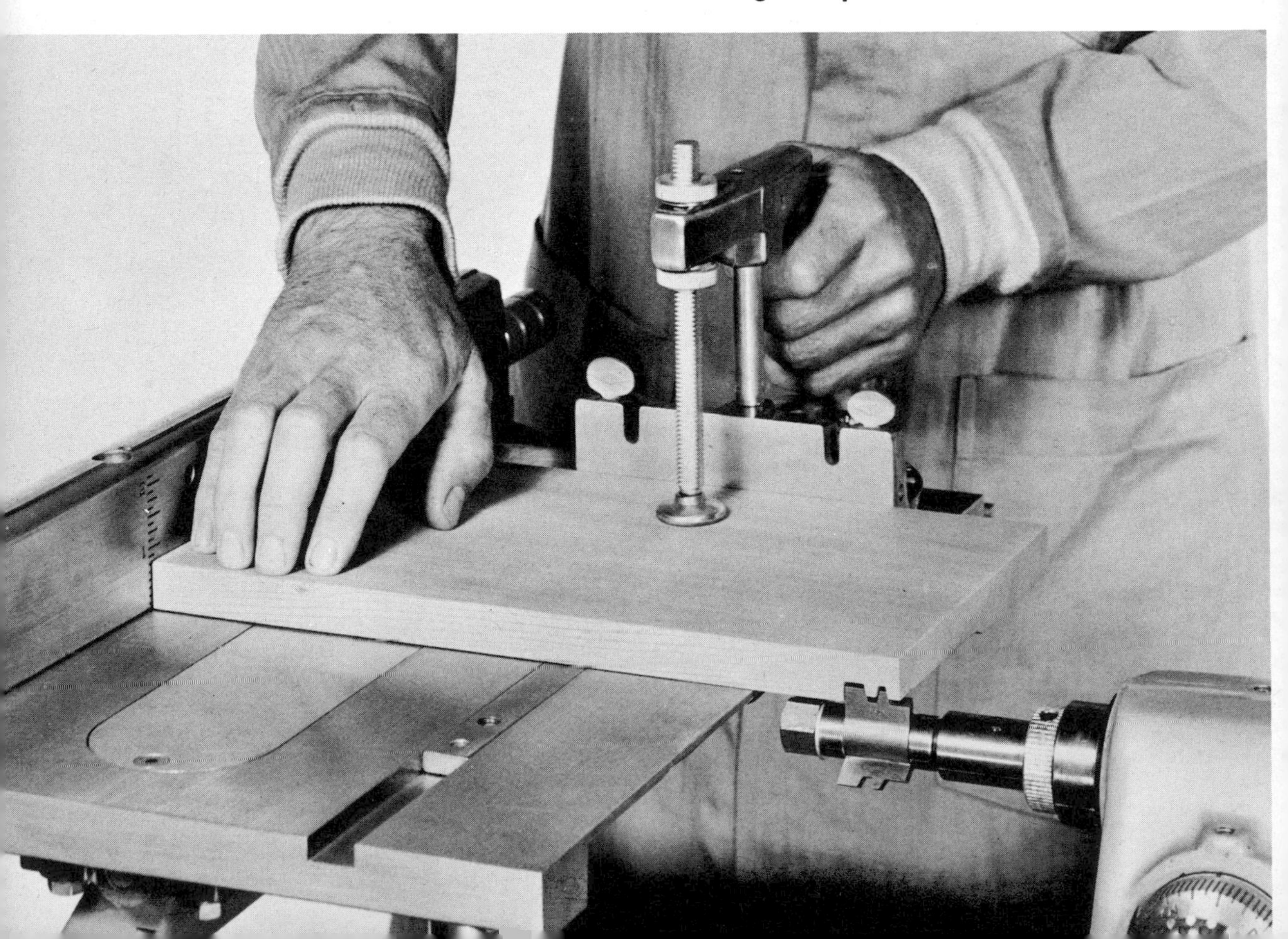

TROUBLE-SHOOTING CHART FOR THE SHAPER

THE TROUBLE	POSSIBLE CAUSES	THE CURE	SEE PAGE
VARIATION IN HEIGHT OF CUT	variation in pressure which holds work down on table	keep pressure firm throughout pass	293
		use hold-downs	294
		make pass slowly and steadily	287
		whenever possible keep cutter under work	287
RAISED AREAS ON SHAPED EDGE	variation in pressure which holds work against cutter	keep work firm against fence or collars throughout pass	293
		use hold-downs	294
NO SUPPORT FROM OUTFEED FENCE EDGE GOUGED AT ONE POINT	misalignment	when removing entire edge, be sure outfeed fence is tangent to cutting circle	292
CUTS NOT SMOOTH	wrong rpm	use faster speed	287
	feeding too fast	slow up pass	287
	working against grain	work with grain whenever possible	296
	dull cutter	sharpen cutter by honing flat side	333
	cutting too deep	on very deep cuts make several passes	296
WORK KICKS BACK AT START OF CUT	no support	use fulcrum pins to start cut when shaping freehand; hold work firmly against fence	298
WORK PULLED FROM HAND	feeding wrong way	always feed against direction of rotation of cutting tool	292
DEPTH OF CUT NOT UNIFORM	misalignment	adjust outfeed fence	292
	side pressure not uniform	use hold-downs; keep pressure against fence or collars consistent	295
WORK BURNS	cutting too deep	on hardwoods take light cuts; attain full depth of cut with several passes	296
	forcing work	feed slowly and steadily	287
	dull cutter	sharpen by honing on flat side	333
COLLARS MARKING WORK	collars dirty or gummed up with pitch	clean with brush and turpentine; keep smooth and store carefully	298
EDGE SPLITS OFF ON CROSS-GRAIN CUT	characteristic of cut	make cross-grain cuts first, then finish with grain	296
		use scrap block to support at end of cut	—

9 SPRAY FINISHING

The compressor • spray gun • air caps • hose preparation and thinning • gun handling • stroking the gun triggering • spraying round objects • broad surfaces • corners flat work • using extra containers • cleaning the gun • masking and shielding • stenciling • more uses for your sprayer • trouble shooting

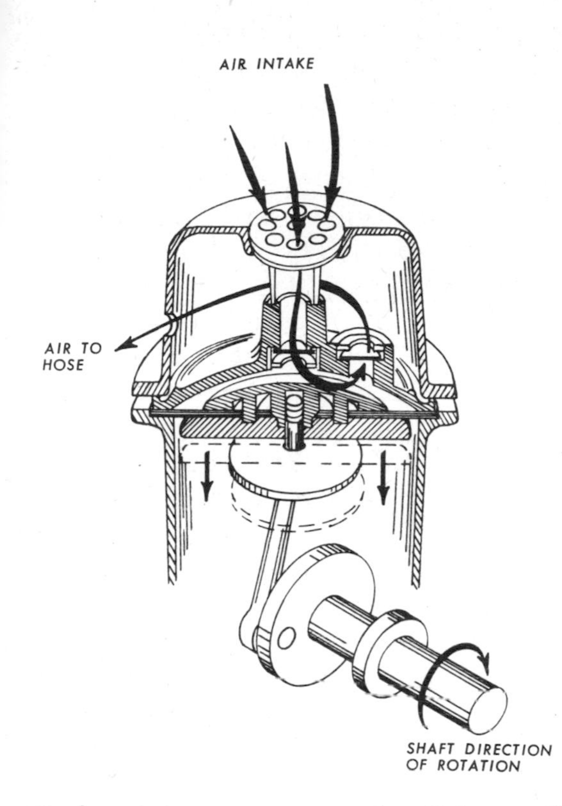

Diaphragm-type compressor is efficient, will deliver oil-free air. Air-intake filter should be checked frequently, replaced when clogged.

This gun has an attached fluid cup and is a combination type, easily set up to do either internal-mix or external-mix spraying.

A POWER SPRAYER will reduce the time and effort required to produce the lasting and professional finish your workshop projects deserve.

A sprayer is not difficult to use. You will be amazed at the speed with which you can spray-finish the largest projects. The difference between a sprayed finish and a hand-brushed one will be immediately obvious and amply rewarding.

A sprayer consists of three parts: compressor, hose, and spray gun.

The compressor, which is motor driven, delivers air through the hose to the spray gun. Here the air picks up the fluid, atomizes it, and sprays it on the work.

The diaphragm-type compressor (sketch above) is a good choice for the home craftsman, since it is simple and does not require an oil bath. This compressor develops air pressure through the reciprocating action of a flexible disc—the diaphragm—which is actuated by an eccentric. The diaphragm is usually made of rubber and does wear. Replacement, however, is quite simple and is required only after many hours of use.

To be capable of handling all the materials you will want to spray, a compressor should have an air displacement of 4 cfm (cubic feet per minute) and should deliver 2.4 cfm of air at the gun.

The spray gun (photograph above) is a tool that uses the air delivered by the compressor to atomize the finishing material and to eject both air and fluid in a pattern controlled by the air cap. Air and fluid enter the gun

Paint-spraying outfit includes gun, hose, and (in right foreground) the compressor.

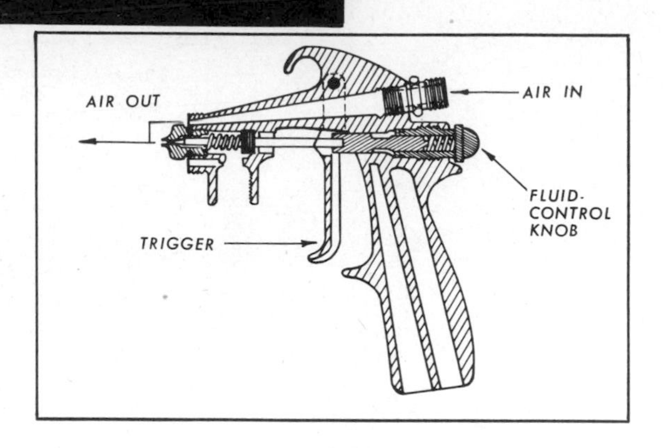

Here is how a bleeder-type gun works.

through separate passages and, after being mixed, are sprayed out through the air cap.

The best kind of gun for the home craftsman is one with an attached fluid cup. It should be a bleeder type, one on which the gun trigger controls fluid flow only, as sketched above. The compressed air continues to pass through the gun, whether or not it is being triggered. This prevents pressure build-up in the lines.

When the gun is set up for siphon feed (external-mix), air passing through the gun creates a vacuum so that atmospheric pressure pushes the fluid up the tube.

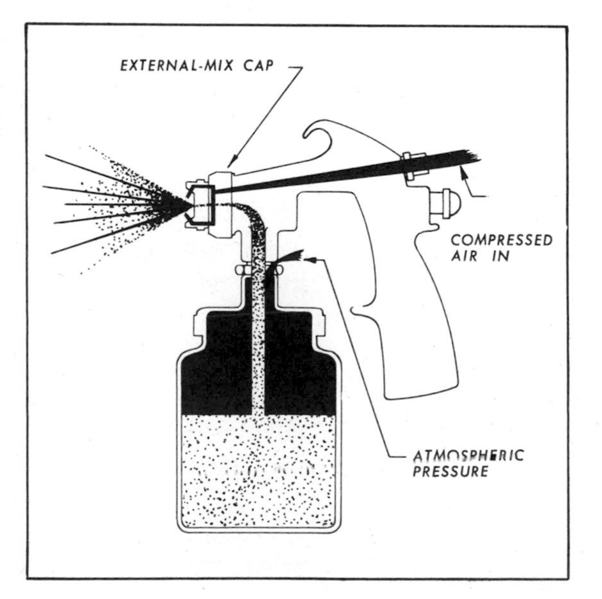

(The non-bleeder gun is equipped with an air valve that shuts off air flow as the fluid is stopped. With this type of gun, special equipment is required to control pressure in the compressed-air-supply system.)

The gun may be a siphon-feed type or a pressure-feed type. In the former (drawing at left, below), air does not enter the cup but passes over it to create a vacuum so that atmospheric pressure forces material from cup to gun. The siphon feed is used with an **external-mix** air cap for spraying thin, fast-drying materials, such as lacquer and shellac. Air and fluid are mixed **outside** the air cap.

Under pressure feed (below), air is fed into the cup so it forces the fluid up into the gun. It is used with an **internal-mix** air cap for spraying heavy-bodied, slower-drying materials. Air and fluid are mixed **inside** the air cap. Because pressure feed builds up considerable force inside the cup, **it should never be used with a glass jar!**

Since you will be working with both types of finishing materials, you will find that a combination gun is the most useful.

When the gun is set up for pressure feed (internal-mix), air enters the cup and builds up the pressure that is needed to force the fluid up the fluid tube.

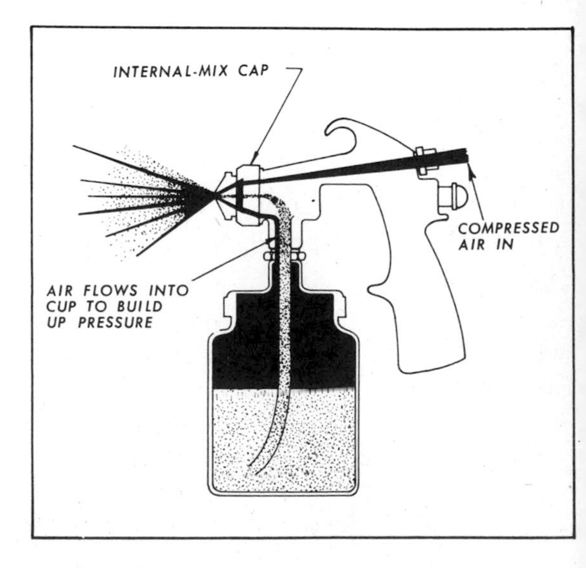

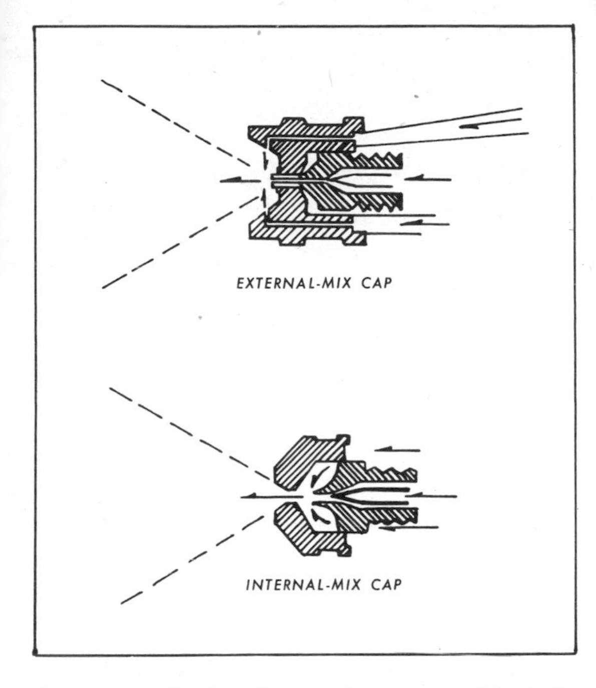

An external-mix air cap (at top—with twin projections) is used when the gun is set up for siphon feed. The internal-mix air cap is used when the gun is set up for pressure feed.

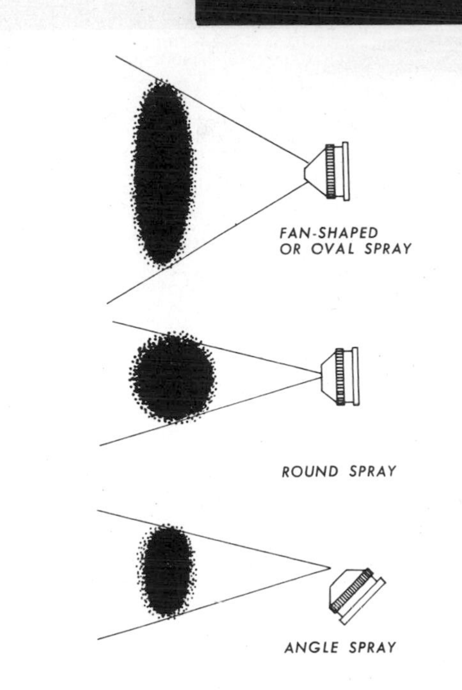

The most commonly used air cap produces a fan- or oval-shaped pattern. A round-pattern cap is also available, as well as one that sprays at a 45° angle and is useful for overhead work.

Air caps (shown above) are referred to as internal-mix or external-mix types.

The external-mix type is easily identified by twin projections on the cap face and the fact that the fluid tube projects outside the cap. Air, pushed out through twin orifices in the projections, atomizes the fluid delivered by the tube and sprays it in a controlled pattern. This action takes place outside the air cap—hence, external mix.

The internal-mix cap does not have the projections, and the fluid tube ends behind the cap surfaces. Air and fluid are mixed inside the cap before being ejected.

Remember: The external-mix cap is used when the gun is set up for siphon feed, the internal-mix cap when the gun is set up for pressure feed.

Caps are further identified by their spray pattern (above), being either round or fan-shaped. The size of the pattern is controlled by the amount of air and fluid allowed to pass through.

The fan air cap gives a long, oval-shaped pattern ideal for large areas, which through control of fluid and air may be reduced in size for working in tight places and corners.

The round air cap produces a small, circular pattern good for small areas and irregular surfaces. The angle cap produces an oval-shaped spray pattern at an angle of 45° for special applications, such as spray painting a ceiling or other overhead object or for horizontal surfaces.

The hose, which is always included with the spray outfit you buy, is exactly the right size to deliver air efficiently from compressor to gun. Any increase in hose length will result in line-drop—considerably reduced air pressure at the gun.

The spray outfit supplied for use on the multi-purpose tool has a two-piece hose. It

A special coupling lets you insert ordinary garden hose. The gun may be used as much as 100 feet away from the compressor.

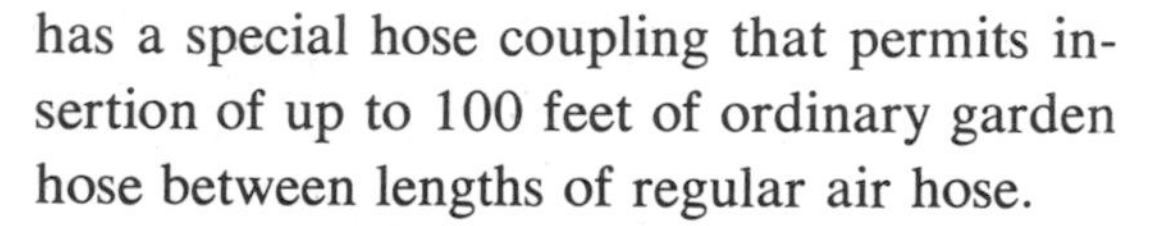

has a special hose coupling that permits insertion of up to 100 feet of ordinary garden hose between lengths of regular air hose.

Garden hose with its greater inside diameter permits efficient delivery of air as much as 100 feet away from the power source. This makes it possible not only to spray-paint fences and house exteriors, as in the photograph below, but also to do all spraying far enough away from the compressor to protect the air filter against clogging by excessive dust or spray particles.

Ordinary garden hose has proven practical for this extension. It should be strong enough to stand an internal pressure of 60 psi (pounds per square inch). Most garden hose will prove adequate, but it should be checked, since there are some varieties of plastic hose that are unable to withstand this pressure.

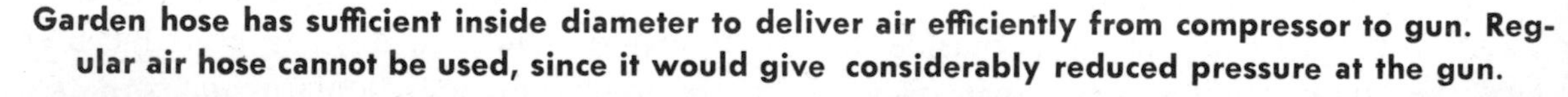

Garden hose has sufficient inside diameter to deliver air efficiently from compressor to gun. Regular air hose cannot be used, since it would give considerably reduced pressure at the gun.

Preparation and Thinning

Moisture in the line, especially when spraying lacquer, shellac, or similar materials, will mar the sprayed surface. Before attaching the gun, always be sure that the hose is dry—particularly when garden hose is being used.

Small metal cylinders called water traps are available for insertion between compressor and gun. These will capture any moisture in the compressed air before it can reach either the gun or the fluid. Trapped water is drained from the cylinder through a valve. Insert the water trap in the line as close to the gun as possible.

Always work in a clean, well-ventilated place—**never** in a closed room or near an open flame. Do not smoke while spraying. If you must work in a confined area, or are doing extensive spraying, wear a respirator.

Almost always the consistency of the material must be reduced with a suitable thinner (see chart below). Thoroughly mix the material in its original container. When pouring it into the gun cup, pass it through a strainer. This is important, for solids or impurities will impair the efficiency of the gun and may be sprayed out onto the work to cause obvious imperfections. When the material is in the gun cup, add a suitable amount of the correct thinner and thoroughly stir it.

Be sure all hose connections are tight.

It is good practice to run the compressor for a few minutes before doing any spraying. Then attach the hose and let air pass through it for a short time to clear it and blow out any moisture. Then attach the gun.

Use this chart to find how to thin your finish and how to apply it. Example: gloss varnish is to be thinned 20% (one-fifth), so add one pint of turpentine for each 5 pints of varnish.

MATERIAL	SOLVENT	PER CENT OF THINNING	AIR CAP	FEED	REMARKS
lacquer (clear) lacquer (pigmented)	lacquer thinners	25-50% 100%	external	syphon	dries quickly; use small pattern; spray full, wet coat
varnish (gloss) varnish (flat-satin)	turpentine	20% 30-50%	internal	pressure	avoid very heavy coats
shellac (4-pound cut)	alcohol	75%	external or internal	syphon or pressure	dries quickly; avoid spraying in wet or humid weather
stain	check container	can consistency	external	syphon	even application necessary
enamel (4-hour)	turpentine (check container)	can consistency—or light thinning if necessary	internal	pressure	do not coat too heavily
house paint	check container	can consistency whenever possible	internal	pressure	do not spray outdoors on a windy day
wall paint (water-mix or rubber-base)	water	as heavy as gun will handle (rubber-base: 10-15%)	internal	pressure	spray as heavily as possible; clean gun with turpentine, after cleaning with water, to avoid rust
synthetics	check container	as is, unless can label instructs otherwise	external or internal	syphon or pressure	spray light coat first; let set; follow with full coat
shingle stain	turpentine (check container)	as is, or thin lightly	external	syphon	even applications necessary
clear sealer	check container	10-20%	external or internal	syphon or pressure	full coat, wiped off after 15-20 minutes, works well
flat wall paint (oil-base)	turpentine	15-30%	internal	pressure	do not coat too heavily

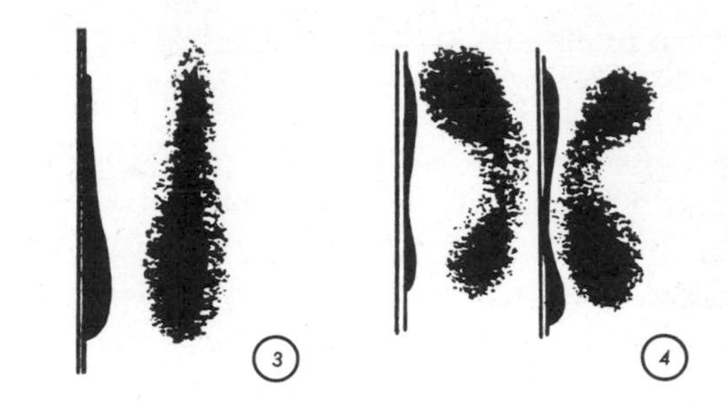

Use this chart to recognize faults in a spraying pattern:

1—GOOD PATTERN, a long oval with even paint distribution, finely atomized at the edges.

2—HEAVY-CENTER PATTERN, with paint too concentrated at center of pattern and atomization poor. This is usually caused by too much of the finishing material, too-heavy material, or not enough air.

3—PATTERN HEAVY AT ONE END, a result of uneven paint distribution caused by a dirty gun. There is usually partial clogging of the air cap or the material nozzle—or both.

4—DISTORTED PATTERN, caused by a dirty gun. There is usually partial clogging of air cap and material nozzle. If the gun is incorrectly adjusted to use too much air, the pattern may split at the center.

Before any job, and especially if you have never handled a spray gun before, you'll find it helpful to spray some experimental patterns on newspaper. Tape the newspaper to a wall, and practice triggering the gun.

Start with the fluid-needle adjustment screw all the way in. Hold the gun about 6″ away from the newspaper and point directly at it. Trigger the gun and gradually turn the adjustment screw counter-clockwise. This will permit fluid to mix with compressed air and be ejected. Notice how body and size of pattern increase as you increase the material flow.

Also notice how the material begins to sag, and finally to run, as you hold the gun motionless. This illustrates a very important point: never hold the gun motionless while it is spraying—or the fluid will continue to pile up on that one spot.

Continue to increase fluid flow until you are getting a pattern about 6″ to 8″ long (4″ to 5″ long if spraying lacquer).

Experiment with the full range of fluid control. You will find that as the pattern length increases, atomization of the paint particles becomes coarser, until you are spraying a heavy, long, hard-to-control pattern. The ideal is an easily handled pattern which still delivers enough paint to cover the surface.

After becoming familiar with how the gun handles and feels, back down the fluid control to a very small pattern and try moving the gun across the paper. The speed with which you move the gun controls the uniformity of the application. Moving too fast is no good, since you will not cover. Moving too slow is even worse, since you will deposit too much paint, and it will sag and run and ruin the job.

Within a short time you will find that after determining the correct pattern you will automatically feed the gun across the work to deliver exactly the right amount of paint uniformly.

Spray experimental patterns on a newspaper and adjust fluid flow and size of pattern before starting to spray the project.

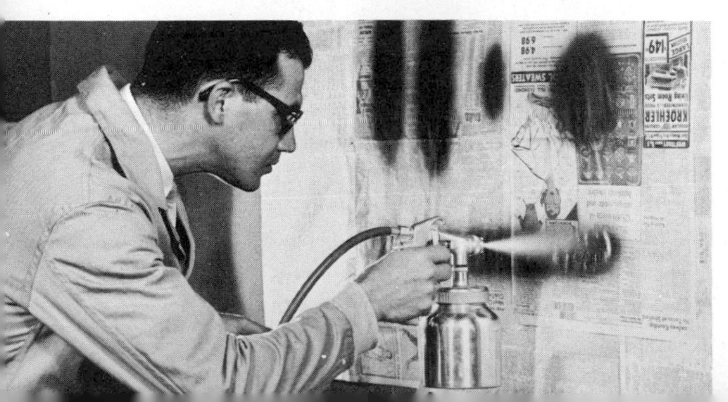

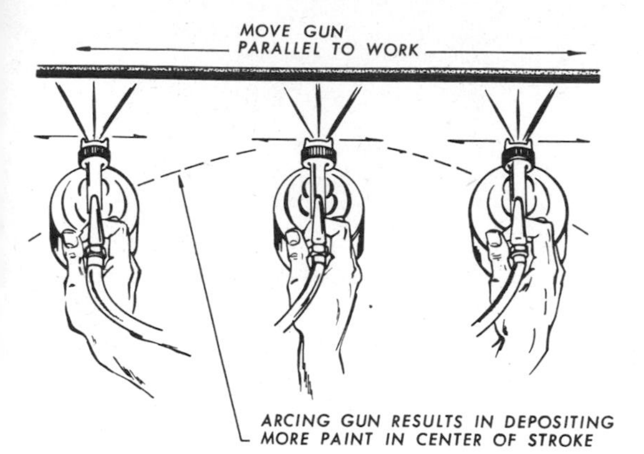

Move the gun parallel to the surface being painted and at a distance of 6″ to 8″ from it.

Stroking the Gun

Hold the gun from 6″ to 8″ from the work. Keep it at right angles and move it parallel to the surface being painted (above).

On all spraying, the perimeter of the pattern is "dusted"—that is, covered by overspray, not really covered with paint. This means that subsequent strokes should overlap previous ones by about 50 per cent (sketch below).

Overlapping more will deposit too much paint. Overlapping less will result in a streaked, uneven surface.

Holding the gun at right angles to the work will guarantee application of a uniform coat.

For full, uniform coverage, strokes should overlap about 50 per cent.

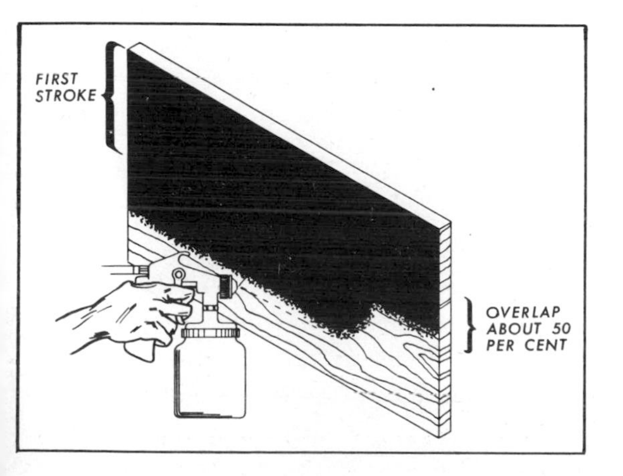

Tilting the gun (sketch below) deposits more paint at one end of the pattern. Arcing the gun deposits more paint at the center of the stroke than at the ends.

The closer the gun is held to the work, the more paint is applied and the faster the stroke must be. The further away the gun is held, the slower the stroke. But extremes are undesirable. Excessive stroke speed will result in careless work, while a stroke that is too slow will tax the patience of the sprayer. In addition, holding the gun too far away will result in excessive dusting and overspraying.

Practice the right and wrong methods of stroking by spraying test patterns on newspaper. You will not only learn to hold and use the gun, but you will also become familiar with the results of right and wrong techniques and will become able to correct any fault that appears on a project.

Proper gun-to-work distance is important.

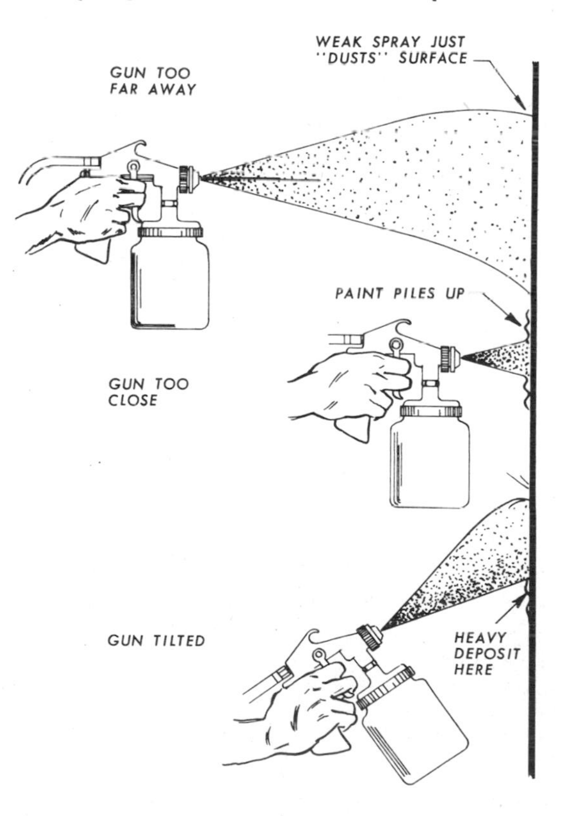

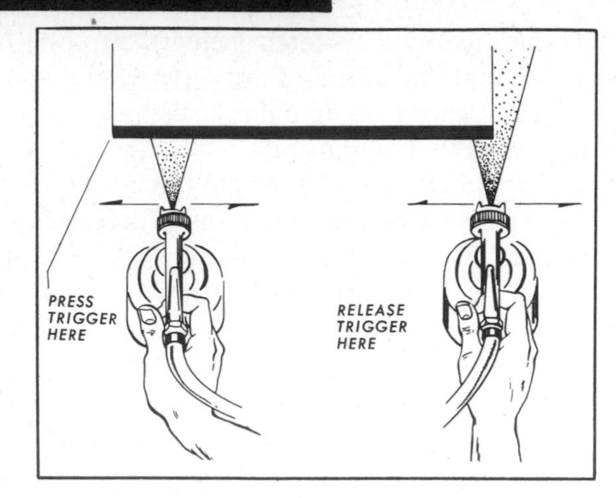

Press trigger just before spray hits work; release it just before the end of the stroke.

Practice by poising the gun to the left of a test panel and pressing the trigger immediately before you start the stroke.

Triggering

If the trigger is pressed and held down until an entire panel is sprayed, considerable paint will be lost and much overspray will hang in the air. Therefore the gun should be triggered just before it hits the work and released at the end of the stroke.

For example, let's assume you are spraying a panel about 2 feet wide, like the one at the right above. Poise the gun just to the left of the panel and press the trigger. As you press the trigger, make a stroke towards the right; as soon as you have passed the right end of the panel, release the trigger. Lower the gun, so the second stroke will overlap the first about 50 per cent, press the trigger, and make the return stroke. At the end of the return stroke, again release the trigger, re-position the gun, press the trigger, and make the third stroke—and so on. This triggering action will soon be automatic and natural.

You can spray vertical end-bands, then area between with overlapping horizontal strokes.

Changing the pattern from vertical to horizontal merely requires rotating the air cap 90°.

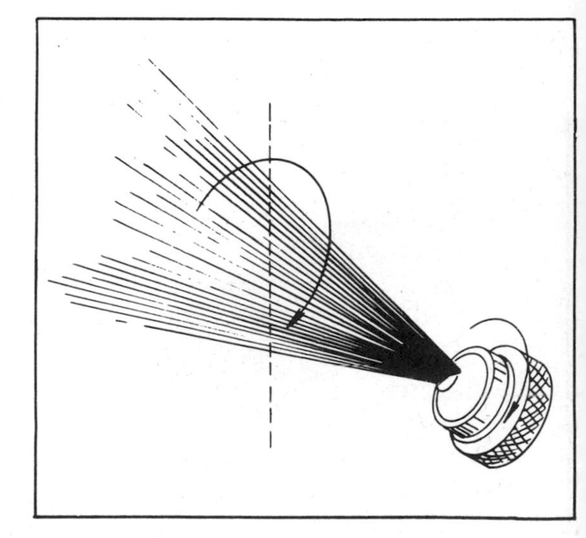

Spraying Round Objects

As sketched at the right, cylinders may be sprayed with overlapping vertical strokes and a small horizontal pattern, or with a medium vertical pattern and overlapping horizontal strokes.

In either case, a smaller spray pattern is preferable to a large one. This also applies to shaped turnings.

Unless the diameter of the object being sprayed is extremely large, use vertical strokes exclusively. Don't try to force the gun stroke to conform to the circumference of the project.

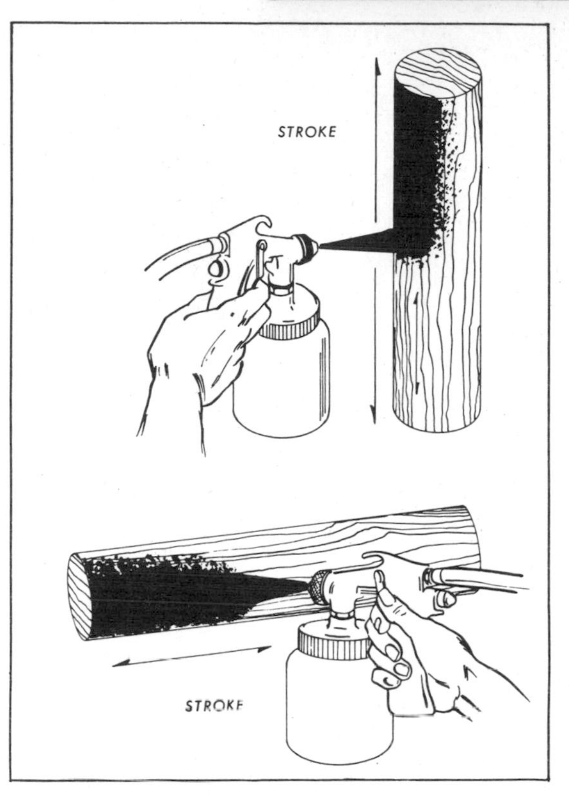

Spray cylinders in either of these ways.

Spraying Broad Surfaces

A small surface is easily sprayed with parallel overlapping strokes. First spraying vertical bands at each end of the work, as sketched at lower left on opposite page, assures sufficient coverage at the ends. It also cuts down on overspray, since the horizontal strokes can end before the edge of the panel is reached.

Work too long to be spanned with single strokes can be sprayed with vertical strokes by turning the air cap 90° and retightening it.

Ends of horizontal strokes used on long work must also be overlapped as in the sketch below. Picture each section of the work being sprayed as a separate small panel easily covered with a single stroke.

Triggering is the same, starting and ending at the ends of each individual stroke.

A vertical pattern and horizontal strokes may be used to spray a very long area. But be sure to overlap the ends of the strokes sufficiently.

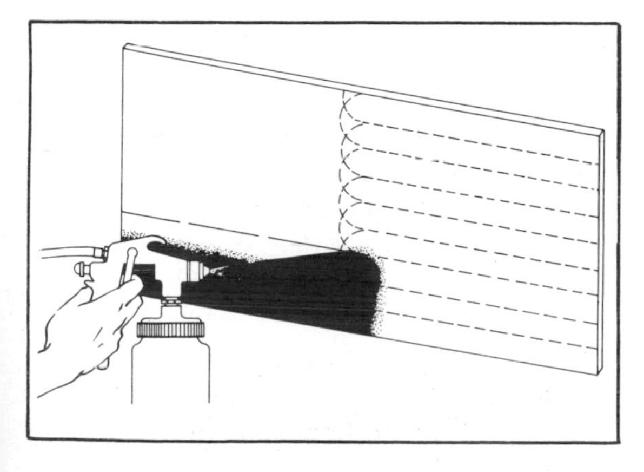

Work that is too long to be sprayed with single horizontal strokes may be painted by using a horizontal pattern and vertical strokes.

An even application is difficult to get when spraying an inside corner by pointing the gun directly at it. So it's a better technique to spray adjacent vertical bands.

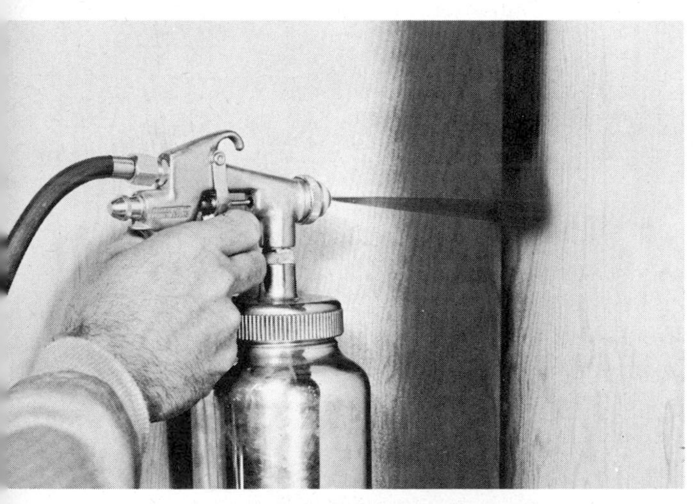

Gun can be tilted to cover an edge and create end band on top surface at the same time.

Spraying Corners

Pointing the spray gun directly at an inside corner (left) may result in an uneven application. It's better to spray vertical bands (center left) that will cover the corner and enough of the adjacent sides to permit overlapping the bands with horizontal strokes.

In an exposed area and especially when spraying lacquer, the banding method is preferred. When the corner is hidden and a slower-drying material is used, it will not matter too much if sides are slightly oversprayed.

Edges, such as on a table top, can be sprayed in the manner shown at bottom left to cover an edge and create end bands in one operation.

To spray a box, spray the corners first, then fill in with conventional strokes.

On outside corners on such slender work as square or tapered chair and table legs, a large horizontal pattern will cover well but will give considerable overspray and dusting. It is best to use a small horizontal pattern, or a fairly large vertical pattern in combination with a vertical stroke.

On **very** slender work, you can use the technique described for table edges—covering two adjacent sides at the same time.

Flat Work

Whenever you can, tilt the work so the gun can be aimed at a 90° angle. When this can't be done, point the gun at a 45° angle.

This results in overspray landing on the work, so do not start from the far side and work toward you; overspray would land on areas already covered with paint. When working with enamels this is not so critical, but overspray landing on a lacquered surface can result in a sandy finish—rough to the touch. So start spraying at the side nearer you.

Don't tilt the gun so far that the paint in the container will cover the lid. The amount a gun may be tilted can be increased by reducing the amount of fluid in the cup.

Using Extra Containers

Extra paint cups are useful, especially when changes from one color to another must be made several times on the same job. The paint may even be stored in the spare cups, if a suitable Mason jar lid is used to seal them.

When the gun is set up for siphon feed, it is possible to use ordinary Mason jars in place of the regular metal cups. However, **remember that this is permissible only when the gun is set up for siphon feed!** When the gun is set up for pressure feed, the pressure built up inside the container makes it dangerous to use anything but the original metal cup.

Other methods possible when the gun is set up for siphon feed are shown in the drawing and photograph at the right.

When the gun is set up for SIPHON FEED, you can dip the fluid tube directly into the paint container (above). Or place the paint can—if it's small enough—inside the gun cup (below).

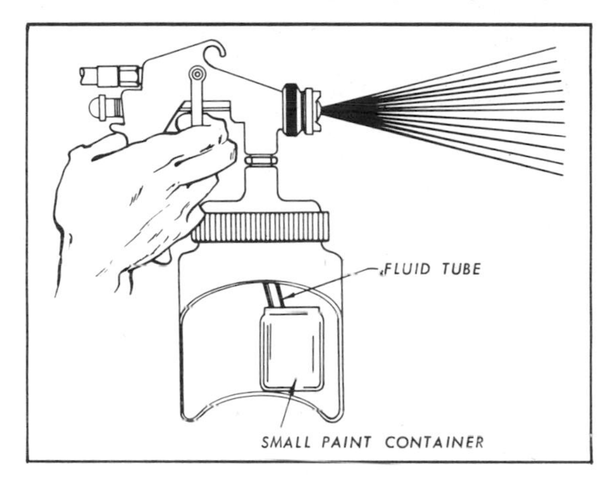

Cleaning the Gun

Spray equipment should be cleaned immediately after use. Following the first step (lower right) pour the remaining paint from the gun cup back into its original container. Then rinse the gun cup with a small amount of suitable solvent. Pour this into the original paint container.

Use a rag moistened with the solvent to clean the inside of the cup, the fluid tube, and the inside of the lid. Pour clean solvent into the cup, screw it to the gun, turn on the compressor, and pull the trigger several times. Then hold a rag over the spray cap and again pull the trigger three or four times. The solvent will "boil" inside the cup and fluid tube. Stop compressor, remove container from gun, and pull trigger to release solvent trapped in tube.

When the gun is set up for siphon feed, you need not pour solvent into the gun cup except to clean it. Clean the gun by dipping the fluid tube directly into the solvent container.

After using water to clean a water-base paint from gun and cup, swish turpentine or lacquer thinner around in the cup and spray it through the gun for a few seconds to prevent rusting of parts.

Before cleaning the gun, hold the tube over the cup and depress the trigger. This will release the paint held in the fluid tube. Then wipe the paint from the outside of the tube.

Use masking tape to make a dividing line between areas. Cardboard is a shield against overspray.

Masking and Shielding

When you are spraying work next to a surface not requiring painting, or are using more than one color, masking or shielding is called for.

Masking is accomplished as shown in the four photographs below.

A combination of masking and shielding may be used, as shown at left, when an adjacent area must be protected from overspray. The shield is moved along with the gun stroke.

This technique is useful when painting baseboards and wainscoting and around windows. Sometimes it is possible to work with the shield only. Be sure to clean it frequently.

1. When using masking tape to lay out a design, first spray the general area with the base color. Then let the paint dry thoroughly.

2. Place the tape, rubbing the edges down with a short piece of dowel. Edges must be pressed down firmly or paint will creep under.

3. Spray the entire panel with the second color. For a clean job, remove the tape . . .

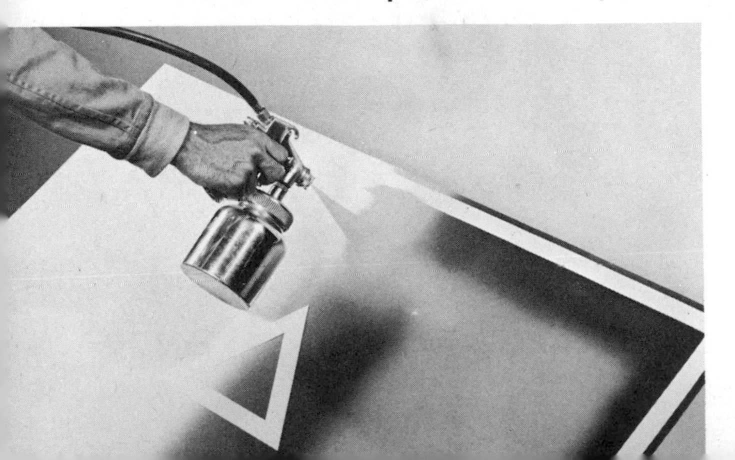

4. . . . before this coat is entirely dry. Pull it off at close to a 90° angle, as shown here.

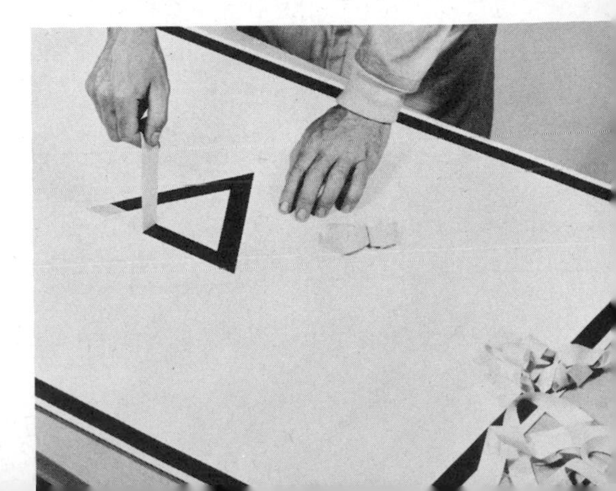

You can cut stencils (above) with a sharp knife or razor blade. Oil-coated stencil papers are available.

Attach the stencil firmly, with all edges perfectly flat. On small designs, a small, round spray pattern (right) is best.

If the stencil was held firmly against the project, the design will have the clean, sharp outlines of the one shown at lower right.

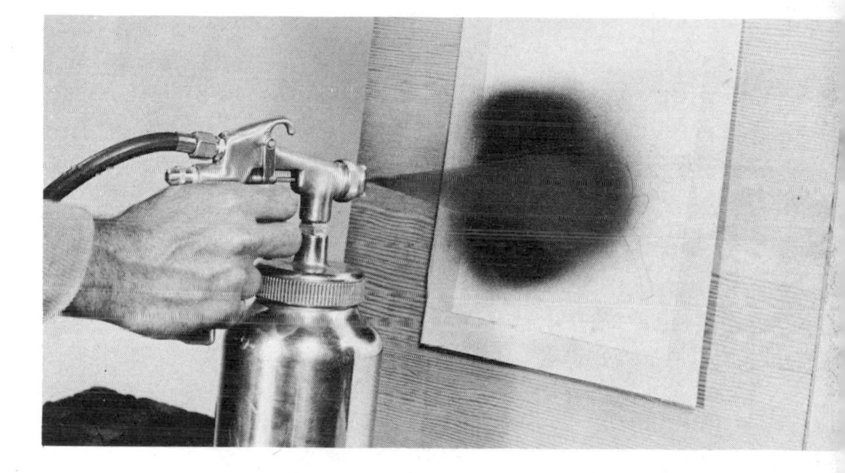

Stenciling

Stencils make it easy to create decorative effects and designs. You can cut your own stencils (above) or purchase ready-made ones.

Stencils are die-cut, oil-coated papers that come ready to use. Best results are obtained when the stencil is attached firmly to the object.

Spray with the gun set for a round pattern suited to the size of the work. Aim the spray head on, and distribute the paint evenly over the entire exposed surface.

Multi-colored designs are possible by using different stencils. Allow sufficient drying time between applications.

Air-jet nozzle helps clean the shop by removing dust and chips from benches and tools.

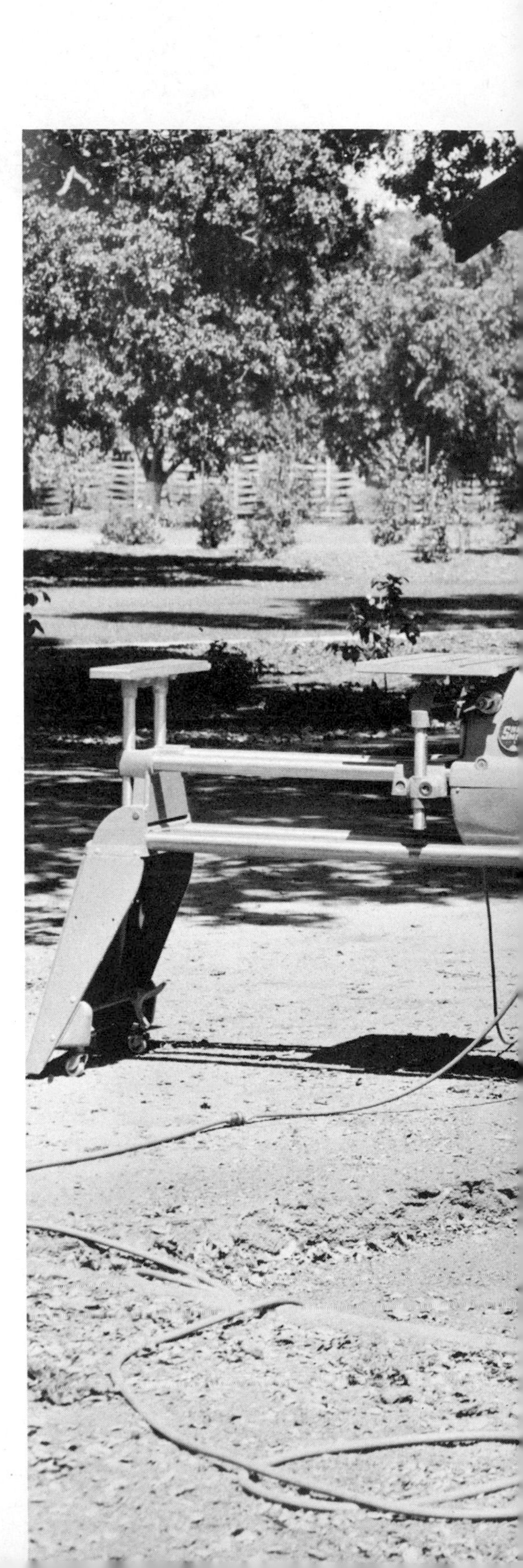

More Uses for Your Sprayer

Some additional uses for your compressor are shown on these two pages.

Compressed air may also be used to get a barbecue fire going well, run a small forge, or inflate plastic toys or swimming pools.

When the garden hose idea is used as shown at right, to extend the reach of the spray gun, be sure to let compressed air run through the hose for a while before attaching gun and cup. This is to make sure that no water or moisture from previous garden use remains in the hose.

With an air-jet nozzle, you can use the compressor to clean hard-to-reach places on shop equipment (above) or to dust a project before spray-finishing it. And with a suitable nozzle you can inflate automobile or bicycle tires—a great help at times.

Garden hose extends the reach of your sprayer. Since you can use as much as 100 feet of hose, you can spray your house—or the fence around it.

TROUBLE-SHOOTING CHART FOR SPRAY FINISHING

THE TROUBLE	POSSIBLE CAUSES	THE CURE	SEE PAGE
GUN SPUTTERS	loose fluid-tube connection	tighten until fluid tube is rigid	see literature supplied with gun
	material nozzle is loose	tighten securely	
	packing around fluid needle is worn or dry	lubricate or replace packing; lock packing nut	
GUN DOES NOT DELIVER PAINT (INTERNAL-MIX)	top connector in wrong position	invert to internal-mix position (pressure feed)	see literature supplied with gun
	worn gaskets	check gaskets on cup-top and connector; replace if necessary	
	clogged air or material passages, or both	clean thoroughly	315
	very low paint level in cup	add correctly thinned and strained paint	309
GUN DOES NOT DELIVER PAINT (EXTERNAL-MIX)	insufficient thinning of material	add proper thinner	309
	low air supply	check all connections and compressor speed	see literature supplied with gun
	air vent on jar-top connector is clogged	clean with thinner	
	dirty or clogged material nozzle or air cap	remove parts and clean thoroughly	
	wrong setup	check for correct combination of air cap and feed for material being used	309
PAINT LEAKS FROM SPRAY GUN	fluid-needle packing nut too tight (paint leaks through spray head)	loosen nut and lubricate packing	see literature supplied with gun
	packing for fluid needle is dry or worn (leaks through packing nut)	tighten packing nut; replace packing if necessary	
	blocked fluid tip	remove tip and clean thoroughly	
	material nozzle or fluid needle damaged	replace damaged parts	
	loose fluid tube	secure wrench-tight	

PAINTED SURFACE "SAGS"	gun held too close to work	keep gun 6" to 8" from work during stroke	311
	heavy paint application	do not make stroke too slowly	311
	paint too thin	follow instructions for correct paint consistency	309
	gun held at angle, causing heavier deposit of paint at one end of pattern	hold gun at right angle to work	311
DISTORTED SPRAY PATTERN	dirty or partially clogged air cap or material nozzle	remove parts and thoroughly clean	310
PAINT "ORANGE-PEELS" (HAS ORANGE-SKIN TEXTURE)	paint too heavy	follow instructions for correct paint consistency	309
	not depositing a full, wet coat	do not stroke gun so fast; be sure to overlap	311
	air pressure low	check all connections and compressor speed	—
	gun stroked too rapidly, causing excessive dusting	practice on newspaper to determine the correct speed for material used	310
	gun held too far from surface	hold gun 6" to 8" away from surface, throughout stroke	311
	overspray on surface already covered	follow instructions for correct spraying procedure	314
EXCESSIVE "FOG" (OVERSPRAY)	gun held too far from surface	hold gun 6" to 8" away from surface throughout stroke	311
	material is much too thin	follow instructions for correct paint consistency	309
	air pressure is too high	decrease speed	see literature supplied with gun
	overspraying	trigger gun at start and end of each stroke	312
	wrong setup	be sure combination of air cap and feed is correct	309
STREAKS IN SURFACE	dirty or clogged air cap or material nozzle	remove parts and thoroughly clean	—
	strokes not parallel or insufficient overlapping	follow instructions for overlapping; keep strokes parallel to each other	311
	stroking too rapidly	practice on newspaper for correct stroke speed	310
	gun held at angle during stroke	keep gun at 90° angle to surface during stroke	311

10 SHARPENING TOOLS

**Sharpening saw blades • jointer knives
lathe chisels • roundnose • parting tool • butt wood chisels
screw drivers • drills • mortising chisels • three-lip shaper cutters
lathe-tool bits • using the honing wheel**

For sharpening, set up the multi-purpose tool with grinding wheel, guard, and tool rest.

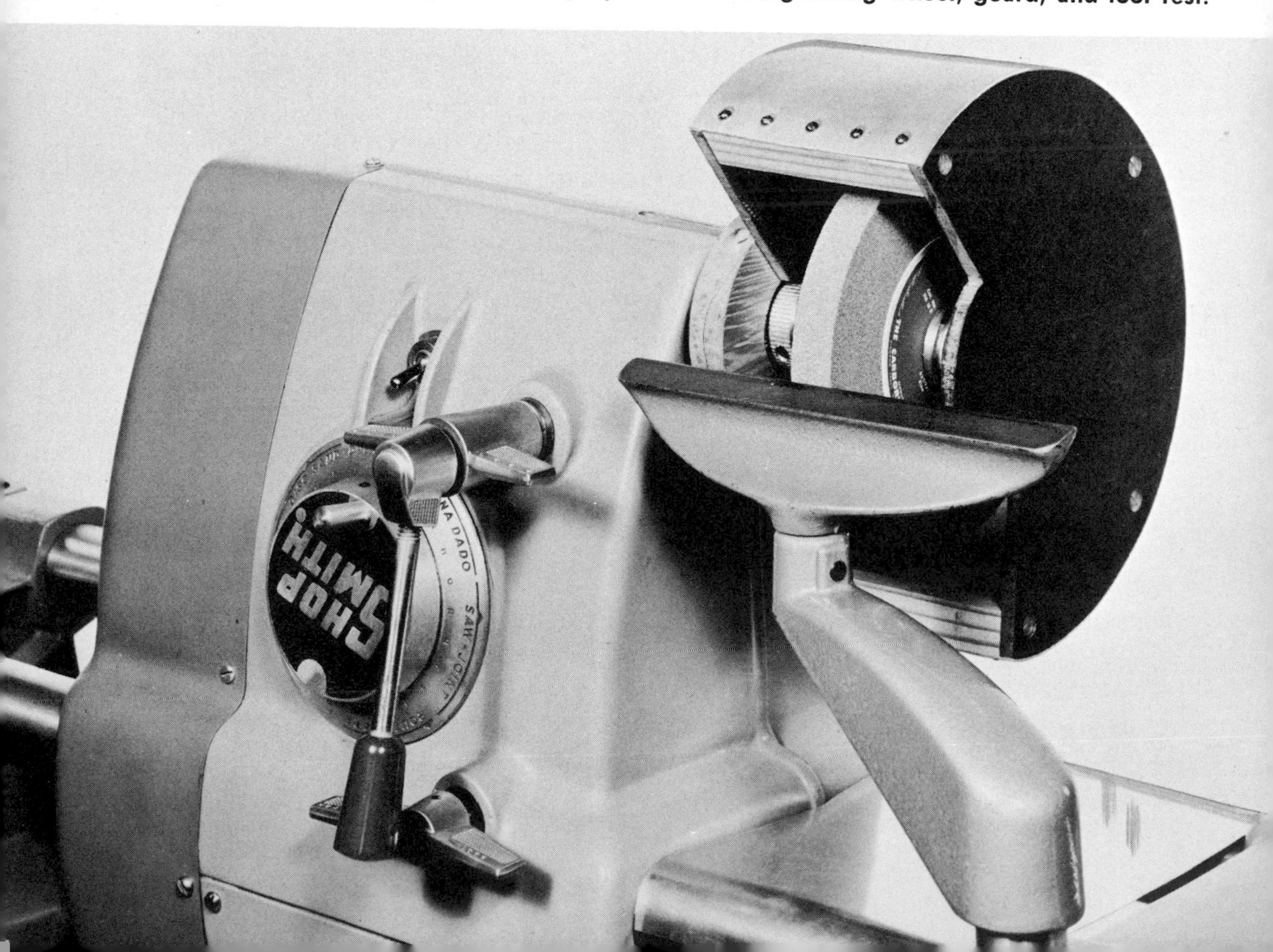

Dull cutting edges waste more time than it would take to make them sharp again.

Dull tools are dangerous, too. A blunt edge won't cut. The work must be forced against it—with increased danger that your hands might slip. A dull blade, especially one improperly set, binds in the kerf and greatly increases the danger of kickback. It also reduces the efficiency of the motor, since more power is required to make the cut.

So keep your tools sharp and clean. They will last longer and do a better job, and you will be safer and more satisfied with your equipment.

The machine most used for tool-sharpening is the grinder. It may be a bench grinder or a bench-mounted polishing-head unit, powered through belt and pulley.

On the multi-purpose tool the grinding wheel is mounted on an arbor and secured to the spindle in the usual manner, as shown on the opposite page. For protection against flying grit, an easily made and widely useful guard is attached to the quill. (Construction details of the guard are given on page 150.)

A sheet-metal shield to protect the tubes from dirt and metal particles is shown at the right. It can be made from a piece of soft sheet-metal, such as copper, aluminum, or even tin. "Do-It-Yourself" aluminum is very good. Cut a piece about 8″ by 10″ and round off the four corners. Clamp it to the tubes, and use a soft-faced mallet, preferably rubber, to bend down the ends over the tubes. Polish the edges with steel wool to remove burrs. Instead of a metal shield, you can place a piece of canvas or cloth over the tubes.

The lathe tool rest functions as a platform for tools being sharpened, and it also provides an adjustable base for sharpening some tools more easily and accurately.

The best general-purpose grinding wheel is about 60-grit aluminum oxide, about 6″ in diameter. Be sure to follow the instructions printed on the wheel. **Never operate a grinding wheel faster than the rpm noted on the paper flanges cemented to the wheel.**

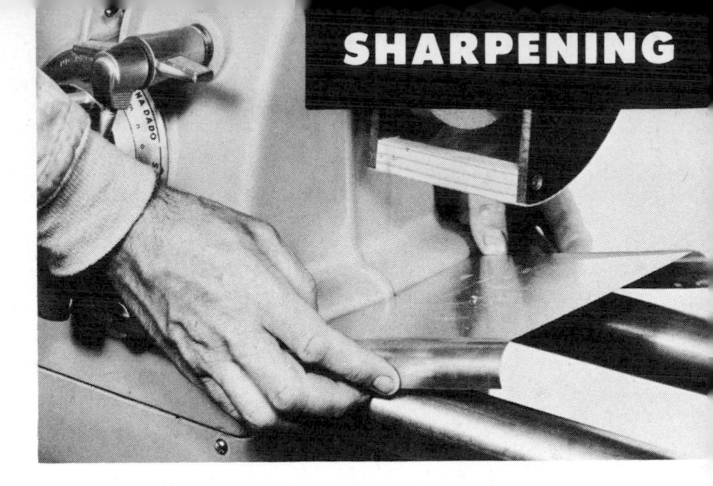

Protect chrome-plated tubular ways from grit, using a sheet-metal or canvas shield. A shield is easily formed right on the tubes (below) if made of "Do-It-Yourself" aluminum. Use a soft-faced mallet when bending the ends.

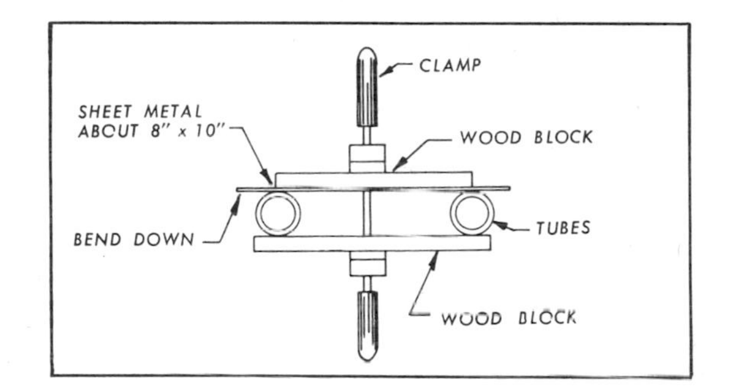

Mount the wheel between washers on the arbor. Use a resilient washer between each metal washer and the wheel; ordinary blotting paper makes good washers for this purpose.

Never use excessive pressure when applying tools to the wheel. Keep tool edges cool by dipping them in water as you work. High-speed steels are best worked dry, with suitable intervals between cuts to prevent overheating the metal. Never take so deep a cut or apply so much pressure that blue spots appear on the edge. This indicates the temper of the metal is being drawn. Work slowly, using a light feed; do not attempt to remove a lot of metal in one bite. Just a light touch to the wheel should be enough to produce an edge that will again cut cleanly and with minimum effort.

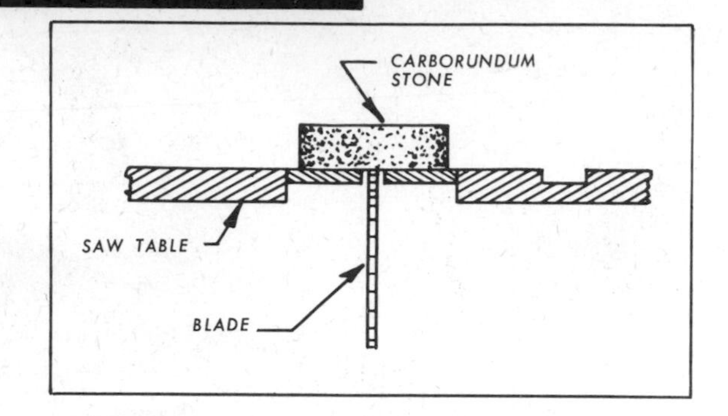

When jointing a saw-blade, be sure to adjust table height so the blade barely touches the stone. Check height with scrap wood first.

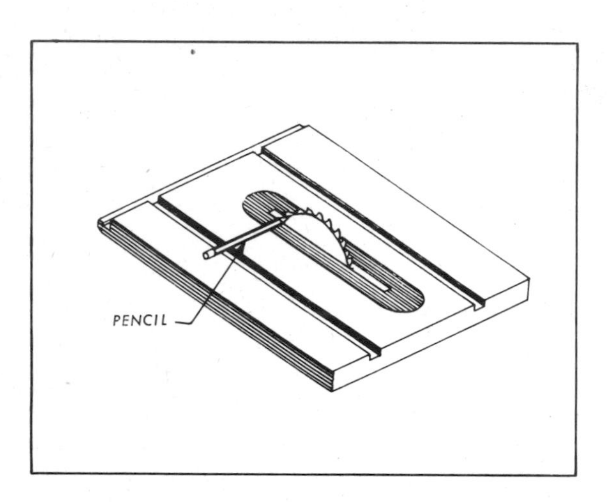

When gumming, place the pencil at the base of the deepest gullet, then slowly turn the blade by hand so the pencil scribes a circle.

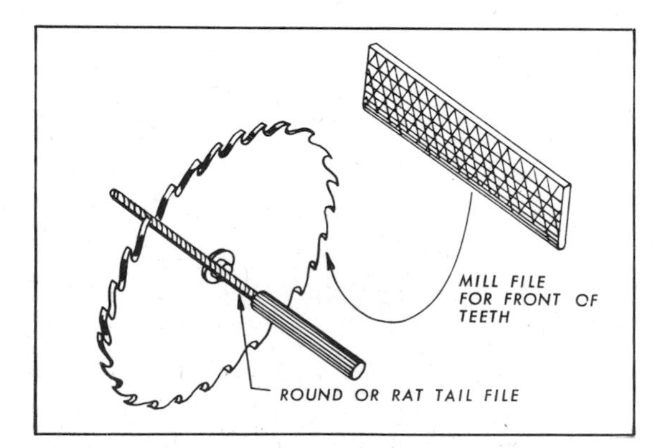

Gullets may be hand-filed with a round or rat-tail file, used lightly. Each gullet should be filed to the pencil line.

Sharpening Saw Blades

A saw blade is sharp and ready for use when you buy it. With reasonable care it will remain so for a long time. When it does get dull, you'll probably want an experienced saw filer and setter to put it in good order again; proper refinishing of saw-teeth is not easy. But if you decide to do the job yourself, it can be accomplished as follows:

The first step, jointing, evens up the circumference of the blade; it makes each tooth-point exactly the same distance from the blade center. This is not necessary on new blades until the teeth have been filed a few times.

To joint a blade, leave it on the machine and raise the table level with the top of the blade. Start the saw and hold a piece of wood over the blade. Adjust table height until the wood is scored **very lightly.** With the saw still running, push a carborundum stone over it (upper left). Flying sparks indicate the teeth are being ground down.

Stop the saw and examine the teeth. If there is a small bright spot on each tooth, the blade has been satisfactorily jointed. **(This applies to the cutting teeth only.** After a few jointing operations it is necessary to file down the raker teeth, which clear wood from the kerf.) If some of the teeth have not been touched, lower the table a fraction and repeat the operation. Some operators prefer mounting the blade backward on the arbor for this operation, but if you check carefully with scrap wood before using the stone, that's not necessary.

The second step, gumming, evens up the depth of the gullets between the teeth. This may be done by hand, or on a grinding wheel in an operation combining gumming and facing thc teeth. Set the blade above the table about 2″, and turn it by hand while you hold a pencil at a point which will touch the base of the deepest gullet (middle drawing at left).

The pencil line indicates how far down to file each gullet.

As shown at bottom left, the next step is to clean out the gullets with a round or rat-tail file.

Use the file lightly. Rotate it on the forward stroke and lift it on the return stroke, so the cutting action is forward only. File to the pencil line. A round-edged mill file is used on the face of the teeth. Be sure to maintain the angle called the rake on the front of each tooth when filing.

The gumming operation shown at the right is a mechanical action that combines filing the gullet depth and refacing the teeth. Sketched below is an adapter to be used in the tool-rest arm so that a regular saw-blade arbor can be mounted. The adapter is made from a length of ¾″ bar stock reduced to ⅝″ diameter at one end. A plywood disc about 6″ in diameter is placed on the arbor, followed by the blade, a washer, and the nut. Set the blade so it is on the horizontal centerline of the wheel.

The grinding wheel should be dressed to fit the size and shape of the gullet. It will have to be changed for different blades, or else different wheels must be kept on hand. The action required here involves advancing the quill and swinging the saw-blade in simultaneously. **With the motor turned off,** bring the wheel forward by advancing the quill, and swing in the blade until the wheel fits snugly in the gullet. Set the depth control dial and use a clamp on the table carriage to control the swing of the saw-blade. With the stops set, go through the motion several times to get the feel of it. Then turn on the motor and do the grinding.

Turn the blade to a new tooth after each pass. The procedure just described is for blades that mount on a conventional ⅝″ arbor. The special 1¼″ arbor, used for the 9″ blades of the multi-purpose tool, can be mounted in a similar manner, but the ply-

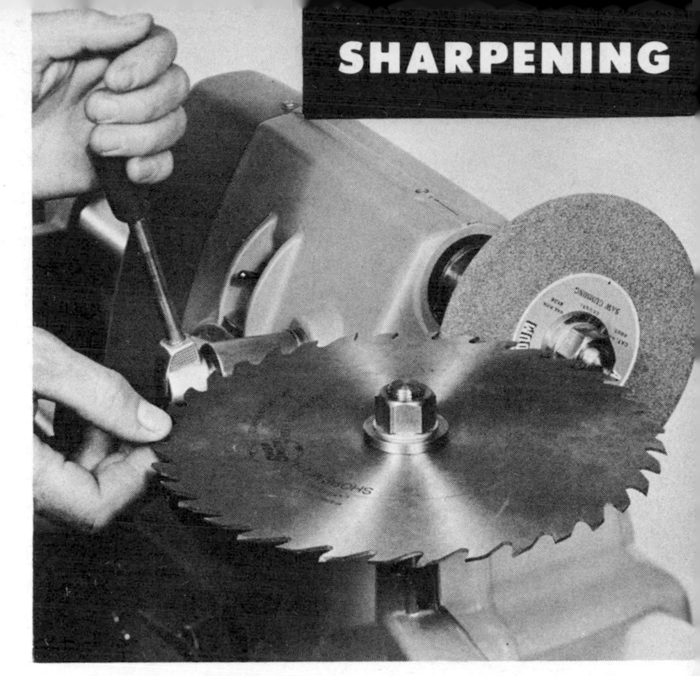

By using a gumming stone and the quill feed, the gullet and face of each tooth may be ground simultaneously. Be sure to practice the action before doing it under power.

Make the adapter below to fit into the tool-rest arm. Any machine shop can easily turn out one of these for you.

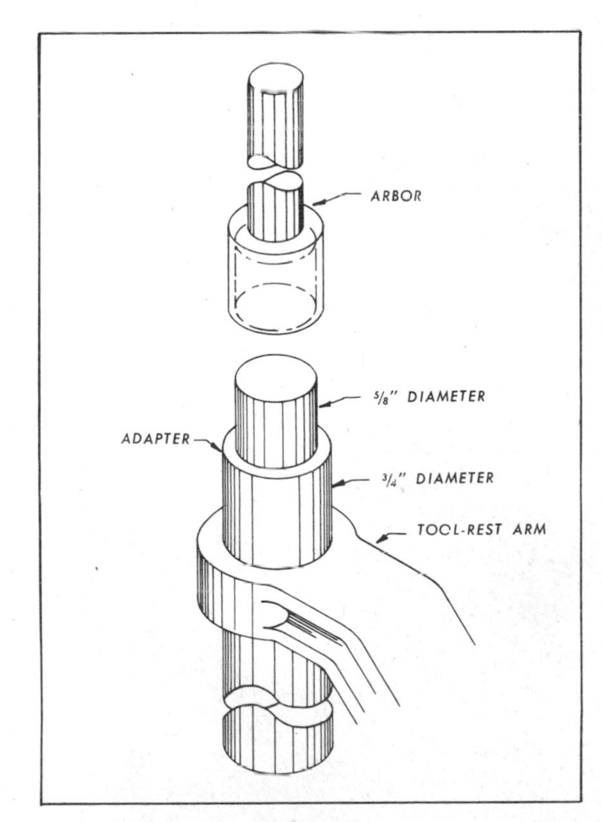

wood disc used between the blade and the arbor nut must be of a suitable thickness.

On most saws—the hollow-ground blade being a typical exception—each tooth is bent in the opposite direction from the one next to it. This is called set. It assures a kerf wide enough to keep the blade from binding. Raker teeth are not set.

The best way to set teeth is to make or buy a little steel anvil and use it in an arrangement similar to the one shown at the right.

Mount the anvil on a steel base long enough so a center bolt can be used through the center hole of the saw blade. This bolt can be made adjustable in a slot so that blades of various sizes can be handled. Once the blade is fixed in the tool, mark one tooth with chalk or a pencil. Set it on the anvil so it projects over the bevel about ⅛″, and strike it a sharp blow with a flatnosed punch and a hammer. Do this on alternate teeth until the marked one comes around again. Then turn the blade over and repeat the operation on the remaining teeth.

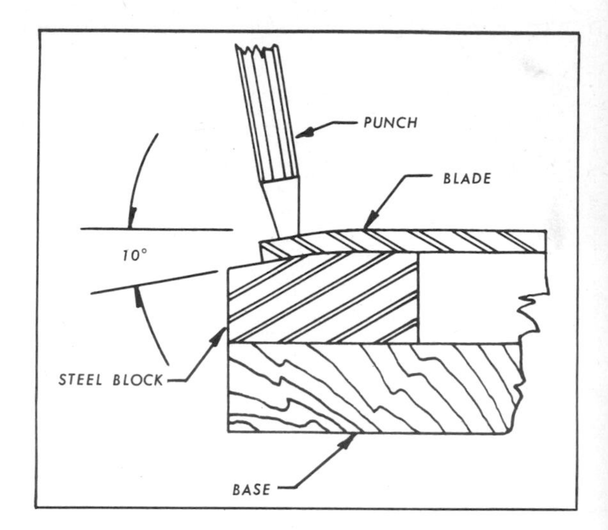

An anvil, beveled to the degree required, is used when setting the teeth on a saw blade. Such an anvil can be purchased in almost any large hardware store.

When filing, grip the blade tightly between blocks in a vise. Be sure to maintain the original bevel-angle of the teeth

The final filing is done with the saw blade mounted between wooden blocks and held tightly in a vise, as in the photograph at the left. The bevels on the cutting teeth will vary with each type. A slim-taper file is good for combination teeth, while a flat file is used on rakers. Be sure to check the teeth and to maintain the same angle when filing. When a saw has been jointed, filing should be just enough to remove the bright spots from the teeth.

Although different blades require different filing angles, the basic techniques are the same. Carefully study the instructions that come with each blade.

Many woodworkers trace the outline of a new blade on a sheet of paper and file it away for future reference. Thus they always have the pattern of the original shape to refer to, no matter what happens to the blade.

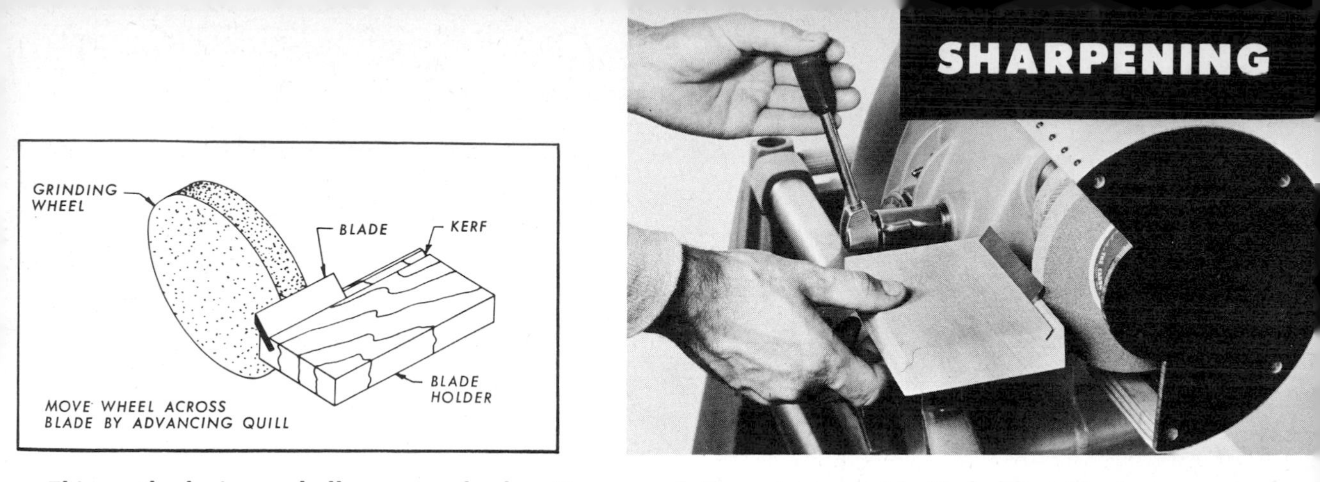

This method gives a hollow-ground edge. It uses a platform to support knife-holding block.

Sharpening Jointer Knives

Because jointer blades are narrow knives, they require a special holding device if they are to be properly sharpened. You can easily make one by cutting a kerf in the **edge** or **surface** of a piece of hardwood, depending on the sharpening method used. The kerf must be angled to suit the bevel on the knife, and must be just wide enough to provide a snug fit.

One method is shown in the pictures above. It uses a special platform (made as shown at the top of the next page) fastened to the tool rest. The knife is placed in the kerf, square to the grinding wheel. The center of the bevel on the knife should be on the horizontal center-line of the wheel. Use the quill-feed lever to move the wheel across the bevel of the knife. Make sure that cuts across the knife are extremely light; and make the pass slowly to avoid overheating the steel. If more than one pass is needed, make the first pass on each knife before changing the setting for the second pass. This operation will produce a hollow-ground edge that can be honed four or five times before the knives must be ground again. Each of the knives is placed in the holder without changing the position of the platform.

A second method, shown below, uses a holder fastened to the miter gauge. The saw table is situated over the grinding wheel, and adjustments are made for a **very** light cut. Then the pass is made across the wheel.

Both methods do a good job of grinding the knives. The first method produces a hollow-ground edge, the second a flat bevel.

This method gives a flat bevel. It uses a jig locked to the miter-gauge head like an extension.

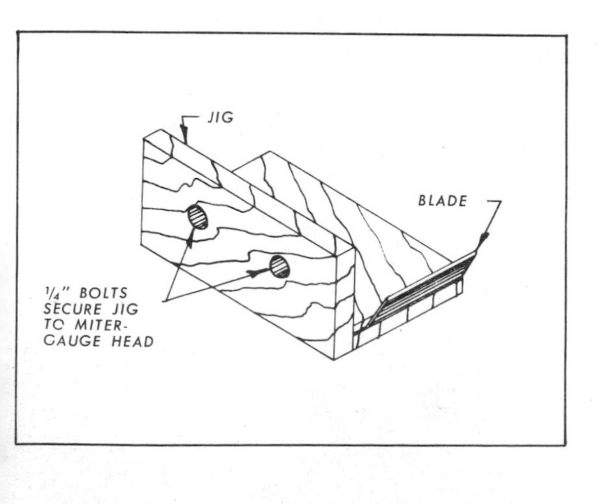

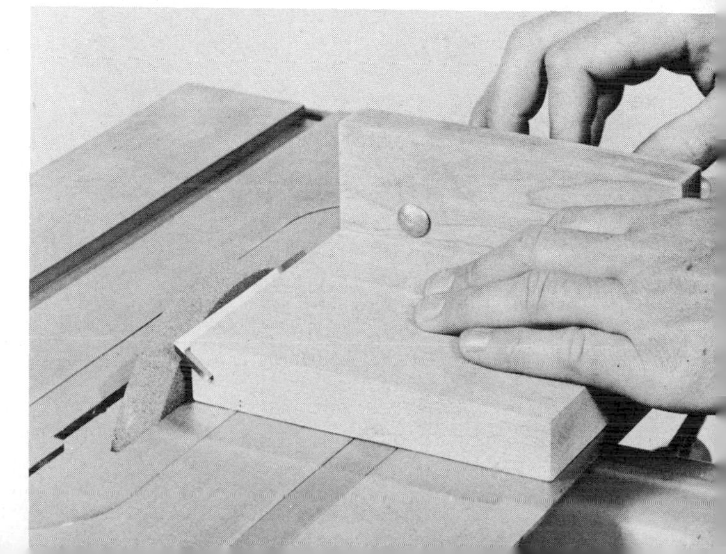

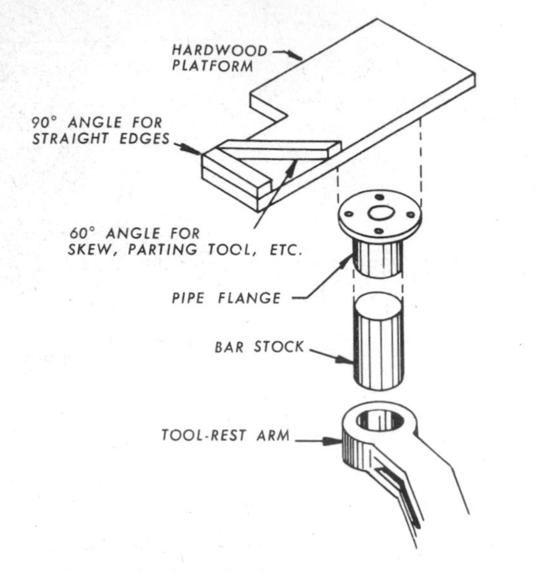

This platform is useful for sharpening many tools. Block is fastened to flange, which is locked to bar stock that fits in tool-rest arm. Be sure platform is square to wheel.

The guides below position the skew for grinding its bevels. They are placed here so each bevel is ground on a different side of the wheel.

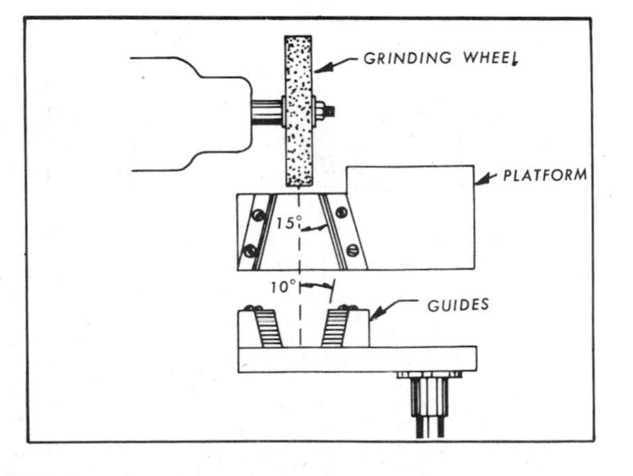

Grinding Lathe Chisels: Skew

Make the simple platform at left for grinding jointer knives and some lathe chisels.

To grind the edge of a skew chisel, use an angle-block on the wooden platform. Clamp the skew into place and make a **light** cut by advancing the wheel, as in the photograph at the left.

Bevels on a skew require a set of bevel-blocks (sketched at lower left) secure to the platform. These blocks are placed so that right and left bevels can be ground on opposite sides of the grinding wheel. If just one side is to be used, place blocks parallel to each other as shown in the two photographs below.

Hone the skew by placing the bevel flat on a fine oilstone and moving it in a circle several times. Do this on both sides.

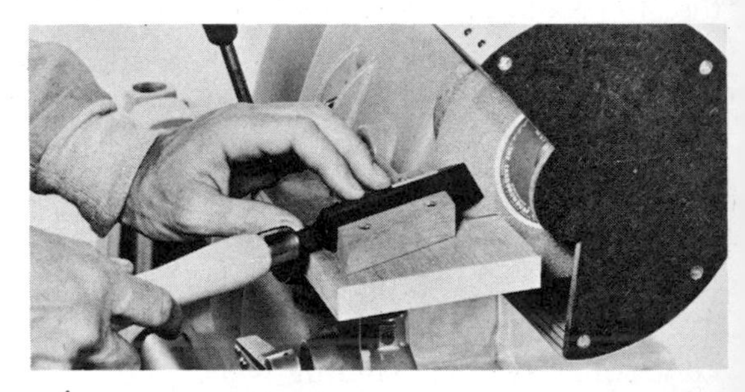

The angle-block will position the skew for re-edging. Be sure it is securely clamped.

When just one side of the wheel is used, the guide blocks are situated parallel to each other. The first bevel is ground with the chisel resting against one block (above). Then (below) the skew is placed against the second guide block for re-grinding the other bevel. The tool may be moved to the wheel, or quill feed used to move wheel against tool.

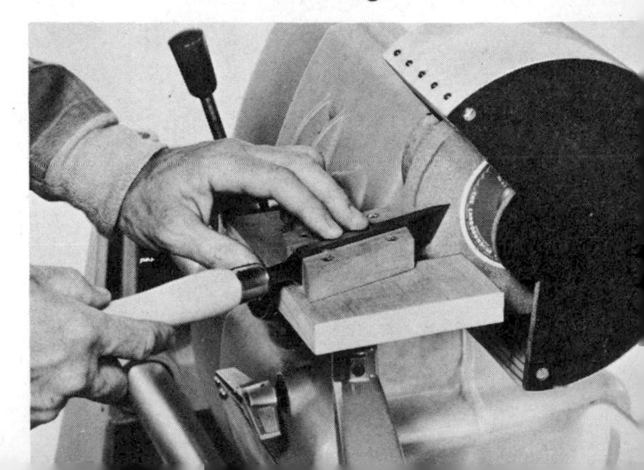

To re-grind the bevel on a gouge, use a cup-wheel (top) or the side of a standard grinding wheel (second photograph from top). Hone on a special fine stone with one round edge, as shown in the middle photograph.

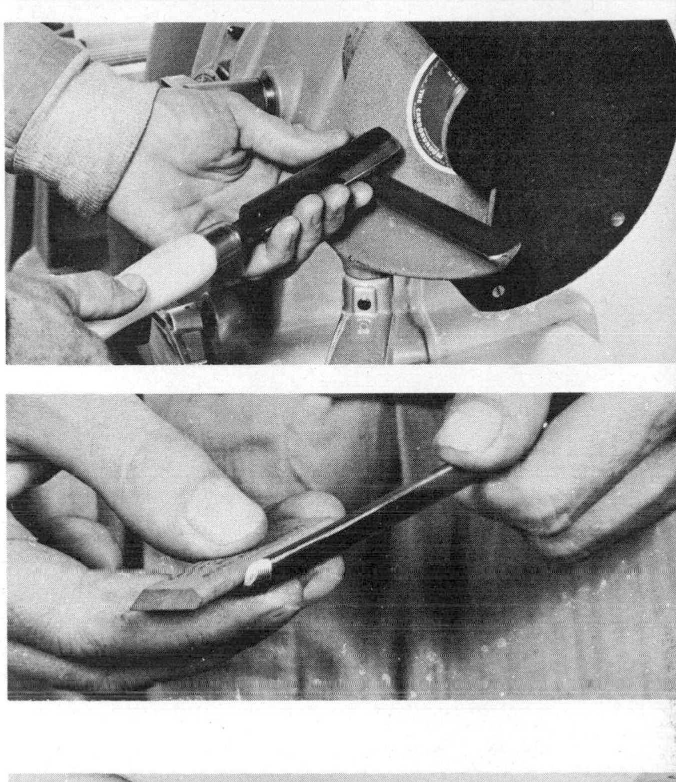

Gouge, Roundnose, Parting Tool

The easiest method of sharpening a gouge is on the inside surface of a cup-wheel mounted on the spindle. Place the tool rest as shown and position the gouge so one end of the curved bevel is flat against the surface of the wheel. As the wheel spins, revolve the gouge in a half-circle, keeping the bevel flat against the wheel.

A second method requires the same movement in turning the chisel, but is accomplished against the flat side of a standard wheel.

A special stone is required for honing the gouge. This may be a flat stone with one rounded edge, or a stone that is convex on one side and concave on the other.

Sharpen the roundnose lathe chisel exactly as you do the gouge. After grinding, place the back of the blade flat on an oilstone and move it in a circle to remove the burr.

The angle-guide used for grinding the edge of the skew is necessary for sharpening the parting tool. Also needed is a small cradle—a block with a shallow V-cut in which the blade of the chisel can rest. The tool is clamped in place and the grinding wheel is moved against the bevel by advancing the quill. The depth dial is set to control depth of cut. The chisel is then turned over and clamped in position to grind the second bevel.

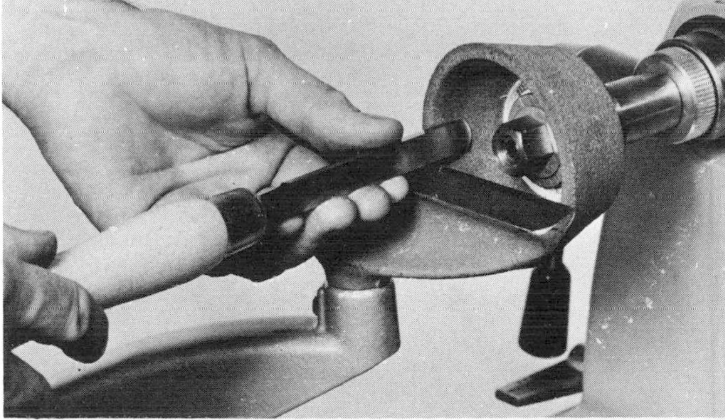

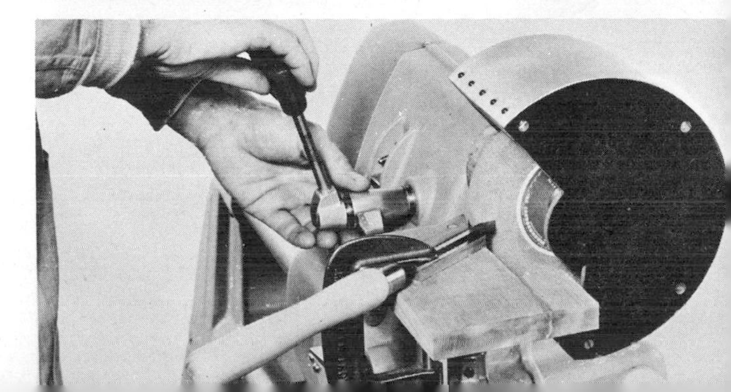

Grind a roundnose lathe chisel on cup-wheel (second photograph from bottom) or regular wheel, just as you would a gouge. Sharpening the parting tool calls for the cradle shown in the bottom picture. It has a shallow V cut into it to fit the shape of the tool.

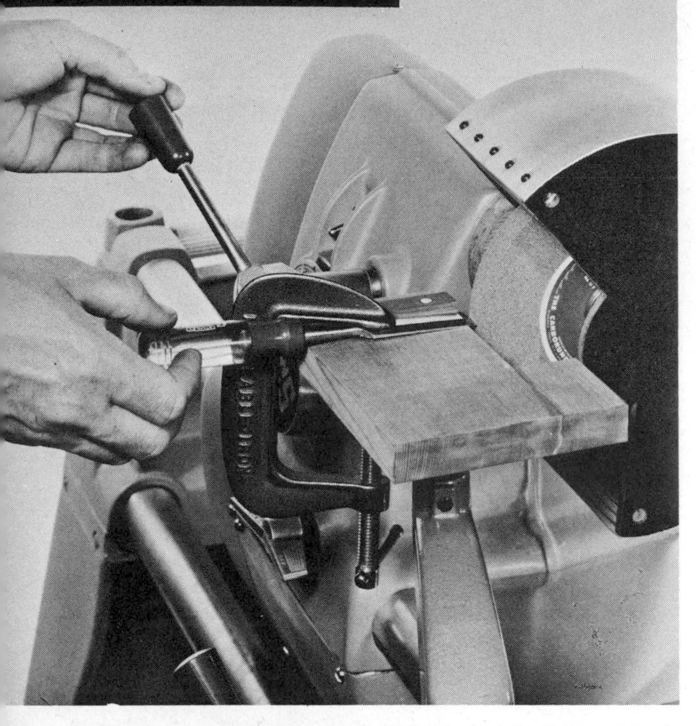

A right-angle guide block holds butt chisels square to the grinding wheel for edging.

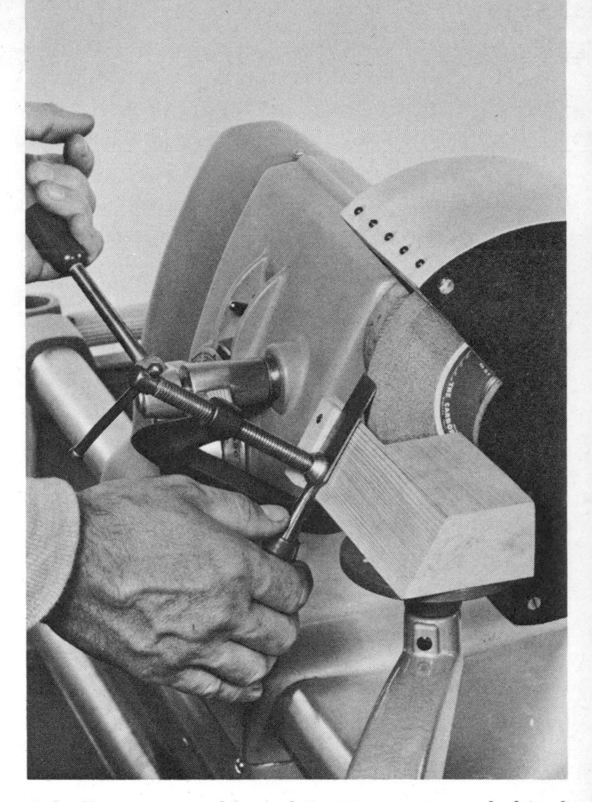

A hollow-ground bevel is put on a wood chisel this way. Be sure the chisel is securely clamped.

Butt Wood Chisels

In order for a butt wood chisel to cut smoothly and hold a keen edge, it must be square across the cutting edge and have a hollow-ground bevel. To square the edge, use the 90° guide block on the wooden platform, and make the pass by advancing the quill (above).

The bevel requires a special platform to hold the chisel in position. Here again, the pass is made by advancing the quill, as shown above. The platform is made from a piece of 2″ stock, shaped as shown at left below. A 90° guide strip holds the chisel square to the wheel.

Once the bevel is ground on the chisel, it will take several honings before it must be ground again. The back side is honed by placing the chisel flat on the stone (as shown in the group of sketches below) and moving it in a circle.

Guide block positions chisel square to wheel. Slant of platform maintains bevel-angle.

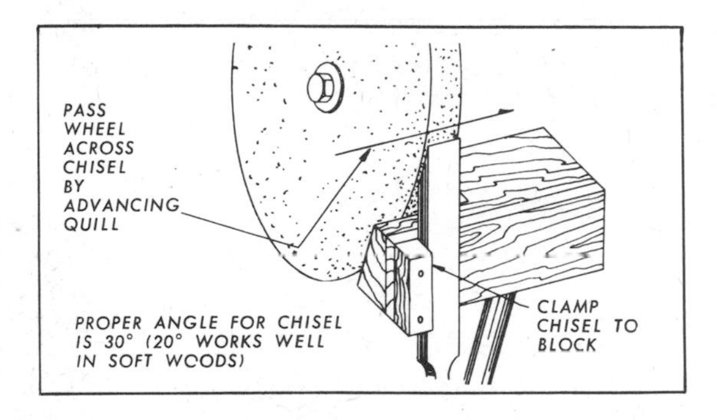

After grinding, butt chisels may be honed on a fine oilstone or a rubber-bonded abrasive wheel.

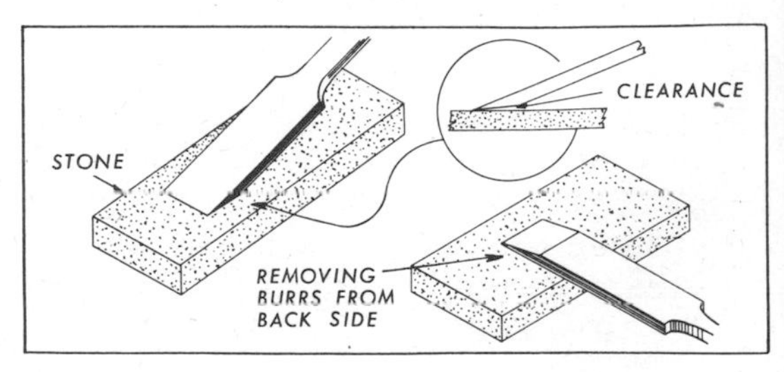

Screw driver edges should be flat and square.

Screw Drivers

While a screw driver does not have to be sharp, its edge should be maintained so it will fit snugly in the screw-head slot.

To make its edge flat and square again, hold the screw driver on the tool rest and advance it directly into the wheel, as in the photograph above.

Grind the side bevels by placing them flat against the side of the wheel, as shown below.

After grinding the edge, refinish the bevels so that the tip of the screw driver will fit snugly in the screw-head slots.

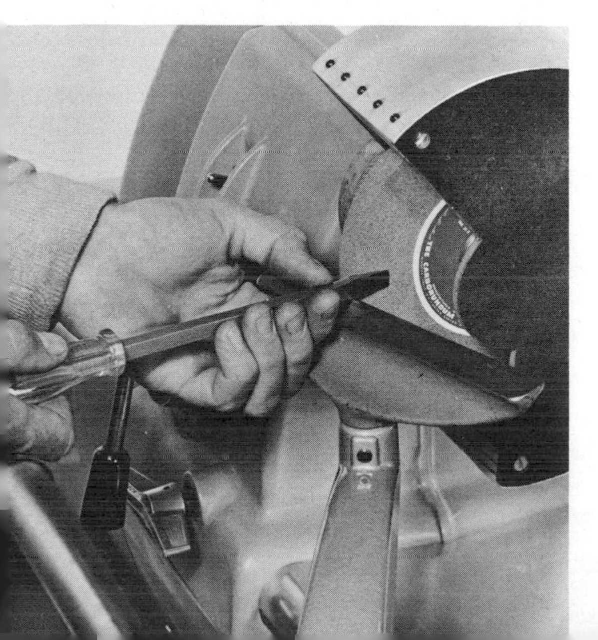

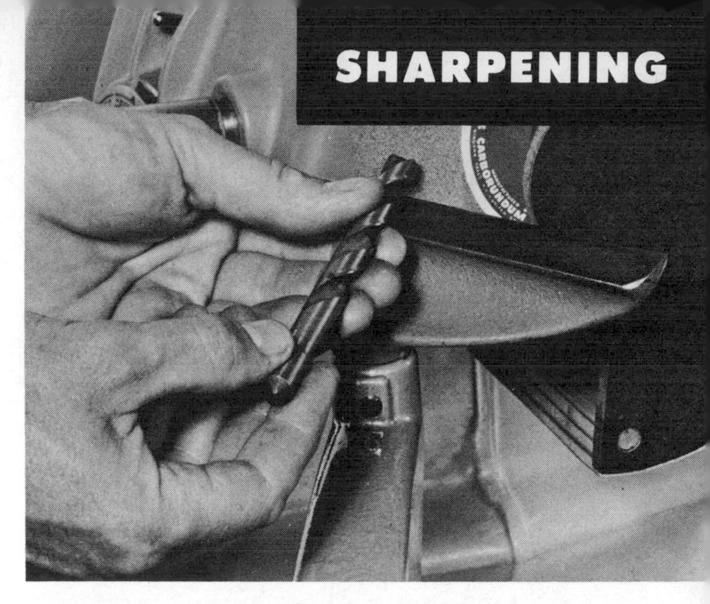

Grinding the point of a drill freehand requires skill that is easily attained through practice. Practice several times with a correctly ground drill before trying to sharpen a dull one.

Drills

The point-angle on drills for general use should be about 59°, and this angle must be maintained when sharpening them. Experienced mechanics reface drill points with a quick flip of the wrist, but it takes practice to master the technique.

The best method is to use the tool rest, as shown above, placing the point-angle flat against the side of the wheel to determine the angle at which it should be held.

A gauge designed to check the point of the drill may be purchased.

One good idea is to set the tool rest so that when the drill is held at a right angle to it, it will be 59° to the side of the wheel. With the drill held correctly, give it a slight twist and at the same time drop the end down.

To get the feel of this, use a properly-ground drill and go through the motion several times with the grinding wheel idle.

Keep the angle constant as you twist and drop the drill. At the end of the stroke, the point of the drill should be down, and it should be flat against the wheel.

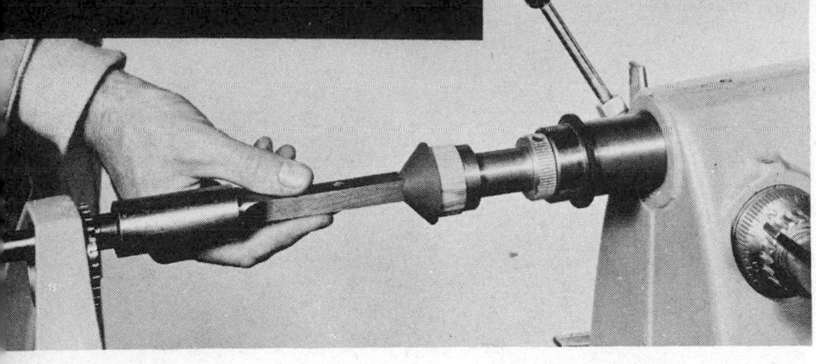

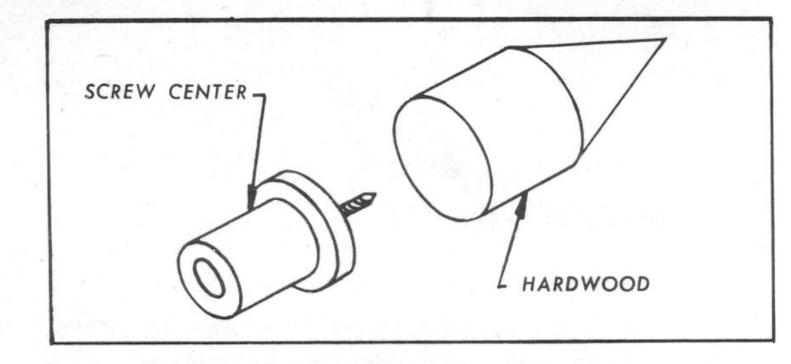

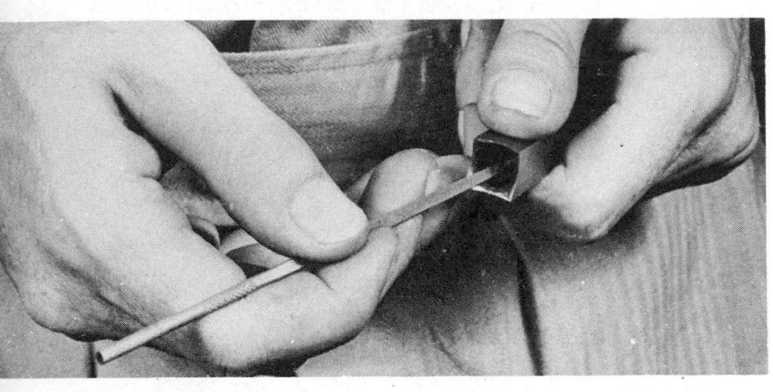

This cone-shaped tool for sharpening mortising chisels can be turned in the lathe on a screw-center. Use it as shown in the photograph at the top of the page. The sleeve of the mortising attachment, which holds the chisel, is locked on the tailstock chuck arbor. Do the sharpening by advancing the quill. Then touch up the inside corners of the mortising chisel by hand (middle photograph), using a small triangular or square file.

Mortising Chisels

Internal faces on mortising chisels should be ground to an included angle of about 78°.

A small grinding wheel with an end shank will do the job if the point is dressed to the angle needed.

Otherwise, a simple cone-shape block can be used. This block is shown in the drawing at the left; and the photograph at the top of the page shows it in use. It is mounted on the lathe screw-center, while the chisel is mounted in the tailstock.

The chisel can be mounted in the tailstock of the multi-purpose tool by using the tailstock chuck arbor and the steel sleeve that is part of the mortising attachment.

The cone, covered with a piece of 120-grit wet-or-dry paper, is advanced into the chisel by means of the quill-feed lever. Do not apply excessive pressure; just touch the abrasive to the chisel, then retract the quill. Repeat this several times.

A small file, square or triangular, is used to clean out the inside corners.

Lathe-Tool Bits

A simple tool post can be used as a holder (as at left) when shaping or sharpening lathe-tool bits.

Since post and tool-rest arm can be adjusted, the bit can be placed so any bevel can be ground on any of its four sides.

The best method is to situate the bit at the correct angle, and then advance the wheel with the quill-feed lever. Feed should be light.

When shaping the bits, retract the wheel often to allow the tool bit to cool.

⇦ Almost any shape can be ground on lathe tool bits by using the setup shown at left. Cutting is done by slowly advancing the grinding wheel.

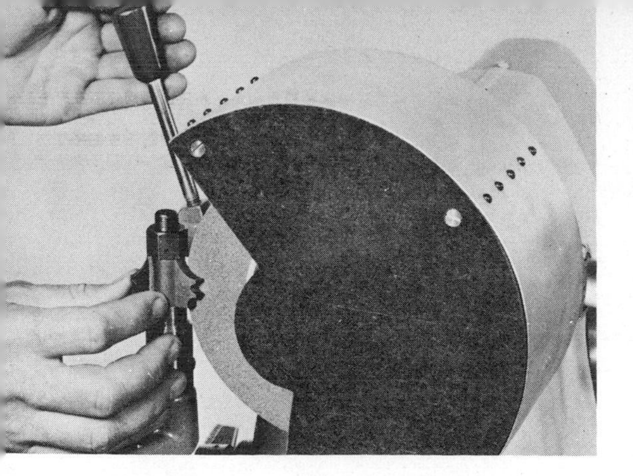

Three-lip shaper cutters are sharpened by lightly grinding the face of each blade.

Three-Lip Shaper Cutters

Shaper cutters can be sharpened by honing the back of each blade on a flat oilstone. If simple honing is not enough, mount the cutter on the shaper adapter and then secure this to the adapter used in the tool-rest arm (above). Advance the quill enough so that the flat side of the cutter is parallel to the side of the wheel. Set the depth dial and retract the quill. Turn on the motor and advance the quill to the limit of the stroke. Then revolve the cutter until the flat side touches the side of the wheel. Again retract the quill, turn the cutter to the next blade, and repeat.

Use the same setup (below) to grind bevels on blank cutters. Adjust quill stroke so bevel on cutter will be flat against side of wheel when you advance the quill.

The bevels on blank blades may be ground in a similar way. Be sure to remove exactly the same amount of material from each edge.

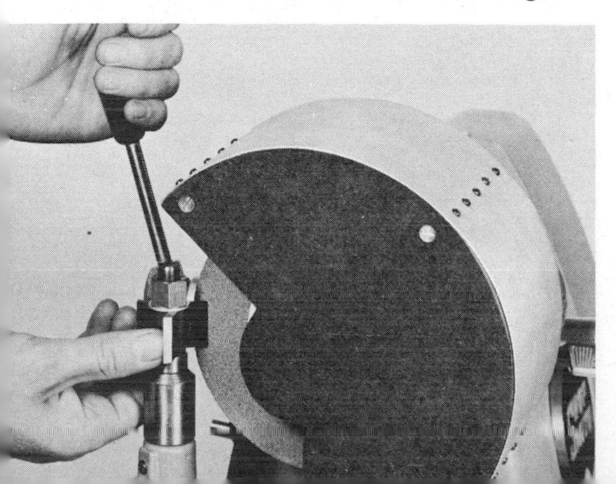

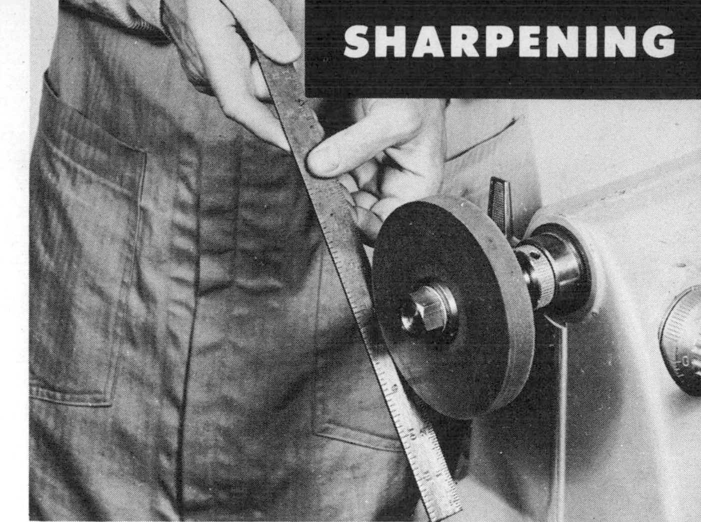

The rubber-bonded abrasive wheel does a good job of polishing metals, including many shop and household items, and honing kitchen knives, plane blades, and scissors.

Using the Honing Wheel

A grinding wheel is always used when an edge is nicked or so dull it must be re-edged. The rubber-bonded abrasive wheel, a high-quality honing tool, is used to add the final keen edge.

On the multi-purpose tool you can mount grinding wheel and honing wheel at the same time, so the honing can immediately follow the grinding job without inconvenience.

Tools carefully ground and used can be honed three or four times before re-edging.

Always wear safety goggles when using any kind of grinding or honing wheel.

Use edge or sides of rubber-bonded abrasive wheel to hone tools after grinding and to maintain keen edges between grinding jobs.

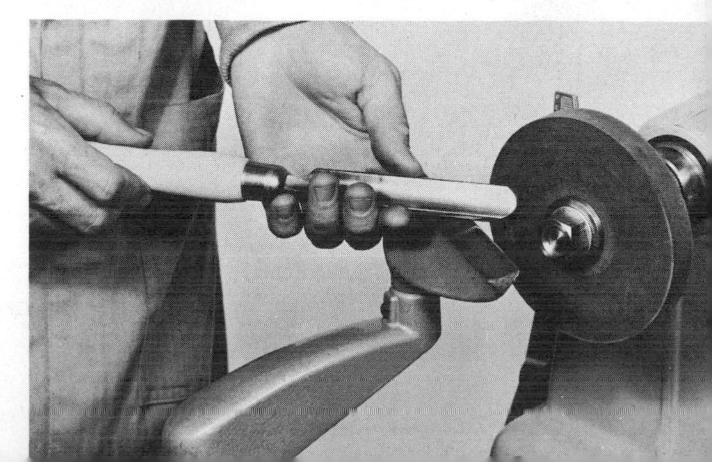

HOW TO HAVE

You can use your shop in comfort and safety if you learn and **follow** the rules that experience has proved to be the basis of good shop practices.

If you're a beginner, don't go right to work on your bright new power tool without reading **all** the printed matter that comes with it. Become familiar with the tool and what it does by making practice cuts first. Don't let yourself become over-confident—even after you have learned all the rules. Often enough it is the man who has learned a rule and deliberately ignores it who gets hurt. **Here are the safety rules. Learn them and obey them.**

Wear Safe Clothes

Keep sleeves buttoned tight at the wrist or rolled well above the elbow, or wear a shop coat with tight cuffs.

Do not wear a necktie or any other loose clothing.

Avoid wearing rings or a wristwatch.

Be Sure Power is Off

Check that the machine is clear, and that the switch is off, before inserting plug into power source.

Be sure switch is off and plug removed from outlet before making any major adjustment or changing tools.

Turn the switch off and pull the plug out when leaving the machine; make this a habit.

Know What You Are Doing

Study instructions so you can plan and perform all operations correctly.

Always provide maximum support for your work.

Be sure all locks are tight before operating machine.

Check machine for operation by turning it by hand before switching it on.

A SAFE SHOP

Keep Alert from the Moment You Begin Work

Keep hands in sight and safely clear of moving tools and parts.

Watch for warning signals that might indicate misalignment or maladjustment.

Never reach across a machine while it is running.

Never push the free end of the work.

Never pick a cutoff from the table while saw is turning.

Never use the rip fence as a stop for the free end of the work.

Never attempt to slow down or stop the machine after switching it off, by grabbing work or tool.

Know Good Shop Practice and Observe it All the Time

Keep tools sharp and correctly set.

Keep saw blade just high enough for the job to be done. Avoid the extremes.

Use saw guard and splitter whenever possible.

Use pusher sticks and hold-downs to avoid getting fingers too close to the saw blade.

Use the Miter-Gauge Safety Grip.

Use miter-gauge extensions.

Always make the return when crosscutting.

Never rip work that does not have a straight edge to bear against the rip fence.

Use correct speeds. If in doubt, use a lower speed.

Never force the work or rush the job.

Never use the rip fence as a stop for the free end of the work.

Make a special table insert when needed.

Whenever possible stand at one side of the cutting tool, not in line with it.

Keep shop floor clean. Sawdust underfoot is slippery.

Never Trust the Machine

By all means have confidence in your machine and its reliability—but always be a little afraid of the machine—never rely on it to think for you.

D

E

F

M

N

O

P

R

S

T

W